Flood Estimation Handbook

Volume 3

Flood Estimation Handbook

Volume 3

Statistical procedures for flood frequency estimation

Alice Robson and Duncan Reed

Institute of Hydrology

© NERC (CEH) 2008

ISBN for complete set of 5 volumes: 978-1-906698-00-3
ISBN for this volume: 978-1-906698-03-4

Originally published by the Institute of Hydrology 1999

Centre for Ecology & Hydrology

Maclean Building, Benson Lane, Crowmarsh Gifford

Wallingford, Oxfordshire OX10 8BB

UK

General and business enquiries: 01491 692562
E-mail: enquiries@ceh.ac.uk
Website: www.ceh.ac.uk

Cover photo: Jude Nutter

Cross-referencing

Cross-references to other parts of the Handbook are usually abbreviated. They are
indicated by the relevant volume number preceding the chapter, section or sub-section
number, with the volume number in bold (e.g. **4** 2.2 refers to Section 2.2 of Volume 4).
Cross-references conventionally prefixed by Chapter, Section or § are to the current
volume.

The Flood Estimation Handbook should be cited as:
Institute of Hydrology (1999) Flood Estimation Handbook (five volumes).
Centre for Ecology & Hydrology.

This volume should be cited as:
Robson, A. J. and Reed, D. W. (1999) Statistical procedures for flood frequency
estimation. Volume 3 of the Flood Estimation Handbook. Centre for Ecology & Hydrology.

Contents

Contents

Contents

Preface

The research for the Flood Estimation Handbook was undertaken at the Institute of Hydrology, Wallingford, Oxfordshire. The Institute is an integral part of the Centre for Ecology and Hydrology, and a component institute of the Natural Environment Research Council. The research programme ran from 1994 to 1999.

Contributors

The core research team comprised Duncan Reed (team leader), Adrian Bayliss, Duncan Faulkner, Helen Houghton-Carr, Dörte Jakob, David Marshall, Alice Robson and Lisa Stewart. David Jones acted as an internal consultant, advising on all aspects of the research. The WINFAP-FEH software package was principally developed by Lawrence Beran, and the FEH CD-ROM was designed and developed by Kevin Black. The Handbook is dedicated in memory of Tanya Jones, a team member whose contribution to hydrological research was tragically cut short by cancer.

Major contributions were also made by David Morris, Susan Morris, Christel Prudhomme and Robert Scarrott, with additional contributions by Val Bronsdon, Victoria Edmunds, Beate Gannon, Stephanie Hills and Nick Reynard.

The team was supported by 1-year Sandwich Course Students from Luton and Sheffield Hallam Universities, including: Mark Bennett, Robert Brookes, Russell Brown, Louisa Coles, Nick Davie, Philip Davies, David Hewertson, Catriona Kelly, Marina Syed Mansor and Paul Nihell.

Sponsors

The research programme was funded by the Ministry of Agriculture Fisheries and Food (MAFF), the Environment Agency, the Department of Agriculture Northern Ireland, and a consortium led by the Scottish Office. The budget for the programme totalled about £1.7m. Indirect support was provided by the Centre for Ecology and Hydrology, the Meteorological Office and river gauging authorities. Costs of final editing and publication of the Handbook, and development of the WINFAP-FEH software, were met by the Institute of Hydrology.

Advisers

The research was reviewed by the Flood Estimation Handbook Advisory Group, comprising:

David Richardson, MAFF Flood and Coastal Defence *(Chair)*
Linda Aucott, Environment Agency
Alan Burdekin, Scottish Office
John Clarke, Department of Agriculture, Northern Ireland
Christopher Collier, University of Salford
Conleth Cunnane, University College Galway, Ireland
John Goudie, MAFF Flood and Coastal Defence *(Technical Secretary)*
Richard Harpin, Sir William Halcrow and Partners
David MacDonald, Binnie Black and Veatch
Andrew Pepper, Consultant to the Environment Agency *(Observer)*
Duncan Reed, Institute of Hydrology
Richard Tabony, Meteorological Office
Howard Wheater, Imperial College

Testers

The main participants in the user test programme were:

David Archer, Consultant to Jeremy Benn Associates
Alan Barr and Grace Glasgow, Kirk McClure and Morton
Don Burn, University of Waterloo, Canada
Jonathan Cooper, Owen Bramwell and Brian Darling, WS Atkins North West
Con Cunnane and Savithri Senaratne, University College Galway
Steve Dunthorne, Sir Alexander Gibb and Partners
Jim Findlay, Murray Dale, Stuart King and Birol Sokmenor, Babtie Group
Mark Futter, Montgomery Watson
Malcolm MacConnachie, Scottish Environment Protection Agency
David MacDonald, Binnie, Black and Veatch
Ian Rose, Emma Blunden and Rob Scarrott, Halcrow
Peter Spencer and David Rylands, Environment Agency
Peter Walsh, Bullen Consultants Ltd
Paul Webster and Anna Lisa Vetere Arellano, University of Birmingham
Howard Wheater and Christian Onof, Imperial College

Acknowledgements

The Flood Estimation Handbook is a product of strategic research funding at the Institute of Hydrology in the 1990s. It would not have happened without the lead shown by MAFF, in particular by Reg Purnell and David Richardson. The dedication of Advisory Group members and the testers is gratefully acknowledged. Alan Gustard (IH) is thanked for managerial assistance in a research programme that did not fit a standard mould.

General thanks go to all those who exchanged ideas with members of the team during the research programme. Those having greatest impact on the course of the research were Don Burn and Jon Hosking. A more general acknowledgement is to all earlier researchers in UK rainfall and flood frequency estimation. It would be invidious to list some and not others.

Coastlines, rivers and lake shorelines shown in the Handbook are based on material licensed from Ordnance Survey and are included with the permission of the controller of Her Majesty's Stationery Office © Crown copyright. Place names are from a gazetteer licensed from AA Developments Ltd.

More specific acknowledgements to individuals and organisations co-operating in the research are made in the relevant volume.

Volumes

1 Overview
2 Rainfall frequency estimation
3 Statistical procedures for flood frequency estimation
4 Restatement and application of the *Flood Studies Report* rainfall-runoff method
5 Catchment descriptors

Notation

The following are the main symbols and abbreviations used throughout this volume of the Flood Estimation Handbook. Other symbols have just a local meaning and are defined where they occur. All the units are metric unless otherwise stated

A_Q	probability that annual maximum $\leq Q$
AE	area exponent
AEP	annual exceedance probability
ALTBAR	mean catchment altitude (m)
AM	annual maximum series / annual maxima
AM_{adj}	climatically adjusted annual maximum series
AREA	catchment drainage area (km²)
ASPWEST	westerly component of the mean direction of slope
BCW	bankfull channel width (m)
BF	baseflow (m³ s⁻¹)
BFI	baseflow index
BFIHOST	baseflow index derived from HOST soils data
C_p	Mallow's C_p
CVRI	coefficient of variation of the intervals between floods
CWI	catchment wetness index
D	discordancy (Chapters 6 and 16); dispersion (Chapter 12)
D_{AE}	dispersion for the annual exceedance series
dist	similarity distance
DPLBAR	mean drainage path length (km)
DPSBAR	mean catchment slope (m km⁻¹)
DPR_{CWI}	dynamic percentage runoff attributable to CWI
DPR_{rain}	dynamic percentage runoff attributable to catchment rainfall
DTM	digital terrain model
E	expected value
e_i	effective record length (years)
F_i	plotting position for i^{th} flow
f(Q)	probability density function
F(Q) or F	cumulative distribution function (non-exceedance probability)
FARL	index of flood attenuation due to reservoirs and lakes
FEH	Flood Estimation Handbook
fse	factorial standard error
FSR	Flood Studies Report
G	Gumbel
GEV	Generalised Extreme Value
GL	Generalised Logistic
GLS	generalised least squares
GP	Generalised Pareto
H_1	heterogeneity (using L-CV)
H_2	heterogeneity (using L-CV and L-skewness)
H_3	heterogeneity (using L-skewness and L-kurtosis)
HOST	Hydrology Of Soil Types
IH	Institute of Hydrology
IHDTM	Institute of Hydrology digital terrain model
k	negative binomial distribution parameter (Chapter 12)
k	shape parameter (flood frequency curve / growth curve)

k^*	permeable-adjusted shape parameter
k'	flood-years shape parameter
l_1	sample L-mean
l_r	r^{th} sample L-moment
L	Logistic
ln	natural logarithm
LN	Log-Normal
LN2	2-parameter Log-Normal
LN3	3-parameter Log-Normal
M	number of sites in pooling-group
MORECS	Met. Office Rainfall and Evaporation Calculation System
M(r)	correlation function for climatic adjustment
n *or* N	record length (years)
n_d	length of donor site record (years)
n_o	length of overlap period between subject site and donor site
n_s	length of subject site record (years)
n_t	total number of years with data for either subject or donor site
NERC	Natural Environment Research Council
NWET	number of spells when soil moisture deficit ≤ 6 mm during 1961-90, defined using MORECS
OLS	ordinary least squares
p	negative binomial distribution parameter (Chapter 12)
PE3	Pearson type 3
POT	peaks-over-threshold
POT1	POT series containing an average of one event/peak per year (annual exceedance series)
POT1#	POT1 counts (number of POT1 floods/year)
POT1m	POT1 flood peak magnitudes
POT3	POT series containing an average of 3 events/floods per year
POT3#	POT3 counts (number of POT3 floods/year)
POT3#adj	climatically adjusted POT3 counts
POT3m	POT3 flood peak magnitudes
P_Q	probability that a POT peak $\leq Q$ given that it is greater than the POT threshold
PR	percentage runoff
PR_{rural}	percentage runoff in the as-rural state
PRESS	predicted error sum of squares
PROPWET	proportion of time when soil moisture deficit ≤ 6 mm during 1961-90, defined using MORECS
PRUAF	percentage runoff urban adjustment factor
PUM	pooled uncertainty measure
q	response runoff peak (m^3 s^{-1})
Q	flow value (m^3 s^{-1})
Q_d	flow at the donor site (m^3 s^{-1})
Q_i	i^{th} largest flow / flood (m^3 s^{-1})
Q_{peak}	peak flow (m^3 s^{-1})
Q_s	flow at the subject site (m^3 s^{-1})
Q(F)	flood frequency curve
Q_T	flood frequency curve/T-year return period flood
QBAR	mean annual maximum flood (m^3 s^{-1})
QD	QMED at the donor site (m^3 s^{-1})

QD_o	QMED at the donor site for the overlap period ($m^3\,s^{-1}$)
QMED	median annual maximum flood ($m^3\,s^{-1}$)
$QMED_{g,cds}$	QMED at gauged donor site obtained from catchment descriptors
$QMED_{g,obs}$	QMED at gauged donor site obtained from flood data
$QMED_{rural}$	median annual maximum flood in the as-rural state ($m^3\,s^{-1}$)
$QMED_{s,adj}$	QMED at subject site adjusted using gauged donor site
$QMED_{s,cds}$	QMED at subject site obtained from catchment descriptors
$Qrural_T$	T-year flood for a catchment in its rural state ($m^3\,s^{-1}$)
QS	QMED at the subject site ($m^3\,s^{-1}$)
QS_{adj}	adjusted QMED at the subject site ($m^3\,s^{-1}$)
QS_d	QMED at the subject site for the donor period ($m^3\,s^{-1}$)
QS_o	QMED at the subject site for the overlap period ($m^3\,s^{-1}$)
r	correlation / risk (as a probability; Chapter 11)
r^2	coefficient of determination
$\bar{r}$	seasonality variable
R	correlation matrix
RESHOST	residual soils term (linked to soil responsiveness)
RMED1	median annual maximum 1-day rainfall (mm)
rmse	root mean square error
RV_i	reduced variate for i^{th} largest flow
S	covariance matrix
S_i	similarity ranking factor
SAAR	standard average annual rainfall 1961-1990 (mm)
SPR	standard percentage runoff
SPRHOST	standard percentage runoff derived from HOST soils data
T	return period (years)
T_{AM}	return period on the annual maxima scale (years)
T_{POT}	return period on the POT scale (years)
t_2	sample L-CV
t_3	sample L-skewness
t_4	sample L-kurtosis
t_{AE}	threshold for the annual exceedance series ($m^3\,s^{-1}$)
t_i^P	i^{th} pooled L-moment ratio
Tp	time to peak (hours)
Tp(0)	time to peak of instantaneous unit hydrograph (hours)
UAF	urban adjustment factor
URBEXT	extent of urban and suburban cover
v	value of a donor site
w	weighting term
W	hydrograph width (hours)
$W_{half-peak}$	hydrograph width at half the peak flow (hours)
WINFAP-FEH	Windows frequency analysis software package
WLS	weighted least squares
x(F)	growth curve
x_T	growth curve / T-year growth factor
x_T^p	pooled growth curve
x_T^*	permeable adjusted growth curve
x_T'	flood-years growth curve
XFLOOD	flood seasonality variable (x component)
$xrural_T$	rural pooled growth curve
YFLOOD	flood seasonality variable (y component)

y_G	Gumbel reduced-variate
y_L	Logistic reduced-variate
Z_{DIST}	goodness-of-fit statistic
α	scale parameter (flood frequency curve) / significance level
β	scale parameter (growth curve)
β^*	permeable adjusted growth curve scale parameter
β'	flood-years growth curve scale parameter
γ	Euler's constant (≈ 0.5772)
Γ	Gamma function
λ_1	1st L-moment (L-mean)
λ_r	rth L-moment
λ_i	exceedance rate for the ith largest flow (Chapter 12)
λ_Q	exceedance rate for a flow Q (Chapter 12)
μ	mean
ξ	location parameter
σ	standard deviation
σ^2	variance
Σ	covariance matrix
τ_2	L-CV
τ_3	L-skewness
τ_4	L-kurtosis
Φ	cumulative distribution function of the Normal distribution
$\bar{\theta}$	seasonality angle
ω	probability of a year containing at least one flood

Chapter 1   Introduction

This volume presents statistical procedures for flood estimation. Much of the content is concerned with estimating a flood peak of given rarity: the so-called T-year flood, where T expresses the event rarity as a return period in years. Concepts and terminology are introduced and explained throughout the volume. The introductory chapter provides a brief overview of what is to follow. In addition, it offers a road-map (Figure 1.1) to the statistical procedures for flood frequency estimation and their arrangement in Volume 3.

Volume 3 is divided into two main parts. Part A (Chapters 2 to 9) provides a 'slim guide' to the statistical procedures for flood estimation. Part B (Chapters 11 to 21) presents the supporting theory and results. This arrangement is designed to support effective use of the statistical procedures, while at the same time encouraging users to understand and explore the methods. These twin targets are addressed by an algorithmic Part A and an expository Part B. Inevitably there is some duplication and restatement. Cross-references are given in chapter headings, to highlight the complementary roles of Parts A and B. Those interested principally in the basis of the methods may wish to refer directly to Part B.

> The first-time user is encouraged to look first at Volume 1, which is a general introduction to the Flood Estimation Handbook and provides guidance on the choice of method to solve particular flood estimation problems (see 1 5).

A final part to the volume (Part C, comprising Chapters 22 and 23) introduces the FEH flood peak datasets and gives broad guidance on the acquisition of flood peak data. Chapter 6 of Volume 1 provides additional advice on finding data.

Do people apply complicated methods before digesting the basic principles? The answer is an unequivocal "Yes". So the important chapter entitled *"Introducing the flood frequency methodology"* has been placed at the beginning of Part B rather than Part A, in the hope that what has not been force-fed will be the more appreciated. It is essential reading to those unfamiliar with statistical frequency analysis, and to all but the most experienced and instinctive user of the WINFAP-FEH software.

It is anticipated that relevant software will evolve during the lifetime of the Handbook. For this and other reasons, Volume 3 presents and illustrates the statistical procedures with relatively little reference to particular software packages.

Because some of the flood estimation procedures are intricate, and much of the guidance in their use is open-ended, many users will inevitably find the FEH difficult to use. But flood frequency estimation is an intrinsically difficult and uncertain task: the user who expects to find it easy is probably not looking deeply enough.

The best flood estimates will combine the effective use of flood data and software with a strong dose of hydrological and statistical judgement, reinforced by detailed understanding of the study objective and the subject catchment – quite a challenge!

Statistical procedures for flood frequency estimation

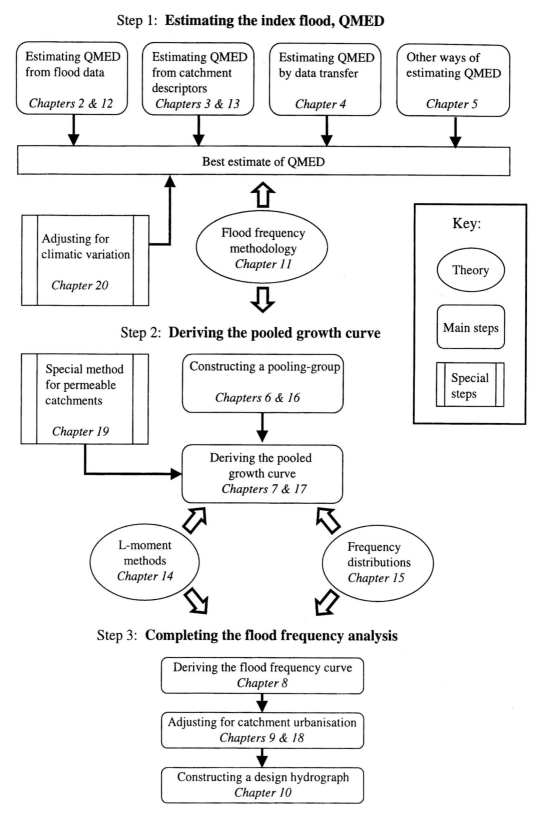

Step 1: Estimating the index flood, QMED

Estimating QMED from flood data *Chapters 2 & 12*	Estimating QMED from catchment descriptors *Chapters 3 & 13*	Estimating QMED by data transfer *Chapter 4*	Other ways of estimating QMED *Chapter 5*

Best estimate of QMED

Adjusting for climatic variation

Chapter 20

Flood frequency methodology
Chapter 11

Key:

Theory

Main steps

Special steps

Step 2: Deriving the pooled growth curve

Special method for permeable catchments

Chapter 19

Constructing a pooling-group

Chapters 6 & 16

Deriving the pooled growth curve
Chapters 7 & 17

L-moment methods
Chapter 14

Frequency distributions
Chapter 15

Step 3: Completing the flood frequency analysis

Deriving the flood frequency curve
Chapter 8

Adjusting for catchment urbanisation
Chapters 9 & 18

Constructing a design hydrograph
Chapter 10

Figure 1.1 *Road-map to the statistical procedures for flood frequency estimation*

Chapter 2   Estimating QMED from flood data (A)

2.1 Introducing QMED

An index flood represents the typical magnitude of flood expected at a given site. It is a peak flow measured in $m^3 s^{-1}$: the unit is often written (and spoken) "cumecs". The Flood Estimation Handbook adopts the *median annual maximum flood, QMED*, as the index flood. This is the flood that is exceeded on average "every other year". *QMED* is formally defined as the middle-ranking value in the series of annual maximum floods, where the annual maximum series comprises the largest flow observed in each year.

Flood peak data are discussed in Part C of this volume: Chapter 22 summarises the datasets used in the research, while Chapter 23 gives guidance in the abstraction of new or updated datasets. The data resources provided in the Handbook are summarised in **1** 2.4, and Chapter 6 of that volume gives guidance on finding gauged and historical flood peak data.

The time-scale over which UK catchments respond to heavy rainfall or snowmelt is generally too short to allow flood frequency estimates to be based on *daily mean flow* data. Thus, the Volume 3 procedures deal exclusively with flood series derived from *instantaneous* (or 15-minute) peak flow data.

Annual maxima

The annual maximum is the largest flood peak in a given year of record. The Handbook follows the convention that, where possible, annual maxima are abstracted and analysed in *water-years* rather than calendar years. The standard UK water-year begins on 1 October: for example, the 1999 water-year begins on 1 October 1999 and ends on 30 September 2000. With the exception of heavily urbanised catchments, winter is the dominant season for river flooding in the UK. The choice of 30 September avoids cutting the series at a flood-prone time of year. Chapter 23 presents guidelines for the abstraction of annual maxima from chart or digital records.

Figure 2.1 shows the annual maximum series for the Dwyryd at Maentwrog flow gauging station, which is numbered 65002 (Station 2 in Hydrometric Area 65).

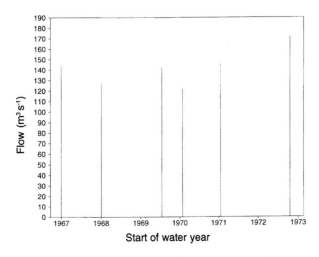

Figure 2.1 *Annual maximum flood peaks ($m^3 s^{-1}$) for the Dwyryd at Maentwrog (65002)*

Estimating QMED from annual maxima

The index flood, *QMED*, can be estimated by ordering the annual maxima and taking the middle-ranking value. In the case of an even number of annual maxima, *QMED* is estimated as the arithmetic mean of the two central values.

Example 2.1
Estimation of QMED from annual maxima: Dwyryd at Maentwrog (65002)

There are six complete water-years of flood data for this approximately 78 km² catchment, draining rugged terrain in Gwynedd, Wales. Arranged in decreasing order of magnitude, the annual maxima are: 171.8, 145.7, **144.4**, **141.8**, 126.7 and 121.9 $m^3 s^{-1}$. There is no middle-ranking value for a sample size of six. Thus the median is estimated as the average of the 3rd and 4th highest values, shown in bold:

$QMED = (144.4 + 141.8) / 2 = 143.1 \ m^3 s^{-1}$.

Note that half the annual maxima are larger than *QMED*, and half are smaller.

2.2 Recommended methods

The site of interest is termed the *subject site*. The gauged record at the subject site should be brought up-to-date prior to analysis. The simplest method of estimating *QMED* is to evaluate the median of the annual maxima (§2.3). This is the recommended procedure if the record length is 14 years or longer. When the record length at the subject site is between two and 13 years, *QMED* is estimated from flood data abstracted in peaks-over-threshold (POT) form (§2.4). Figure 2.2 summarises recommendations for *QMED* estimation when there are two or more years of data at the subject site.

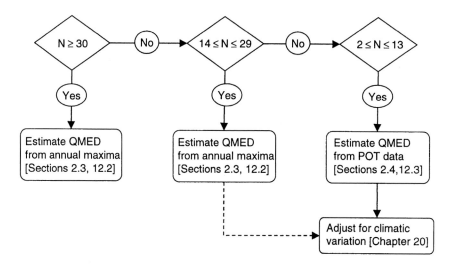

Figure 2.2 *Recommended method for QMED estimation when the flood record at the subject site is longer than 2 years: N denotes the number of water-years of record.*

Special considerations are required when the record length is shorter than two years. In such cases, the gauged data are unlikely to provide a reliable estimate of *QMED* directly. Recommendations are then quite complicated, depending on whether a data transfer from a much longer record at a nearby donor site is possible (see Box 2.1 and Figure 2.3).

Box 2.1 Data transfers, donor sites and analogue catchments

Volume 1 introduces the broad philosophy of *data transfers* (1 2.3) and gives guidance on the selection of donor and analogue catchments (1 3.3). A *donor site* is a gauged site that is sufficiently close to the subject site to make its flood data of special relevance. Usually it will be on the same river, directly upstream or downstream of the subject site. An *analogue catchment* is a more distant catchment that is thought to be hydrologically similar. Data transfers for *QMED* estimation are discussed in Chapter 4.

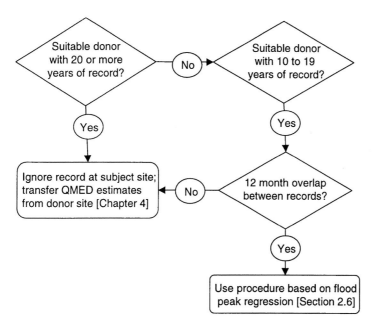

Figure 2.3 *Recommended method for QMED estimation when the record length at subject site is shorter than two years **and** there is a good donor site*

When the record length is shorter than two years but there is no long-record site nearby, various methods can be considered. Approaches include:

- Estimate *QMED* from a very short POT record (see Additional Note 12.1);
- Treat the subject site as if it is ungauged: if possible, applying a data transfer (see Chapter 4);
- Apply personal judgement to combine the above estimates.

A better strategy will be to defer the analysis until a longer period of flood data is available for the subject site. Where this is impractical, and no useful donor or analogue catchment can be found, it will be advisable to abstract flood event data and apply the rainfall-runoff method (Volume 4). This last option is particularly recommended when the subject catchment is urbanised.

Influence of climatic variability

Climatic variability leads to some periods being unusually *rich* or *poor* in terms of flood occurrences. Estimates of *QMED* from short or moderate records should therefore be adjusted for *period-of-record effects* (see Figure 2.2). The novice user will reduce the sensitivity to period of record by updating the flood series beyond that published. The more experienced user will both update the flood series and, if the record is still a lot shorter than 30 years, make a specific adjustment for climatic variation (see Chapter 20).

Influence of land-use change

The index flood can be affected by land-use change. When estimating *QMED*, it is usually necessary to discard the part of a flood series that pre-dates a major catchment change, such as completion of a large impounding reservoir. The treatment of progressive land-use change is problematic. The advantage of being up-to-date in terms of land use – by only analysing the most recent flood data – has to be weighed against the increased sampling error (and period-of-record sensitivity) if *QMED* is estimated from a shortened record.

2.3 QMED estimation from annual maxima

QMED is estimated from annual maxima by taking the median of the series. This is the recommended method if there are 14 or more years of record, or if peaks-over-threshold (POT) data are unavailable or incomplete.

Example 2.2
Estimation of QMED from annual maxima: Lambourn at Welford (39031)

Hydrographs from this exceedingly permeable (approx. 176 km^2) catchment are dominated by a slowly varying baseflow component. This makes it difficult to determine whether successive flood peaks are independent. It is therefore impractical to abstract flood peak data in peaks-over-threshold (POT) format. Thus, *QMED* is estimated from the annual maximum series, despite the record being less than 14 years long.

There are 11 annual maxima for the Lambourn at Welford (39031). The sample median, i.e. the middle-ranking value, is 1.95 m^{3}s^{-1}. Because the record is a lot shorter than 30 years, an adjustment for climatic variation may be appropriate (see Chapter 20).

Tied values

In some flood series, several floods are ascribed identical magnitudes. These are termed *tied values*. The feature arises from the limited resolution of water level recording or from data being rounded at an early stage of data processing. The data are said to be *granular*. If the granularity is marked (e.g. more than 20% of observations are tied) it is advisable to re-abstract or reprocess the flood data prior to *QMED* estimation. Alternatively, an extreme value plot of the data will reveal the extent of the granularity, and may confirm whether the sample median provides a reasonable estimate of *QMED*.

Example 2.3
Estimation of QMED from annual maxima: Dane at Congleton (68018)

The flood record for the Dane at Congleton Park (68018) comprises 32 annual maxima. The sample median is 37.6 m³ s⁻¹. Ten of the values are tied, of which four are equal to the median. It is therefore advisable to check whether granularity in the data has compromised the estimate of *QMED*.

An extreme value plot of the data, using the Logistic reduced variate, confirms that the granularity has not influenced the *QMED* estimate unreasonably. The fitted flood frequency curve – shown for reference – is a Generalised Logistic distribution. The GL distribution, and plotting positions based on the Logistic reduced variate, are discussed in §15.3.

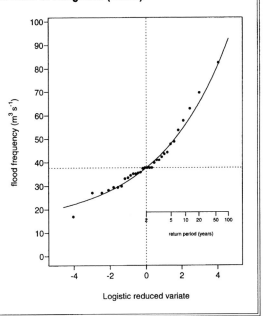

2.4 QMED estimation from peaks-over-threshold (POT) data

Peaks-over-threshold (POT) data comprise a series of flood peaks which are bigger than a selected threshold. They provide a more complete description of flood behaviour than annual maximum data. They can be useful in estimating the index flood, even though *QMED* is defined as the median of the annual maxima. The abstraction of POT data from chart or digital records is discussed in Chapter 23.

Figure 2.4 shows peaks-over-threshold data for the six complete water-years of record for the Dwyryd at Maentwrog (65002), displaying all flood peaks exceeding 110 m³ s⁻¹. It is seen that the two highest floods in the 6-year period

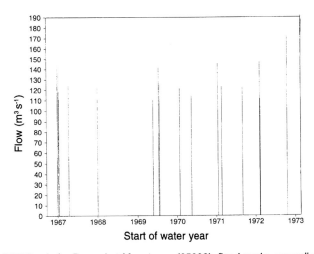

Figure 2.4 POT floods for Dwyryd at Maentwrog (65002): flood peaks exceeding 110 m³ s⁻¹

occurred in the same (1972/73) water-year. This illustrates that the POT series provides a more complete description of flood behaviour than the annual maximum series: only the larger of the two events appears in the annual maximum series of Figure 2.1. In traditional POT analyses, the choice of threshold can be problematic. However, as will now be seen, this is not an issue in the method for estimating *QMED* from POT data devised for the Handbook.

Method

The number of years of POT record is noted. Part-years of record are ignored. Using values of i and w from Table 2.1, *QMED* is estimated as a weighted average of the ith and $(i+1)^{th}$ highest floods:

$$QMED = w\,Q_i + (1 - w)Q_{i+1} \tag{2.1}$$

Table 2.1 Positions and weight for QMED estimation from UK flood data in POT format

POT record length (years)	i^{th} position	$(i+1)^{th}$ position	Weight w
1	1	2	0.602
2	2	3	0.895
3	2	3	0.100
4	3	4	0.298
5	4	5	0.509
6	5	6	0.725
7	6	7	0.945
8	6	7	0.147
9	7	8	0.349
10	8	9	0.557
11	9	10	0.769
12	10	11	0.983
13	10	11	0.185

Example 2.4
QMED estimation from POT data: Feugh at Heugh Head (12008)

There are ten complete water-years of flood data for the Feugh at Heugh Head (12008), a 229 km^2 tributary of the Dee in east Scotland. The 12 largest POT floods are: 261.6, 202.9, 162.7, 160.8, 155.8, 141.6, 139.3, **133.4**, **124.4**, 120.0, 113.3 and 110.4 m^3 s^{-1}.

For a ten-year record, the required values of $i = 8$ and $w = 0.557$ are read from Table 2.1. Inserting w, and the 8th and 9th highest flood peaks (in bold) into Equation 2.1 yields:

$$QMED = (0.557)\,133.4 + (1 - 0.557)\,124.4 = 129.4\ \text{m}^3\,\text{s}^{-1}.$$

This is somewhat smaller than the sample median of the ten annual maxima (not shown) of 137.5 m^3 s^{-1}. Because of the shortness of the record, the *QMED* estimate from POT is preferred, and an adjustment for climatic variation may be appropriate (see Chapter 20).

This is the recommended method when the flood record is two to 13 years long, provided that the POT series is as long as the annual maximum series. The parameter values in Table 2.1 have been specially calibrated for use with UK flood peaks, which have a perceptible tendency to cluster in time (see §12.3).

When estimating *QMED* from POT data, it is conventional (and preferable) to count years in water-years (i.e. beginning 1 October). Nevertheless, the user can choose to count years from another start-date, e.g. 1 June, if this allows an additional year of data to be analysed. This relaxation of the water-year convention is reasonable for *QMED* estimation from short flood records using the POT approach. However, the Volume 3 procedures require that, where possible, annual maximum series are abstracted and analysed in water-years beginning on 1 October.

Example 2.5
QMED estimation from POT data: Dwyryd at Maentwrog (65002)

Figure 2.4 shows the six complete water-years of POT flood data for this catchment. The 5th and 6th highest floods are 141.8 and 138.0 $m^3 s^{-1}$. This gives a *QMED* estimate of:

$$QMED = (0.725)\,141.8 + (1 - 0.725)\,138.0 = 140.8\ m^3 s^{-1}$$

which is slightly smaller than the *QMED* estimate from annual maxima in Example 2.1.

Because of the shortness of the record, it is reasonable to relax the preference for water-years and to analyse the full POT record. The gross period of record is 4 May 1967 to 30 January 1974 (6.75 years). It transpires that the highest and 3rd highest floods in the 6.75-year period fell outside the six water-years analysed above. If the full POT record is used (and assumed to represent a 7-year period) the revised calculation yields:

$$QMED = (0.945)\,144.4 + (1 - 0.945)\,141.8 = 144.3\ m^3 s^{-1}.$$

Alternatively or additionally, it may be appropriate to adjust the *QMED* estimate for climatic variation, by reference to longer-term records at nearby stations (see Chapter 20).

2.5 Confidence intervals for QMED estimates

A confidence interval expresses the uncertainty in an estimate. Typical values are summarised in Table 2.2, taken from §13.8.

These confidence intervals represent the uncertainty arising from use of a limited sample size. The true uncertainty – taking account of measurement and model errors as well as the sample error – is likely to be somewhat larger, but is difficult to quantify.

2.6 Record extension by regression

When there is a very short record at the subject site (perhaps as short as one year), which overlaps a much longer record nearby, it may be practical to extend the record by a regression method. A predictive relationship is sought to estimate the flood peak at the subject site Q_s from the corresponding flood peak at the donor site Q_d. Suitable model forms to consider are:

Example 2.6
95% confidence intervals for QMED for the Feugh at Heugh Head (12008)

General
Station 12008 has POT and annual maximum series of equal length (i.e. 10 water-years). The recommended method is to estimate *QMED* from the POT series (Example 2.4). From Table 2.2, the typical 68% confidence interval when estimating from a 10-year POT record is (0.89 *QMED*, 1.13 *QMED*). The corresponding 95% confidence interval is obtained by squaring the factors, i.e. (0.89² *QMED*, 1.13² *QMED*). For the *QMED* estimate of 129.4 m³ s⁻¹ derived in Example 2.4, this yields 95% confidence intervals for *QMED* of (102, 165) m³ s⁻¹.

Specific
Rather than using the general estimate of uncertainty from Table 2.2, it is possible to obtain a specific estimate of the confidence interval by resampling from the POT series and evaluating *QMED* in each case. Using balanced resampling on water-years, taking 199 resamples, the 95% confidence interval for *QMED* for this station is found to be (101, 159) m³ s⁻¹. The principles of resampling are introduced in 1 A.3.

Table 2.2 *Typical 68% confidence intervals for QMED estimation from annual maxima, POT series and catchment descriptors. For a given record length, the recommended method (corresponding to the narrowest interval) is shown in bold.*

Record length (years)	Typical 68% confidence intervals for *QMED* estimation		
	From annual maxima	From POT series	From catchment descriptors
0			(0.65 *QMED*, 1.55 *QMED*)
1	(0.66 *QMED*, 1.52 *QMED*)	**(0.67 *QMED*, 1.48 *QMED*)**	(0.65 *QMED*, 1.55 *QMED*)
2	(0.75 *QMED*, 1.34 *QMED*)	**(0.76 *QMED*, 1.31 *QMED*)**	(0.65 *QMED*, 1.55 *QMED*)
3	(0.77 *QMED*, 1.29 *QMED*)	**(0.80 *QMED*, 1.25 *QMED*)**	(0.65 *QMED*, 1.55 *QMED*)
5	(0.82 *QMED*, 1.22 *QMED*)	**(0.85 *QMED*, 1.18 *QMED*)**	(0.65 *QMED*, 1.55 *QMED*)
10	(0.88 *QMED*, 1.14 *QMED*)	**(0.89 *QMED*, 1.13 *QMED*)**	(0.65 *QMED*, 1.55 *QMED*)
15	**(0.90 *QMED*, 1.11 *QMED*)**	(0.90 *QMED*, 1.11 *QMED*)	(0.65 *QMED*, 1.55 *QMED*)
20	**(0.93 *QMED*, 1.08 *QMED*)**	(0.92 *QMED*, 1.09 *QMED*)	(0.65 *QMED*, 1.55 *QMED*)

$$Q_s = a + bQ_d \qquad (2.2)$$

$$\ln Q_s = c + d \ln Q_d \qquad (2.3)$$

If *a* is not significantly different from zero, or *d* is not significantly different from 1, these models reduce to the simpler form:

$$Q_s = bQ_d \qquad (2.4)$$

Provided the regression is convincing – e.g. explaining more than 90% of the variance in flood peaks at the subject site – the model can be used to extend the flood series at the downstream site. *QMED* can then be estimated by the method of §2.4. The nature of the POT method is such that it suffices to use the regression model to transfer the two flood values that straddle the *QMED* value at the donor site, i.e. Q_i and Q_{i+1} in Equation 2.1.

Judgement is required in determining how many flood events (from the short period of overlap) to use in the regression analysis. Preferably, the flood events should be selected according to threshold exceedances at the *donor* site. It is prudent to check the fit of the model visually, to confirm whether flood peaks close to *QMED* are well modelled or based on extrapolation. A time-series plot of the model residuals (i.e. observed minus predicted) provides a check for any unexpected trend effects.

Example 2.7
Record extension by regression

Modelling
It is required to estimate *QMED* at a site some distance downstream of a permanent gauging station. A temporary gauging station is established at the subject site and, in one wet winter, ten distinct floods are measured at both sites. A regression analysis yields a model that explains 99% of the variance in flow at the subject site, Q_s, in terms of the flow measured at the donor site, Q_d. The model is:

$$Q_s = -26.0 + 1.267 \, Q_d$$

The intercept term is found to be not significantly different from zero, allowing the simpler model:

$$Q_s = 1.208 \, Q_d$$

A plot (see inset figure) confirms that the model provides a good description of the data.

QMED estimation
The model is used to extend the very short flood series at the subject site to form a 10-year record: a period long enough for *QMED* estimation using the POT method of §2.4. The record extension yields a POT series at the subject site in which the 8th and 9th largest floods are 499.7 and 479.6 $m^3 \, s^{-1}$ respectively. Applying Equation 2.1, *QMED* at the subject site is estimated to be 491 $m^3 \, s^{-1}$.

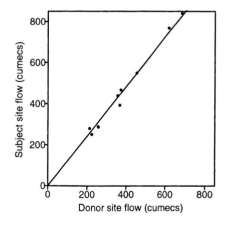

Commentary
Although a hypothetical application, the example uses real data. A regression model – calibrated on flood data for the 1982/83 water-year – is used to generate a 10-year POT record for the Dee at Park (12002) from the POT series measured upstream at Woodend (12001). The catchment area to Park is 33% greater than that to Woodend, a moderately large difference. The *QMED* estimate of 491 $m^3 \, s^{-1}$ thus obtained compares with an estimate of 460 $m^3 \, s^{-1}$ derived by direct analysis of the Park POT series for the relevant period, namely the ten years commencing 1 October 1982. Perhaps because the winter of 1982/83 included an impressive array of flood peaks, the record extension approach has in this case performed well. Sometimes the regression analysis will be much less convincing, e.g. because it is based on minor events or yields an r^2 value of less than 0.90. In such cases, it may be preferable to discard the very short flood series at the subject site, and to adopt the more usual data transfer procedure of Chapter 4.

Chapter 3   Estimating QMED from catchment descriptors (A)

Many flood estimation problems arise at sites for which there are no flood peak data. This chapter presents a procedure for estimating *QMED* from catchment descriptors. Catchment descriptors are measures that seek to capture key features of the drainage basin. For example, *AREA* is the drainage area in km². The catchment descriptors used in the FEH are based on digital data, and are discussed fully in Volume 5.

3.1 Scope of applications

Flood estimates made from catchment descriptors are, in general, grossly inferior to those made from flood peak data, even those estimated from short records. Nevertheless, Chapter 3 is important for two reasons. First, it allows preliminary estimates of *QMED* to be made relatively simply. Second, it forms an integral part of the procedures presented in Chapter 4, whereby estimates of *QMED* are transferred from a gauged (donor) site to an ungauged (subject) site.

Recommendation

The recommended procedure (1 5.3) for *QMED* estimation at sites for which there are no flood peak data is to transfer data from a nearby donor site or from a more distant analogue catchment. A prerequisite for such transfers is that the donor/analogue catchment is hydrologically similar to the subject catchment. Data transfer procedures for *QMED* estimation are presented in Chapter 4.

It is recommended that the Chapter 3 procedure is only used in preliminary assessments or for minor flood design problems. Estimating *QMED* from flood data (Chapter 2) or by data transfer (Chapter 4) is preferable.

Exceptionally, in cases where no suitable data transfer can be found, the Chapter 3 method may form the sole basis of *QMED* estimation.

Warning

The estimation of *QMED* from catchment descriptors is inappropriate for flood frequency estimation in many situations, for example:
- Where there is a threat to life;
- In the design of major flood defence schemes;
- In justifying non-structural flood defence measures (e.g. major investment in flood warning, increased flood insurance premiums, downgrading or abandoning land use);
- In support of decisions to site development in the perceived margins of floodplains.

Ignoring gauged flood data close to the site (see §4.3) can never be condoned, and failure to look further afield (§4.5) may leave the flood estimation open to criticism.

3.2 Ingredients

There are two steps in *QMED* estimation from catchment descriptors. This chapter discusses the first step, which yields an estimate of $QMED_{rural}$. For rural catchments, this is the only step necessary. Where required, the estimate is adjusted for catchment urbanisation in a second step (see Chapter 9). The variable $QMED_{rural}$ denotes an estimate of *QMED* in the *rural state*, i.e. in the absence of urban development. It is an estimate of the *as-rural* index flood.

$QMED_{rural}$ is estimated from five catchment descriptors: drainage area (*AREA*), average annual rainfall (*SAAR*), soil drainage type (represented by *SPRHOST* and *BFIHOST*), and storage attenuation (represented by *FARL*). The catchment descriptor *FARL* is an index of flood attenuation due to reservoirs and lakes; *SPRHOST* and *BFIHOST* are estimates of standard percentage runoff (*SPR*) and the baseflow index (*BFI*) obtained from the HOST soil classification. Application of an urban adjustment factor (see Chapter 9) is recommended if the FEH index of urban extent, *URBEXT*, exceeds 0.025. The FEH catchment descriptors are summarised in Appendix C, and defined more fully in Volume 5.

It is important to verify that the digital data provide a realistic representation of the catchment. In particular, the user must confirm that the estimate of drainage area, *AREA*, is consistent with locally held information, and that the estimates of *URBEXT* and *FARL* are up-to-date.

Checking the catchment boundary

The FEH catchment descriptors are based on drainage boundaries defined by a digital terrain model, IHDTM. Catchment-descriptor values are supplied on the FEH CD-ROM. The associated software displays the catchment boundary used to calculate the descriptors.

It is important to note that catchment boundaries derived from contour data – whether through digital terrain data or subjectively from paper maps – may misrepresent the effective drainage area for flood runoff. The user should therefore check the catchment boundary using a combination of personal knowledge, local information, and maps. Inconsistencies are likely to arise principally on small catchments, on urbanised catchments, on very flat catchments, and in cases where natural drainage paths have been diverted by channels, culverts or embankments.

Although principally based on contour data, IHDTM uses blue-line information from 1:50000 maps to guide the position of principal drainage paths. This occasionally leads to incorrect representations where stream junctions are not explicitly shown on the 1:50000 map, e.g. because of culverting.

Where there is scope for the drainage area to be under or over-represented, the user should refer to contour data at least as detailed as those shown (in Great Britain) on OS 1:25000 maps. A 5% error in *AREA* should certainly be considered unacceptable. In cases of doubt, the site should be visited and, if appropriate, surveyed. Volume 5 gives advice on how to adjust descriptor values manually, in cases where the effective catchment boundary differs from the one given by the FEH CD-ROM (see **5** 7.2).

3.3 *Estimation of QMED$_{rural}$*

The as-rural index flood $QMED_{rural}$ is estimated from:

$$QMED_{rural} = 1.172\ AREA^{AE}\left(\frac{SAAR}{1000}\right)^{1.560} FARL^{2.642}\left(\frac{SPRHOST}{100}\right)^{1.211} 0.0198^{RESHOST}$$

(3.1)

Here, *AE* denotes the *area exponent* given by:

$$AE = 1 - 0.015\ \ln\left(\frac{AREA}{0.5}\right)$$

(3.2)

The variable *RESHOST* is a residual soils term obtained from HOST data (see **5** 5) and defined by:

$$RESHOST = BFIHOST + 1.30\left(\frac{SPRHOST}{100}\right) - 0.987$$

(3.3)

The FEH catchment-descriptor methods are applicable to catchments no smaller than 0.5 km², the lower limit for which the FEH CD-ROM supplies catchment descriptors. Thus, the area exponent given by Equation 3.2 is never greater than 1.0.

The factorial standard error associated with Equation 3.2 is 1.549. Thus, only about two out of three estimates made using the catchment-descriptor model will yield an estimate of $QMED_{rural}$ that lies within the range (0.65 $QMED_{rural}$, 1.55 $QMED_{rural}$). This 68% confidence interval is much wider than those for $QMED$ estimation from flood peak data, even when the record length is very short (see Table 2.2). Catchment-descriptor estimates of $QMED$ should therefore not be used if there is scope to obtain flood peak data at the subject site, or to transfer an estimate from a gauged site (see Chapter 4).

Example 3.1
Estimation of QMED from catchment descriptors: Dwyryd at Maentwrog (65002)

Catchment descriptors to ungauged sites are found using the FEH CD-ROM. Descriptors for gauged catchments, including station 65002, are listed in the Appendix to Volume 5. The relevant values are:

$$AREA = 78.15 \text{ km}^2 \qquad SAAR = 2212 \text{ mm}$$
$$BFIHOST = 0.378 \qquad SPRHOST = 47.2 \qquad FARL = 0.938$$

Note that *FARL* is markedly less than the (unreservoired) default value of 1.0, reflecting the many lakes and several reservoirs in the catchment, including those associated with the Tan-y-Grisiau pumped-storage hydroelectric scheme.

Application of Equations 3.2 and 3.3 yields:

$$AE = 0.924 \qquad RESHOST = 0.005$$

From which Equation 3.1 gives:

$$QMED_{rural} = 75.7 \text{ m}^3\text{s}^{-1}$$

The Dwyryd at Maentwrog catchment is almost entirely rural, with $URBEXT = 0.006$. This is well within the limit ($URBEXT = 0.025$) for the catchment to be judged essentially rural. Thus, the estimate from catchment descriptors is:

$$QMED = 75.7 \text{ m}^3\text{s}^{-1}$$

Extensive slate quarries and spoil-heaps within the Dwyryd catchment may influence flood behaviour, but are not accounted for in this generalised estimate.

The estimate above is very much smaller than the 144.3 m^3s^{-1} estimated from POT flood data (see Example 2.5). If the latter is taken as a true estimate of *QMED*, the factorial error of the catchment-descriptor estimate is 1.906 (where 75.7/144.3 = 1/1.906). This compares with the factorial standard error of 1.549 associated with Equation 3.1. The error in ln*QMED* is 0.645 (i.e. ln1.906), which is 1.47 times greater than the standard error in ln*QMED* by the catchment-descriptor model of 0.438 (i.e. ln1.549). Assuming that errors in estimating ln*QMED* are Normally distributed, about one in seven estimates using the Chapter 3 procedure can be expected to be worse than this.

This example shows why *QMED* should be estimated from catchment descriptors only as a method of last resort. Where practical, the methods of Chapter 2 or 4 are always preferable.

Chapter 4 Estimating QMED by data transfer

4.1 Context

Whenever possible, a *QMED* estimate at an ungauged site should be adjusted by data transfer from a gauge on a hydrologically similar catchment. The preferred approach (Sections 4.2 to 4.4) is to transfer a *QMED* estimate from a gauge that is local and highly relevant to the subject site. The reserve option (§4.5) is to transfer a *QMED* estimate from a more distant catchment that is hydrologically similar.

The rationale for data transfers is the relative imprecision of generalised estimates from catchment descriptors (e.g. Chapter 3) compared to specific estimates made from gauged data (e.g. Chapter 2). Data transfers provide a halfway house. The concepts of donor and analogue catchments are introduced in Box 4.1.

The basic transfer procedure (§4.2) can be applied to *any* generalised *QMED* estimate made at an ungauged site. A generalised estimate is one made by a substantially general procedure without recourse to gauged flood data. Most commonly, it will be a *QMED* estimate based on catchment descriptors (Chapter 3).

Box 4.1 Donor and analogue catchments

A *donor site* is a local catchment offering gauged data that are particularly relevant to flood estimation at the subject site. The ideal donor catchment is one sited just upstream or downstream of the subject site. More typically, it will be sited some distance upstream or downstream, draining an area rather smaller or larger than the subject catchment. A similar-sized catchment on an adjacent tributary can also make a good donor if the physiography and land-use of the two catchments are broadly similar.

An *analogue catchment* is a more distant gauged catchment that is sufficiently similar to the subject catchment to make a transfer of information worthwhile. Judging a suitable analogue requires hydrological understanding and experience.

4.2 Basic transfer procedure

The basic transfer procedure comprises six steps:
1. Select a donor site;
2. Derive the preferred estimate of *QMED* at the donor site (Chapter 2);
3. Evaluate a generalised estimate of *QMED* at the donor site (e.g. by Chapter 3);
4. Evaluate the generalised estimate of *QMED* at the subject site (using the same method as in Step 3);
5. Compare the two estimates of *QMED* at the donor site, determining the factorial under or over-estimation of the generalised estimate;
6. Adjust the generalised estimate of *QMED* at the subject site to reflect the factorial under- or over-estimation seen at the donor site.

The selection of a donor site (Step 1) is discussed in §4.3. Where there is more than one potential donor, either the most suitable is selected or a multi-site adjustment procedure is used (see §4.4). The preferred estimate of *QMED* at the donor site (Step 2) follows the §2.2 recommendations, summarised in Figure 2.1. Steps 3 and 4 require no particular comment. Steps 5 and 6 are more straightforward than they appear and are crystallised in the *transfer equation*:

$$QMED_{s,adj} = QMED_{s,cds}\left(\frac{QMED_{g,obs}}{QMED_{g,cds}}\right) \qquad (4.1)$$

where the subscripts *s* and *g* refer to the subject site and gauged site respectively, and *cds* and *obs* refer to estimates deriving from catchment descriptors and observed data respectively. $QMED_{s,adj}$ is the adjusted estimate of *QMED* at the subject site, resulting from the data transfer.

Dividing through in the equation by $QMED_{s,cds}$ yields:

$$\frac{QMED_{s,adj}}{QMED_{s,cds}} = \left(\frac{QMED_{g,obs}}{QMED_{g,cds}}\right) \qquad (4.1')$$

This reveals that the adjustment works on the principle that the proportional error in the generalised estimate *seen* at the gauged site is indicative of the *unseen* proportional error in the generalised estimate at the subject site. For this assumption to be reasonable, it is essential that the estimates of *QMED* used in Steps 3 and 4 should derive from the same procedure. Typically, the generalised estimates will use the catchment-descriptor model of Equation 3.1. However, the same principle might apply to generalised estimates of QMED made in other ways, e.g. using the channel-width model of §5.2.

4.3 Selection of donor site

A donor site is a gauged record that is sufficiently close to the subject site to make its flood data of special relevance. Usually it will be on the same river, directly upstream or downstream of the subject site. Exceptionally, it may be on an adjacent river. To be accepted as a donor site, the gauged catchment must also be hydrologically similar to the subject catchment. Judging catchment similarity is as much an art as a science.

When there is more than one potential donor catchment, relative suitability has to be judged in terms of both similarity to the subject catchment and quality of *QMED* estimate. In most cases, the choice of donor site will either be obvious (only one reasonable candidate – use §4.2) or fraught (no reasonable candidate – see §4.5). However, in a minority of cases there will be merit in applying a multi-site adjustment procedure.

4.4 Multi-site adjustment procedure

4.4.1 Formulation

The simplest approach is to treat each donor site separately, forming *M* adjusted estimates of $QMED_{s,adj}$ at the subject site: $QMED_{s,adj1}$, $QMED_{s,adj2}$ ... $QMED_{s,adjM}$. The main difficulty is the notation. The final *QMED* estimate is obtained as a weighted average of the individually transferred estimates. It is recommended that the average be taken by geometrical weighting, i.e.

$$QMED_{s,adj} = \prod_{i=1}^{M} (QMED_{s,adji})^{w_i} \qquad (4.2)$$

where w_i are relative weights, chosen to sum to unity. Taking logarithms gives the friendlier form:

$$\ln QMED_{s,adj} = \sum_{i=1}^{M} w_i \ln QMED_{s,adji} \qquad (4.2')$$

4.4.2 Weights

The choice of weights w_i is a matter of judgement. The weight should reflect both similarity to the subject site and the quality of the $QMED$ estimate at the gauged site. The weights would not normally be very different from each other. If one or two donor sites are clearly the most relevant, the adjustment of $QMED$ should be based on those transfers alone.

4.5 Using an analogue catchment

A common situation is that a flood estimate is required for an ungauged site, and that no gauged catchment within the river basin is at all similar. In this circumstance, the recommendation is to transfer a $QMED$ estimate from an analogue catchment (see Box 4.1). Such a catchment is hydrologically similar to the subject catchment but falls in a different river basin.

The FEH approach to flood growth curve estimation (see Chapters 6 and 7) groups catchments in terms of their hydrological similarity rather than their

---

Box 4.2 Guidance on judging catchment similarity

The judgement of catchment similarity is discussed throughout the FEH, in 1 3.3 and 4 2.1.3, as well as in Chapters 4, 6 and 16 of this volume. The essence is to identify and summarise the degree of inter-site similarity in those catchment properties thought to influence or represent flood behaviour.

The basic concept is clear, yet the advice given in the Handbook is far from regimented. While this may reflect imperfect co-ordination of the methods and their presentation, there are important factors which conspire against uniform guidelines:

● There are different possibilities in different situations; for example, it is possible to use river flow data in the judgement of similarity between gauged catchments, but not between gauged and ungauged catchments;

● In some situations it is pragmatic to use an objective criterion of catchment similarity (e.g. in research to develop generalised procedures) whilst, in others, subjective judgement is fully warranted (e.g. in site-specific studies where the analyst has local knowledge);

● It is sometimes necessary to find a gauged catchment that is *local* to the subject catchment, e.g. in the adjustment of $QMED$ for climatic variation (see Chapter 20); in other cases, this is merely desirable, e.g. in transferring an estimate of unit hydrograph time-to-peak (see 4 2.2.5).

geographical proximity. Some pooling-groups are found to comprise gauged catchments that are widely dispersed across the UK. This suggests that an extensive search is required before it can be concluded that a particular transfer is the most appropriate or that there is no suitable analogue catchment.

4.5.1 Judging suitability of an analogue catchment for *QMED* transfer

There are opposite perspectives on how to judge catchment similarity for *QMED* transfers. According to the Chapter 3 model, the most important catchment features influencing *QMED* on rural catchments are those indexed by *AREA, SAAR, BFIHOST, SPRHOST* and *FARL*. Thus, one view of catchment similarity is that each of these features should be broadly similar between the subject catchment and the analogue catchment. The opposing view is that the $QMED_{rural}$ model (§3.3) accounts adequately for the variations in *QMED* that arise from the listed features. Thus, the important test in judging similarity is whether the catchments are similar in *other* respects.

Example 4.1
QMED estimation for the Kenwyn at New Mill: data transfer from the Kenwyn at Truro (48005)

Truro was severely flooded from the River Kenwyn on 27 January 1988 and 11 October 1988. Flood estimates were needed in 1990 to support the construction of a flood storage reservoir at New Mill, some 3 km upstream of the city centre. For verisimilitude, the transfer is carried out using data available in late 1989, when New Mill Dam was being designed.

Step 1 The choice of donor site is obvious: the Kenwyn at Truro gauging station ($AREA$ = 19.1 km^2) lies about 2 km downstream of New Mill ($AREA$ = 16.6 km^2).

Step 2 Annual maxima are available for 18 water-years: 1968/69 to 1981/82 and 1985/86 to 1988/89. The recommended method is therefore to estimate *QMED* as the median of the annual maxima. This yields the preferred estimate of *QMED* at the gauged site:

$QMED_{g,obs}$ = 5.62 m^{3}s^{-1}.

Step 3 Applying the catchment-descriptor model (§3.3) to the gauged site yields: $QMED_{g,cds}$ = 4.74 m^{3}s^{-1}. Strictly, this is an estimate of the as-rural *QMED* at the gauged site. The donor catchment has an urban extent of 0.031, which is slightly greater than the 0.025 limit for the catchment to be judged *essentially rural* (see Chapter 9). Because the degree of urbanisation is minor, and concentrated close to the catchment outlet, an adjustment for urbanisation is judged unnecessary in this case. Consequently, the catchment-descriptor estimate from §3.3 is accepted as an estimate of *QMED*.

Step 4 Applying the catchment-descriptor model to the subject site gives:

$QMED_{s,cds}$ = 4.13 m^{3}s^{-1}.

Steps 5 and 6 Application of Equation 4.1 completes the data transfer, yielding: $QMED_{s,adj}$ = 4.13 (5.62 / 4.74) = 4.90 m^{3}s^{-1}. The outcome is to increase the *QMED* estimate at New Mill from 4.13 to 4.90 m^{3}s^{-1}.

Neither view is wholly right or wrong. A pragmatic approach is to require that the features listed in the *QMED* model are broadly similar and that the catchments do not differ radically in some influential unlisted feature. Particular caution is required when proposing a transfer to or from a catchment affected by urbanisation, reservoir development, or other major land-use change (see §4.6).

Example 4.2
Ae Water at Ae Village

A flood estimate is required for the Ae Water at Ae Village, in southern Scotland (Figure 4.1). No flood records are held for the Ae, but there are two flood series on the Kinnel Water. The Kinnel Water at Redhall (78004) has 31 annual maxima. This is a neighbouring catchment of similar size and wetness, but slightly more permeable soils. The Kinnel Water catchment to Bridgemuir (78005) also has similar wetness and slightly more permeable soils, but is three times larger than the subject catchment. The *QMED* estimate at this gauge derives from 14 annual maxima. All three catchments are forested, the subject catchment the most extensively.

The natural solution appears to be to transfer a *QMED* estimate from station 78004, using the basic transfer procedure. However, station 78005 has the compensating advantage of lying downstream of the subject site; in other words, station 78005 gauges the combined flow of the Ae and Kinnel Waters. Thus a transfer from station 78005 is also relevant.

Such a situation can inspire quite complicated adjustment schemes, e.g. an attempt might be made to attribute the *difference* in flood behaviour at the two Kinnel stations to the contribution of the Ae. While an adjustment based on adding or subtracting flows can sometimes be useful in studies of typical river-flow, the approach is unsound when applied to a typical *extreme* river-flow, such as *QMED*.

The approach taken is therefore to apply the multi-site adjustment procedure (§4.4). Somewhat greater weight ($w_1 = 0.6$) is accorded to station 78004 than to station 78005 ($w_2 = 0.4$), but the choice of weights is subjective.

All three catchments are essentially rural. Applying the catchment-descriptor model of §3.3 to the subject site yields:

$$QMED_{s,cds} = 48.3 \text{ m}^3\text{s}^{-1}$$

Applying the basic transfer procedure of §4.2 to each site in turn:

$$QMED_{s,adj1} = QMED_{s,cds} \left(QMED_{78004,obs} / QMED_{78004,cds} \right) = 48.3 \,(69.4 / 40.6) = 82.6 \text{ m}^3\text{s}^{-1}$$
$$QMED_{s,adj2} = QMED_{s,cds} \left(QMED_{78005,obs} / QMED_{78005,cds} \right) = 48.3 \,(128.9 / 94.1) = 66.2 \text{ m}^3\text{s}^{-1}$$

Hence, from Equation 4.2:

$$QMED_{s,adj} = \left(QMED_{s,adj1} \right)^{0.6} \left(QMED_{s,adj2} \right)^{0.4} = (82.6)^{0.6} \,(66.2)^{0.4} = 75.6 \text{ m}^3\text{s}^{-1}$$

Thus the effect of the data transfer is to revise the *QMED* estimate at Ae Village from 48.3 to 75.6 m³s⁻¹, an increase of 57%.

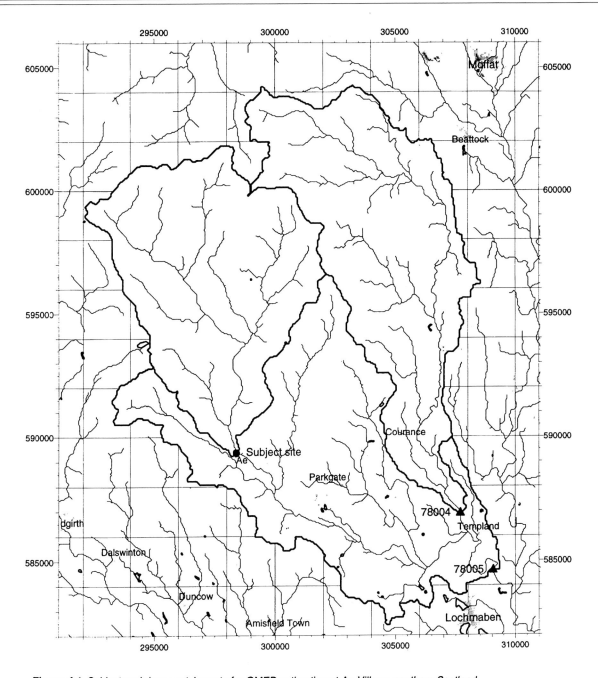

Figure 4.1 *Subject and donor catchments for QMED estimation at Ae Village, southern Scotland*

4.5.2 Transfer procedure

Once a credible analogue catchment has been found, the basic transfer procedure of §4.2 is applied as previously. If two or more useful analogues are found, the multi-site adjustment procedure of §4.4 should be followed.

There is an important distinction between the use of donor and analogue catchments. Suitable *donor* catchments will be few in number and their suitability will generally be clear from their relative location and the relative quality of their *QMED* estimates. Thus, it would be unusual to transfer data from more than one or two donor catchments. In contrast, the relevance of a particular analogue catchment to *QMED* estimation at the subject site will often be supposed rather than manifest. In such circumstances, it may be prudent to involve several analogue catchments in the transfer procedure than place reliance on one alone.

4.6 Additional guidance

4.6.1 Urbanised catchments

It is generally recommended that donor/analogue catchments used in *QMED* estimation by data transfer should be essentially rural. A suitable test is that the FEH index of urban extent, *URBEXT,* should be less than 0.025. Some relaxation of this rule is warranted – as in Example 4.1 – when, in all other respects, the gauged catchment makes an excellent donor.

When applying the transfer method, there is no requirement for the subject catchment to be rural. If the subject site is urbanised, the data transfer can be used to adjust the as-rural index flood, $QMED_{rural}$. The allowance for catchment urbanisation is then applied in the normal way, using the procedure given in Chapter 9.

Catchments having large but comparable degrees of urbanisation (indicated by *URBEXT*) should not be judged similar if the layout or character of development is very different. An important consideration is the location of urbanisation within the catchment, both with regard to the main drainage paths and relative to any important permeable/impermeable soil-class divisions. The effect of urbanisation on flood frequency is influenced by the permeability of the parent soils, and the relative position of development within the catchment. The auxiliary descriptors of urban location (*URBLOC*) and urban concentration (*URBCONC*) may help in the judgement of catchment similarity.

These (and other) catchment descriptors are summarised in Appendix C, with full details in Volume 5. A particular worry is that apparently similar urbanised catchments may differ in the extent to which remedial works have offset the adverse impact of development on flood frequency (see Chapter 18). This is largely unquantifiable. Experience and local knowledge are therefore essential if a *QMED* estimate is to be transferred from one urbanised catchment to another (see also **1** 5.7).

In principle, the transfer procedure of §4.2 can be applied to *QMED* estimates on urbanised catchments obtained from Chapter 9. However, it may be necessary to make the uncomfortable assumption that the urban adjustment part of the *QMED* model is correct, using the §4.2 procedure to transfer an estimate of $QMED_{rural}$ rather than *QMED*. At the donor site, the gauged estimate of $QMED_{rural}$ is inferred by back-calculation from the urban adjustment model. Such transfers should only be attempted exceptionally, when the subject and donor catchments are broadly similar in all respects, including the degree of urbanisation. Section 9.4 provides further advice.

4.6.2 Reservoired catchments

The presence of a major impounding reservoir on either the subject or donor catchment should discourage any routine transfer of information. A suitable test is to query the transfer if either donor or subject site has a *FARL* index less than 0.95.

FARL is an index of flood attenuation due to reservoirs and lakes (see Appendix C). If the main effect is due to a lake – or a reservoir kept permanently full – it may be reasonable to permit the transfer, on the assumption that the flood attenuation effect is adequately represented within the catchment-descriptor model. If the main effect is due to an impounding reservoir, it may be better to base the flood frequency estimation on the rainfall-runoff method (Volume 4). Where there are useful flood peak data to exploit, a hybrid method can be adopted (see **1** 5.6).

4.6.3 Other special cases

Soils are an important influence on flood magnitude. Activities such as opencast mining and quarrying can lead to dramatic losses in the natural permeability and porosity of soils. Without adequate remedial works, the effects can be pronounced and sustained. With few exceptions, it is never possible to restore worked ground to a condition where the soils are as permeable as in the virgin state. Arterial, forest and field drainage accelerate flood response and are liable to increase flood magnitudes. None of these features is explicitly represented in the *QMED* estimation from catchment descriptors. Circumspection is needed if the subject or donor catchment is unusual in such respect.

Floodplain effects are only indirectly represented in the FEH procedures. While floodplains can have a marked effect on the flood frequency curve at longer return periods, they may not always present a problem for estimating *QMED* (see §5.2).

4.6.4 Assistance in judging catchment similarity

A tool within the WINFAP-FEH software package identifies the gauged catchments that are most similar to a given subject catchment in terms of catchment size (*AREA*), wetness (*SAAR*), and soil properties (*BFIHOST*). Having identified a pool of catchments, the software provides extensive diagnostic information to assist in judging catchment similarity in terms of other features (*FARL, PROPWET* and *URBEXT*) and flood behaviour (flood seasonality and flood statistics). Figure 6.2 illustrates the types of display provided.

While designed primarily to assist in the construction of pooling-groups for growth curve derivation (Chapter 6), the tool can help to narrow down the search for an analogue catchment for *QMED* data transfer. However, it is still important to make a specific search for a possible donor site, i.e. local to the subject site. A gauged record upstream or downstream of the subject site is always of special interest, even if its drainage area is several times larger or smaller than the subject catchment. The check is necessary both because the software tool is preoccupied with judging similarity in terms of *AREA, SAAR* and *BFIHOST*, and because there may be additional gauged records held locally that are not in the FEH flood peak datasets.

Chapter 5   Other ways of estimating QMED

Flood frequency estimation is a developing science, and methods will continue to evolve. For estimating the very rarest floods, it appears likely that extreme value analysis, and systematic pooling of data, will remain key ingredients. However, because *QMED* represents a not-very-extreme event, there is scope to consider alternative methods of estimation. *QMED* is the flood that is exceeded on average every other year.

5.1 QMED from continuous simulation modelling

The continuous simulation approach to flood frequency estimation is based on river flow simulation using a catchment model. The primary data input is a medium-to-long record of catchment hourly rainfall. The approach has extensive data and modelling requirements, and falls outside the scope of the FEH. Only a brief introduction is provided here.

The FSR rainfall-runoff approach (see FEH Volume 4) is a relatively intricate *design event method*, which makes assumptions about the storm and antecedent conditions that give rise to the *T*-year flood. In contrast, the continuous simulation approach is in principle straightforward. River flows are simulated continuously over many years and the largest flood peaks in the runoff series are analysed as if they formed an observed peaks-over-threshold (POT) series (Calver and Lamb, 1996). A potent feature of the approach is that simulations can be re-run using a modified rainfall input to reflect projected climate change, or with a modified catchment model to represent land-use change (Naden *et al.*, 1996).

The approach generally requires continuous hourly rainfall records, and a catchment model that simulates the full range of flow conditions. Where appropriate, different models can be used for different subcatchments, and can be combined with hydraulic modelling of key river reaches. In some catchments, simulations may need to take explicit account of snow and snowmelt, posing extra requirements for modelling and meteorological data (notably, air temperature). Application of the approach to ungauged catchments requires generalisation of the model parameters so that appropriate values can be estimated from catchment descriptors. The development of fully generalised catchment models is dependent on extensive data gathering and research (see also **1** 9.6)

Situations in which continuous simulation might be a useful route to estimating *QMED* are relatively specialised. High quality rainfall and flow data are required, with a flow record long enough for calibration of the rainfall-runoff model yet too short to allow direct estimation of *QMED* (using Chapter 2). Another situation in which continuous simulation might be useful is if there are unusual hydraulic or storage effects locally, which caution against transferring a *QMED* estimate using the procedure in Chapter 4.

5.2 QMED from channel dimensions

QMED estimation from channel dimensions provides an alternative to estimation from catchment descriptors (Chapter 3). It can form the basis of a second opinion, in cases where the *QMED* estimate from catchment descriptors proves contentious or problematic.

Background

The form and size of river channels provide a natural source of information about flood potential. It is generally held that, in many natural rivers in the UK, the water level in the main channel reaches *bankfull* every year or so. Thus, there is scope to estimate *QMED* from channel dimensions. Wharton *et al.* (1989) estimate typical flood quantiles from channel dimension data in a study of 72 UK catchments. Both channel width and cross-sectional area are found to be useful predictors of the 1.5-year and 5-year floods estimated from annual maxima.

Estimates of *QMED* from the FEH flood peak datasets – obtained by the relevant Chapter 12 method – were regressed against channel dimension data, yielding the model below. Figure 5.1 illustrates the catchment and channel sizes in the 65-site dataset used in calibration.

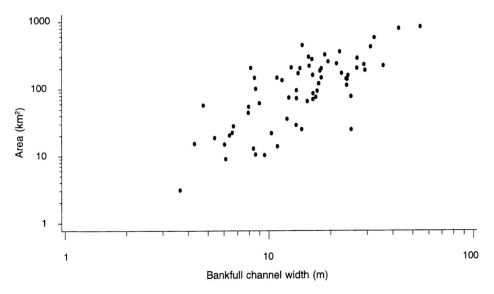

Figure 5.1 *Catchment and channel sizes used in calibration of Equation 5.1 model: channel dimension data taken from Wharton (1989)*

Method

QMED can be estimated from the bankfull channel width, *BCW* (metres). The relevant formula

$$QMED = 0.182 \, BCW^{1.98} \tag{5.1}$$

explains over 80% of variation in ln*QMED* with a factorial standard error of 1.73. This means that 68% of estimates are expected to lie within the interval (0.58 *QMED*, 1.73 *QMED*). The fit of the model is shown in Figure 5.2.

Given the simplicity of the model and the modest sample size, it is unsurprising that Equation 5.1 is typically outperformed by the catchment-descriptor model of Equation 3.1, which has a tighter 68% confidence interval of (0.65 *QMED*, 1.55 *QMED*). Nevertheless, Wharton's method provides a useful alternative in problematic cases.

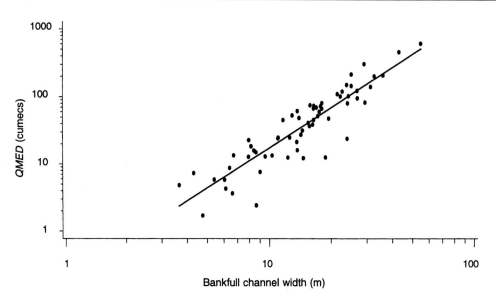

Figure 5.2 *Fit to sample data provided by Equation 5.1 model*

Discussion

The channel dimension approach should not be applied to strongly channelised (i.e. 'engineered') rivers, or to recently modified catchments, unless a fluvial geomorphologist confirms that the channel system has adjusted to the new flow regime. It is evident from Figure 5.1 that Equation 5.1 has been calibrated using data from wide and moderately wide rivers. It is not recommended for use on streams where the channel width at bankfull is much less than 5 metres.

Boxes 5.1 and 5.2 provide guidance on the suitability and use of the approach in particular cases. These are a précis of Wharton (1992).

Box 5.1 Suitability of river reach for QMED estimation by channel width method

Select a reach that is natural, substantially straight, and at least four times as long as the channel width. The reach need not be exactly at the subject site. The following cases should be avoided:

- Reaches that have been artificially modified;
- Reaches with bedrock banks;
- Braided and geomorphologically active reaches;
- Reaches with large pools or locally steep gradients.

The drainage area at the upstream and downstream ends of the selected reach should be very similar, both to each other and to the drainage area at the subject site; i.e. there should be no intervening tributary. Preferably, the bankfull level should be substantially the same on both sides of the river, and relatively uniform along the reach.

Box 5.2 Guidelines for applying the channel width method

Choosing cross-sections
Where possible, select three rectangular-to-trapezoidal sections, spaced at least one channel width apart. Avoid cross-sections of unusual shape. Flow velocities should be relatively symmetrical across the section.

Identifying bankfull level
Bankfull is defined as the (minimum) elevation of the active floodplain. The height of the *lower limit* of perennial vegetation, usually trees, should be used as an aid.

Measuring channel width
Measure the bankfull channel width, *BCW*, by tape or tacheometer. Where one bank is higher than the other, care should be taken to measure horizontally from the level of the lower bank across to the opposite bank. Adopt a reach-average value of *BCW*, calculated as an arithmetic mean.

Example 5.1
QMED estimation from channel width

The subject site drains a 27.22 km² headwater catchment of the Wye. A 100-metre-long reach was chosen about 500 m downstream of the subject site. Three relatively regular sections were identified, about 25 m apart. Bankfull channel width was measured by tape, following the guidelines in Box 5.2 and adopting suitable safety precautions.

The reach-average value of bankfull channel width is:

$$BCW = (17.78 + 16.10 + 20.25) / 3 = 18.0\ m$$

Applying Equation 5.1:

$$QMED = 0.182\,(18.0)^{1.98} = 55.7\ m^3 s^{-1}.$$

Adjusting for the slightly smaller drainage area at the subject site:

$$QMED = 55.7\,(27.22 / 27.95) = 54.2\ m^3 s^{-1}.$$

The subject site is in fact gauged (station 55010). The median of 40 annual maxima yields:

$$QMED = 51.8\ m^3 s^{-1}.$$

In this instance the estimation from channel width performs well.

Chapter 6   Selecting a pooling-group (A)

6.1 Introduction

For most gauging stations, flood records are too short to allow reliable estimation of the long return-period floods typically required in design assessments. The recommendation is therefore to *pool* data from groups of catchments. This is essential when estimating flood frequency at an ungauged site. If the guidance in Chapter 8 (and **1** 5.3) is followed, the only situation in which a pooled analysis might be deemed superfluous is when the record length at the site exceeds 2*T*. Here, *T* denotes the *target return period*, i.e. the return period of primary interest.

"The regions are dead; long live the pooling-groups"

The subheading is inspired by Acreman and Wiltshire (1989). The Flood Studies Report (NERC, 1975) pooled flood data within fixed geographical regions. The pooling-groups recommended in the FEH are fundamentally different:

- Catchments are grouped according to their perceived hydrological similarity rather than their geographical position;
- Catchment groupings are individual to the subject site for which the flood frequency estimate is required;
- The size of pooling-group is adjusted to reflect the return period of interest.

To convey these differences – and to avoid ambiguity in the meaning of *region* – a new vocabulary is used (see Table 6.1).

Table 6.1   *Terminology for pooled frequency analysis*

Flood Studies Report	Flood Estimation Handbook
Region	Pooling-group
Regional frequency analysis	Pooled frequency analysis
Regional growth curve	Pooled growth curve
Regionalisation scheme	Pooling scheme

Essentials

Each subject site is considered to lie at the heart of a group of gauged catchments to which it is hydrologically similar. The pooling-group is sized to provide sufficient data to underpin estimation of the flood growth curve at the subject site. All stations in the pooling-group influence the resultant growth curve to some extent. However, greater weight is given to the longer-record stations, and to those catchments judged most similar to the subject catchment.

The number of stations included in the pooling-group is determined by a rule of thumb: the *5T rule*. This specifies that the pooled stations should collectively supply five times as many years of record as the target return period, *T*. Thus, the pooling-group is sized to provide at least 5*T* *station-years* of flood data.

The objective is to select gauged catchments that are hydrologically similar to the subject catchment. The initial selection is made in terms of catchment descriptors representing three key features: size (*AREA*), wetness (*SAAR*), and soil properties (*BFIHOST*). Next, sites in the pooling-group are reviewed using station and catchment information, and by reference to additional indicators of hydrological similarity. This part of the procedure is subjective and gives considerable scope for the experienced user to apply hydrological judgement to adapt the pooling-group. Finally, the flood peak data themselves are examined, and checks made for discordant sites and group heterogeneity. Unless further review of the pooling-group is indicated, the user proceeds to growth curve derivation (Chapter 7).

The process is summarised in Figure 6.1. There are two options. Experienced users will choose a *precautionary approach*, in which the initial pooling-group is reviewed as a matter of course. Otherwise, a *reactive approach* is recommended, in which the pooling-group is reviewed only if a specific problem arises in testing. Tests in §6.5 explore the statistical properties of the pooled flood data, and determine whether the group includes discordant sites or is strongly heterogeneous.

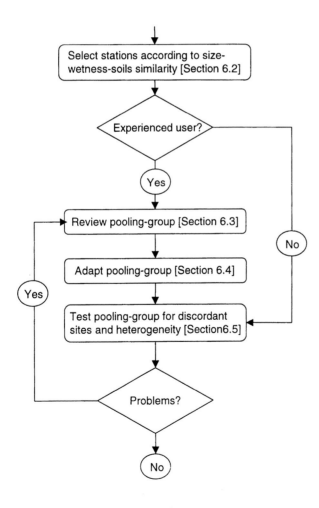

Figure 6.1 *The main steps in constructing a pooling-group*

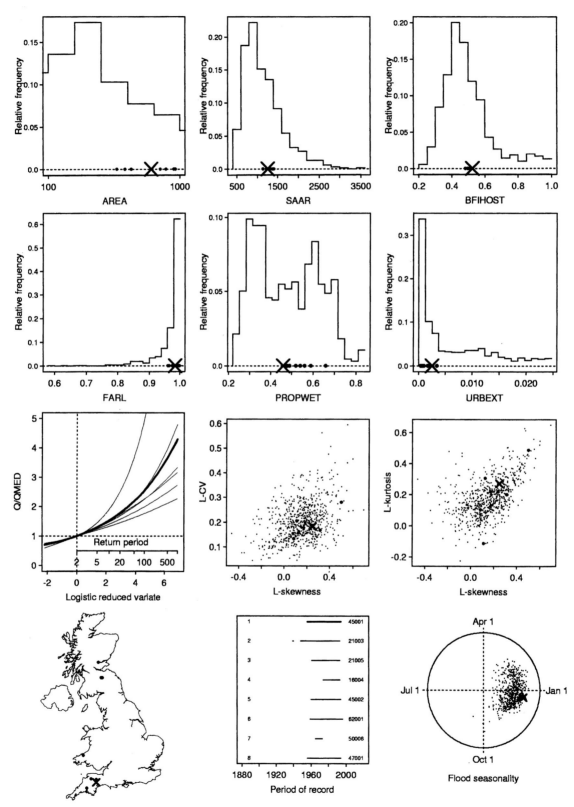

Figure 6.2 *Diagnostic diagrams for reviewing the 50-year pooling-group for the Exe at Thorverton (45001) – see text for explanation: the subject catchment is marked* X

6.2 Initial selection of pooling-group

Searching for catchments that are hydrologically similar to the subject site is onerous, and software support is essential, e.g. using the WINFAP-FEH package. The search is made over all essentially rural catchments in the annual maximum flood dataset that offer at least eight annual maxima. In the FEH, an *essentially rural* catchment is defined as one for which *URBEXT* < 0.025. Where the subject site is itself urbanised, the pooling-group is formed for the *as-rural* condition, i.e. as if the subject catchment were rural (and ungauged). Flood frequency estimates are adjusted for urbanisation in a subsequent step (Chapter 9).

The initial pooling-group is constructed objectively, by seeking those gauged catchments that are nearest to the subject catchment in *size-wetness-soils space*. This is a 3-dimensional space defined by the *AREA*, *SAAR* and *BFIHOST* variables. The specially devised co-ordinate system (see Chapter 16) is (0.528 ln*AREA*, 2.63 ln*SAAR*, 6.67 *BFIHOST*). A *similarity ranking* is assigned to each catchment, rank 1 denoting the gauged catchment that is nearest to the subject catchment in size-wetness-soils space. When the subject site is gauged, there are special rules as to whether to include the station in its own pooling-group (see §6.6). When it is included, it is of course the rank 1 station.

In order to allow for wastage – i.e. rejection of stations in the review process of §6.3 – it is helpful to select more stations than are strictly needed to meet the 5*T* rule. For clarity in the example, these reserve stations are *not* shown in Figure 6.2.

Example 6.1a
Initial pooling-group for T = 50 years: Exe at Thorverton (45001)

This example considers flood frequency estimation for a 600 km^2 gauged catchment in south-west England: the Exe at Thorverton. For a target return period of 50 years, the stations pooled should provide at least 250 station-years of data. The initial pooling-group for the Exe at Thorverton comprises eight stations, including the subject site. Together, these yield 252 station-years of record.

The first set of diagnostic diagrams (top row in Figure 6.2) confirms the manner in which the stations have been selected. The eight catchments are closely grouped in terms of size (*AREA*), wetness (*SAAR*) and soils (*BFIHOST*). The background histogram in each diagram denotes the distribution of values in the sample of catchments potentially available for selection; these are the 698 essentially rural catchments for which the FEH-adopted flood peak dataset provides eight or more annual maxima.

6.3 Reviewing the pooling-group

This important task is open-ended. An experienced user will take a *precautionary approach*, vetting the group membership prior to the statistical analysis of flood peaks. The review should examine factors such as:

- Station locations and their periods of record;
- Similarity in terms of flood seasonality;
- Similarity in terms of further catchment descriptors;

- Standard comments, and other information, about stations and their catchments;
- Known special features of the subject catchment.

Less experienced users will proceed straight to testing the pooling-group (§6.5). In this *reactive approach*, the pooling-group is reviewed only if a specific problem arises.

Station locations and periods of record

Geographical location plays no explicit role in the initial pooling, which is carried out in size-wetness-soils space (§6.2). Neighbouring catchments do, however, often have similar soils and landform, and experience a similar climate. Thus, there will often be a degree of geographical cohesion in FEH pooling-groups. Stations that lie on the same river as the subject site are of particular relevance, and may warrant special promotion in the similarity ranking.

Example 6.1b Review of station locations and periods of record

The bottom row of diagrams in Figure 6.2 illustrates the locations and periods of record for stations in the 50-year pooling-group for the Exe at Thorverton example. The group members are quite widely dispersed across Britain, with about half in south-west England and half elsewhere.

In the central diagram in the bottom row of Figure 6.2, the stations are listed in *similarity rank* order. The gauged catchment most similar to the subject catchment is, of course, the Exe at Thorverton (45001) itself. Under the size-wetness-soils criterion, the next most similar catchments are in south and east Scotland: two on the Tweed (21005 and 21003) and one on the Earn (16004). The period of record for the Tweed at Peebles (21003) encompasses that for the upstream station at Lyne Ford, making station 21005 a candidate for possible removal from the pooling-group. The 5th ranking station is the Exe at Stoodleigh (45002). Being on the same river as the subject site, this station is potentially of higher relevance than that accorded by size-wetness-soils similarity ranking. However, the period of record at Stoodleigh does not add to that at Thorverton, suggesting that no special promotion is warranted in this case. The 7th ranking station (50006) has only eight annual maxima. Because the method of growth curve derivation (see Chapter 7) weights by similarity ranking and record length, this station will have little weight; the decision whether or not to retain it in the pooling-group is unlikely to be consequential.

Example 6.1c
Review of flood seasonality

All the stations in the Exe at Thorverton pooling-group have POT data as well as annual maxima. It is therefore possible to assess and compare the flood seasonality of all members of the pooling-group. The display of flood seasonality (bottom right diagram in Figure 6.2) indicates that the eight catchments share a broadly similar seasonal distribution of floods. In this case, the review reveals nothing untoward.

Similarity in terms of flood seasonality

Flood seasonality can be examined by looking at the dates of peaks-over-threshold (POT) events (see Box 6.1). This step is recommended on the premise that catchments having distinctly different seasonal signatures are unlikely to be hydrologically similar. Even when the subject catchment is itself ungauged, a review of flood seasonality can help to identify any unusual stations in the pooling-group.

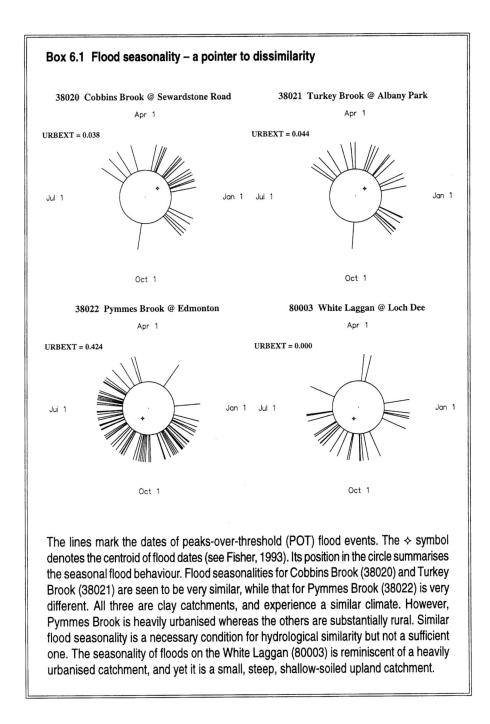

Box 6.1 Flood seasonality – a pointer to dissimilarity

The lines mark the dates of peaks-over-threshold (POT) flood events. The ✧ symbol denotes the centroid of flood dates (see Fisher, 1993). Its position in the circle summarises the seasonal flood behaviour. Flood seasonalities for Cobbins Brook (38020) and Turkey Brook (38021) are seen to be very similar, while that for Pymmes Brook (38022) is very different. All three are clay catchments, and experience a similar climate. However, Pymmes Brook is heavily urbanised whereas the others are substantially rural. Similar flood seasonality is a necessary condition for hydrological similarity but not a sufficient one. The seasonality of floods on the White Laggan (80003) is reminiscent of a heavily urbanised catchment, and yet it is a small, steep, shallow-soiled upland catchment.

Similarity in terms of further catchment descriptors

Catchments in the pooling-group can be compared and contrasted with respect to any property, including FEH catchment descriptors (see Appendix C) further to those used in forming the initial pooling-group.

Example 6.1d
Review of further catchment descriptors

Diagrams in the second row of Figure 6.2 indicate catchment similarity in terms of reservoir/lake effects (*FARL*), typical soil wetness (*PROPWET*), and degree of urbanisation (*URBEXT*).

The attenuating effect of reservoirs and lakes – represented by *FARL* taking a value less than the (no lake) default of 1.0 – is stronger on some catchments in the pooling-group than others. However, it is judged that none of the *FARL* values is excessively different from the Exe at Thorverton's own value of 0.985. Should a selected station show a very marked reservoir/lake effect, it is advisable to confirm that the *FARL* value is relevant to the period of flood record. The FEH flood peak datasets include some records gathered prior to the construction of major reservoirs, and it is helpful to check station (and catchment) comments for such exceptions.

PROPWET denotes the proportion of the time that catchment soils are wetter than a chosen reference level (see **5** 5.7.1 for full definition). The pooling-group for the Exe at Thorverton has rather a dispersed sample of *PROPWET* values (see central diagram in 2nd row of Figure 6.2). Soils on the Tweed at Lyne Ford catchment (21005) are typically rather wetter (*PROPWET* = 0.66) than other catchments in the pooling-group, and much wetter than those for the subject catchment (*PROPWET* = 0.46). This is enough of a difference to add to the suspicion that station 21005 may be an inappropriate member of the pooling-group.

The sample variation of *URBEXT* values is of no great concern. The limited range of values serves as a reminder that only essentially rural (*URBEXT* < 0.025) catchments are pooled.

Station comments and other information

Additional information is available from several sources, including the *Hydrometric Register and Statistics 1991-95* (IH/BGS, 1998). The flood peak datasets accompanying the FEH include several sets of station comments, some based on standard descriptions taken from the National River Flow Archive. These comments may draw attention to exceptional features. For example, a *catchment comment* may identify karstic geology or a major diversion to/from the topographic drainage area. Such comments might immediately rule the station out of the pooled analysis. When a *station comment* refers to the quality of flow data, it is important to check that this relates to flood-flow rather than low-flow measurements. General uncertainty in flood-flow measurement would not normally be reason to exclude a station. However, a site might be rejected from the pooling-group if the comment suggests that the measurement of flood flows is systematically flawed.

If the *subject* catchment has a special feature that is thought to be highly influential on flood growth behaviour, but has not been indexed numerically (e.g. unusually extensive floodplain storage), considerable judgement will be required to determine an appropriate pooling-group. It is important to bear in mind that the pooling-group serves to define the ratio of the *T*-year flood to the 2-year flood (i.e. *QMED*); it plays no direct part in the estimation of *QMED*.

Example 6.1e Review of other information

For the seven catchments selected to join the Exe at Thorverton in its pooling-group, several station comments express doubt about the quality of flood-flow measurement, and some refer to impounding reservoir effects on the flow regime. However, the comments provide no strong signal to discard a particular site from the pooling-group.

Flood statistics

Statistics of the flood magnitudes can contribute to judgements about which stations belong, or do not belong, in the pooling-group. Formal measures of *discordancy* and *heterogeneity* (§16.3) based on L-moment ratios (§14.3) are used to test the pooling-group in §6.5.

The FEH recommendation is that these tests should be used to *trigger* a review, or further review, of the pooling-group, but should not form the prime basis for removing particular sites. A flood series may yield unusual L-moment ratios simply because the catchment has experienced exceptional floods within the period of record, rather than because the catchment is intrinsically different. It is recommended that stations with unusual L-moment ratios be given particular scrutiny, and checked for possible data error. However, such stations should not be removed from the pooling-group without good cause.

Box 6.2 Important note on the removal of stations from pooling-groups

A station should be discarded from a pooling-group only if it is fundamentally mismatched in terms of an important hydrological feature: both mismatched to the subject catchment in particular and the pooling-group in general. A station should not be removed simply because its recorded flood statistics are different.

6.4 Adapting the pooling-group

If the review indicates that a particular station does not belong in the pooling-group, the general practice is to replace it by the 1st station held in reserve from the initial pooling (see §6.2). However, if the station omitted is a short-record station, it is possible that the revised pooling-group will meet the 5T rule without need of a substitute. A pooling-group that nearly meets the 5T rule does not need to be augmented. As a further rule of thumb, a pooling-group providing 4.9T

Example 6.1f
Adapting the pooling-group

The detailed review in §6.3 suggests that station 21005 is somewhat anomalous in terms of soil wetness (i.e. *PROPWET*). It also appears to be an unprofitable member of the pooling-group, because its period of record is duplicated by a longer record at a downstream station (21003), which is a higher-ranking member of the pooling-group.

The 1st reserve station is the Teifi at Llanfair (62002). This short-record station lies upstream of 62001 (already a member of the pooling-group) and does not provide any years of record not also seen at 62001. The 2nd reserve station is the Annan at Bridekirk (78003) in central southern Scotland, for which 26 annual maxima are available.

On balance, it is judged appropriate to replace station 21005 by station 78003. After this change, the combined record length in the pooling-group is 246 years, broadly meeting the 5T target of 250 station-years.

---

station-years could be considered adequate, but one providing 4.8T station-years should not. This additional rule has little scientific basis, but is designed to promote consistent use of the procedures. The experienced flood analyst should not feel bound to follow either the additional rule or the underlying 5T rule.

6.5 Testing for discordant sites and heterogeneity

The statistical properties of the pooled flood data are examined in terms of their L-moment ratios (Chapter 14). Standard software tools are available to assist in testing, and only brief descriptions of the methods are given here. The methods are discussed in detail in §16.3. The first step is to calculate L-moment ratios for each site in the pooling-group (Table 6.2).

L-CV is a measure of the variability of annual maxima. L-skewness represents the skewness of the set of values: a high value typically means that some of the annual maxima are particularly large relative to the main body of data. L-kurtosis is more difficult to interpret, but a value of zero shows a platykurtic (flat-topped) distribution, and may indicate that the annual maxima are rather evenly distributed in magnitude.

Table 6.2 *L-moment ratios for sites in Exe at Thorverton pooling-group*

Station	No. of annual maxima	L-CV	L-skewness	L-kurtosis	Discordancy, D
45001	38	0.18	0.25	0.27	0.19
21003	46	0.28	0.50	0.49	1.90
16004	19	0.13	0.08	0.10	0.85
45002	34	0.18	0.17	0.22	0.66
62001	37	0.17	0.31	0.20	0.68
50006	8	0.20	0.11	-0.11	2.15
47001	38	0.19	0.24	0.22	0.06
78003	26	0.11	0.29	0.23	1.50

Testing for discordant sites

The discordancy measure D draws attention to potentially unusual or influential sites, and is used (see §16.3) to detect whether the distribution of annual maxima at an individual station is strongly different from the group-average. The discordancy is calculated from the L-moment ratios (e.g. Table 6.2). The critical value for D, i.e. the value at which a site is judged discordant from the group, depends on the number of sites in the group. Details are given in §16.3.1.

Example 6.1g
Discordancy test

For a pooling-group of eight members, the critical value of D is 2.14 (see Table 16.1). It is seen from Table 6.2 that the Mole at Woodleigh (50006) is judged potentially discordant to the pooling-group. However, the discordancy value is only slightly greater than the test value (2.15 compared to 2.14). Even if the station were strongly discordant, it would be excluded from the pooling-group only if judged to be hydrologically dissimilar to the subject catchment.

Station 50006 is a short-record site, and it is common for such sites to appear discordant. Because the growth curve derivation (see Chapter 7) weights by similarity ranking and record length, this station will have little weight. Thus, the decision whether or not to retain it in the pooling-group is unlikely to be consequential.

In practice it will often be necessary to apply judgement. There will be cases when a non-discordant station will be removed from a pooling-group because hydrologically (e.g. judged by the methods of §6.3) its catchment is thought to be strongly dissimilar to the subject catchment. In other cases, a discordant station will be allowed to remain in the pooling-group because, hydrologically, there is no strong argument to exclude it.

Testing for heterogeneity

One of the basic ideas of pooled frequency analysis is that the distribution of flood growth is broadly similar at all sites in the group. In the FEH, the distribution of values is represented by the L-moment ratios, and a pooling-group is judged *homogeneous* if there is no evidence that these ratios differ significantly from site to site. Otherwise, the pooling-group is said to be *heterogeneous*. The recommended test uses the H_2 statistic (see §16.3.2). This examines the variability in L-CV and L-skewness values across the pooling-group. Table 6.3 summarises the terminology, and recommended rules, for testing for heterogeneity. Further details are given in Chapter 16.

The ideal situation is that the selected stations form an acceptably homogeneous pooling-group for flood growth curve derivation. Unfortunately, this will often not be the case. Typically, there is a conflict between choosing a very small set of stations which form a homogeneous pooling-group (a 1-station pooling-group is guaranteed to be homogeneous!) and choosing a large number of stations to provide ample flood data to extend the growth curve to the target return period.

Table 6.3 *Guidance on pooling-group heterogeneity (judged from H_2 statistic)*

Value of H_2	Pooling-group is said to be:	Review of pooling-group is:
$H_2 \leq 1$	Acceptably homogeneous	Not required
$1 < H_2 \leq 2$	Possibly heterogeneous	Optional
$2 < H_2 \leq 4$	Heterogeneous	Desirable
$H_2 > 4$	Strongly heterogeneous	Essential

When the pooling-group is judged to be heterogeneous, or strongly heterogeneous, the recommendation is to review the pooling-group. This means that the user should consider making reasoned changes to the pooling-group. However, if there is no hydrological justification for changes, or if the pooling-group remains heterogeneous despite changes, it will be necessary to tolerate heterogeneity in the pooling-group. Hosking and Wallis (1997) advise that, in the critical application of estimating very long-return-period events, "Heterogeneity is less important as a source of error, whereas mis-specification of the frequency distribution is more important". The FEH paraphrases this in the maxim: "Better to tolerate heterogeneity than to use too few data".

Example 6.1h
Heterogeneity test

For the Exe at Thorverton pooling-group summarised in Table 6.2, the heterogeneity calculation yields $H_2 = 0.43$. Thus the pooling-group is judged to be acceptably homogeneous, and no changes are required.

In some applications, even after careful review by the methods of §6.3, the pooling-group will still be judged strongly heterogeneous ($H_2 > 4$). There are various ways in which the user can massage the heterogeneity, e.g. by shortening the target return-period or by withdrawing short-record stations from the pooling-group (replacing them with a smaller number of stations from the reserve list). Both these actions will lead to the pooling-group comprising fewer stations, thus promoting the possibility that the group will be judged less heterogeneous. However, it may be better simply to acknowledge the heterogeneity, and to proceed to growth curve derivation (Chapter 7).

6.6 When to exclude the subject site from its own pooling-group

In the above example, the subject site is treated as a member of its own pooling-group. It is natural that construction of the pooling-group should be focused on the subject catchment. There are, however, situations when the flood record at the subject site should be excluded from the pooling-group when deriving the pooled growth curve.

The first exception is when the subject catchment is urbanised. Urban catchments are *never* included in a pooling-group. The allowance for catchment urbanisation is made separately (see Chapter 9). Judgement can be applied if the extent of urban development is only slightly greater than the FEH cutoff (*URBEXT* = 0.025) for an 'essentially rural' catchment.

The second exception is when there is a long enough record at the subject site to make a single-site analysis of flood growth also relevant. Excluding the site from the pooling-group permits a comparison to be drawn between what the subject-site flood data are saying (in a single-site analysis) and what flood data for similar catchments are saying (in the pooled analysis). Depending on various factors, the final growth curve is based either on the pooled analysis alone or on a weighted-average of the pooled and single-site analyses. In the former case, the subject site is reintroduced into the pooling-group, whereas in the latter it continues to be excluded. Full guidance is given in Chapter 8, with an overview in **1** 5.3.

6.7 Further guidance

Pooling-group construction is a new field. It is therefore anticipated that further guidance in judging catchment similarity, and in retaining/discarding sites from pooling-groups, will be developed, based on experience with the Volume 3 procedure and additional research. In addition to exploring the more detailed descriptions and discussions in Chapter 16, users may wish to be alerted to further guidance disseminated (or referenced) via the FEH homepage. The Internet address is http://www.nwl.ac.uk/ih.

Chapter 7   Deriving the pooled growth curve (A)

The procedure for choosing a pooling-group (see Chapter 6) is relatively intricate. In contrast, the Flood Estimation Handbook recommends a mechanistic approach to growth curve derivation, once the pooling-group has been chosen. The general method is summarised in §7.1. A special variation for highly permeable catchments is introduced in §7.2. In all cases, some simple checks are recommended once the growth curve has been derived (§7.3).

7.1 General method

The ingredients from which the growth curve is derived are the sample L-moment ratios for the *M* sites in the pooling-group. These have already been calculated for use in testing the properties of the pooling-group (§6.5).

Pooling the L-moment ratios

The L-moment ratios for the pooling-group are formed by a weighted-average of the L-moment ratios for the individual sites. Thus:

$$\text{L-CV}_{pooled} = \frac{\sum_{i=1}^{M} w_i \text{L-CV}_i}{\sum_{i=1}^{M} w_i} \quad (7.1) \qquad \text{L-skewness}_{pooled} = \frac{\sum_{i=1}^{M} w_i \text{L-skewness}_i}{\sum_{i=1}^{M} w_i} \quad (7.2)$$

where *M* is the number of sites in the pooling-group and the weight w_i is an *effective record length* at the ith site defined by:

$$w_i = s_i n_i \qquad (7.3)$$

Here, the actual record length n_i is reduced by a *similarity ranking factor* S_i:

$$S_i = \frac{\sum_{j=i}^{M} n_j}{\sum_{j=1}^{M} n_j} \qquad (7.4)$$

The denominator is the total number of station-years of record in the pooling-group, while the numerator is the number of station-years in the pooling-group provided by sites that are no more-similar (to the subject site) than is the ith site. Thus, the similarity ranking factor assigned to the most-similar site is:

$$S_1 = (n_1 + n_2 + \dots + n_M) / (n_1 + n_2 + \dots + n_M) = 1.0$$

while that assigned to the Mth-most similar site is:

$$S_M = n_M / (n_1 + n_2 + \dots + n_M)$$

Example 7.1
Deriving the pooled L-moments for the Exe at Thorverton pooling-group

Calculating the weights
This is a continuation of Example 6.1. It is seen that the second-most similar station (21003) is given slightly greater weight than station 45001, because of its longer record. The final column shows the relative weight accorded to each station. Together, stations 45001 and 21003 account for half of the total weight. It is seen that the short-record station (50006) – assessed in Example 6.1g as a potentially discordant member of the pooling-group – is given very little weight. This means that the resultant growth curve is largely unaffected by the decision whether to retain this station in the pooling-group.

i	Station	No. of annual maxima, n_i	Similarity ranking factor S_i	Weight $w_i = S_i n_i$	Relative weight $w_i / \sum w_j$
1	45001	38	246 / 246 = 1.000	38.0	0.270
2	21003	46	208 / 246 = 0.846	38.9	0.277
3	16004	19	162 / 246 = 0.659	12.5	0.089
4	45002	34	143 / 246 = 0.581	19.8	0.141
5	62001	37	109 / 246 = 0.443	16.4	0.117
6	50006	8	72 / 246 = 0.293	2.3	0.016
7	47001	38	64 / 246 = 0.260	9.9	0.070
8	78003	26	26 / 246 = 0.106	2.7	0.020
		$\Sigma = 246$ station-years		$\Sigma = 140.5$	$\Sigma = 1.000$

Deriving the pooled L-moment ratios
Applying Equations 7.1 and 7.2 to the L-moment ratios given in Table 6.2 yields L-CV$_{pooled}$ = 0.202 and L-skewness$_{pooled}$ = 0.298. A similar formula embodying the same weighting system yields L-kurtosis$_{pooled}$ = 0.289.

The pooling of the L-moment ratios is shown in Figure 7.1 below.

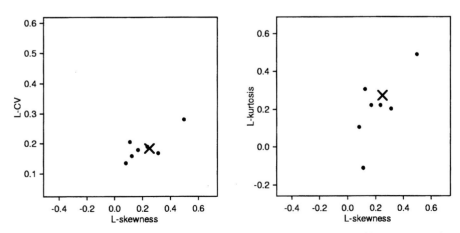

Figure 7.1 *L-moment ratios for the Exe at Thorverton pooling-group: the subject catchment is marked* X

Deriving the growth curve

The FEH recommends adoption of the Generalised Logistic (GL) distribution to describe flood growth in the UK. Although the distribution has three parameters, only two are required when it is used to represent flood growth. The third parameter is determined by the constraint that – for a growth curve standardised by $QMED$ – the distribution takes a value of 1.0 when the non-exceedence probability $F = 0.5$.

The GL distribution of flood growth is specified by:

$$x(F) = 1 + \frac{\beta}{k}\left\{1 - \left(\frac{1-F}{F}\right)^{k}\right\} \tag{7.5}$$

Chapter 11 introduces the flood frequency methodology underlying Volume 3, while details of the GL distribution are given in §15.3.

It is conventional (e.g. Hosking and Wallis, 1997) to denote the 2nd and 3rd L-moment ratios by t_2 and t_3, and to use the superscript R to denote regional-average values. Because the regions used in Volume 3 are pooling-groups, P is an alternative notation to R. For brevity, the superscript is omitted below.

The required parameter values of the Generalised Logistic distribution are estimated from the 2nd and 3rd regional-average L-moment ratios, t_2 and t_3, by:

$$k = -t_3 \tag{7.6}$$

$$\beta = \frac{t_2 k \sin \pi k}{k \pi (k + t_2) - t_2 \sin \pi k} \tag{7.7}$$

The T-year growth factor x_T is then evaluated by setting $F = 1 - 1/T$ in Equation 7.5, i.e.:

$$x_T = 1 + \frac{\beta}{k}\left\{1 - (T-1)^{-k}\right\} \tag{7.8}$$

Note that, when k>0,

$$x_T \rightarrow 1 + \frac{\beta}{k} \quad \text{as} \quad T \rightarrow \infty$$

In such cases the fitted distribution is said to have an 'upper bound', implying a maximum possible growth factor of $1 + \beta/k$. It is advisable to be wary of routinely adopting such a growth curve, if the implied upper bound appears unrealistically low (see ¶ 10.1).

Choice of distribution

Although the general recommendation is to adopt the Generalised Logistic (GL) distribution, there will be situations in which the experienced user will choose another distribution. Section 17.3 explains the background to the general recommendation and describes a goodness-of-fit measure (§17.3.1) that can inform

---

Example 7.2
Fitting the growth curve distribution for the Exe at Thorverton pooling-group

Taking values from Example 7.1, the L-CV and L-skewness for the pooling-group are 0.202 and 0.298 respectively. Thus $t_2 = 0.202$ and $t_3 = 0.298$.

Substituting t_2 and t_3 into Equations 7.6 and 7.7 yields: $k = -0.298$ and $\beta = 0.198$. The growth curve (see inset plot) is constructed by multiple calculation from Equation 7.8 using a range of values of the return period T.

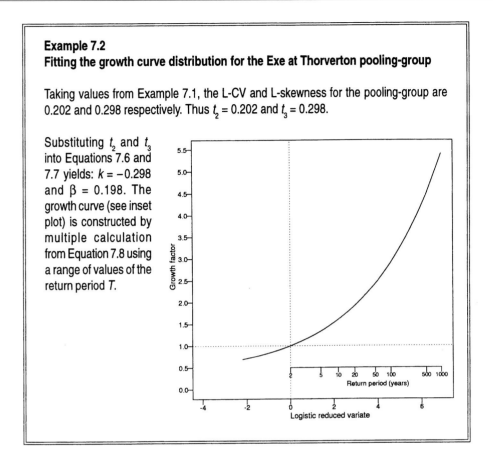

the experienced user. This measure should be used in association with growth curve plots, also known as 'extreme value plots' (see §15.3).

When plotting the Generalised Logistic (GL) distribution, it is appropriate to adopt the Logistic reduced variate scale. Under this convention, the Logistic distribution (which is the special case of the GL distribution when $k = 0$) plots as a straight line.

Prior to publication of the Flood Estimation Handbook, the distribution most widely used to describe flood growth in the UK was the Generalised Extreme Value (GEV). For the GEV distribution, it is appropriate to plot the growth curve against the Gumbel reduced variate. Because of its former widespread use, the Gumbel reduced variate is often referred to simply as 'the reduced variate'. To lessen the scope for confusion between the Gumbel and Logistic reduced variates, the FEH strongly discourages this abbreviation.

When to adopt the simpler Logistic distribution

The above solution method is unsuitable when the L-skewness (the 3rd L-moment ratio, t_3) is close to zero. If t_3 lies in the range [-0.01, 0.01], it is recommended that the simpler Logistic distribution (§15.5.1) is fitted using:

$$\beta = t_2$$

> **Box 7.1 Choice of distribution**
>
> Standardisation on a particular distribution – the Generalised Logistic – should be considered advisory rather than mandatory. However, selection of another distribution needs to be supported by properties of the gauged flood data or hydrological understanding of the catchment, rather than by a desire to see a higher or lower result.

7.2 Special method for permeable catchments

Chapter 19 presents a special method for growth curve estimation on permeable catchments. This is motivated by recognition of the exceptional properties of highly permeable catchments, and of the desire that growth curve derivation is not unduly influenced by small annual maximum values in flood-free years.

The FEH defines a permeable catchment as one for which SPRHOST, the standard percentage runoff estimated from HOST soils data, is less than 20%.

7.3 Checking whether the derived growth curve implies an upper bound

Problem

The distribution recommended to describe UK flood growth is the Generalised Logistic (GL). In common with the widely used Generalised Extreme Value (GEV) distribution, the GL sometimes indicates that there is an upper bound (i.e. maximum possible value) to flood peaks expected on the catchment.

In some cases, the implied upper bound is many times larger than the largest observed $Q/QMED$ value. The slow approach towards the upper bound means that the feature is of little consequence within the return-period range for which flood frequency estimates are typically required.

In other cases, the upper bound to the fitted growth curve is scarcely higher than some of the values of $Q/QMED$ observed within the pooling-group, and the fitted growth curve approaches the upper bound within the return-period range for which flood growth estimates are required. Such a feature is nearly always physically unrealistic. Various examples and discussions are to be found in §15.3, §15.4, Chapter 19 and 1 10.1.

The recommendation to adopt the Generalised Logistic (GL) distribution for pooled growth curve derivation is based on goodness-of-fit criteria (see §17.3). A perceived additional advantage of the GL distribution is that, in application to UK flood peak data, the model gives rise to pooled growth curves with an upper bound in far fewer instances than does the GEV distribution.

Treatment

The technique presented in Chapter 19 for permeable catchments may circumvent the behaviour if this arises from 'non-floods' exerting an undue influence on the pooled growth curve. However, there are situations in which the growth curve behaviour may reflect a real feature, such as the attenuating action of floodplain storage. Such situations warrant special study. In exceptional cases, it may be appropriate to favour a single-site analysis and/or to seek to strengthen the flood frequency estimation in other ways. These might include use of the FSR rainfall-runoff method (see Volume 4), or innovative approaches based on continuous simulation modelling (see §4.1 and 1 10.6).

Alternatively, an undesired upper bound can be avoided by choosing to fit the 2-parameter Logistic distribution (see §15.5.1). This is a special case of the GL distribution that has no upper (or lower) bound.

Chapter 8   Deriving the flood frequency curve

When estimating flood frequency on an urbanised catchment, Chapter 8 must be read in conjunction with Chapter 9.

8.1 Summary of recommendations

The statistical approach constructs the flood frequency curve Q_T as the product of the index flood $QMED$ and the growth curve x_T:

$$Q_T = QMED\, x_T \tag{8.1}$$

where T denotes the return period in years. The choice of method for estimating $QMED$ is summarised in Table 8.1. For a gauged site, the main criterion is the length of flood record. For an ungauged site, the choice of method is dictated by the availability of a suitable donor/analogue catchment from which to transfer an estimate of $QMED$. In essence, the data transfer procedure (Chapter 4) provides a 'local correction' to the estimate of $QMED$ from descriptors, by examining the proportional error that the Chapter 3 estimate makes at the gauged site.

Table 8.1   *Method for estimating index flood, QMED*

Length of record	QMED estimation method
< 2 years	Data transfer from donor/analogue catchment (Chapter 4)
2 to 13 years	From peaks-over-threshold (POT) data (Sections 2.4 and 12.3)
> 13 years	As median of annual maxima (Sections 2.3 and 12.2)

Table 8.2   *Recommended methods for growth curve estimation: when T ≤ 27 years*

Length of record	Site analysis	Pooled analysis [†]	Shorthand description
< T/2 years	No	Yes	Pooled analysis
T/2 to T years	For confirmation	Yes	Pooled analysis prevails
T to 2T years	Yes	Yes [‡]	Joint (site and pooled) analysis
> 2T years	Yes	For confirmation [‡]	Site analysis prevails

[†] Size of pooling-group chosen to provide 5T station-years of record
[‡] Subject site excluded from pooled analysis

Table 8.3   *Recommended methods for growth curve estimation: when T > 27 years*

Length of record	Site analysis	Pooled analysis [†]	Shorthand description
< 14 years	No	Yes	Pooled analysis
14 to T years	For confirmation	Yes	Pooled analysis prevails
T to 2T years	Yes	Yes [‡]	Joint (site and pooled) analysis
> 2T years	Yes	For confirmation [‡]	Site analysis prevails

[†] Size of pooling-group chosen to provide 5T station-years of record
[‡] Subject site excluded from pooled analysis

Uncorrected use of the catchment-descriptor method (Chapter 3) is not recommended. It should be applied only in preliminary assessments or where no suitable donor/analogue catchment can be found. Advice on selecting donor and analogue catchments is given in Chapter 4, with further guidelines in **1** 3.3. Where the record length used is much shorter than 30 years, a period-of-record correction is recommended (see Chapter 20). This procedure seeks to insulate the *QMED* estimate from the effects of climatic fluctuation.

The recommended method for estimating the growth curve x_T depends on both the length of gauged record and the target return period, *T.* This is the return period for which the flood frequency estimate is principally required. The guidelines are summarised in Tables 8.2 and 8.3. The choice between tables depends on *T.* Table 8.3 is relevant to most river flood design problems, where the target return period is typically longer than 27 years.

The FEH recommends that the growth curve is estimated from flood data in annual maximum form. A 'site analysis' is one based on annual maxima at the subject site alone. A 'pooled analysis' draws on data from a network of gauged catchments chosen to be hydrologically similar to the subject catchment. In Tables

---

Example 8.1
Deriving the flood frequency curve for the Exe at Thorverton (45001)

This catchment has been used earlier to illustrate construction of the pooling-group (Example 6.1) and derivation of the pooled growth curve (Example 7.2). It is a gauged site, with annual maxima available for 38 years. The target return period is 50 years.

QMED estimation
Following the recommendation of Table 8.1, *QMED* is estimated as the median of the annual maxima. This yields: $QMED = 175$ m³ s⁻¹.

Growth curve estimation
For a record length of 38 years and a target return period of 50 years, Table 8.3 recommends adoption of the pooled growth curve (from Example 7.2), but that a site analysis is undertaken as a precaution. In this instance, the site growth curve is in good agreement with the pooled growth curve (see inset figure), and the latter is adopted without further examination.
Thus: $x_{50} = 2.45$.

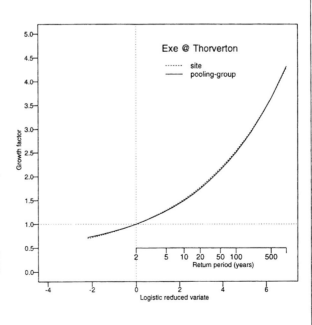

Flood frequency curve
The required flood estimate in m³ s⁻¹ is the product of *QMED* and the 50-year growth factor. Applying Equation 8.1:
$Q_{50} = 175 \times 2.45 = 429$ m³ s⁻¹.

8.2 and 8.3, "for confirmation" means that the relevant analysis is undertaken for comparison only: unless there are exceptional factors, the other analysis should prevail. A detail (indicated in a footnote) concerns whether the subject site is included in its own pooling-group for growth curve derivation. In essence, if the site record is long enough for the site analysis to play a direct role in growth curve estimation in its own right, the site is excluded from the pooled analysis. However, such cases will not arise very often, because the gauged record is rarely as long as the target return period. Typically, the growth curve will be based on a pooled analysis. An urbanised catchment is never included in a pooled analysis.

Where the subject site is gauged, the recommended method for growth curve derivation is often 'pooled analysis prevails', in which both site and pooled analyses are undertaken but the latter is generally adopted. Special care is warranted if the site growth curve is much steeper than the pooled growth curve. If the site growth curve is considered particularly reliable, it may be reasonable to move to the next category in Table 8.3: adopting the joint analysis method (see §8.2).

8.2 Detailed guidance

The recommendations in Table 8.3 assume that the flood record at the subject site is of average quality. The record length in the table should be informally reduced if the gauged record is considered unusually poor. Evidence of non-stationarity in the flood series (see Chapter 21) would be good reason, but doubt about the flood rating would not. Doubts about flood ratings are commonplace, and any specific concern about the rating at the subject site should be addressed prior to analysis. Conversely, if the quality and stationarity of the record are thought to be unusually good, the record length used in Table 8.3 could be informally increased.

The less experienced analyst is expected to follow Table 8.3 (or Table 8.2). An experienced analyst will interpret the guidelines less rigorously, allowing the choice to be influenced by personal knowledge, and a detailed appraisal of the catchments and their data.

The conditions under which flood data at the subject site are used in growth curve derivation are less restrictive than they appear. In those cases where the flood growth curve is wholly or principally based on pooled analysis, the subject site is included in its own pooling-group as the rank 1 member. The only circumstances in which the site record is ignored in growth curve derivation are if the catchment is urbanised or if the record is shorter than eight years (see §16.2.3).

Data transfers when subject and donor catchments are both urbanised

The FEH recommends that only 'essentially rural' catchments (those where $URBEXT < 0.025$) are used in transferring an estimate of $QMED$ (by the Chapter 4 procedure) and in pooled growth curve construction. A subsequent adjustment is then made for catchment urbanisation (see Chapter 9). An exception to this rule is warranted when the (ungauged) subject site is urbanised and there is a similarly urbanised (gauged) donor site close by. Most often, this will apply where the subject and donor sites lie a short distance apart on the same river. In this instance, application of the Chapter 4 approach is less clear-cut. The key difficulty is that a discrepancy between the gauged and catchment-descriptor estimates at the donor site might reflect an abnormal 'urban effect', rather than a poor estimate of $QMED_{rural}$ (see Example 9.3).

QMED estimation when there is a very short record at the subject site

There are various possibilities if there is a good donor catchment close by. One approach is to apply the data transfer method (Chapter 4), as if the subject site were ungauged. However, if several flood events have been recorded at both the subject and donor sites, an alternative is to extend the flood series at the subject site by correlation (see §2.6).

Where there is no suitable donor or analogue catchment, it may be prudent to install a temporary gauging station at the subject site. If two or more years of data can be gathered, *QMED* can be estimated by peaks-over-threshold analysis. If only one year of data can be gathered, a 'compromise' estimate of *QMED* might be derived as an average of the POT estimate (see §12.1.4) and that derived from catchment descriptors (see Chapter 3). It is generally recommended that any averaging (or weighted-averaging) of flood estimates is undertaken in the log domain; thus, values of ln *QMED* would be averaged before transforming back to obtain *QMED*.

Growth curve by pooled analysis

The method for deriving the pooled growth curve is given in Chapter 7, with further details in Chapter 17. A special variant of the method is appropriate when dealing with highly permeable catchments (see Chapter 19).

Growth curve by site analysis

The site growth curve is obtained by a single-site analysis of flood growth. The method of growth curve derivation is essentially the same as in the pooled analysis case (i.e. §7.1). The one difference is that the L-moment ratios used are those for the annual maxima at the particular site, whereas, in the pooled case, they are weighted averages of the L-moment ratios at several sites.

The method of growth curve fitting recommended in the FEH (see §15.3) can be termed the 'L-median' method. Whereas the classical L-moment method (e.g. Hosking and Wallis, 1997) fits the growth curve so that the mean of the distribution is 1.0, the L-median method fits the growth curve so that the median of the distribution is 1.0. In both cases, when a 3-parameter distribution such as the Generalised Logistic is adopted, the derived growth curve respects the L-CV and L-skewness of the annual maxima.

When using the L-median method of fitting, the growth curve produced by site analysis can be distorted by an unfortunate estimate of *QMED*. The most common cause of a poor estimate of *QMED* is when the annual maximum series (or POT series) of ranked observations has a big jump in magnitudes close to the values/value which determine/determines *QMED*. This is one of several reasons why it is essential to inspect an extreme value plot of the site data against the site and/or pooled growth curve. In case of doubt, a useful check is to refit the growth curve using the classical L-moment method, to see whether satisfying the required median value has distorted the resultant growth curve.

Growth curve by joint analysis

The joint analysis method provides a compromise between the pooled growth curve and the site growth curve. It is appropriate when the record at the subject site is longer than the target return period, but not twice as long.

The recommended procedure for combining the site and pooled growth curves is to take a weighted average of their L-moment ratios. Thus:

$$L\text{-}CV = w\ L\text{-}CV_{site} + (1 - w)\ L\text{-}CV_{pooled} \tag{8.2}$$

and

$$L\text{-}skewness = w\ L\text{-}skewness_{site} + (1 - w)\ L\text{-}skewness_{pooled} \tag{8.3}$$

where w is a weight reflecting the record length N at the subject site relative to the target return period T. The recommended weight is:

$$w = \frac{N}{2T} \tag{8.4}$$

If the recommendations of Table 8.3 (or, where appropriate, Table 8.2) are followed, w will be found to lie between 0.5 and 1.0. Note that, in the joint analysis method, the subject site is excluded from its own pooling-group when deriving the pooled growth curve. This is because the site receives weight directly, as is evident in Equations 8.2 and 8.3.

8.3 Catchment factors that may warrant special consideration

Allowances for catchment urbanisation are considered in Chapter 9. This section discusses other factors that may warrant special consideration when interpreting flood frequency curves.

8.3.1 Floodplain storage

Many larger rivers have notable floodplains, especially at, or close to, major confluences. The temporary storage of a large volume of water on the floodplain can lead to appreciable attenuation of the flood hydrograph between upstream and downstream sites. In some cases, flood water overflows into gravel pits or low-lying land adjacent to the river and plays no direct part in flooding at downstream sites. In other cases, the floodplain represents an important ephemeral channel, so that part of the flood flow passes down the river channel and part down the 'floodplain channel'.

Spillage of water onto the floodplain leads to a decrease in the rate of water level rise, both at the site of overflow and at sites downstream. Where they are pronounced, such effects are often evident in the water level hydrographs recorded. Where the residence time of flood water on the floodplain is much longer than that of flood water in the river channel, the floodplain storage attenuates the rate of flow. This delays and reduces the peak of the flood hydrograph at downstream sites. The effect can best be likened to that of a lake, although the analogy is imperfect: a lake usually has a defined outlet, whereas a floodplain generally does not.

It was not possible to develop an index of floodplain storage as part of the FEH studies and consequently the general methods make no explicit allowance for floodplain storage effects. It is therefore necessary to be particularly circumspect where such effects are thought to have a strong influence on flood frequency. This concern may relate to the subject site or to one or more of the long-record sites that influence the particular flood frequency estimation.

The anticipated effect is a slackening of the gradient of the flood frequency curve above the threshold flow at which major spillage occurs. If the site analysis reveals such an effect, this may be one instance when it is inappropriate to allow the pooled analysis to overrule or dilute it. A particular concern in U-shaped valleys is that the floodplain storage effect may weaken in the largest floods, with the result that the gradient of the flood frequency curve steepens at long return period. Such situations warrant special study.

8.3.2 Reservoirs and lakes

The regression model for *QMED* estimation from catchment descriptors (Chapter 3) includes *FARL*, an index of the flood attenuation due to reservoirs and lakes. This represents water bodies appearing on 1:50000 OS maps that lie on a major DTM drainage path (see **5** 4).

This is one aspect in which the catchment-descriptor data supplied with the FEH – both the values for gauged catchments tabulated in Volume 5 (and supplied in WINFAP-FEH) and the values for ungauged catchments supplied on the FEH CD-ROM – are not entirely reliable. In some cases the digital data fail to detect correctly that a given water body is 'on line' with the drainage system. Comparing *FARL* values for sites upstream and downstream of the water body will generally confirm whether its attenuating effect has been registered correctly. If the descriptor shows a suitably large effect (i.e. if *FARL* is considerably less than 1.0), it will be correct. However, if the descriptor indicates an attenuation effect less than anticipated (i.e. if *FARL* has a value closer to 1.0 than expected), the value should be corrected subjectively, by reference to experience gained on other catchments. The defect may be remedied in later editions of the FEH software, but particular care is required until authoritative updates are issued.

Regardless of the warning above, special consideration is required where the *FARL* index or local knowledge indicates a likely strong effect on flood flows arising from one or more impounding reservoirs. Unless these are ornamental/amenity reservoirs that are kept permanently full – and thus behave like natural lakes – it may be advisable to use the rainfall-runoff approach (see **4** 8) to take explicit account of the reservoirs. More generally, Volume 1 gives guidance on choosing between, and reconciling, flood estimates obtained by the statistical and rainfall-runoff methods (see **1** 5.5 and **1** 5.6).

8.3.3 Agricultural drainage

The regression model for *QMED* estimation from catchment descriptors does not explicitly represent field drainage, forestry ditching or arterial drainage (e.g. moorland gripping). Where agricultural drainage is a strong feature of the subject catchment, particular care is warranted in selecting a donor catchment for transferring an estimate of *QMED* by the Chapter 4 procedure. These and other land-use effects are reviewed in Sections 9.3 to 9.6 of Volume 4.

Chapter 9   Adjusting for urbanisation (A)

9.1 Introduction

Urbanisation has a marked effect on the flood behaviour of a catchment. Typically, it accelerates and intensifies the flood response, and widens the seasonal distribution of flood occurrences.

Earlier chapters describe the statistical procedure for flood frequency estimation on an essentially rural catchment, i.e. one for which *URBEXT* is less than 0.025. The adjustment procedure introduced in this chapter allows flood frequency estimation to be performed on urbanised catchments. The recommended approach (§9.2) is to estimate the flood frequency as if the catchment were rural, and then to make an explicit adjustment for urbanisation. Variations on the general method are required when the subject site is gauged (§9.3), or if there is a similarly urbanised donor catchment close by (§9.4).

Box 9.1 Index of catchment urbanisation, *URBEXT*

The FEH index of catchment urbanisation is the fractional urban extent *URBEXT*, judged from detailed land-cover mapping (see **5 6**). This differs systematically from the urban index *URBAN$_{FSR}$* used in the Flood Studies Report and related procedures. It is essential not to confuse values of the two indices.

It is important to appreciate that the adjustment procedure represents only the net effect of urbanisation: i.e. the residual effect after typical drainage works have been carried out. Put another way, the adjustment represents that part of the aggravating effect (of development on flood frequency) for which, historically, attenuation works have typically failed to cater. Though significant (see §18.3.3), the urban adjustment in the FEH statistical method models only a small part of the overall increase in flood frequency that would be experienced if all runoff-control works (e.g. soakaways, storage ponds, strategic flood storage reservoirs) were omitted.

Box 9.2 When to use another method

The user who seeks a method to design works to counter the gross effect of urbanisation must look elsewhere. One option is to apply the rainfall-runoff method of Volume 4, where the adjustment for urbanisation is partly founded on experimentation in the late 1970s to extend the applicability of the FSR rainfall-runoff method.

Another option is to apply engineering judgement, i.e. to design works based on the accumulated experience of what has been found to be effective. This experiential approach can most readily be justified on very small catchments – such as those met in the development of greenfield sites – for which few data have been brought together nationally to support a more formal approach.

The adjustment procedure introduced in §9.2 is described more fully in Chapter 18. The difficulties of allowing for catchment urbanisation are also discussed in 1 8.

9.2 Adjustment procedure

9.2.1 Notation

The flood frequency curve is obtained in Chapter 8 by 'scaling up' the growth curve by the index flood, i.e. multiplying the growth factor x by the index flood $QMED$:

$$Q_T = QMED\ x_T \tag{8.1}$$

where T denotes the return period in years. It is helpful to introduce notation to emphasise that the basic method is applicable only to essentially rural catchments. Thus:

$$Qrural_T = QMED_{rural}\ xrural_T \tag{9.1}$$

The notation $QMED_{rural}$ was introduced in Chapter 3 to denote an estimate of $QMED$ on an essentially rural catchment. The catchment-descriptor model developed there (Equations 3.1 to 3.3) can be used to provide an estimate of the 'as-rural' index flood on urbanised catchments. This assumes that – in their original rural condition – urbanised catchments in the UK would be represented adequately by the rural catchments used in calibration of the $QMED_{rural}$ model (see §18.3.3).

Equation 9.1 provides an estimate of the as-rural flood frequency, $Qrural_T$. The notation Q_T is then reserved for the estimate of flood frequency after it has been adjusted for urbanisation. For rural catchments, Q_T is simply $Qrural_T$.

9.2.2 Steps

In the absence of gauged data, the adjustment for urbanisation comprises three steps:

- Adjust $QMED$ for urbanisation (§9.2.3);
- Adjust growth curve for urbanisation (§9.2.4);
- Obtain the flood frequency curve as the product of $QMED$ and the growth curve (§9.2.5).

The first step is not required where flood data are available at the subject site (see §9.3).

9.2.3 Adjustment of QMED_rural to QMED

Urbanisation typically has its strongest effect on floods of short return period, such as the median annual maximum flood, $QMED$. The effect is represented by an urban adjustment factor, UAF:

$$QMED = UAF\ QMED_{rural} \tag{9.2}$$

where

$$UAF = PRUAF\ (1 + URBEXT)^{0.83} \tag{9.3}$$

and

$$PRUAF = 1 + 0.615\ URBEXT\left(\frac{70}{SPRHOST} - 1\right) \tag{9.4}$$

The term *PRUAF* is a percentage runoff urban adjustment factor inferred from the rainfall-runoff method (see §18.3.2 and **4** 2.3.1). It reflects that the effect of urbanisation on *QMED* is influenced by the parent soil type. The effect is expected to be weaker when the soils are particularly impermeable (e.g. *SPRHOST* in the range 50 to 70), and stronger when they are particularly permeable (e.g. *SPRHOST* less than 20). The expectation is based on the argument that the change in infiltration characteristics (from rural to urbanised) is more dramatic for naturally permeable soils. This is supported by the regression result underlying the adjustment procedure (see §18.3).

In applying the urban adjustment, *URBEXT* should be taken as the urban extent relevant to the current (or projected) catchment urbanisation, according to the FEH definition of urban extent (see **5** 6).

9.2.4 Adjustment of xrural$_T$ to x$_T$

The as-rural flood growth curve *x* is adjusted for urbanisation by:

$$x_T = UAF^{-\left(\frac{\ln T - \ln 2}{\ln 1000 - \ln 2}\right)} xrural_T \tag{9.5}$$

where *T* is the return period and *UAF* is the urban adjustment factor for *QMED* (defined by Equations 9.3 and 9.4). When *T*=2, the exponent in Equation 9.5 reduces to zero, confirming that the urban adjustment preserves x_T as a growth curve (since $x_2 = xrural_2 = 1.0$). For return periods longer than two years, the urban adjustment given by Equation 9.5 reduces the growth factor from its rural value. When *T* = 1000, Equation 9.5 yields $x_{1000} = xrural_{1000}/UAF$. This fully offsets the urban effect on $QMED_{rural}$ provided by Equation 9.2, i.e. $QMED = UAF\ QMED_{rural}$, so that $Q_{1000} = Qrural_{1000}$.

The choice of 1000 years as the end-point for the urban effect on flood frequency is arbitrary, since it was not practical to support a particular choice empirically (see §18.4). The urban-adjustment procedure is intended principally for use in the return-period range 2 to 200 years, and should never be used outside the range 2 to 1000 years.

9.2.5 Estimation of flood frequency curve

The estimate of the growth factor x_T (from §9.2.4) is multiplied by the estimate of *QMED* (from §9.2.3) to give the flood frequency curve:

$$Q_T = QMED\ x_T \tag{8.1}$$

9.3 Exploiting flood data at the subject site

If the catchment is currently gauged, *QMED* can be estimated directly from the gauged data by peaks-over-threshold or annual maximum analysis (Chapter 2). Unless the urban extent of the catchment is set to expand further, this is all that is required. The estimate of *QMED* can be used in place of the estimate by §9.2.3.

Where urbanisation has expanded appreciably during the period of record, one approach is to estimate *QMED* only from the recent record. Five years of data – indicative of the catchment in its current condition – will usually provide a useful estimate of *QMED*, and would be preferable to estimating *QMED* from a 30-year record during which the catchment has progressively urbanised. In other situations, it may be appropriate to analyse the full period of record, associating the resultant *QMED* value with the urban extent at the mid-point of the record. The value of *URBEXT* can then be updated to the current (or projected) state of

---

Example 9.1
Estimation of the 50-year flood for the Tawd at Skelmersdale New Town

A preliminary estimate is required of the 50-year flood on the Tawd at Stormy Corner, a heavily urbanised catchment draining most of Skelmersdale New Town in north-west England. The subject site is ungauged.

As-rural calculation
The first step is to estimate the 50-year flood as if the catchment were rural. Applying the method of Chapter 3 yields an estimate of $QMED_{rural}$ = 4.45 m³s⁻¹. One gauged catchment (52017) was eliminated from the initial pooling-group because its flow regime is strongly influenced by Blagdon reservoir (*FARL* = 0.89). Nevertheless, the pooling-group was still found to be heterogeneous (H_2 = 3.34). Inspection revealed a highly varied group of catchments, but no reason could be found to make further specific changes. The 50-year growth factor was found to be x_{50} = 2.92. Thus:

$$Qrural_{50} = 2.92 \times 4.45 = 13.0 \text{ m}^3\text{s}^{-1}$$

For illustrative purposes, it is assumed that the developed part of the catchment has expanded by 10% since 1990. Thus, the value of *URBEXT* is taken as 1.1 times the value of $URBEXT_{1990}$ read from the FEH CD-ROM, i.e.

$$URBEXT = 1.1 \times 0.159 = 0.175$$

Adjusting QMED for urbanisation

$$PRUAF = 1 + 0.615\,(0.175)\,(70.0/23.2 - 1) = 1.22 \tag{9.4}$$

$$UAF = 1.22\,(1 + 0.175)^{0.83} = 1.39 \tag{9.3}$$

so that

$$QMED = 1.39 \times 4.45 = 6.19 \text{ m}^3\text{s}^{-1} \tag{9.2}$$

Adjusting the growth factor for urbanisation

$$x_{50} = UAF^{-(\ln 50 - \ln 2)/(\ln 1000 - \ln 2)}\,xrural_{50} = 1.391^{-3.219/6.215}\,2.92 = 2.46 \tag{9.5}$$

Thus, the 50-year flood is estimated to be:

$$Q_{50} = QMED\;x_{50} = 6.19 \times 2.46 = 15.2 \text{ m}^3\text{s}^{-1}$$

This is seen to be 17% greater than the as-rural 50-year flood.

catchment urbanisation. §8.2 of Volume 1 suggests three ways that an *URBEXT* value might be updated for urban expansion. Such techniques can also be used to backdate an *URBEXT* value (see Example 9.2).

Example 9.2
Adjusting a QMED estimate from one era of urbanisation to another: the Fender at Ford (68010)

Flood frequency estimates are required in the year 2000 for a heavily urbanised catchment draining part of the Wirral. The subject site is not currently gauged but flood peak data are available for eight water-years commencing in October 1973. This example illustrates the adjustment of *QMED* from the era of gauging to the era of application.

Because the record length is shorter than 14 years, *QMED* is estimated from the peaks-over-threshold series. Applying the method of §2.4 yields $QMED = 4.45 \text{ m}^3\text{s}^{-1}$.

Inferring a value of $QMED_{rural}$
The approximate mid-point of the period of record is 1977. An $URBEXT_{1990}$ value of 0.204 is read from the FEH CD-ROM. Development of the catchment is estimated to have expanded at the national-average rate between 1977 and 1990. Applying the inverse-tangent model derived in **5 6**, the urban extent in 1977 is estimated to be:

$$URBEXT_{1977} = 0.186$$

An estimate of $QMED_{rural}$ is then unravelled by applying Equation 9.2 in reverse. The relevant steps are:

$$PRUAF = 1 + 0.615 (0.186) (70.0/37.2 - 1) = 1.10 \qquad (9.4)$$

$$UAF = 1.10 (1 + 0.186)^{0.83} = 1.27 \qquad (9.3)$$

$$QMED_{rural} = QMED/UAF = 4.45/1.27 = 3.50 \text{ m}^3\text{s}^{-1} \qquad (9.2)$$

A further application of the inverse-tangent model of urban expansion yields a year 2000 estimate of:

$$URBEXT_{2000} = 0.212$$

Finally, the required estimate of *QMED* is obtained:

$$PRUAF = 1 + 0.615 (0.212) (70.0/37.2 - 1) = 1.15 \qquad (9.4)$$

$$UAF = 1.15 (1 + 0.212)^{0.83} = 1.35 \qquad (9.3)$$

$$QMED = UAF\ QMED_{rural} = 1.35 \times 3.50 = 4.73 \text{ m}^3\text{s}^{-1} \qquad (9.2)$$

9.4 Data transfers

When estimating flood frequency at an ungauged site, Chapter 4 strongly encourages transferring an estimate of *QMED* from a suitable donor or analogue catchment, rather than relying on an estimate from catchment descriptors alone. This recommendation is maintained for urbanised catchments, but particular care is needed in choosing the donor catchment. Usually, an essentially rural donor catchment will be chosen, and the *QMED* value transferred to provide an improved estimate of *QMED*~rural~ at the subject site. Exceptionally, a *QMED* value can be transferred from one urbanised catchment to another if the catchments are both: (i) hydrologically similar in their as-rural condition, and (ii) similar in terms of the extent, type and layout of urbanisation. It is also relevant that urban drainage practice across the subject and donor catchments should be similar. General guidance in transferring estimates from a suitable donor catchment is summarised in Box 9.3.

Box 9.3 Data transfer from one urbanised catchment to another

Where the subject site is ungauged but there is a useful donor site nearby, a flood estimate can sometimes be transferred from one urbanised catchment to another. In this context, a useful donor site is one draining a hydrologically similar, and similarly urbanised, catchment.

In such an exceptional case, it is recommended that the effect of urbanisation is unravelled before transferring the estimate. The first step is to derive a best estimate of flood frequency at the donor site. Then the relevant urban adjustment is applied in reverse, to estimate the as-rural flood frequency curve at the donor site. Next, the estimate is transferred from the donor site to the subject site, as if both catchments were rural. Finally, the estimate at the subject site is re-adjusted for urbanisation. This approach can be applied to estimates by the statistical procedure or by the rainfall-runoff method. However, the adjustment model used to represent the urban effect at the subject site must be the same as that used to remove the urban effect at the donor site. The reader who considers this 'unravelling' approach to be unnecessarily complicated is referred to Example 9.3.

Particular circumspection is warranted before making such a transfer. It should be attempted only when:
- The gauged data at the donor site are of good quality;
- The donor and subject catchments are hydrologically similar in their rural condition;
- Urbanisation and drainage provision in the catchments are of similar character, and their layout relative to soil types is similar.

The final example is a continuation of Example 9.1, re-appraising the effect of Skelmersdale New Town on flood frequency in the Tawd by reference to a gauged site downstream. The example provides a reminder of the inherent uncertainty in estimating *QMED* from catchment descriptors, and illustrates the judgements required when interpreting gauged flood data from an urbanised catchment for effecting a data transfer.

Granting wide scope to use local data to judge the effect of urbanisation could lead to anomalous assessments: for example, in which local flood data are held to demonstrate no adverse effect from urbanisation. The standard procedure is to transfer a *QMED*~rural~ estimate from a rural catchment to an urbanised catchment. Occasionally, as in Example 9.3, a transfer might be attempted between urbanised catchments, again focusing on adjusting the *QMED*~rural~ estimate. However, a transfer should never be attempted from an urbanised catchment to a rural catchment.

A limitation of the urban adjustment procedure presented in §9.2.3 is the assumption that catchment urbanisation has a greater proportional effect on the 2-year flood than on rarer flood peaks. This may not always be realistic.

Example 9.3
Interpreting a QMED estimate from flood data for an urbanised catchment: the Tawd at Skelmersdale New Town

Flood data are available for the Tawd at Newburgh gauging station (70006), about 3 km downstream of Stormy Corner (see Example 9.1). The gauged catchment is more than a third larger than the subject catchment, the intervening subcatchment being largely rural. Nevertheless, because it lies on the same river, and there are no marked differences in soils, the Tawd at Newburgh is a potentially useful donor catchment.

QMED from gauged data at Newburgh
With 14 water-years of gauged flood data, *QMED* can be estimated as the sample median of the annual maxima, yielding $QMED = 12.6$ m^{3}s^{-1}. The period of record is centred on 1972.

Catchment-descriptor estimate of QMED at Newburgh
The Chapter 3 procedure is used to estimate *QMED* from catchment descriptors, yielding $QMED_{rural} = 5.8$ m^{3}s^{-1}. When adjusting for urbanisation – in order to interpret the gauged estimate – it is appropriate to use the urban extent in 1972. In the absence of more detailed information, the $URBEXT_{1990}$ value of 0.117 is backdated from 1990 to 1972 using the inverse-tangent model of urban expansion (see **5 6**), yielding an $URBEXT_{1972}$ value of 0.101. Applying the urban adjustment procedure of §9.2.3 then leads to an urban-adjusted catchment-descriptor estimate of $QMED = 7.1$ m^{3}s^{-1}.

Interpretation at Newburgh
In this example, the catchment-descriptor estimate of *QMED* (7.1 m^{3}s^{-1}) is much less than the gauged *QMED* estimate (12.6 m^{3}s^{-1}). The analyst must decide whether the discrepancy reflects a poor catchment-descriptor estimate of $QMED_{rural}$ or if the actual urban effect differs from that implied by the standard adjustment procedure (i.e. §9.2.3). The former hypothesis might be tested by examining *QMED* estimates for essentially rural catchments that are similar to the Tawd at Newburgh in its as-rural condition. The latter hypothesis is difficult to test. However, morphological evidence that channel cross-sections used to be much smaller (before the New Town development was built) might be convincing. Exceptionally, if the discrepancy is thought to be due to an unusually strong urban effect, it is suggested that the exponent of the $(1 + URBEXT)$ term in Equation 9.3 should be increased to obtain a match at the donor site. The varied model would then be applied at the subject site. The general recommendation is to attribute the discrepancy to a poor estimate of $QMED_{rural}$, as below.

Interpretation at Stormy Corner
The estimate of $QMED_{rural}$ at Stormy Corner is multiplied by the ratio of the observed to modelled values at Newburgh, i.e. $12.6/7.1 = 1.77$. The net effect is to increase all the urban-adjusted flood estimates at Stormy Corner by 77%, so that the Q_{50} estimate of 15.2 m^{3}s^{-1} (obtained in Example 9.1) is increased to 26.9 m^{3}s^{-1}.

Chapter 10 Defining a design hydrograph

10.1 Introduction

In some applications – for example, the design of flood storage areas – a design hydrograph rather than a peak flow estimate is required. Strictly, there is no such thing as a *T*-year flood hydrograph: all hydrographs are different and a rarity can only be ascribed to a particular aspect of a hydrograph, such as its peak flow or its maximum 1-day volume, or to a particular impact (e.g. level of inundation). The less ambitious objective met in this chapter is to supply a typical hydrograph which has a peak of the required rarity.

A flowchart in the introduction to the Flood Studies Report encourages users to adopt a rainfall-runoff approach whenever a design hydrograph is required. This is necessary for dam safety appraisals in the UK, where the relevant guide (ICE, 1996) implies that spillway design floods should not be based on the statistical analysis of peak flows. Reed and Field (1992) suggest that this advice reflects the unacceptable degree of extrapolation required to estimate extremes such as the 10 000-year flood by statistical analysis alone. However, in less exacting settings, it is legitimate to consider deriving the design hydrograph in other ways, so that it is compatible with the best estimate of flood (peak) frequency.

Three methods are presented here: adjusting the rainfall-runoff model parameters (§10.2), borrowing a standard hydrograph shape from the FSR rainfall-runoff method (§10.3), and applying a generalised model of hydrograph shape (§10.4). No one method is explicitly recommended. However, circumstances will often suggest which method is most appropriate to the particular catchment and its data. A final section (§10.5) briefly mentions the statistical analysis of flood volumes.

10.2 Adjusting the parameters of the FSR rainfall-runoff model

Volume 4 presents a technical restatement of the FSR rainfall-runoff method and its application. One approach to obtaining a design hydrograph is to adjust the parameters of the rainfall-runoff model by trial and error (i.e. successive approximation) until the flood frequency curve synthesised by the rainfall-runoff method (4 3) agrees with the flood frequency curve obtained by statistical analysis. The design hydrograph is then provided by the (adjusted) rainfall-runoff method.

In some cases, adjusting the standard percentage runoff (*SPR*) parameter suffices to gain reasonable agreement. Otherwise, it may be necessary to adjust both *SPR* and the unit hydrograph time-to-peak, *Tp*. The goal of matching a particular flood frequency curve should not override other aspects. It is reasonable to adjust a parameter value that experience shows to be typically poorly estimated. For example, it is known that 1:250000 soil maps provide only a broad-brush estimate of *SPR* – via the HOST classification (5 5.4) – especially on small catchments. Thus, an estimate of *SPR* from soil mapping might reasonably be adjusted to gain agreement between statistical and rainfall-runoff estimates of flood frequency. However, it would be unreasonable to re-adjust an estimate of *Tp* that had come from a direct analysis of flood events on the subject catchment.

The adjustment of model parameters can be unconvincing if the flood frequency curves produced by the statistical and rainfall-runoff methods have widely different gradients, or if a very large adjustment is required. The flood frequency estimates may disagree because the assumptions made in the rainfall-

D.W. Reed & D.C.W. Marshall   **59**

runoff method (specifically, the ingredients of the design event) are inappropriate to the catchment, rather than because the *SPR, Tp* and baseflow (*BF*) parameters have been poorly estimated.

10.3 Borrowing a standard hydrograph shape from the rainfall-runoff method

Design hydrographs generated by the FSR rainfall-runoff method come from one of two families of hydrograph shape, according to whether the design rainfall is distributed using the '50% summer profile' (moderate to heavily urbanised catchments) or the '75% winter profile' (rural and lightly urbanised catchments). The appropriate hydrograph shape is taken from Fig. **4** 3.9. The procedure is summarised in Box 10.1.

Box 10.1 Procedure for borrowing a standard hydrograph shape

Step 1
Evaluate the baseflow per unit area from *SAAR* using Figure **4** 3.8; multiply by *AREA* to obtain the baseflow component, *BF*.

Step 2
Subtract the baseflow from the preferred estimate of *T*-year peak flow to estimate the response runoff peak, *q*:
$$q = Q - BF \qquad [4.3.4]$$

Step 3
Select a standard hydrograph shape from Figure **4** 3.9, estimating the required indicator variable '*D/Tp*' by:
$$D/Tp = 1 + SAAR/1000 \qquad [4\ 3.1]$$

Choose the '50% summer' case if the catchment is moderately to heavily urbanised (*URBEXT* > 0.15) and the '75% winter' case otherwise.

Step 4
Estimate unit hydrograph time-to-peak using:

$$Tp = 1.1 \left\{ 4.270\ DPSBAR^{-0.35}\ PROPWET^{-0.80}\ DPLBAR^{0.54}\ (1+URBEXT)^{-5.77} \right\} \quad [10.1]$$

or from flood event analysis (see **4** 2). Equation 10.1 is a minor modification to Equation **4** 2.10, in which the multiplier 1.1 adjusts the estimate of *Tp(0)* to *Tp*, where the data interval of the unit hydrograph has been nominally set to *Tp(0)*/5 (see **4** 2.2).

Step 5
Read ordinates of the standard hydrograph shape from Figure **4** 3.9 at convenient time intervals *t*, indexed by *t/Tp*.

Step 6
Multiply the ordinates by *q* to 'scale-up' the standard hydrograph shape to form the response runoff hydrograph.

Step 7
Add the baseflow *BF* to obtain the required design hydrograph: $Q = q + BF$.

10.4 Applying a simplified model of hydrograph shape

An alternative approach is based on an analysis of the shapes of flood hydrographs. At gauged sites, a direct analysis can be made of the hydrographs recorded in the largest floods. In some applications, it will suffice to characterise the upper part of the design hydrograph (i.e. the part that threatens inundation), and to adopt an upper hydrograph shape based on a simplified model. If required, the lower part of the design hydrograph can be sketched in.

Let Q_{peak} be the peak flow estimate for which a design hydrograph is required. In the simplified model, $W_{half-peak}$ denotes the width of the hydrograph at half peak-flow, measured in hours. Thus, $W_{half-peak}$ is the duration for which a flow of $Q_{peak}/2$ is exceeded during the event (see Figure 10.1). Two variants of the hydrograph-width procedure are summarised in Box 10.2.

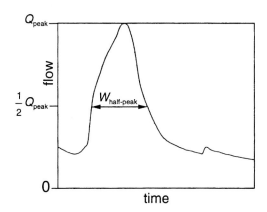

Figure 10.1 *Definition of hydrograph width at half peak-flow*

10.5 Statistical analysis of flood volumes

One option for studying volumetric characteristics of flood hydrographs is to analyse both instantaneous and 1-day flood peaks. The Flood Studies Report presents a method (FSR **I** 5) based on calendar-day extremes. However, the assumption – that instantaneous, 1-day and longer-duration peaks coincide – is an uncomfortable one, and use of the method is not especially encouraged. In the short term, use of the methods outlined in Sections 10.2 to 10.4 is preferred. In the longer term, the need to construct design hydrographs may be circumvented by flood frequency estimation based on 'continuous simulation modelling' (see §5.1 and **1** 9.6).

Although sometimes minor, a recurrent problem is that the source data for daily mean flow calculation – typically 15-minute water levels – are rarely held in computer-compatible form for the whole period of record. This means that it is difficult to confirm that the 1-day and instantaneous peaks are internally consistent, and impractical to adjust the 1-day extremes for any revised flood rating. This was the chief reason why the statistical analysis of calendar-day flood volumes was not pursued in development of the Flood Estimation Handbook.

> **Box 10.2 Hydrograph-width procedure for synthesising the upper part of the design hydrograph**
>
> **Step 1a**
> Estimate $W_{half\text{-}peak}$ by direct analysis of hydrograph widths for recorded flood events, taking a median of values observed in the largest floods.
>
> **Step 1b**
> Alternatively, estimate $W_{half\text{-}peak}$ from the formula:
>
> $$W_{half\text{-}peak} = 2.99 \ Tp(0)^{0.77} \hspace{2cm} [10.2]$$
>
> where $Tp(0)$ is the equivalent time-to-peak of the instantaneous unit hydrograph in the FSR rainfall-runoff method (**4** 1.3), derived either from flood event analysis or from catchment descriptors (**4** 2.2).
>
> **Step 2**
> Construct the hydrograph using the formula:
>
> $$Q / (0.5 \ Q_{peak}) = 2 - 0.65 \ (W/W_{half\text{-}peak}) - 0.35 \ (W/W_{half\text{-}peak})^2 \hspace{1cm} [10.3]$$
>
> where W denotes the hydrograph width at flow Q (see Figure 10.2). Q_{peak} denotes the peak flow at which, by definition, the hydrograph width is zero.
>
> Note that the method assumes a symmetrical shape about the time of peak flow, and that the hydrograph is constructed from the centre outwards. For example, if ordinates are required at hourly intervals, Equation 10.3 is applied to estimate flow values (Q) for hydrograph widths of 2, 4, 6, 8, ... hours.

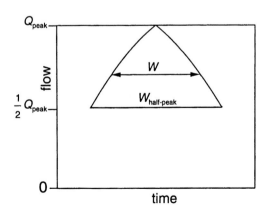

Figure 10.2 *Model for upper hydrograph shape*

Chapter 11 Introducing the flood frequency methodology

11.1 Introduction

This chapter introduces the statistical flood frequency methodology. It concentrates on single-site analysis and uses this to introduce important flood frequency concepts.

In single-site analysis, only the flood data from the subject site are used. This represents the simplest flood frequency estimation case. More commonly it will be necessary to carry out a pooled analysis in which flood data from a group of similar catchments are used (Chapters 16 and 17). The steps required for single-site analysis are very similar to those necessary for pooled analysis, but are simpler. Describing flood frequency analysis for the single-site case provides a general introduction to the methodology.

Section 11.2 introduces the flood peak data; §11.3 presents fundamental concepts such as the return period, the index flood and the flood frequency and flood growth curves. The final sections summarise how these components fit together within single-site analysis, and introduce pooled frequency analysis.

11.2 Flood data series

Two main types of flood data series are used here: the annual maximum series and the peaks-over-threshold (POT) series. Chapter 22 describes the annual maxima and POT series and the methods used in abstracting and validating the flood peak data. Only a brief introduction to these data sets is given here.

Both annual maximum and POT series are usually analysed in terms of the water year, which in the UK runs from 1 October to 30 September (§23.5.2).

Annual maximum series

The annual maximum series consists of the largest observed flow in each water year. It is straightforward to obtain and to analyse, and is the most commonly available form of flood data. Annual maximum data do not indicate whether several major floods occurred in a water year; only the single largest flow is recorded. An annual maximum series sometimes includes values that arise from poorly defined peaks of flow. This occurs when a catchment has not experienced any floods in a water year. Such occurrences are typical of highly permeable catchments and can require special treatment (Chapter 19).

Peaks-over-threshold series

A peaks-over-threshold (POT) series consists of all distinct peak flows that are greater than a selected *threshold* flow. Usually the abstraction threshold is set so that the series contains an average of four or more peaks per year. Independence rules, to determine when peaks can be considered distinct, must be carefully applied (§23.5.1). The resulting POT series is irregular; in some years there may be many floods, in other years there will be no floods.

POT data provide a more complete picture of the flood regime than annual maxima, but are also more difficult to abstract and are not always available. The methodology adopted in the FEH is pragmatic and mainly relies on annual maximum data. However, when available, use of POT data is recommended, notably for *QMED* estimation (Chapter 12), testing for trends (Chapter 21) and in summarising flood seasonality (Additional Note 16.1).

Statistical procedures for flood frequency estimation

There are two main types of flood data, the annual maximum series and the peaks-over-threshold (POT) series. Two POT series are used in the FEH for flood frequency analysis: these are the POT1 and POT3 series containing an average of one and three events per year, respectively. Another term for the POT1 data is the annual exceedance series.

The POT abstraction threshold is ideally set low, so that there is flexibility for future analyses. A low threshold allows a large number of peaks to be included: these will include small and medium-sized events as well as the largest floods. For analytical purposes, the threshold level may be raised above the abstraction threshold: peak flows smaller than this level are then ignored. This thins out the POT series. Varying the threshold allows different aspects of the data to be emphasised. For example, a high threshold means that only the very largest events are used. A low threshold gives a more frequent POT series that indicates a wider range of flood events. The thresholds in this volume are usually set so that the average frequency of POT events is either one per year or three per year. The three events per year series (POT3) contains medium and large peak flows and is used for trend analysis and to calculate seasonality variables. The one event per year series (POT1) contains only the largest floods. It includes the same number of floods as the corresponding annual maximum series, but typically there are some years with no flood event and some years with several flood events.

Annual maximum and POT series are closely related to one another; the annual maximum flow for a year is just the largest POT event in the water year (providing that a POT event has occurred during the year). This relationship is shown in Figure 11.1, where three threshold levels for POT data are shown (abstraction, POT1 and POT3). In most years, the annual maximum values are also part of the POT series. However, 1972 and 1975 had no sizeable flows and the annual maximum values for these years are less than the POT abstraction threshold. The POT record contains many more floods than the annual maximum series. If the POT series is 'thresholded' at a higher level, fewer years contain POT events. For example, using the one event per year POT1 series, there are no POT events in 1972, 1973, 1975, 1982 and 1983.

11.3 Flood frequency fundamentals

11.3.1 Return period

The *return period T* of a flood is a measure of its rarity, defined as the average interval between occurrences of floods that exceed it. The longer the return period, sometimes referred to as the *recurrence interval*, the rarer the flood. In practice T is usually represented differently for the two common hydrological datasets: T_{POT} in the context of POT data and T_{AM} in the context of annual series.

> T_{POT}, the return period on the POT scale, is the average interval between floods exceeding Q. T_{POT} is the *true* return period.

> T_{AM}, the return period on the annual maximum scale, is the average interval between years containing one or more floods exceeding a flow Q. T_{AM} is a *convenient* return period to use.

T_{AM} is not the true return period, because of the distortion caused by measuring time in units of whole years, and because there may be multiple floods within a year. T_{POT} is always slightly shorter than T_{AM}, but the difference between T_{AM} and T_{POT} usually becomes less important for longer return periods and is often considered unimportant for return periods longer than about 20 years. The approximate interrelationship between T_{POT} and T_{AM} has been derived by Langbein (1949) and is given by

$$\frac{1}{T_{AM}} = 1 - \exp\left(-\frac{1}{T_{POT}}\right) \tag{11.1}$$

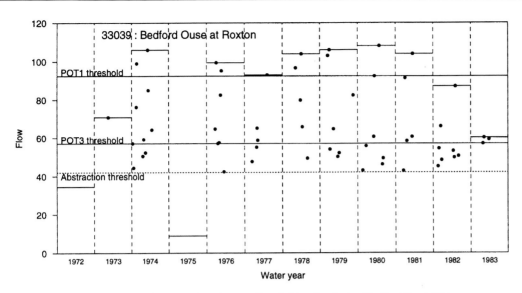

Figure 11.1 *Annual maximum and peaks-over-threshold series for the Bedford Ouse. The horizontal dotted line shows the abstraction threshold. Solid horizontal lines show the POT1 (1 event/year) and POT3 (3 events/year) thresholds. The points show the POT events and the horizontal bars the annual maxima.*

In the FEH, the return period generally refers to T_{AM} and is written as T. It is important to remember that, with this definition, return period represents the average interval between years containing large floods and not the average interval between large floods.

In the FEH, the return period for a flood peak flow Q is the average time interval between years with annual maximum flows greater than Q. The flood with a return period of T years is called the *T-year flood*.

The flood with a return period of T years is denoted by Q_T and referred to as the *T-year return period flood* or just the *T-year flood*. Since Q_T is the flood that, on average, is exceeded in one year out of every T years, this gives

$$\text{Pr (annual maximum } > Q_T) = \frac{1}{T} \qquad (11.2)$$

The left hand side of this equation is termed the *annual exceedance probability*, *AEP*. Thus

$$AEP = \frac{1}{T} \qquad (11.3)$$

For example, for the 50-year flood Q_{50} the *AEP* is 1/50, i.e. there is a 1-in-50 chance of one or more floods greater than Q_{50} occurring in any year.

The return period can be related to $F(Q)$, the non-exceedance probability (or cumulative distribution function: Box 11.1). To see this, note that

$$
\begin{aligned}
AEP &= \text{Pr (annual maximum } > Q) \\
&= 1 - \text{Pr (annual maximum } \leq Q) \\
&= 1 - F(Q)
\end{aligned}
\qquad (11.4)
$$

Combining Equations 11.3 and 11.4 gives

$$T = \frac{1}{1 - F(Q)} \qquad (11.5)$$

Box 11.1   Some statistical fundamentals

A *sample* is a set of observations or measurements derived from an *underlying population*. Thus, a 20-year annual maximum series is a sample from a much longer series (population), stretching forwards and backwards in time. Sample observations may take either discrete or continuous values. An example of *discrete data* is the number of floods in a year: it is always a whole number. Flood flows are an example of *continuous data*: flows can take any value within a range.

A statistical distribution describes the underlying population. It describes the values that observations (past, present or future) are likely to have. A *discrete distribution* is one that takes discrete values: it is usually defined by giving the probability of each possible value. An example of a discrete distribution that could be used to describe the number of floods in a year is the Poisson distribution (see §12.3). A *continuous distribution* is one that can take continuous values. It is defined in terms of either the probability density function or the cumulative distribution function (see Example 11.1). The *probability density function* $f(x)$ can be thought of as the equivalent of the probabilities used to describe the discrete case. Thus, if $f(x)$ is high at x, there is a relatively high probability of observing a value close to x. The *cumulative distribution function* $F(x)$ gives the probability of observing a value less than or equal to x: it takes a value between 0 and 1 and is often referred to as the *non-exceedance probability*. $F(x)$ and $f(x)$ are related to one another by

$$F(x) = \int_0^x f(x)\, dx$$

and are illustrated in Example 11.1.

An *extreme value distribution* is taken here to mean a statistical distribution used to describe extreme events. Often an extreme value distribution is characterised by there being a significant chance of some very big value occurring (an extreme). Examples of extreme value distributions include the Generalised Extreme Value (GEV), Log-Normal (LN) and Generalised Logistic (GL) distributions (see Chapter 15 for more details).

The notation Q is used throughout the FEH to refer to a peak flow. When referring to a distribution that describes flood flows, the link with flow is emphasised by writing the probability density function and the cumulative distribution function as $f(Q)$ and $F(Q)$ respectively.

It is often useful when considering return periods to include more general ideas related to risk: for example, the probability of a flood happening within 100 years. Additional Note 11.1 discusses some of these risk concepts.

11.3.2 Flood frequency curves

The flood frequency curve is a curve that relates flood size to flood rarity (return period).

A *flood frequency curve* relates flood-size to flood-rarity. In a typical analysis, it will be necessary to estimate the flood frequency curve and to interpret this curve

---

Example 11.1
An illustration of the probability density function and the cumulative distribution function for the exponential distribution

The exponential distribution is a simple continuous distribution that might be used to describe the distribution of an annual maximum series. It has probability density function

$$f(Q) = \lambda e^{-\lambda Q}$$

where λ is a parameter describing the spread of the distribution. The cumulative distribution function, obtained by integration, is

$$F(Q) = \text{Pr (annual maximum} \leq Q) = 1 - e^{-\lambda Q}$$

The figure shows these functions for $\lambda = 0.5$: the probability density function decays away at larger values and shows that there is a higher probability of observing an annual maximum value close to 1 than near to 10.

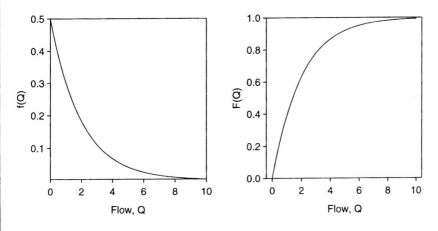

Probability density function f(Q) and cumulative distribution function F(Q) for the exponential distribution with parameter $\lambda = 0.5$

---

for the study in question. The methods presented in this volume are used to obtain the flood frequency curve.

Here, the discussion of the flood frequency curve is based on the Generalised Logistic distribution; similar principles apply when other distributions are used. The Generalised Logistic (GL) distribution is the recommended default distribution for standard flood frequency analysis (§15.3 and §17.3.2). Other distributions are discussed in Chapter 15.

For the GL distribution, the flood frequency curve can be expressed in equation form in terms of either the return period T or the non-exceedance probability F:

$$Q_T = \xi + \frac{\alpha}{k}\left\{1-(T-1)^{-k}\right\} \qquad (k \neq 0) \qquad\qquad (11.6)$$

$$Q(F) = \xi + \frac{\alpha}{k}\left\{1-\left(\frac{1-F}{F}\right)^{k}\right\} \qquad (k \neq 0) \qquad\qquad (11.7)$$

where Q_T is the T-year return period flood, ξ is the location parameter, α the scale parameter and k the shape parameter. Rearranging Equation 11.6 gives the return period T for a flow Q as:

$$T = 1 + \left\{1 - \frac{k}{\alpha}(Q-\xi)\right\}^{-\frac{1}{k}} \qquad\qquad (11.8)$$

Example 11.2 shows a flood frequency curve and how it is used to link flood frequency (return period) and flood size.

Note that when the flood frequency curve has been fitted to a relatively small sample of flood peak data it may be appropriate to adjust the return period estimates obtained from Equation 11.8. This correction, called the *expected probability adjustment,* is analogous to the better known property that regression of x on y differs from the regression of y on x. Further details are given in Additional Note 11.2.

Flood frequency diagram and extreme value plot

It is always helpful to plot the flood frequency curve. The *flood frequency diagram* depicts the flood frequency curve with flood magnitude on the vertical axis, and information about the frequency (and return period) on the horizontal axis. The horizontal axis is usually presented using a *reduced-variate scale*; this is a special scale that is selected so that: (i) a straight line indicates that a simpler 2-parameter distribution applies, in this case the Logistic distribution (see Chapter 15), (ii) a line that curves down and away from a straight line indicates a frequency distribution that is bounded above (i.e. it has a maximum possible value), and (iii) an upwards curving line indicates a flood frequency curve that is unbounded above. A return-period scale is usually also shown on the graph.

Observed flood data can usefully be added to the flood frequency diagram: this is often then referred to as an *extreme value plot.* Chapter 15 presents more details on the reduced variate scale and on plotting positions for the observed data. The most important uses of flood frequency diagrams are as a simple way of relating flood magnitude and return period, and as a means of comparing possible frequency curves with observed flood behaviour: Example 11.2 is typical.

11.3.3 The index flood

The index flood can be thought of as a typical flood for a particular catchment. It tends to increase with catchment size and with average annual rainfall. The index flood is used to link the flood frequency and growth curves (see below): the flood frequency curve is obtained by multiplying the index flood and the growth curve.

In the margin:

In the FEH, the index flood is *QMED*, the median annual maximum flood. It is the flood that on average is exceeded in exactly half of all years.

In the FEH, the index flood is defined to be the *median annual maximum flood, QMED.* In fact *QMED* is the two-year return period flood on the annual maximum scale. This can be deduced as follows. First observe that, on average, half of all annual maxima values are greater than *QMED* (because *QMED* is the median). This means that the annual exceedance probability *AEP* is a half at *QMED* and, from Equation 11.3, the return period is two years.

In the Flood Studies Report, the mean annual flood *QBAR* was used as the index flood. *QMED* is preferred over *QBAR* because:

- *QMED* is a more robust measure: *QMED* is unaffected by the size of an exceptionally large flood event, whereas *QBAR* can change markedly.

- *QMED* can be directly interpreted as the two-year return period flood: this simplifies growth curve construction.

Example 11.2
Using the flood frequency curve plotted below, (i) find the 50-year return period flood, (ii) estimate the return period of a flood of 600 m³ s⁻¹.

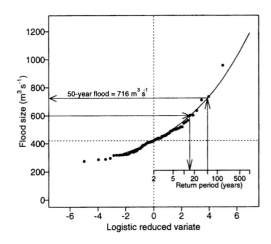

The above plot shows the flood frequency curve for the Wye at Belmont (55002).

(i) To read the 50-year flood off the graph: find the point $T = 50$ on the return period axis, move vertically upwards to the flood frequency curve and then horizontally across to read off the flood magnitude. This gives $Q = 716$ m³ s⁻¹. Note that the flood frequency equation for the curve plotted above is

$$Q_T = 416 + \frac{51}{-0.2}\cdot\left[1 - (T-1)^{0.2}\right]$$

Substituting $T = 50$ in this equation gives the desired $Q_{50} = 716$ m³ s⁻¹

(ii) To read the return period for a flood of 600 m³ s⁻¹ off the graph: find the 600 m³ s⁻¹ flood on the vertical axis, move across to the curve and down to the return period axis. This gives the return period as 16 years.

Alternatively, using Equation 11.8, we have

$$T = 1 + \left\{1 - \frac{-0.2}{51}(Q - 416)\right\}^{\frac{1}{0.2}}$$

Substituting $Q = 600$ m³ s⁻¹, we again obtain $T = 16$ years.

Statistical procedures for flood frequency estimation

11.3.4 The growth curve

The growth curve is a scaled version of the flood frequency curve. It allows the flood behaviour of different catchments to be compared easily and is therefore particularly important for pooled analysis.

The growth curve x_T is defined by

$$x_T = \frac{Q_T}{QMED} \tag{11.9}$$

where Q_T is the flood frequency curve. The growth curve can be thought of as a scaled version of the flood frequency curve. It has the same shape as the flood frequency curve, but is scaled to have a value of 1.0 at the two-year return period. It is used in a somewhat similar way to the flood frequency curve.

Because all growth curves are scaled to have a value of 1.0 at the index flood, growth curves from different catchments can be easily compared. For pooled analysis, the pooled growth curve represents an average of all the individual growth curves from sites in the pooling-group.

The *growth factor* is the value of the growth curve at a particular return period. The T-year growth factor is written as x_T and can be used to estimate the T-year flood, Q_T:

$$Q_T = x_T\, QMED \tag{11.10}$$

Like the flood frequency curve (see §11.3.2), the growth curve is usually based on an extreme value distribution, and can be used in equation or graphical form.

Using the Generalised Logistic distribution as an example, the growth curve may be defined in terms of either the return period T or the non-exceedance probability F:

$$x_T = 1 + \frac{\beta}{k}\left\{1 - (T-1)^{-k}\right\} \qquad (k \neq 0) \tag{11.11}$$

$$x(F) = 1 + \frac{\beta}{k}\left\{1 - \left(\frac{1-F}{F}\right)^{k}\right\} \qquad (k \neq 0) \tag{11.12}$$

where $\beta = \alpha / \xi$, and ξ and α are the location and scale parameters from the flood frequency curve (Equation 11.6).

The growth curve is illustrated in Example 11.3. Note that the constraint that the growth curve has a value of 1.0 at the index flood means that only two parameters are required to describe the GL growth curve, whereas three parameters are needed for the GL flood frequency curve.

11.4 Outline of single-site frequency analysis

11.4.1 Main stages

In single-site analysis only the data from the subject site are used. The recommended procedure is to treat the problem in two steps:

1. Estimation of the index flood, QMED
    The catchment flood data are used to estimate the index flood. *QMED* estimation methods are detailed in Chapter 12. In most cases, *QMED* is found by taking the median of the annual maximum values.

2. Derivation of the growth curve
    Derivation of the growth curve involves selection of the distribution and estimation of the growth curve parameters. In most situations, use of a

Example 11.3
Using the growth curve plotted below (i) find the 50-year growth factor, (ii) find the 50-year flood, (iii) estimate the return period of a flood of 600 m³ s⁻¹. In this example QMED is known to be 421 m³ s⁻¹.

This example repeats the analysis of Example 11.2, but presents the growth curve rather than the flood frequency curve.

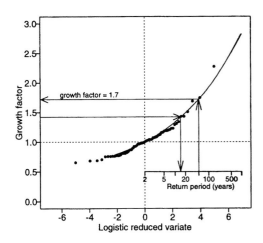

(i) The 50-year growth factor can be read off the graph: it is 1.7. Note that the growth curve for this site is

$$x_T = 1 + \frac{0.122}{-0.2}\left\{1 - (T-1)^{0.2}\right\}$$

Substituting $T = 50$ in this equation also gives a growth factor of 1.7.

(ii) Since $QMED = 421$, the 50-year flood is estimated by

$$Q_{50} = x_{50}\, QMED = 1.7 \times 421 = 716\,\text{m}^3\text{s}^{-1}.$$

(iii) To find the return period for a flood of 600 m³ s⁻¹, first convert the flood size to a growth factor.

$$\text{growth factor} = x = Q/QMED = 600/421 = 1.43$$

From the graph, find the growth factor equal to 1.43 on the vertical axis. Move across to the curve and down to the return period axis. This gives a return period of 16 years. In equation form, the growth curve can be rewritten as

$$T = 1 + \left\{1 - \frac{-0.2}{0.122}(x_T - 1)\right\}^{\frac{1}{0.2}}$$

Substituting $x = 1.43$, we again obtain $T = 16$ years.

Generalised Logistic growth curve is recommended for UK flood data. Estimation of the growth curve parameters is achieved using an L-moment method. L-moments are introduced in Chapter 14, and use of L-moments for estimation of growth curve parameters is described in Chapter 15. More details of the Generalised Logistic distribution and of using extreme value plots to visualise the fit to the observed data are also given in Chapter 15.

Once the growth curve has been derived, the flood frequency curve is obtained by multiplying the growth curve by *QMED*.

By structuring single-site analysis as described above, it is relatively easy to generalise to pooled analysis (see below). Using the same basic framework for single-site and pooled analyses, has the advantage that specialised procedures developed for the pooled case are readily transferable to single-site analyses. Examples of this include: handling urban effects (Chapter 18), correcting for climatic variation (Chapter 20) and local data transfers (Chapter 4).

> For single-site analysis, *QMED* and the growth curve are estimated. The flood frequency curve then equals *QMED* × the growth curve.

11.4.2 When is single-site analysis used?

Single-site analysis is used when there is a reliable and long record at the site of interest and when the target return period *T* is not too long. Single-site analysis is not usually appropriate if the record length is shorter than *T*. If the record is between *T* and 2*T* years in length, it is recommended that both a single-site analysis and a pooled analysis are carried out (see §8.1). If the record length is more than 2*T* years long, then a single-site analysis is usually sufficient, but comparison with a pooled analysis is recommended as a precaution.

11.5 Introducing pooled frequency analysis

Pooled frequency analysis is required unless the flood record is particularly long, i.e. at least twice as long as the return period of interest. The basic principle of the pooling approach is to combine data from the subject site with flood data from other similar sites. The flood frequency curve is estimated using this more extensive data set.

Pooled frequency analysis involves the same basic steps as single-site analysis. Thus it is necessary to (i) estimate the index flood, and (ii) derive the growth curve. For pooled analyses, the methods used in these two steps are generally more complex than in the single-site case.

> Pooled frequency analysis involves the same main steps as single-site analysis but uses flood data from other similar catchments. A pooled analysis is necessary unless the flood record is particularly long compared to the return period of interest.

1. Estimation of the index flood

For pooled flood frequency analysis, there are two main methods for estimating *QMED*. The first (and the preferred method) is to estimate it directly from the subject site's flood record. This is likely to give the best estimate of *QMED* and is described in Chapter 12. If this is not possible, the catchment descriptor method is used, where *QMED* is estimated using a catchment descriptor equation that links it to measures such as catchment area, soils and wetness (Chapter 13). The catchment descriptor equation gives only very approximate estimates of *QMED* and data transfer techniques should generally be used to refine the estimate using flood data from another nearby site (Chapter 4).

2. Estimation of the pooled growth curve

The pooled growth curve is derived using the data from sites in the pooling-group. This consists of gauged catchments with similar characteristics to the subject site. The pooling-group is custom-built for each site, with sites being included if they have similar size, wetness and soils to the subject site (Chapter 16). Once the pooling-group is known, a pooled growth curve is fitted to the data (Chapter 17). As with single-site analysis, the recommended distribution for the pooled growth curve is the Generalised Logistic distribution (Chapter 15) and it is obtained using L-moment methods (Chapter 14).

Chapters 12 to 17 cover in depth the methods outlined above. More specialised topics, such as flood frequency estimation for urban catchments and correcting for climatic variation, are discussed in the remaining chapters of Part B.

Additional Note 11.1   Risk

It is often necessary to interpret information about flood frequency in terms of the risk of exceedance, i.e. the probability of a flood exceeding a threshold value. There are simple relationships between risk and return periods. A summary of some of the most useful results follows.

Let Q_T be the T-year flood, more formally the T-year return period flood. The probability (or risk) of Q_T being exceeded at least once in any one water year is $1/T$. For example, there is a 1 in 50 (0.02) risk of one or more 50-year floods occurring in a given year.

The risk equation describes the risk r of the T-year flood occurring one or more times in an M-year period. It is given by

$$r = 1 - \left(1 - \frac{1}{T}\right)^M \qquad (11.13)$$

The risk equation is derived as follows:

$$\text{Pr} \ (T\text{-year flood occurs during a year}) \ = \ \frac{1}{T}$$

$$\text{Pr} \ (\text{no } T\text{-year flood in a year}) \ = \ 1 - \frac{1}{T}$$

$$(11.14)$$

$$\text{Pr} \ (\text{no } T\text{-year flood in } M \text{ years}) \ = \ \left(1 - \frac{1}{T}\right)^M$$

$$\text{Pr} \ (\text{one or more } T\text{-year floods in } M \text{ years}) \ = \ 1 - \left(1 - \frac{1}{T}\right)^M$$

Table 11.1 shows the risk of various return-period floods occurring during selected M-year periods. It can be seen that there is an approximately two-thirds risk of observing a T-year flood in T years ($r = 0.63$ for T greater than 100 years).

The risk equation can also be used to estimate the typical return period of the largest flood in an M-year period. For the typical largest flood, the associated risk is 0.5 (there is an even chance of a largest flood being smaller or larger than the typical largest flood). The return period can therefore be obtained by solving the risk equation (Equation 11.13) for T. For example, consider the typical return period of the largest flood in 100 years. Since the associated risk is 0.5, this flood must have a return period T that satisfies Equation 11.13, i.e.

Table 11.1 *The risk of one or more T-year floods occurring during a selection of M-year periods. The risk of one or more T-year floods in T years is highlighted in bold.*

Period length M (years)	Return period, T (years)					
	5	10	20	50	100	500
1	0.20	0.10	0.05	0.02	0.01	0.00
2	0.36	0.19	0.10	0.04	0.02	0.00
5	**0.67**	0.41	0.23	0.10	0.05	0.01
10	0.89	**0.65**	0.40	0.18	0.10	0.02
20	0.99	0.88	**0.64**	0.33	0.18	0.04
50	1.00	0.99	0.92	**0.64**	0.39	0.10
100	1.00	1.00	0.99	0.87	**0.63**	0.18
500	1.00	1.00	1.00	1.00	0.99	**0.63**

$$0.5 = \left(1 - \frac{1}{T}\right)^{100}$$

This gives

$$T = \left(1 - 0.5^{\frac{1}{100}}\right)^{-1} \tag{11.15}$$

$$= 145 \text{ years}$$

The largest flood in a 100-year period will therefore typically have a return period of 145 years. More generally, if M is large, the largest flood in an M-year flood has a return period of approximately $1.44M$ years.

Additional Note 11.2 Expected probability adjustment

The expected probability adjustment is an adjustment that is made to the annual exceedance probability (AEP: §11.3.1). It is required because a method which gives the 'best' estimate of flood size, does not necessarily give the 'best' estimate of flood frequency. This note explains why an adjustment is sometimes needed and broadly indicates the likely size of the adjustment. For details on how to calculate the adjustment the reader is referred to Stedinger (1983), Australian Rainfall Research (IE Australia, 1987) and Arnell (1988).

The FEH statistical methods are designed primarily to estimate flood size, e.g. what is the size of the 50-year flood? The methods give (relatively) unbiased estimates of flood size. This means that if, for example, the 50-year flood could be estimated many times using the FEH methods, the average of these estimates would be pretty near to the true 50-year flood. More formally, an estimator is said to be unbiased if the average of many estimations is very close to the true value.

The FEH methods give an unbiased estimate of flood size but a biased estimate of flood frequency (AEP) and return period. In the case of the 50-year flood, the estimated 50-year flood will on average be exceeded more than once every 50 years. This bias occurs because of sampling uncertainties. The bias diminishes as record length increases, and is relatively small if the record length is long compared to the return period. The use of FEH pooling-groups is likely to result in a relatively small bias, since this method uses a large number of station-years of data for flood frequency estimation (Chapter 16).

Table 11.2 and Figure 11.2 show the approximate level of the bias in the *AEP* for various *T*-year flood estimates. The table is obtained by taking a GL distribution that is typical of FEH flood data (this corresponds to L-CV = 0.20 and L-skewness = 0.15: see Chapter 15). Samples of selected record lengths are derived

Table 11.2 *Mean values of AEP for selected record lengths and return periods obtained by simulation from a GL distribution. The bracketed number is the average recurrence interval between exceedances. The top line gives actual values.*

Record length		Return period, T (years)			
		10	20	50	100
	True value	0.1 (10)	0.05 (20)	0.02 (50)	0.01 (100)
10		0.14 (7.2)	0.082 (12)	0.052 (19)	0.034 (29)
20		0.12 (8.5)	0.066 (15)	0.034 (29)	0.023 (44)
30		0.12 (8.6)	0.062 (16)	0.031 (32)	0.018 (54)
40		0.11 (9.0)	0.059 (17)	0.028 (36)	0.016 (62)
50		0.11 (9.3)	0.058 (17)	0.026 (39)	0.015 (67)
100		0.11 (9.5)	0.054 (19)	0.023 (43)	0.013 (79)

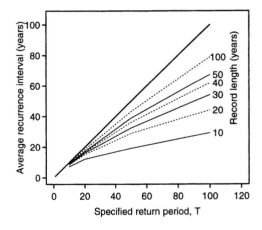

Figure 11.2 *Mean recurrence interval between exceedances (1/AEP) for a selection of record lengths. For short records and long return periods, the estimated T-year flood may be exceeded considerably more often than once in T years.*

from this distribution and used to estimate the *T*-year flood. For each estimate of the *T*-year flood, the corresponding *AEP* value is calculated and the average of these *AEP* values, taken over 1000 samples, is reported. The table illustrates the extent to which sample *AEP* values tend to exceed the true *AEP* values. For example, the table says that for a 50-year flood that is estimated using a 20-year record, the corresponding *AEP* is 0.034. Thus, the estimated 50-year flood will actually be exceeded about once every 1/0.034 = 32 years. For easier interpretation, the bracketed values in Table 11.1 show $1/AEP$, i.e. a measure of the associated return period (N.B. this is not the average return period). The bias in AEP is largest when the return period is long relative to the record.

Adjusting for the bias in AEP is non-trivial, and no simple formula is available for use with the GL distribution — the adjustment depends on the precise form of the fitted flood frequency distribution. An adjustment can be obtained either by simulation (Monte-Carlo) approaches (Arnell, 1988), or using Bayesian techniques (Stedinger, 1983; Kuczera, 1997). Arnell (1988) presents relationships for a correction that applies to the GEV distribution.

The issue of when the adjustment should be applied is a sensitive one (IE Australia, 1987). If the objective is to obtain the 50-year design flood, then use of the adjustment would not normally be appropriate. If the objective is to estimate the rarity of a flood then an adjustment should be used. The issue becomes more complex if an assessment of risk is to be made (Stedinger *et al.*, 1993) and depends critically on the precise approach taken to risk estimation.

Chapter 12 Estimating QMED from flood data (B)

12.1 Introduction

12.1.1 QMED as the index flood

In the FEH, the index flood is used to scale the pooled growth curve in order to obtain the site frequency curve. The recommended index flood is the *median annual maximum flood*, referred to as *QMED* (see Chapter 11). This is the flood that is exceeded in exactly half of all years.

12.1.2 Choosing whether to use POT or annual maximum series

QMED estimates can be derived from either peaks-over-threshold (POT) or annual maximum series. In general, POT data give improved estimates of *QMED*, especially for shorter record lengths. Using POT data is of equivalent value to collecting another one or two years of annual maximum data (see §12.4.2).

Data for estimating QMED

POT data are used to estimate *QMED* when
- the POT record is as long as the annual maximum record, and
- there are fewer than 14 years of record

In all other cases, *QMED* is derived from the annual maximum series.

If *QMED* is estimated using a record shorter than 14 years, an adjustment for climatic variation is recommended (see Chapter 20). Note that in the FEH methodology, the growth curve is always estimated using annual maximum data, even when POT data are used to derive *QMED*.

12.1.3 Summary of estimation from annual maximum series

QMED is estimated from annual maxima by taking the median of the series (§12.2).

12.1.4 Summary of estimation from POT series

A POT estimate of *QMED* can be obtained with the aid of the standard coefficients given in Table 12.1.

Estimating QMED from POT data

To calculate *QMED* using POT data, the recommended procedure is:
- remove incomplete water-years and determine the record length,
- obtain the required values of i, $i+1$ and w from Table 12.1,
- arrange floods in descending order of magnitude,
- find the ith largest and $(i+1)^{th}$ largest flows in the POT series (i.e. Q_i, Q_{i+1}),
- estimate *QMED* by taking a weighted average of these two flows:

$$QMED = w\,Q_i + (1-w)\,Q_{i+1}$$

A.J. Robson   **77**

In general, only complete water-years of POT records are used for *QMED* estimation. However, where a record is particularly short, special methods that make use of part-records may be appropriate (Additional Note 12.1). It should be remembered that a year in which no POT event occurs forms a valid and important part of a POT record. Further details, examples and background information on estimating *QMED* from POT data are given in §12.3.

Table 12.1 *Summary information for estimating QMED from POT data. The ordered positions (i, i+1) show that the ith largest and i+1th largest POT floods are just bigger and just smaller than QMED respectively. A weighted average of these two flood peaks is taken, using the weights w. POT data are most beneficial for estimating QMED from records shorter than 14 years. Values for longer records are italicised here.*

POT record length (years)	i	i+1	Weight w
1	1	2	0.602
2	2	3	0.895
3	2	3	0.100
4	3	4	0.298
5	4	5	0.509
6	5	6	0.725
7	6	7	0.945
8	6	7	0.147
9	7	8	0.349
10	8	9	0.557
11	9	10	0.769
12	10	11	0.983
13	10	11	0.185
14	*11*	*12*	*0.389*
15	*12*	*13*	*0.597*
16	*13*	*14*	*0.807*
17	*13*	*14*	*0.018*
18	*14*	*15*	*0.221*
19	*15*	*16*	*0.426*
20	*16*	*17*	*0.634*

12.2 Estimating QMED from annual maxima

12.2.1 Calculation of the median annual maximum flood

Calculation of the median annual maximum flood using annual maximum data is very straightforward. The median is the middle-ranking value of a series of numbers. To find the median, the series is sorted into decreasing order of size, so that Q_i is the ith largest annual maximum. If the total record length is n, then

$$QMED = \begin{cases} Q_{\frac{n+1}{2}} & \text{for } n \text{ odd} \\ \frac{1}{2}\left(Q_{\frac{n}{2}} + Q_{\frac{n}{2}+1}\right) & \text{for } n \text{ even} \end{cases} \qquad (12.1)$$

Example 12.1
Estimate QMED from annual maximum data for the Bedford Ouse at St Ives Staunch (33017).

Annual maximum series in
decreasing order of magnitude

	Water year	Flow $(m^3 s^{-1})$	
1	1967	142.1	
2	1950	133.9	
3	1968	124.0	
4	1949	119.4	
5	1954	118.5	
6	1953	116.7	
7	1963	107.6	
8	1970	104.2	
9	1966	97.0	←
10	1961	94.3	←
11	1969	92.4	
12	1951	88.7	
13	1965	84.0	
14	1952	83.7	
15	1962	69.9	
16	1964	55.4	
17	1971	52.0	
18	1972	51.0	

The annual maximum series runs from 1949 to 1954 and 1961 to 1972.

Order the annual maxima from largest to smallest. Since there are 18 years of data, QMED is the average of the 9th and 10th largest floods.

$$QMED = \frac{1}{2}(Q_{18/2} + Q_{18/2+1})$$
$$= \frac{1}{2}(Q_9 + Q_{10})$$
$$= \frac{1}{2}(97.0 + 94.3)$$
$$= 95.6 \, m^3 s^{-1}$$

12.3 Estimating QMED from peaks-over-threshold series

This section gives background information on how *QMED* can be estimated from peaks-over-threshold (POT) data. Practical application of the method is summarised in §12.1.4.

In the following sections, some important aspects of POT data are introduced (§12.3.1 and §12.3.2) and the importance of clustering in POT data is discussed (§12.3.3). UK data show a noticeable degree of clustering, and because of this the negative binomial distribution is used here to describe POT occurrences (§12.3.4).

The final two sections examine the theoretical relationship that forms the key to estimating *QMED* from POT data. It is shown how this relationship is used to calculate the table for estimating *QMED* from POT data (Table 12.1).

12.3.1 Some peaks-over-threshold basics

The peaks-over-threshold (POT) data comprise a series of floods that are bigger than a selected threshold (see §11.2 and Chapter 23 for details). If a low threshold is used, the POT series contains numerous floods, some of which are of moderate or small size. Using a high threshold leaves just a few large events in the POT series. In *QMED* estimation, the main interest is in the rarer floods, so a high threshold is most useful. In other circumstances, for example when studying flood seasonality, a lower threshold is more appropriate.

Peaks-over-threshold and annual maximum data are closely linked. Provided the POT threshold is low enough, the annual maximum will be the maximum of the POT events in a year. Because POT records contain more floods than annual maximum records, a better estimate of *QMED* can often be obtained from the POT data. The benefit of using POT data is most marked when record lengths are shorter than 14 years (§12.4).

12.3.2 Exceedance rates and the annual exceedance series

To estimate *QMED* from POT requires knowledge about exceedance rates.

Definition

A POT *exceedance rate* describes how often a river is likely to produce a flood that exceeds a threshold flow. For any flood flow Q the exceedance rate λ_Q is defined as the average number of floods per year which exceed Q. A high threshold corresponds to a low exceedance rate and *vice versa*.

> The POT exceedance rate λ_o is the average number of floods per year that are greater than a flow Q.

Estimating exceedance rates

Let Q_i be the i th largest POT flood in an N-year POT record. Consider Q_i^*, a flow level just above Q_i. There are $i-1$ floods bigger than Q_i^*, so the exceedance rate at Q_i^* (= the average number of floods bigger than Q_i^*) can be estimated by

$$\hat{\lambda}_{Q_i}^+ = \frac{(i-1)}{N} \tag{12.2}$$

For Q_i^-, a flow level just below Q_i, there are i floods bigger than Q_i^- and the exceedance rate is

$$\hat{\lambda}_{Q_i}^- = \frac{i}{N} \tag{12.3}$$

The exceedance rate can be seen to take a step jump at Q_i and the exceedance rate at Q_i can be estimated by taking an average of Equations 12.2 and 12.3,

$$\hat{\lambda}_{Q_i} = \frac{(i-0.5)}{N} \tag{12.4}$$

Note that this estimate of λ_{Q_i} depends only on the ordered position of the POT flow i and on the length of the POT record N. It does not depend on the magnitudes of the ordered flows Q_i. Because λ_{Q_i} depends only on i, it is often convenient to write it simply as λ_i.

The annual exceedance series

> The POT1 or annual exceedance series is a POT series that contains an average of one event per year.

The annual exceedance series is the POT series that contains an average of one event per year. Thus the annual exceedance series for an N-year POT record will contain N floods. The annual exceedance series is identical to the POT1 series (§11.2). In this chapter, the POT exceedance process plays an important role and the term annual exceedance series is therefore preferred.

12.3.3 Dispersion and clustering in POT data

It is found that the procedure for obtaining *QMED* depends on the level of clustering in the POT data. This makes it necessary to delve into the stochastic process by which POT floods occur or arrive: the arrival process. Three cases are considered:

- Flood events occur randomly in time: a *Poisson* process;
- Flood events are more clustered than a random process;
- Floods events are less clustered than a random process.

It is important to allow for the degree of clustering in POT data because systematic over- or under-estimation of *QMED* could otherwise occur.

The *index of dispersion* (Cox and Lewis, 1966) is used to measure the degree of clustering in the POT data. It is a scaled measure of the variability of the number of floods per year, defined by:

$$D = \frac{\text{variance (no. of floods per year)}}{\text{mean (no. of floods per year)}} \qquad (12.5)$$

The terms *dispersion* and *index of dispersion* are used interchangeably in this volume.

The relationship between the degree of clustering and the dispersion is shown in Figure 12.1. For a random (Poisson) process, the theoretical dispersion is 1.0. A dispersion higher than 1.0 indicates clustering at the annual scale (i.e. notably more floods in some years than others). A dispersion less than 1.0 shows that the number of floods per year is unusually regular (i.e. more regular than would be expected of a random process). Because dispersion is calculated from the number of events per year, the effect of any seasonality in the data is reduced.

The dispersion is dependent on the choice of POT threshold. In the FEH, dispersions are generally calculated for the annual exceedance series, i.e. data where the threshold has been chosen so that the series contains an average of one event per year. The dispersion corresponding to this is written D_{AE}. In general, the higher the threshold, the less clustering is likely to be present. Use of the annual exceedance series means that there is minimal clustering in the data; yet there are still sufficient data for *QMED* to be estimated.

Note that when calculating the dispersion it is necessary to take account of *ties* in the data. A tie occurs in a flood series when there are two or more floods that are recorded as having the same size. Most ties arise because water levels are

> The index of dispersion D describes clustering in a POT record. D_{AE} is the dispersion for the annual exceedance (POT1) series.

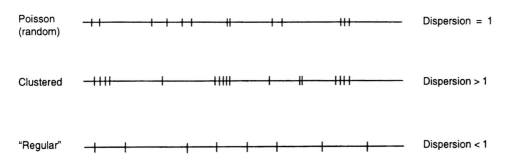

Figure 12.1 *An illustration of stochastic series, such as flood event occurrences, that (i) occur randomly, (ii) are more clustered than random data, and (iii) are more regular (less clustered) than random data*

recorded or abstracted with limited precision (e.g. for many gauging stations, levels read from charts are accurate to within about 5 mm). For dispersion, ties are only important if they occur at the threshold level. For example, an annual exceedance series for a 9-year record should contain nine floods. If the 8th, 9th and 10th largest flows are recorded as being identical, it is difficult to define the annual exceedance series and to calculate the dispersion. In practice, if there are T tied floods, of which only t values need to be included for an annual exceedance series, the dispersion is obtained by calculating the dispersion for all possible selections of t floods from T ties, and adopting the mean value.

Example 12.2 shows how the dispersion is calculated, and how it is dependent on the threshold.

Dispersion properties of UK floods data

For all sites with POT data, the dispersions of the annual exceedance series were determined and are shown in Figure 12.2. The main findings are:

- UK POT data tend to be somewhat clustered: 70% of sites have a dispersion greater than 1.0;
- 20% of gauges are significantly more clustered than a Poisson (random) process (95% significance level);
- Short records show greater variability in the dispersion;
- The average value of D_{AE}, weighted by record length, is 1.38.

In the UK, POT data tend to be somewhat clustered. Flood arrivals cannot be considered to behave as a truly random process.

The tendency for clustering in UK data may be due to climatic variations, combined with the role that antecedent conditions play in determining catchment response. The UK climate shows a tendency for groups of wet years and groups of dry years to occur together (§20.2). This appears to cause sequences of flood-rich and flood-poor years. The antecedent soil conditions are also important, particularly when catchments have become fully saturated. A catchment that is fully wetted up gives a larger flood response than one that is in an average state. Such factors can encourage flood events to cluster seasonally.

These results suggest that the POT arrival process is not always behaving as a random process. Consequently, processes other than the Poisson process need to be considered.

In the recommended method for estimating *QMED* from POT data, an estimate of the dispersion of the annual exceedance series D_{AE} is needed. In general, it is recommended that the UK-average value of D_{AE} (1.38) is used. Simulation studies were used to compare this with using site-specific values of D_{AE} (§12.4). The UK-average dispersion gave better overall performance, probably because dispersion tends to be poorly defined for short flood records. Use of locally derived values of D_{AE}, e.g. the site dispersion for a long record or a regionally averaged dispersion value, could be preferable in some circumstances, and experienced analysts may sometimes wish to consider using local alternatives to the UK-average dispersion.

12.3.4 Using the negative binomial distribution for POT occurrences

In the FEH, the negative binomial distribution is used to describe the number of POT events that occur each year. This distribution allows for some clustering in the data and, in particular, can be parameterised so that its dispersion equals the observed UK-average (D_{AE} = 1.38).

Example 12.2
Estimate the dispersion for exceedance rates of one, two and three events per year for the Allan Water at Bridge of Allan (18005).

The POT series for the Bridge at Allan is shown below and is marked with the threshold levels for one, two and three events per year (93.5, 81.2 and 74.9 $m^3 s^{-1}$ respectively). The abstraction threshold is 58.0 $m^3 s^{-1}$. There are 20 water-years of data.

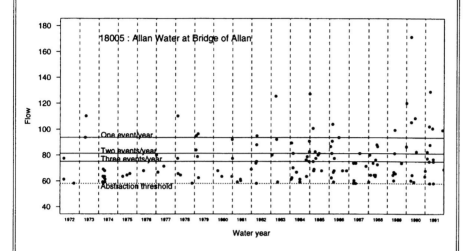

The number of POT events per year is found for the three thresholds:

	1 event	2 events	3 events		1 event	2 events	3 events
1972	0	0	1	1982	1	2	3
1973	2	2	2	1983	1	2	3
1974	0	0	0	1984	1	5	8
1975	0	0	0	1985	1	3	6
1976	0	0	0	1986	2	5	6
1977	0	0	1	1987	0	1	1
1978	1	1	2	1988	0	2	4
1979	2	3	4	1989	1	2	2
1980	0	1	1	1990	4	6	6
1981	0	0	1	1991	4	6	10

From these three series, the mean, variance and dispersion (= variance/mean) of the number of floods per year are calculated.

	1 event	2 events	3 events
Mean	1.00	2.05	3.05
Variance	1.579	4.155	8.050
Dispersion	1.579	2.027	2.639
Dispersion$_{ties}$	1.579	2.042	2.547

For the two and three events per year thresholds, the mean number of events per year is slightly higher than it should be: e.g. 2.05 instead of 2.00. This is because there are ties at the threshold. If ties are allowed for in calculating the dispersion (see main text) a slightly different dispersion is found: this is shown in the final row. As expected dispersion is found to be greater at lower thresholds.

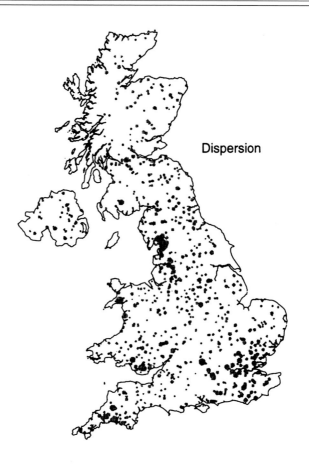

Dispersion

Figure 12.2 *Map of dispersion values for annual exceedance (POT1) series for FEH gauging stations. Grey circles show dispersion values that are greater than one (they show clustering), black circles show sites where the dispersion is less than or equal to one. Circle radii are proportional to the calculated dispersion.*

Some common 1- and 2-parameter distribution functions, including the negative binomial and Poisson distribution, are detailed in Table 12.2. Of these distributions, only the negative binomial is able to match a non-integer dispersion greater than 1.0. The negative binomial distribution uses one more parameter than the Poisson distribution. Simulation studies show that the negative binomial distribution either outperforms or gives very similar results to the Poisson distribution when used in estimating *QMED* (§12.4).

The negative binomial distribution

The 2-parameter negative binomial distribution is used to describe the distribution of the number of POT events per year. Its parameters are chosen to match the observed clustering in the POT data.

The negative binomial distribution is a 2-parameter distribution function with a dispersion that is greater than 1.0. The negative binomial distribution results if the number of peaks in a year comes from a Poisson distribution with mean μ, where μ varies from year to year with a gamma distribution. A negative binomial distribution also results if there is a Poisson number of episodes per year with prescribed proportions of these episodes having one peak, two peaks, three peaks, and so on. The negative binomial distribution is therefore a reasonable choice to account for clustering of floods in particular years.

Table 12.2 *Some discrete distribution functions. D denotes dispersion and D_{AE} the dispersion for the special case of an annual exceedance (POT1) series. For an annual exceedance series, the mean number of events is 1.*

Distribution	No. of parameters (range)	Possible values	Point probability	Mean	Variance	D	D_{AE}
Binomial	2 $(n \geq 0)$ $(0 \leq p \leq 1)$	$0 \leq r \leq n$	$\binom{n}{r} p^r (1-p)^{n-r}$	np	$np(1-p)$	$(1-p)$	$1 - \frac{1}{n}(<1)$
Poisson	1 $(\mu \geq 0)$	$r \geq 0$	$\dfrac{e^{-\mu}\mu^r}{r!}$	μ	μ	1	1
Geometric	1 $(0 \leq p \leq 1)$	$r \geq 0$	$p(1-p)^r$	$\dfrac{1-p}{p}$	$\dfrac{1-p}{p^2}$	$\dfrac{1}{p}$	2
Negative binomial	2 $(0 \leq p \leq 1)$ $(k \geq 0)$	$r \geq 0$	$\binom{k+r-1}{r} p^k (1-p)^r$	$\dfrac{k(1-p)}{p}$	$\dfrac{k(1-p)}{p^2}$	$\dfrac{1}{p}$	$1 + \frac{1}{k}(>1)$

The negative binomial process is defined by

$$Pr\ (r\ events) = \binom{k+r-1}{r} p^k (1-p)^r$$
$$= \frac{(k+r-1)!}{(k-1)!r!} p^k (1-p)^r \tag{12.6}$$

where k and p are parameters. For this distribution the dispersion is $1/p$. The negative binomial distribution is not defined for a dispersion of 1. However, as the dispersion tends to 1, the distribution tends towards the Poisson distribution.

The mean of a negative binomial series is just the average number of events per year: this is the exceedance rate λ and can be written, using Table 12.2,

$$\text{Mean} = \lambda = k\frac{1-p}{p} \tag{12.7}$$

Parameters of the negative binomial distribution for an annual exceedance series

For an annual exceedance (POT1) series, the average number of events per year is one, i.e. $\lambda = 1$. From Equation 12.7 and Table 12.2, the parameters for a negative binomial distribution with mean of 1 can be written:

$$p = \frac{1}{D_{AE}} \tag{12.8}$$

$$k = \frac{1}{D_{AE}-1} \tag{12.9}$$

where D_{AE} is the dispersion for the annual exceedance series.

12.3.5 Theoretical link between POT and annual maximum series

This section introduces the equation that provides a theoretical link between POT and annual maximum series. The equation forms the basis for calculating the table used in estimating $QMED$ from POT data (Table 12.1). The full mathematical derivation of the equation is provided in Additional Note 12.2.

The equation linking POT and annual maximum series is

$$AEP_Q = 1 - \left\{1 + \lambda_Q (D_{AE} - 1)\right\}^{\frac{-1}{D_{AE}-1}} \qquad (D_{AE} > 1) \qquad (12.10)$$

where AEP_Q is the annual exceedance probability (i.e. the probability that an annual maximum exceeds Q), λ_Q is the exceedance rate for the flow Q and D_{AE} is the dispersion for the annual exceedance series. This links AEP and λ for a given flow Q. It assumes that the POT arrivals follow a negative binomial distribution.

Equation 12.10 holds for any dispersion greater than 1, but is not defined for a dispersion equal to 1 (corresponding to the Poisson distribution). However, it can be shown that, as the dispersion becomes very close to one, the relationship reduces to

$$AEP_Q = 1 - e^{-\lambda_Q} \qquad (12.11)$$

Observing that $AEP = 1/T_{AM}$ (Equation 11.3) and $\lambda = 1/T_{POT}$, this equation can be shown to give Langbein's relationship (§11.3.1). Equation 12.10 can be seen as a generalisation of Langbein's relationship that allows for clustering in POT data.

Equation 12.10 says that, if the dispersion of the annual exceedance series is known, then the probability of an annual maximum exceeding Q can be found for any flow in the POT record. When $Q = QMED$, there is an even chance of an annual maximum value being greater than $QMED$ in any one year, so

$$AEP_{QMED} = 0.5 \qquad (12.12)$$

> The annual exceedance probability (AEP) is 0.5 at $QMED$. The peaks-over-threshold $QMED$ estimation method looks for the POT flow for which the $AEP = 0.5$. The AEP of a POT flow can be found if the dispersion of the POT annual exceedance series is known.

Finding $QMED$ using POT data is therefore equivalent to finding a flow for which $AEP_Q = 0.5$. In practice, a POT series is unlikely to contain an observed flow for which AEP_Q is exactly 0.5. Instead, the POT floods for which the AEP is just above and just below 0.5 are selected and $QMED$ is estimated by taking a weighted average of these two flows (Examples 12.3 and 12.4). Equation 12.10 therefore enables $QMED$ to be estimated from the POT series.

12.3.6 Understanding the table for estimating QMED from POT data

Table 12.1 summarises the information required for estimation of $QMED$ from POT data (assuming a negative binomial distribution and a dispersion of 1.38). This section describes how the $QMED$ estimation table is used and how the information contained in the table is derived.

Using the QMED estimation table

To use Table 12.1, the POT data are ordered from largest to smallest. The relevant values of i, $i+1$ and w are extracted from the table, in accordance with the number of years of record. $QMED$ is then estimated by taking a weighted average of the ith and $i+1^{th}$ flows:

$$QMED = w\,Q_i + (1-w)Q_{i+1} \qquad (12.13)$$

Two examples showing how to use Table 12.1 to calculate $QMED$ are given in Example 12.3.

Example 12.3
Estimate QMED for the Gwash and White Laggan Burn.

(1) Gwash at Belmesthorpe (31006)

There are 6 years of POT data at this site and no additional years of annual maximum data. $QMED$ is therefore estimated from the POT series. The largest 8 flows ($m^3 s^{-1}$) are:

Rank:	1	2	3	4	5	6	7	8
Flow:	26.5	21.0	16.4	14.4	13.4	11.5	11.2	10.4

From Table 12.1, for a record length of 6 years, the 5th and 6th flows are required and the weight is 0.725. $QMED$ is therefore estimated as

$$QMED = 0.725 \times 13.4 + (1 - 0.725) \times 11.5 = 12.9\ m^3 s^{-1}$$

(2) White Laggan Burn at Loch Dee (80003)

There are 11 years of POT record and no additional annual maximum data. $QMED$ is therefore estimated using the POT series.

The largest 14 flows ($m^3 s^{-1}$) for this site are:

Rank:	1	2	3	4	5	6	7	8	9	10	11	12	13	14
Flow:	26.9	9.54	9.38	9.22	9.22	8.76	8.76	8.76	8.61	8.61	8.61	8.46	8.46	8.46

From Table 12.1, we see that, for a record length of 11 years, the 9th and 10th flows are required and the weight is 0.769. Here, the 9th and 10th largest flows are tied values.

$$QMED = 0.769 \times 8.61 + (1 - 0.769) \times 8.61 = 8.61\ m^3 s^{-1}$$

Deriving the QMED estimation table

The methods used to derive Table 12.1 enable the recalculation of equivalent information for other record lengths and other values of dispersion.

There are two stages to deriving the table. The first stage identifies the positions of the flows that lie just above and just below $QMED$. For this,

- calculate $\lambda_1, \lambda_2, \lambda_3, \ldots$ the exceedance rates for the 1st, 2nd, 3rd … largest POT flows. Note that for the ith largest flow of an N-year record, the exceedance rate is (from Equation 12.4):

$$\lambda_i = \frac{i - 0.5}{N} \qquad (12.14)$$

- convert these exceedance rates into *AEP* values using Equation 12.10;
- identify the positions of the flows with *AEP* values that bracket *AEP*=0.5.

Example 12.4 shows how this proceeds for the case of a 9-year flood record.

The second stage is to calculate the weights that are used to average the two POT floods found from stage one. The recommended weighting scheme uses a Logistic reduced variate scale based on the *AEP* values of the two POT floods. A reduced variate scheme is recommended because simulation studies (for the GEV distribution) indicate that a reduced variate scale gives slightly better estimates than a linear weighting scheme.

The Logistic reduced variate for a flow Q_i is defined (§15.3.4) by

$$RV_{Q_i} = \ln \frac{AEP_{Q_i}}{1-AEP_{Q_i}} \qquad (12.15)$$

If Q_i is the ith largest POT flood, and if Q_i and Q_{i+1} are the flows which bracket *QMED*, then *QMED* is estimated as the weighted average:

$$QMED = wQ_i + (1-w)Q_{i+1} \qquad (12.16)$$

where w is defined as

$$w = \frac{RV_{Q_{i+1}} - RV_{QMED}}{RV_{Q_{i+1}} - RV_{Q_i}}$$

$$= \frac{RV_{Q_{i+1}}}{RV_{Q_{i+1}} - RV_{Q_i}} \qquad (12.17)$$

since

$$RV_{QMED} = \ln \frac{AEP_{QMED}}{1-AEP_{QMED}} = \ln \frac{0.5}{1-0.5} = 0 \qquad (12.18)$$

Table 12.1 shows the values of w for a dispersion of 1.38 for record lengths of up to 20 years. Example 12.4 illustrates how w is determined for a 9-year record.

12.4 Analyses used in selecting the recommended QMED estimation methods

The recommended *QMED* estimation methods were selected from a number of possibilities. This section summarises the analyses that were used to choose between estimation methods. The preferred estimation method changes with record length and the analyses are used to decide when estimation from POT data should be favoured over use of annual maximum data. The analyses also provide information on uncertainty in *QMED*, which is discussed further in §12.5.

Example 12.4
For a 9-year POT record, find (a) the positions of two POT flows that bracket QMED, and (b) the corresponding weights for averaging them.

This example shows how the data in Table 12.1 are obtained for a POT record with 9 years of data and a dispersion of 1.38.

(a) For any POT record of 9 years, the annual exceedance (POT1) series contains 9 floods. The exceedance rate for each flood can be calculated using Equation 12.4 and the AEP from Equation 12.10: e.g. for the 3rd largest flood:

$$\lambda_3 = \frac{(i-0.5)}{N} = \frac{(3-0.5)}{9} = 0.28$$

$$AEP_3 = 1 - \{1 + (D_{AE} - 1)\,\lambda_3\}^{\frac{-1}{D_{AE}-1}}$$

$$= 1 - \{1 + (1.38 - 1)\,0.28\}^{\frac{-1}{1.38-1}} = 1 - 1.106^{-2.63} = 0.23$$

i.e. there is a probability of 0.23 of an annual maximum being larger than the 3rd largest POT flood.

The table below gives λ and AEP values for the nine flows in the annual exceedance series and identifies the required positions for the flows bracketing QMED:

n	λ	AEP	
1	0.056	0.053	
2	0.167	0.149	
3	0.278	0.232	
4	0.389	0.304	
5	0.500	0.367	
6	0.611	0.423	
7	**0.722**	**0.472**	← the 7th and 8th largest floods have
8	**0.833**	**0.515**	← AEP values just above and below 0.5,
9	0.944	0.554	i.e. they bracket QMED.

(b) The weight w used to obtain QMED is found by substituting the AEP values of the selected floods into Equation 12.17:

$$w = RV_8 / (RV_8 - RV_7)$$

where
$$RV_7 = \ln\{AEP_7 / (1 - AEP_7)\} = \ln\{0.472 / (1 - 0.472)\} = -0.112$$
$$RV_8 = \ln\{AEP_8 / (1 - AEP_8)\} = \ln\{0.515 / (1 - 0.515)\} = 0.060$$
giving
$$w = 0.060 / (0.060 + 0.112) = 0.349$$

So, for any 9-year record, QMED is estimated by POT data by

$$QMED = 0.349\,Q_7 + (1 - 0.349)\,Q_8$$

and the following information can be included in Table 12.1 for a 9-year record:

$$i = 7; \quad i+1 = 8; \quad w = 0.349$$

The approach illustrated in this example can be used to obtain i and w for alternative record lengths and dispersions.

12.4.1 Approach to comparing QMED estimation methods

Four main methods were tested in the analyses:

1 AM   estimation from annual maxima;

2 POT_{UK} estimation assuming a negative binomial distribution with UK-average dispersion;

3 POT_{site} estimation assuming a negative binomial distribution with site-dependent dispersion;

4 POT_{Pois} estimation assuming a Poisson distribution.

Case 1 uses only annual maximum data. Case 2 forms the recommended method for estimation from POT data. Case 3 is considered because of the possibility that *QMED* estimates would be improved by using the site dispersion instead of a UK-average dispersion. The final case uses a Poisson distribution: theoretically this is the simplest POT approach because it corresponds to random arrival times for POT events.

The analysis used a resampling approach. Only stations with at least 30 years of POT record were used: there are 100 such stations. The method relies on the assumption that the true *QMED* is well estimated from the annual maximum series for long-record sites and thus that the error in estimating *QMED* from a short sub-record can be judged by comparing the sub-record and full-record *QMED* values. This is likely to be a good assumption for short sub-records, but not when the sub-record is quite long compared with the full record. The *QMED* estimate derived using the full data series at a site is termed $QMED_{full}$.

Consider evaluating how each of the four methods would perform for stations with, say, 11 years of data. This can be tested by using the long-record sites to generate sample records of length 11 years. For each long-record site, pick out 100 random subsets of 11 years (random sampling without replacement). Estimate *QMED* from these sub-records by each of the four methods and call these estimates $QMED_{sub}$. The ratio of $QMED_{sub}$ to $QMED_{full}$ provides a measure of the factorial error (§12.5.1) in estimating *QMED* for 11-year records.

The resampling approach used to compare estimation methods works as follows: for *N* between 1 and 20 years,

- make 100 selections of *N* years from every long-record site;
- for each selection, estimate *QMED* using each of the four methods;
- evaluate the error as the ratio $QMED_{sub} : QMED_{full}$.

Difficulties arise when the required record-length is only one or two years long. For some subsets of the POT record there are insufficient POT events to estimate $QMED_{sub}$. These are years in which there were either few or no POT events above the abstraction threshold. Of course, if POT data had really been extracted for just these years, a lower abstraction threshold would have been used and enough data would be available. However, *QMED* estimates obtained from these years are likely to underestimate *QMED* substantially. It is not acceptable to reject these subset selections because this would introduce bias.

The problem was tackled as follows. First any additional useful information contained in the annual maximum record is used: in years when no POT flood occurs, the annual maximum for that year is treated as being a POT event. If the number of POT events is still insufficient then the abstraction threshold is used as a substitute POT event. This is not a perfect solution but is an improvement over discounting these troublesome subsets completely. For the preferred POT method, the errors are presented both with and without the selections that had insufficient POT data. This provides an indication of the overall effect that these samples may have. The proportion of cases in which this problem occurs is relatively small.

12.4.2 Summary of analysis results

The results of the analyses are summarised in Table 12.3 and Figure 12.3. Table 12.3 shows values of the factorial standard error (fse) for each of the methods. The factorial standard error is a multiplicative error (see §12.5.1). Values of fse close to 1.0 represent good estimates.

The main findings from this are:
- The negative binomial POT estimate gives the lowest error for 1 to 13 years of data and for 15 years of data; POT methods using a Poisson approach or a site-dependent dispersion approach are less good;
- Annual maximum data give results that are similar to the POT methods for 14 years and for greater than 16 years of data;
- Using POT data is roughly equivalent to obtaining an extra year of annual maximum data.

This leads to the following recommendations:
- For records less than 14 years, POT data give the best estimate of *QMED*;
- For records of at least 14 years of data, *QMED* can be estimated from annual maxima.

For records of 14 years or more, estimation from POT data is likely to give very similar results to estimation from annual maxima, and there is no clear advantage in using the POT record. Note that, theoretically, POT data should always give a better estimate of *QMED* than the annual maxima. The fact that the test results do not show this is probably because the procedure compares POT estimates with *QMED* estimates based on 30 years of annual maxima, as if the latter were error-free. This will tend to bias results in favour of estimation from annual maxima.

Analysis of UK data shows that POT data generally give improved *QMED* estimates for records of less than 14 years.

12.5 Uncertainty in QMED

This section examines the uncertainty associated with *QMED* estimation. A method based on a factorial standard error approach is presented in §12.5.2 and is applicable to short records. For longer records, confidence intervals can be found using an alternative approach, as described in §12.5.3.

12.5.1 Confidence intervals and the factorial standard error

A *confidence interval* expresses the uncertainty in an estimate. To say that an estimate has a 95% confidence interval of (A, B), means that, in repeated application of the same methods, 95% of the intervals (A, B) will contain the true value of *QMED*. A confidence interval is useful because it gives a feel for how much is really known about the estimate. Narrow confidence intervals indicate that the estimate is likely to be a good one. Wide confidence intervals indicate that much less is known and the estimate may only be rather approximate.

For *QMED* estimation, it is usual to consider the uncertainty in terms of the multiplicative error, i.e. the ratio between true and estimated value. Multiplicative errors are usually estimated by the *factorial standard error*, *fse*, which is the exponential of the standard error *s* on the logged scale:

Statistical procedures for flood frequency estimation

Table 12.3 *Errors of estimation for a selection of methods: (1) using annual maxima, (2) using POT data with the UK-average dispersion, (3) using POT data with site-dependent dispersion and (4) using POT data assuming a Poisson distribution (i.e. dispersion = 1.0). The errors are presented as factorial standard errors. Numbers in brackets give the error for method (2) if problem subsets are removed (see text). Values in bold indicate the best estimate at each record length.*

Number of years	(1) AM	Method (2) POT$_{UK}$	(3) POT$_{site}$	(4) POT$_{Pois}$
1	1.522	(1.349)**1.484**	1.485	2.606
2	1.342	(1.283)**1.315**	1.326	1.493
3	1.294	(1.247)**1.248**	1.253	1.279
4	1.234	(1.204)**1.204**	1.215	1.259
5	1.218	**1.179**	1.189	1.194
6	1.187	**1.164**	1.172	1.174
7	1.179	**1.154**	1.160	1.164
8	1.156	**1.143**	1.147	1.155
9	1.153	**1.137**	1.142	1.148
10	1.138	**1.128**	1.132	1.141
11	1.136	**1.125**	1.127	1.138
12	1.121	**1.118**	1.121	1.129
13	1.117	**1.113**	1.114	1.124
14	**1.108**	1.110	1.113	1.123
15	1.109	**1.105**	1.109	1.119
16	**1.097**	1.102	1.105	1.114
17	**1.096**	1.100	1.102	1.112
18	**1.087**	1.096	1.099	1.110
19	**1.086**	1.093	1.096	1.106
20	**1.079**	1.092	1.094	1.106

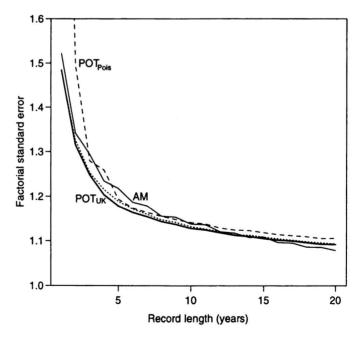

Figure 12.3 *Factorial standard errors for the four estimation schemes. The recommended POT approach is shown in the thick solid line, the annual maximum approach is shown in the thin solid line. The dashed line marks the results if a Poisson distribution is assumed and the dotted line the results if site-dependent dispersion is used. Note the slightly 'stepped' appearance of the annual maximum line due to the difference between taking the median of an odd and even number of points.*

$$fse = e^s \qquad (12.19)$$

For multiplicative errors, confidence limits are proportional to the estimated value. For example, approximate 68% and 95% confidence intervals for *QMED* are given by

68% confidence interval = $(QMED/fse, QMED\,fse)$

95% confidence interval = $(QMED/fse^2, QMED\,fse^2)$.

These confidence intervals assume that errors on the log scale are approximately normally distributed.

The factorial standard error is a measure of the multiplicative (proportional) error of an estimate. It can be used to calculate confidence intervals.

12.5.2 Approximate confidence intervals for QMED when estimated from short records

The empirically derived factorial standard error values shown in Table 12.3 can be used to obtain approximate confidence intervals for *QMED* estimates from short records. For example, the fse for a 6-year POT record, using the recommended method (2), is 1.164. Thus the confidence intervals for *QMED* are

68% confidence limits for *QMED* = (0.86 *QMED*, 1.16 *QMED*)

95% confidence limits for *QMED* = (0.74 *QMED*, 1.35 *QMED*)

Example 12.5 also illustrates how confidence limits are calculated. Note that the factorial standard errors shown in Table 12.3 are likely to underestimate the true error. This is because the method assumes that there is no error in a *QMED* value obtained from a 30-year record. For short records ($N < 10$), this approximation will have only a small effect on the confidence intervals. For records of 10 to 15 years, confidence intervals obtained using Table 12.3 give a useful guide to uncertainty, but users may also consider the techniques described in §12.5.3.

12.5.3 An alternative approach to estimating confidence intervals for QMED

Section 12.5.2 shows how to estimate confidence intervals for *QMED* when the record is short. That approach will tend to underestimate uncertainty for longer records. Here, an alternative approach is presented for the case where *QMED* is estimated from annual maximum data. This is a distribution-free approach and is suitable for use with records that are at least ten years long.

Suppose that there are N annual maxima, sorted from the largest to the smallest, $Q_1, Q_2, ..., Q_N$. One approach to obtaining a confidence limit for *QMED* is to look for an interval of the form (Q_r, Q_{N-r}), where r is less than $N/2$.

The relationship between r and the significance level α of the confidence interval (Q_r, Q_{N-r}) is given by Kendall and Stuart (1979):

$$1-\alpha = 2^{-N} \sum_{i=r}^{N-r} \binom{N}{i} \qquad (12.20)$$

where

$$\binom{N}{i} = \frac{N!}{i!\,(N-i)!} \qquad (12.21)$$

Values of r and $N–r$ corresponding to 68% and 95% confidence intervals are shown in Table 12.4. The values have been interpolated in order to obtain approximately the required coverage probabilities. They can be used to find the required confidence intervals by taking a weighted geometric average of the flood peaks on either side of the quoted positions. For example, for a 15-year record, the positions given in Table 12.4 for a 95% confidence interval are 4.2 and 11.8. The confidence intervals are obtained by taking a weighted geometric average of the 4th and 5th, and of the 11th and 12th largest floods:

$$\text{Upper} = Q_4^{5-4.2} Q_5^{4.2-4} = Q_4^{0.8} Q_5^{0.2}$$

$$\text{Lower} = Q_{11}^{12-11.8} Q_{12}^{11.8-11} = Q_{11}^{0.2} Q_{12}^{0.8}$$

(12.22)

Example 12.6 also illustrates this approach.

Table 12.4   *Positions of the ordered flow values for constructing 68% and 95% confidence intervals for QMED, for annual maximum series of ten years or longer*

No. of years	68%		95%	
	upper	lower	upper	lower
10	3.9	7.1	2.3	8.7
11	4.3	7.7	2.7	9.3
12	4.7	8.3	3.1	9.9
13	5.2	8.8	3.4	10.6
14	5.6	9.4	3.8	11.2
15	6.1	9.9	4.2	11.8
16	6.4	10.6	4.5	12.5
17	6.9	11.1	5.0	13.0
18	7.3	11.7	5.3	13.7
19	7.8	12.2	5.7	14.3
20	8.2	12.8	6.1	14.9
25	10.5	15.5	8.1	17.9
30	12.7	18.3	10.1	20.9
35	15.1	20.9	12.2	23.8
40	17.3	23.7	14.3	26.7
45	19.6	26.4	16.4	29.6
50	22.0	29.0	18.5	32.5
60	26.6	34.4	22.9	38.1
70	31.3	39.7	27.3	43.7
80	36.0	45.0	31.7	49.3
90	40.8	50.2	36.2	54.8
100	45.5	55.5	40.7	60.3

Example 12.5
Obtain confidence intervals for the QMED estimates of Example 12.3

(1) Gwash at Belmesthorpe (31006)

For this site, a 6-year POT record gives $QMED = 12.9 \, \text{m}^3\text{s}^{-1}$

The approximate fse for a 6-year record is 1.164. So the confidence intervals are

68% confidence interval = (12.9/1.164, 12.9 × 1.164) = (11.1, 15.0) m^3s^{-1}
95% confidence interval = (12.9/1.164^2, 12.9 × 1.164^2) = (9.5, 17.5) m^3s^{-1}

(2) White Laggan Burn at Loch Dee (80003)

There are 11 years of POT record and *QMED* is estimated as 8.61 m^3s^{-1}

The fse for an 11-year record is 1.125, and thus the confidence limits for *QMED* are

68% confidence interval = (8.61/1.125, 8.61 × 1.125) = (7.7, 9.7) m^3s^{-1}
95% confidence interval = (8.61/1.125^2, 8.61 × 1.125^2) = (6.8, 10.9) m^3s^{-1}

Example 12.6
Estimate the 95% confidence intervals for QMED for (a) the Rase at Bishopbridge (29005) and (b) the East Dart at Bellever (46005).

(a) The Rase at Bishopbridge has a 13-year annual maximum record, from which $QMED = 7.25 \, \text{m}^3\text{s}^{-1}$.

For this example, we calculate confidence intervals using both the fse and quantile based methods.

(i) The fse for a 13-year annual maximum record is 1.117 (Table 12.3). This gives

95% confidence interval = (7.25 / 1.117^2, 7.25 × 1.117^2) = (5.8, 9.0) m^3s^{-1}

(ii) Using Table 12.4, the flow positions for a 95% confidence interval on a 13 year record are 3.4 and 10.6. Using the same approach as in Equation 12.22,

Lower = $Q_3^{0.6} Q_4^{0.4}$ = 4.24$^{0.6}$ 4.97$^{0.4}$ = 4.52 m^3s^{-1}
Upper = $Q_{10}^{0.4} Q_{11}^{0.6}$ = 9.88$^{0.4}$ 10.88$^{0.6}$ = 10.47 m^3s^{-1}

This gives a 95% confidence interval for *QMED* of (4.5, 10.5) m^3s^{-1}

The second approach results in a wider (and probably more realistic) estimate of the confidence interval.

(b) The East Dart at Bellever has a 30-year record with $QMED = 39.1 \, \text{m}^3\text{s}^{-1}$. Using Table 12.4, the flow positions are 10.1 and 20.9. These values are sufficiently close to 10 and 21 for it to be reasonable just to use the 10th and 21st largest flows as the confidence interval. This gives a 95% confidence interval for *QMED* of (32.3, 46.5) m^3s^{-1}.

12.6 QMED values for UK sites

QMED estimates have been calculated for all FEH gauges using the recommended methods described above. The results are mapped in Figure 12.4 and summarised in Table 12.5. In general, *QMED* values are higher in the north and west, and (of course) on larger catchments.

Table 12.5 *Summary of UK QMED values (m³ s⁻¹) for 986 FEH gauging stations. Selected percentiles of the data are shown.*

				Percentile			
	Min	**10%**	**25%**	**50%**	**75%**	**90%**	**Max**
QMED	0.1	4	11	32	100	230	950

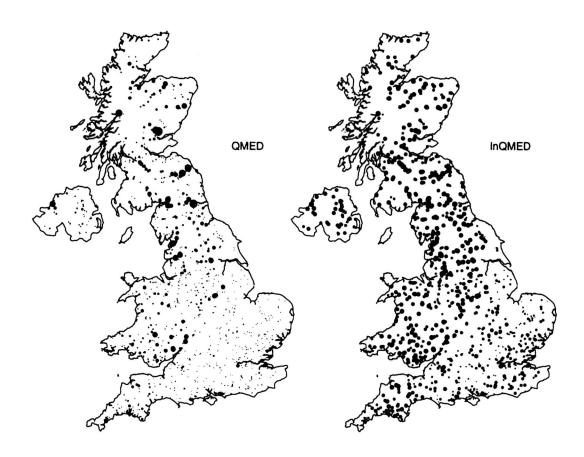

Figure 12.4 *QMED and lnQMED values for FEH gauging stations*

Additional Note 12.1 Handling incomplete water-years of data for short-record stations

For *QMED* estimation from POT, it is generally recommended that only complete water-years of record are used. However, if the record length is very short then a small amount of additional data can result in greatly improved estimates of *QMED*. This means that part-year POT records should sometimes be used.

Moving the start of the analysis-year

The simplest approach to make better use of the POT data is often to start the analysis-year at an alternative date (rather than 1 October). For example, for a record starting in March 1992 and ending in February 1995, the analysis-year would be selected to start on 1 March.

Treating a part-year as a full year

To use a part-year POT record is possible, but requires care. The main problem arises if the data are strongly seasonal. If the main flood season is included within the part-year record it may be acceptable to treat the data as if the year's record were complete. If the main flood-season is not included it is probably best not to use the part-year record. In some cases, it may be possible to ascertain that no flood occurred during a gap in the record in which case the data may be treated as coming from a full year (see §23.5.1).

Joining up gaps in the data

If there are gaps in the data it may be possible to reduce the number of incomplete water-years in the record by combining part-years to obtain additional water-years of data. In Figure 12.5 below, data from 1990 and 1991 are combined and used as if they were from a single water-year. Only a small part of the data from 1990 are unused. Note that combining part-records should respect seasonality in the data.

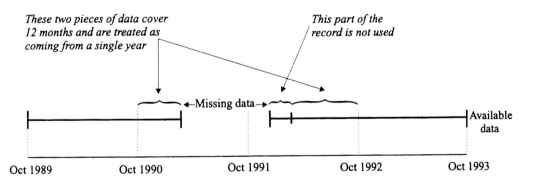

Figure 12.5 *Illustration of how to maximise use of data when there is a gap in the record. The example shows a record beginning in October 1989 and ending in October 1993. A 10-month gap in the record interferes with data for two water-years (1990 and 1991). This leaves just two complete water-years of data (1989 and 1992). By removing a small part of the record and combining the remaining two part-years, a valuable third water-year of data can be obtained.*

Additional Note 12.2   Derivation of an equation linking POT and annual maximum series

This note describes the theory behind the equation that links the annual exceedance probability to the POT series (Equation 12.10).

Let t_{AE} be the threshold level for the annual exceedance (POT1) series. For any flow Q, greater than t_{AE}, define

$$A_Q = \text{Pr (annual maximum event} \leq Q) \qquad (12.23)$$

and, for any single POT event,

$$P_Q = \text{Pr (POT event} \leq Q \mid \text{POT event} > t_{AE}) \qquad (12.24)$$

where $\text{Pr}(A \mid B)$ denotes the probability of A given that B has occurred. Note that the annual exceedance probability is given by

$$AEP = 1 - A_Q \qquad (12.25)$$

For any POT flow Q the exceedance rate λ_Q is defined by

$$\lambda_Q = \text{average number of POT events} > Q \qquad (12.26)$$

For $Q > t_{AE}$, λ_Q is equal to $1-P_Q$. To show this, it is necessary to consider the number of floods larger than Q and the number of floods in the annual exceedance process. In the following, only the number of events occurring in a single year is considered. Observe that

$$\lambda_Q = \text{E(no. of events} > Q)$$
$$= \sum_{r=0}^{\infty} \text{E(no. of events} > Q \mid r \text{ events} > t_{AE}) \text{Pr}(r \text{ events} > t_{AE}) \qquad (12.27)$$

Also

$$\text{E(no. of events} > Q \mid r \text{ events} > t_{AE}) = \sum_{r=0}^{\infty} k \, \text{Pr}(k \text{ events} > t_{AE} \mid r \text{ events} > t_{AE})$$

$$= \sum_{k=1}^{r} k \binom{r}{k} P_Q^{r-k} (1-P_Q)^k$$

$$= r(1-P_Q) \sum_{k=0}^{r-1} \binom{r-1}{k} P_Q^{r-1-k} (1-P_Q)^k$$

$$= r(1-P_Q) \sum_{k=0}^{r-1} \text{Pr}(k \text{ events} > Q \mid r-1 \text{ events} > t_{AE})$$

$$= r(1-P_Q) \qquad (12.28)$$

Inserting this in Equation 12.27, and using the fact that the average number of events greater than t_{AE} is 1, gives

$$\lambda_Q = \sum_{r=0}^{\infty} r(1-P_Q) \text{Pr}(r \text{ events} > t_{AE})$$

$$= (1-P_Q) \, E(\text{no. of events} > t_{AE})$$

i.e.
$$\lambda_Q = 1-P_Q \tag{12.29}$$

as required.

In any year where a POT event occurs, the annual maximum will be the maximum of the POT events. So P_Q and A_Q can be related as follows:

$$A_Q = \text{Pr (annual maximum event} \leq Q)$$

$$= \text{Pr (all POT events during year} \leq Q)$$

$$= \sum_{n=0}^{\infty} \text{Pr}(n \text{ POT events} \leq Q \mid n \text{ POT events} > t_{AE}) \, \text{Pr}(n \text{ POT events} > t_{AE})$$

$$= \sum_{n=0}^{\infty} \text{Pr}(\text{POT event} \leq Q \mid \text{POT event} > t_{AE})^n \, \text{Pr}(n \text{ POT events} > t_{AE})$$

$$= \sum_{n=0}^{\infty} (P_Q)^n \, \text{Pr}(n \text{ POT events} > t_{AE}) \tag{12.30}$$

If the POT data come from a negative binomial process, $\text{Pr} \, (n \text{ POT events} > t_{AE})$ will be given by Equation 12.6. This can be substituted in the above equation for A_Q and rearranged to give

$$A_Q = \sum_{k=0}^{r-1} (P_Q)^n \binom{k+n-1}{k} p^k (1-p)^n$$

$$= \frac{p^k}{\{1-P_Q(1-p)\}^k} \sum_{k=0}^{r-1} \binom{k+n-1}{k} \{1-P_Q(1-p)\}^k \{P_Q(1-p)\}^n$$

$$= \left\{ \frac{p}{1-P_Q(1-p)} \right\}^k$$

$$= \left\{ \frac{1}{p} - P_Q \frac{1-p}{p} \right\}^{-k} \tag{12.31}$$

Using Equations 12.31 and 12.25, *AEP* can be written as

$$AEP_Q = 1 - A_Q = 1 - \left\{ \frac{1}{p} - P_Q \frac{1-p}{p} \right\}^{-k} \tag{12.32}$$

and substituting for P_Q from Equation 12.29,

$$AEP_Q = 1 - \left\{ \frac{1}{p} - (1-\lambda_Q) \frac{1-p}{p} \right\}^{-k} \tag{12.33}$$

For the annual exceedance series, the negative binomial parameters are given by $p = 1/D_{AE}$ (Equation 12.8) and $k = 1/(D_{AE}-1)$ (Equation 12.9). This gives the required relationship:

$$AEP_Q = 1 - \{1 + \lambda_Q(D_{AE}-1)\}^{\frac{-1}{D_{AE}-1}} \tag{12.34}$$

Chapter 13 Estimating QMED from catchment descriptors (B)

13.1 Overview

QMED is the median annual maximum flood and is used as the index flood. The catchment descriptor method allows *QMED* to be estimated from catchment descriptors using a catchment descriptor equation. This chapter primarily describes the derivation and use of the catchment descriptor equation.

13.1.1 When is the catchment descriptor method used?

The catchment descriptor method is used when there are no data or only a very short record at the subject site. Otherwise *QMED* is estimated from flood data (Chapter 12).

The catchment descriptor method uses the catchment descriptor equation together with the data transfer method (Chapter 4). The transfer method allows the *QMED* value obtained from the catchment descriptor equation to be refined using data from another site. It uses a longer flood record at a suitable nearby transfer site. Exceptionally, *QMED* may be estimated at a site using only the catchment descriptor equation. This is not generally recommended because, compared to other methods, it gives poor estimates of *QMED*. Even a two-year record can be expected to provide a better estimate of *QMED* than the catchment descriptor equation (§13.8). Direct use of the catchment descriptor equation is only appropriate if (i) the site record is less than two years long, and (ii) there are no suitable nearby sites with a longer record.

> The catchment descriptor method is used for *QMED* estimation for ungauged sites, or sites with very few flood data. The method involves use of the catchment descriptor equation and is usually used in conjunction with flood data from nearby sites. Direct use of the catchment descriptor equation without reference to other sites typically yields poor estimates of *QMED*.

13.1.2 QMED catchment descriptor equation

> The catchment descriptor equation (Equation 13.1) relates *QMED* to
> - area (*AREA*)
> - wetness (*SAAR*)
> - soils (*SPRHOST* and *RESHOST*)
> - reservoirs and lakes (*FARL*)
>
> It applies to rural UK catchments of at least 0.5 km².

The recommended equation for estimation of *QMED* is

$$QMED_{rural} = 1.172\, AREA^{AE} \left(\frac{SAAR}{1000}\right)^{1.560} FARL^{2.642} \left(\frac{SPRHOST}{100}\right)^{1.211} 0.0198^{RESHOST} \tag{13.1}$$

where

$$AE = \text{area exponent} = 1 - 0.015 \ln\left(\frac{AREA}{0.5}\right) \tag{13.2}$$

with r^2 (on $\ln QMED$) = 0.916 and fse = 1.549.

RESHOST is a residual soils term obtained from HOST data, defined by

$$RESHOST = BFIHOST + 1.30\left(\frac{SPRHOST}{100}\right) - 0.987 \tag{13.3}$$

The *QMED* model (Equation 13.1) applies to rural catchments with area of at least 0.5 km^2 (urban catchments are discussed in Chapter 18). The terms in the model represent catchment size (*AREA*), typical wetness (*SAAR*), soils (*SPRHOST* and *RESHOST*) and reservoir/lake effects (*FARL*). Further details about the interpretation and limitations of this equation are given in §13.7. Uncertainty and errors are discussed in §13.8.

Table 13.1 shows the range of each variable and of the contribution it makes to the catchment descriptor equation. Contributions with a wide range (e.g. *AREA* and *SAAR*) have the greatest influence in the equation.

Table 13.1 *The range, mean and 25- and 75-percentiles for variables in the QMED catchment descriptor equation, and for the corresponding terms (shown in bold). Values are calculated using the rural FEH gauging stations.*

	Min	25%	Mean	75%	Max
AREA	1.1	62.8	358	344	6850
SAAR	547	807	1160	1420	3470
FARL	0.67	0.97	0.97	1.00	1.00
SPRHOST	5.0	32.7	37.9	44.6	59.9
RESHOST	-0.152	-0.028	-0.004	0.02	0.19
AREA^{AE}	1.1	46.5	172	194	1940
$(SAAR/1000)^{1.560}$	0.38	0.71	1.37	1.76	7.28
$FARL^{2.642}$	0.35	0.92	0.93	1.00	1.00
$(SPRHOST/100)^{1.211}$	0.03	0.26	0.31	0.38	0.54
RESHOST	0.48	0.93	1.03	1.12	1.81

13.1.3 Chapter structure

The remainder of this chapter describes the derivation of Equation 13.1 and provides further details on use of the equation. Sections 13.2 to 13.6 cover the derivation of the model, its structure, the data and the statistical analysis.

Sections 13.7 and 13.8 discuss model interpretation and uncertainty: users are encouraged to pay particular attention to these sections. The final section makes comparisons with some similar approaches.

13.2 Choosing the model

13.2.1 A multiplicative structure

The index flood to be estimated is the median annual flood, *QMED*. The model used here for describing *QMED* in terms of catchment descriptors is of the form

$$QMED = A\ Var_1^{\ b}\ Var_2^{\ c}\ Var_3^{\ d}... \tag{13.4}$$

where Var_1, Var_2, ... are catchment descriptors and *A*, *b*, *c*, ... are constants. This model says that changes in catchment descriptors have a *scaling effect* on the index flood. The degree of scaling is affected by the exponent terms *b, c, d, ...*

Analysis of this model is simplified by a logarithmic transformation, yielding

$$\ln QMED \;=\; a + b \ln Var_1 + c \ln Var_2 + d \ln Var_3 + \ldots \qquad (13.5)$$

where $a = \ln A$ (the natural logarithm of A). The constants $a, b, c, \ldots$ are unknowns that have to be estimated. Writing the equation in this form gives a linear structure that allows standard multivariate statistical procedures to be applied.

13.2.2 Other approaches to modelling

A regression approach is not without limitations. One alternative, considered but not applied here, is that of *dimensional correctness* (Buckingham, 1914). This is an approach in which the model structure is constrained so that the dimensions of the model are consistent with the predicted variable. A physically-based model of any system should ideally respect dimensional correctness. A simple example of a dimensionally correct flood estimation model is the *rational formula*:

$$Q \;=\; c\,I\,AREA \qquad (13.6)$$

which relates a flood peak Q (dimensions $L^3 T^{-1}$) to rainfall intensity I (dimensions LT^{-1}) and drainage area (dimensions L^2): c is a dimensionless constant. This equation has been widely used, with values of c chosen by experience and various formulae for the duration to be used in estimating I. Calibration of a dimensionally correct model has generally not met with success in the context of UK flood estimation, and has not been attempted here.

> The catchment descriptor equation is an empirically derived model and not a physically based law. It should not be applied to catchments that are very different to the calibration set.

Linear regression tends to produce dimensionally incorrect models. This can occur because of cross-correlations between variables of different dimensions. An explanatory variable within a model may act as a surrogate for one or more physical quantities that may not even have been measured. Such models provide useful results, but do not transfer well to other flood regimes. The fact that the final equation is dimensionally incorrect reminds us that the *QMED* model should be recognised as an empirical result, rather than a physically based law. It should not be applied on catchments that are very different to the calibration set.

13.3 Flood and catchment descriptor data

13.3.1 Sites used in model development

Model development is broken down into two stages: selecting variables and calibrating parameters. For selecting variables, 687 mainland UK catchments were used. For calibrating parameters, a further 41 stations from Northern Ireland were included bringing the total to 728 sites. The sites were selected from the flood gauging stations described in Chapter 22 and Appendices A and B. They include those stations for which

- The area is 0.5 km^2 or greater;
- Digital catchment data are available;
- The catchment is essentially rural (*URBEXT* < 0.025).

Here, URBEXT is the FEH index for urban extent and is the fraction of the catchment revealed to be urbanised from 1990 satellite imagery (5 6). Short records were included in the analysis but given little emphasis.

In the course of the analysis, some catchments were found to show unusual behaviour. These catchments were mostly retained in the analysis, but in a few cases there were grounds for doubting the appropriateness of a particular gauge. Specific details of the gauges omitted are given in Additional Note 13.1.

13.3.2 QMED estimates

The *QMED* values used in deriving the catchment descriptor equation were estimated using the methods described in Chapter 12. In most cases, *QMED* is estimated as the median of the annual maxima. However, for shorter records, use is made of peaks-over-threshold data where available. The *QMED* estimates were adjusted for climatic variation using the methods described in Chapter 20. These adjustments were applied to records shorter than 30 years; the adjustment has greatest effect on the short-record sites.

13.3.3 Catchment descriptors

Around 30 explanatory catchment descriptors were considered for inclusion in the *QMED* equation. Definitions of catchment descriptors are reproduced in Appendix C: full details of the main ones are given in Volume 5. All the variables considered derive from digital catchment data. They include measures of catchment size, wetness, soil type, slope and land use. Logarithms were taken of most explanatory variables, in keeping with the model structure (Equation 13.5): using logarithms is especially advantageous for variables such as *AREA* with very wide-ranging values.

All variables were screened by plotting against all other variables and against ln*QMED*. The plots were used to identify cross-correlations and any non-linear relationships, and to highlight possible outliers and influential points. Figure 13.1 shows a matrix scatterplot of selected catchment descriptors. Examples of high correlation occur between ln*AREA* and ln*DPLBAR* (the mean drainage path length), and between a number of variables related to catchment wetness (e.g. ln*SAAR*, ln*RMED1*, and ln*NWET*). The reservoir/lake index ln*FARL* shows few marked cross-correlations.

Spearman's rank correlation coefficients were also calculated: Table 13.2 shows correlations for the descriptors in Figure 13.1. Overall, the variables have a

Table 13.2 Table of Spearman's rank correlation for selected variables. Correlations over 0.9 are shown in bold. Correlations between 0.6 and 0.8 are shown in italics and underlined.

	ln*QMED*	ln*AREA*	ln*DPLBAR*	ln*SPRHOST*	ln*BFIHOST*	ln*SAAR*	ln*RMED1*	ln*NWET*	ln*ALTBAR*	ln*FARL*
ln*QMED*	1.00	*0.70*	*0.67*	0.42	−0.37	0.50	0.44	0.32	0.51	−0.20
ln*AREA*	*0.70*	1.00	**0.96**	−0.06	0.10	−0.07	−0.13	−0.11	0.02	−0.37
ln*DPLBAR*	*0.67*	**0.96**	1.00	−0.07	0.11	−0.08	−0.14	−0.11	0.03	−0.36
ln*SPRHOST*	0.42	−0.06	−0.07	1.00	**−0.93**	0.54	0.48	0.25	0.58	−0.03
ln*BFIHOST*	−0.37	0.10	0.11	**−0.93**	1.00	−0.44	−0.40	−0.23	−0.47	−0.03
ln*SAAR*	0.50	−0.07	−0.08	0.54	−0.44	1.00	**0.95**	*0.69*	*0.79*	−0.03
ln*RMED1*	0.44	−0.13	−0.14	0.48	−0.40	**0.95**	1.00	*0.69*	*0.73*	−0.01
ln*NWET*	0.32	−0.11	−0.11	0.25	−0.23	*0.69*	*0.69*	1.00	0.49	0.09
ln*ALTBAR*	0.51	0.02	0.03	0.58	−0.47	*0.79*	*0.73*	0.49	1.00	0.02
ln*FARL*	−0.20	−0.37	−0.36	−0.03	−0.03	−0.03	−0.01	0.09	0.02	1.00

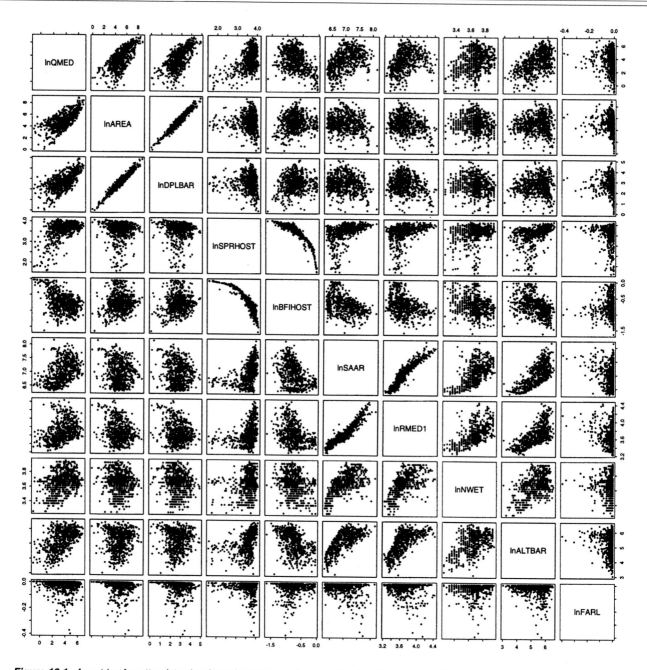

Figure 13.1 *A matrix of scatterplots showing relationships between pairs of catchment descriptors and QMED after logarithmic transformation*

complex correlation structure. Only three pairs of variables have correlations of 0.9 or more, but six pairs have correlations in the range 0.6 to 0.8.

An ideal model would contain only variables with low correlations. The presence of high correlations in the catchment descriptors is problematic for two reasons. First, it leads to a large number of possible model choices, all of which give similar fits, and many of which may have poorly specified parameters. Second, it means that a variable may be favoured by the model in lieu of another variable, confounding hydrological interpretation. In some cases, highly correlated variables can be reconstructed into new uncorrelated variables. For example, ln*SPRHOST* and ln*BFIHOST* show appreciable correlation (Spearman's $r = -0.93$), but both appear important in the model: a new variable *RESHOST* was introduced to replace ln*BFIHOST*. *RESHOST* is designed to have low correlation with *SPRHOST* but to capture the additional information contained in *BFIHOST* (§13.3.4).

13.3.4 RESHOST and other additional variables

Additional derived variables were considered for use in the regression models, including product terms such as ln*AREA* ln*SAAR* (none of those tried were found to be useful), quadratic terms such as $(\ln AREA)^2$ (used where there was evidence of non-linearity), and variables constructed to reduce correlation. Of these, three variables were found to be useful and two were incorporated into the final model.

RESHOST

There are two primary variables that summarise soil characteristics: *SPRHOST* and *BFIHOST*. *SPRHOST* and *BFIHOST* are generalised estimates of standard percentage runoff (*SPR*) and the baseflow index (*BFI*) made from soil mapping. Both variables are derived from the HOST soil digital database (see 5 5). *SPR* represents the typical quick responsiveness of river flow to heavy rainfall, whereas *BFI* reflects the typical proportion of annual river flow that is attributable to baseflow rather than quick-response runoff. A large baseflow index typifies a permeable catchment with extensive groundwater storage. *BFIHOST* tends to decrease with increasing *SPRHOST* (Figure 13.2).

SPRHOST is large (up to 60%) for impermeable catchments, and small for permeable catchments (Chapter 19 defines catchments as being permeable if *SPRHOST* is less than 20%). The *BFIHOST* values range between 0.17 and 0.97 for the FEH catchments. *SPRHOST* and *BFIHOST* are found to be closely correlated (correlation = -0.91) but nevertheless, if used together, both variables make important contributions to the *QMED* model. In view of this, a new variable, *RESHOST*, was constructed.

RESHOST is the residual from a linear regression of *BFIHOST* on *SPRHOST*, based on a dataset consisting of 1 in every 1000 UK ungauged sites that drain at least 0.5 km^2 (Figure 13.2):

$$RESHOST = BFIHOST + 1.30\left(\frac{SPRHOST}{100}\right) - 0.987 \qquad (13.7)$$

> *RESHOST* gives a measure of the relative responsiveness of a catchment. It is the residual of a regression between *BFIHOST* and *SPRHOST*

$r^2 = 0.85$ using 3463 catchments.

RESHOST provides a measure of the relative responsiveness of the catchment. It describes whether *BFIHOST* is indicating that a catchment is more or less responsive than would be anticipated from *SPRHOST*. A positive value of *RESHOST* suggests a less responsive regime than indicated by *SPRHOST* alone (*BFIHOST* higher than expected). Examples of this situation arise for some highland and moorland catchments with blanket peat (e.g. the Findhorn at Shenachie, 7001) where *SPRHOST* is high but BFI is moderate (instead of low). A negative value of *RESHOST* suggests a more responsive regime, with *BFIHOST* lower than expected given the value of *SPRHOST*. Examples include some Carboniferous catchments (Millstone Grit, shales, Coal Measures) such as the Crimple at Burn Bridge (27051) where *SPRHOST* is moderate but *BFIHOST* is low (instead of moderate).

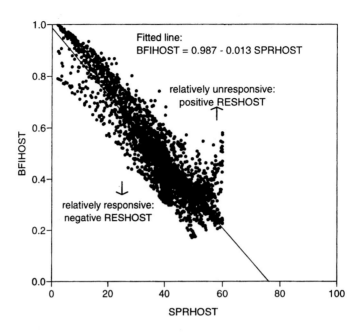

Figure 13.2 *Calibrated relationship between SPRHOST and BFIHOST (3463 gauged catchments). RESHOST is the residual from this relationship and can be thought of as a measure of relative responsiveness.*

lnAREAsq

The term ln*AREAsq* allows for some non-linearity in the effect of *AREA* in the *QMED* model. ln*AREAsq* is the square of ln*AREA*. Without this variable, the *AREA* term in the *QMED* equation is raised to a constant power (exponent). The additional variable $(\ln AREA)^2$ allows the exponent to change with *AREA*. For example, the model

$$\ln QMED \;=\; a + b\ln AREA + c\ln AREAsq + \ldots \tag{13.8}$$

can be written

$$\ln QMED \;=\; a + \ln AREA\,(b + c\ln AREA) + \ldots \tag{13.9}$$

giving

$$QMED \;=\; A\;\;AREA^{\,b+c\ln AREA}\;\ldots \tag{13.10}$$

In the final model, it was found that the *AREA* exponent ($b + c\ln AREA$) is close to 1.0 for very small catchments and declines towards 0.85 for the largest catchments (see also §13.7.2).

lnSAARsq

This variable allows for a non-linear *SAAR* effect. ln*SAARsq* is the square of ln*SAAR*. It does not appear in the final model.

13.4 Multiple least-squares regression

13.4.1 Approach

The *QMED* catchment descriptor equation was derived by multiple least-squares regression techniques. This section provides a background to the use of least squares methods and the generalised least-squares approach.

The simplest least-squares approach is ordinary least-squares. For this, all observations are treated as being independent and having residual errors of equal variance. Such assumptions are not valid for estimation of *QMED*. First, the variance of *QMED* varies from station to station because of differences in record length and in natural variability. Second, the assumption of independence fails because flood data are spatially correlated and flood records overlap in time. In such circumstances, generalised least-squares techniques are more appropriate (Stedinger and Tasker, 1985; Tasker and Stedinger, 1989).

Further information on multiple regression techniques can be found in standard statistical texts such as Weisberg (1980) and Draper and Smith (1981), or in statistical hydrology texts such as Holder (1985) and Hirsh *et al.* (1993).

13.4.2 Ordinary, weighted and generalised least-squares

Three least-squares methods are considered here:

- *Ordinary least-squares (OLS)*, the classical multivariate least-squares approach in which observations are treated as being equally reliable and mutually independent, i.e. errors are assumed independent of each other and of constant variance;

- *Weighted least-squares (WLS)*, similar to OLS except that observations are weighted to allow for differences in reliability, i.e. errors are assumed independent but with differing variances;

- *Generalised least-squares (GLS)*, in which cross-correlations in the data are allowed for, i.e. errors are modelled as having differing variances and as being mutually correlated (Stedinger and Tasker, 1985; Tasker and Stedinger, 1989).

More formally, consider the regression model

$$\mathbf{y} = \mathbf{X}\boldsymbol{\beta} + \mathbf{e} \tag{13.11}$$

where **y** is a vector of the dependent variable (in our case ln*QMED*), **X** is a matrix of explanatory variables (here, a matrix of catchment descriptors, augmented by a column of ones corresponding to the intercept term in Equation 13.5) and **β** is a vector of regression coefficients (i.e. *a, b, c, ...* in Equation 13.5).

The OLS approach assumes that the errors, **e**, have uniform variance (i.e. the same at each site) and are mutually independent. The covariance matrix for **e** is given by

$$\boldsymbol{\Sigma} = \sigma^2 \mathbf{I} \tag{13.12}$$

where **I** is the identity matrix (a matrix with ones along the diagonal and zeros everywhere else) and σ^2 is a constant.

In WLS, the assumption that all error terms have the same variance is relaxed, with **Σ** taking the form:

The *QMED* catchment descriptor equation is fitted using multiple regression techniques. A generalised least-squares approach is used. This takes account of spatial correlations in the data.

$$\mathbf{\Sigma} = \text{diag}(\mathbf{\sigma^2}) \qquad (13.13)$$

where $\mathbf{\sigma^2} = (\sigma^2_1, \sigma^2_2, \sigma^2_3, ..., \sigma^2_n)$ is a vector of variances. Thus, $\mathbf{\Sigma}$ takes the form of a diagonal matrix with the variances along the diagonal. In practical terms, WLS is usually handled by applying a weighting term to each observation and its explanatory variables, and then using OLS. The optimal scheme is for the weights to be inversely proportional to the standard deviations. Often the error is assumed proportional to record length, in which case the weights are proportional to the square root of the record lengths (Weisberg, 1980).

The GLS approach relaxes the assumption of independent errors, so that $\mathbf{\Sigma}$ becomes a full variance-covariance matrix representing the spatial correlations in the data as well as differences in variability between sites. Though more complex, this approach provides a much more realistic representation of hydrological data and GLS is recommended for improved estimation of flood quantiles (Stedinger and Tasker, 1985). In practice, GLS models are fitted by transforming the problem into one that can be solved using OLS methods. In particular, $\mathbf{\Sigma}$ is taken to be of the form $\mathbf{\Sigma} = \sigma^2 \mathbf{R}$, where σ^2 is a constant that is to be estimated and $\mathbf{R}$ is a known matrix reflecting the relative variances and correlations in the errors. For brevity, $\mathbf{R}$ is loosely referred to as the correlation matrix. It is possible to use OLS techniques providing the inverse square root of the correlation matrix, i.e. $\mathbf{R}^{-1/2}$, can be derived. Both dependent and independent variables ($\mathbf{y}$ and $\mathbf{X}$ in Equation 13.11) are transformed by multiplying by $\mathbf{R}^{-1/2}$ to give an OLS model form. Thus the major step in fitting the GLS model is to obtain and invert a suitable matrix $\mathbf{R}$.

> A critical step in fitting a GLS model is to obtain and invert a matrix that describes the variability and correlation in the data.

13.4.3 Characterising site variability

This section considers how differences in site variability can be characterised. It serves as an introductory step towards deriving the variance-covariance matrix $\mathbf{\Sigma}$ required for the generalised least-squares method.

Two main sources of error contribute to the overall regression error at a site. The first is the *sample error* in the ln*QMED* value. This has a variance that is, to a first-order approximation, inversely proportional to the record length. The second source of error is associated with imperfections in the fitted model. This *model error* is unaffected by how many observations are available at the site. The variance of the *overall regression error* for the ith site can then be written as

$$\sigma^2_i = \sigma_m^2 + \sigma_s^2 / N_i \qquad (13.14)$$

where N_i is the record length, σ_m^2 is the variance associated with model error and σ_s^2 is the variance linked with the sample error. Note that a more complex model would be required to account for differences in natural variability between sites. This is not attempted here.

For modelling purposes, it is convenient to write Equation 13.14 in the form

$$\sigma^2_i = \sigma^2 (c + 1/N_i) \qquad (13.15)$$

where c is the ratio of σ_m^2 to σ_s^2, and σ_s^2 is replaced by σ^2, which represents an unknown constant to be estimated in the GLS analysis.

The constant c cannot be readily obtained, but can be roughly estimated. An estimate of σ_s^2 may be obtained from the analyses in §12.4. For example, the factorial standard error (fse) for *QMED* estimated from a 15-year record is 1.10, from which σ_s^2 is estimated to be 0.14 (see §12.5.1 for an introduction to fse). An estimate of σ_i^2 is obtained via an intermediary OLS six-variable regression model: the average value of the mean square error from this model is 0.15 and can be thought of as a typical value of σ_i^2. The average record length is 23 years and σ_m^2 is estimated using Equation 13.14 as

$$\sigma_m^2 = \sigma_i^2 - \sigma_s^2/23 = 0.15 - 0.14/23 = 0.14$$

This suggests that σ_m^2 and σ_s^2 are of a similar size and that c is approximately 1.0: this value is used below.

13.4.4 Selecting the covariance matrix for generalised least-squares

The covariance matrix Σ describes the correlations and relative variances of the QMED regression errors at the gauging stations. The form of covariance model used here is

$$\Sigma_{ij} = \sigma^2 R_{ij} = \begin{cases} \sigma^2 (1 + 1/N_i) & i = j \\ \\ \sigma^2 r_{ij}\{1 + M_{ij}/(N_i N_j)\} & i \neq j \end{cases} \qquad (13.16)$$

where N_i is the number of years of data at site i, M_{ij} is the number of years of overlap between sites i and j, and r_{ij} describes the decreasing correlation with distance (see below).

    The above covariance model represents at-site variance (the diagonal terms) using the structure outlined in the previous section, i.e. incorporating terms to reflect both model error and sample error. For non-diagonal terms, the two error components are modified slightly. The term $M_{ij}/(N_i N_j)$ replaces $1/N_i$ and characterises the between-site correlation arising from sample error: the greater the overlap, and the shorter the record length, the higher the correlation. Sample correlations arise because sites close to one another may experience the same weather conditions and are therefore not fully independent. In the above model, spatial correlation due to model error and spatial correlation due to sample error are assumed to decline with distance at the same rate (as represented by r_{ij}). Spatial correlations resulting from model error arise because sites close to one another may share local peculiarities that are not adequately accounted for in the generalised catchment descriptor model for QMED (see also §13.6.2).

A function to describe spatial correlation

To fit the GLS model requires characterisation of the spatial correlation in the overall regression errors, as represented by r_{ij} (Equation 13.16). It is assumed here that the between-site correlations in annual maximum flood data provide a reasonable approximation to the correlations in the regression errors. It is generally necessary to choose a smooth function for r_{ij} so that $\mathbf{R}^{-1/2}$ can be obtained (Stedinger and Tasker, 1985). Here r_{ij} is modelled as decaying exponentially with distance

$$\hat{r}_{ij} = e^{-\alpha d_{ij}} \qquad (13.17)$$

where d_{ij} is the distance between catchment centroids in kilometres.

    This relationship is calibrated using annual maximum data for all catchment pairs within 200 km of each other. For each pair of gauges, Spearman's rank correlation is calculated and, using this, a fitted value of $\alpha = 0.016$ is obtained. The resultant curve is plotted in Figure 13.3. The correlation falls to a half at an inter-site distance of around 45 km.

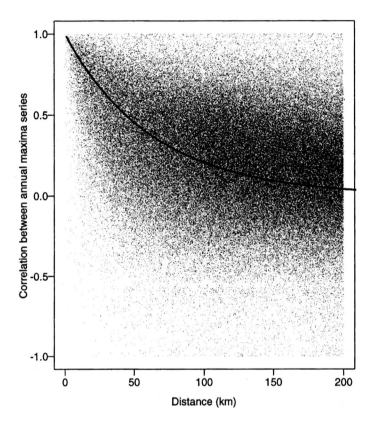

Figure 13.3 *Form of the fitted model for inter-station correlation r_{ij}. Points show observed correlations in annual maximum data for catchments up to 200 km apart.*

13.5 Variable selection

This section introduces the criteria for variable selection and summarises the results of the analyses.

13.5.1 Criteria for selecting variables

Choosing between variables is a complex task requiring balances to be struck. The overall objective is to select a relatively small set of variables that provides a good statistical fit to the *QMED* data and gives a hydrologically sound model. The final choice of variables evolved from an iterative process combining statistical analysis and hydrological knowledge. Initial model forms were investigated, looking for outliers and non-linear relationships. The exploratory analysis motivated refinements to the model, identifying sites requiring investigation and suggesting possible additional variables. At each stage, exhaustive search techniques were used to ensure that no useful model was missed. Using exhaustive searches also lessened the need to pre-select between highly correlated catchment descriptors.

Hydrological criteria

Hydrological judgement was used to determine whether models made physical sense and to help to choose between very highly correlated variables. Hydrologically unrealistic models were rejected.

For a model to be hydrologically sound, the selected variables and fitted coefficients needed to be acceptable. Variables such as geographical location (Easting and Northing) were considered undesirable: they encapsulate variations in other variables (e.g. climate, catchment geology) but do not themselves directly affect flood behaviour. Catchment altitude can be considered in a similar light. Model coefficients also needed to make sense: e.g. $\ln QMED$ should increase with catchment area and wetness. Models with inappropriate coefficients were rejected.

Statistical criteria

A number of criteria were used to decide how many variables should be included in the model and which these should be. Including too many variables can give the appearance of better fit, but results in worse predictions. The following statistical 'stopping' criteria were used to help decide on an appropriate size of model.

Coefficient of determination, r^2

This is the proportion of the total variation in the dependent variable that is explained by the regression model. A high r^2 is often used as a measure of how well a model fits. Note, however, that r^2 always increases as further variables are added into the model. The point at which the increase in r^2 starts to slow down can indicate a suitable model size.

Adjusted r^2, adj_r^2

This measure is based on r^2 but includes a penalty for including extra variables. The best-fitting model should be indicated by the adjusted r^2 attaining a maximum.

Predicted error sum of squares, PRESS

The *PRESS* statistic measures how well the model performs in prediction mode. Each site is removed in turn from the analysis and its value predicted using data from the remaining sites (Allen, 1974). The difference between observed and predicted values is the *jackknifed* residual. *PRESS* is the sum of the squares of these residuals and is calculated here using Miller's approximation (Miller, 1984). A minimum *PRESS* value is sought.

A further test for a suitable model size was carried out by introducing *artificial variables*. During the final stages of the analysis, 30 artificial explanatory variables were constructed from random variables. These were considered, alongside the catchment descriptors, for possible inclusion in the model. The selection of an artificial variable as an explanatory variable strongly suggests that the model contains too many variables.

Statistical criteria such as Mallow's C_p and Mallow's adjusted C_p (Mallow, 1973; Miller, 1984) were also calculated. They were found to give very similar results to the adjusted r^2 and *PRESS* statistics.

13.5.2 Results of selection analyses

The recommended catchment descriptor model incorporates six explanatory variables. Selection of the final model was a lengthy iterative process and it is not possible to present all stages here. Seven gauging stations were eliminated during the course of the analysis (see Additional Note 13.1) and the results reported below are based on 687 essentially rural sites (§13.3.1). Various additional variables were considered along the route. For the searches reported here, the dataset includes the three additional explanatory variables *RESHOST*, ln*SAARsq* and ln*AREAsq*, as introduced in §13.3.4. The focus in the current section is on selecting which variables to include in the model. Final coefficients were obtained using a larger dataset and a modified model form (§13.6, §13.7).

GLS search results

An exhaustive generalised least-squares search was used to select the optimal set of variables. For this, every possible combination of variables was fitted, up to a maximum model size of nine variables. Fitted models were graded by size and r^2 and the best few models in each size group were examined. Tables 13.3 and 13.4 show the best fitting model of each size. WLS and OLS searches were also performed as a check; they gave a similar ordering for up to six variables in the model, but deviated from GLS thereafter.

The r^2 values for the best-fitting models improve rapidly for up to five variables and flatten off by seven variables (Table 13.4; Figure 13.4). This suggests that the final model should contain at least five and at most seven variables. Note that the *PRESS* and adjusted r^2 statistics do not attain a maximum but increase by only a small amount beyond six variables. Models that include more than seven variables were generally found to be hydrologically unacceptable and to be sensitive to which sites were excluded: different variable selections resulted from relatively minor modifications to the dataset. Thus, there is the danger that a seventh or subsequent variable is incorporated simply to accommodate an unusual site.

Use of artificial variables

The inclusion of artificial variables (§13.5.1) in the GLS search gave revealing results (Table 13.5). The third best 7-variable model includes an artificial variable. However, the best 7-variable model has an r^2 that is only marginally better than the model that includes the artificial variable. It is concluded that the largest acceptable number of variables is six.

Partial residual plots

The above analyses indicate that either five or six variables should be used in the fitted model. The 5-variable model is based on ln*AREA*, ln*SPRHOST*, ln*SAAR*, *RESHOST* and ln*FARL*. The 6-variable model uses the additional variable ln*AREAsq*. This was considered as a possible explanatory variable because, at an earlier stage of the analysis, partial residual plots suggested a non-linear effect due to catchment size. A partial residual plot illustrates the relationship between the dependent variable and the candidate explanatory variable after the effects of all the other explanatory variables have been allowed for. Figure 13.5 shows partial residual plots for each of the variables in the 5-variable model. In the case of *AREA*, the data appear slightly banana-shaped indicating possible non-linearity and justifying the use of ln*AREAsq* in the model.

Selection analyses suggest six variables should be used to explain *QMED*: ln*AREA*, ln*SPRHOST*, ln*SAAR*, *RESHOST*, ln*FARL* and ln*AREAsq*.

Summary

The above analyses suggest that the 6-variable model containing ln*AREA*, ln*SAAR*, ln*SPRHOST*, *RESHOST*, ln*FARL* and ln*AREAsq* is the preferred set of variables. This model is further investigated to check that it gives an acceptable fit and has a suitable hydrological interpretation.

Table 13.3 GLS search results: the best-fitting set of variables for model sizes of one to nine variables. For each model the r² value is given.

No.	r²	Selected variables
1	0.807	ln*AREA*
2	0.880	ln*AREA*; ln*SPRHOST*
3	0.887	ln*AREA*; ln*SPRHOST*; ln*SAAR*
4	0.896	ln*AREA*; ln*SPRHOST*; ln*SAAR*; ln*FARL*
5	0.904	ln*AREA*; ln*SPRHOST*; ln*SAAR*; ln*FARL*; *RESHOST*
6	0.906	ln*AREA*; ln*SPRHOST*; ln*SAAR*; ln*FARL*; *RESHOST*; ln*AREAsq*
7	0.907	ln*AREA*; ln*SPRHOST*; ln*SAAR*; ln*FARL*; *RESHOST*; ln*AREAsq*; ln*ASPWEST*
8	0.908	ln*AREA*; ln*SPRHOST*; ln*SAAR*; ln*FARL*; *RESHOST*; ln*AREAsq*; ln*ASPWEST*; ln*ALTBAR*
9	0.909	ln*AREA*; ln*SPRHOST*; ln*SAAR*; ln*FARL*; *RESHOST*; ln*AREAsq*; ln*ASPWEST*; ln*ALTBAR*; ln*DPLBAR*

Table 13.4 Summary statistics for the models shown in Table 13.3

Size	r²	adj_r²	PRESS
1	0.807	0.807	875
2	0.880	0.880	544
3	0.887	0.887	514
4	0.896	0.895	476
5	0.904	0.904	439
6	0.906	0.906	431
7	0.907	0.906	427
8	0.908	0.907	424
9	0.909	0.908	423

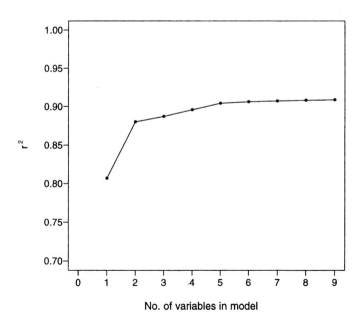

Figure 13.4 r² value for the best-fitting model of each size

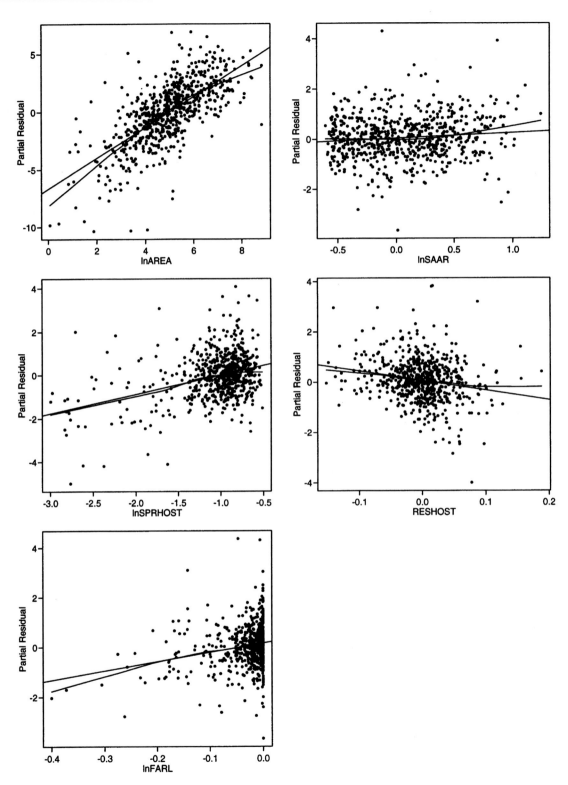

Figure 13.5 *Partial residual plots for a 5-variable regression model. Each plot shows the relationship between a particular explanatory variable and the dependent variable, after allowing for the effects of the other explanatory variables in the model. The straight line is the fitted relationship. A smoothing curve is used to highlight possible non-linearities. Non-linearity in lnAREA is suggested.*

Table 13.5 *Results of an exhaustive GLS search in which 30 artificial variables (a1–a30) were introduced as possible explanatory variables. The best three models including r² values are shown for 5- to 8- variable models. Variables are listed in alphabetical order.*

		r^2	Variables
5-var	1	0.904	ln*AREA*; ln*SPRHOST*; ln*SAAR*; ln*FARL*; *RESHOST*
	2	0.902	ln*AREA*; ln*ALTBAR*; ln*SPRHOST*; ln*FARL*; *RESHOST*
	3	0.901	ln*AREA*; ln*SPRHOST*; ln*RMED2*; ln*FARL*; *RESHOST*
6-var	1	0.906	ln*AREA*; ln*SPRHOST*; ln*SAAR*; ln*FARL*; *RESHOST*; ln*AREAsq*
	2	0.905	ln*AREA*; ln*ALTBAR*; ln*SPRHOST*; ln*SAAR*; ln*FARL*; *RESHOST*
	3	0.905	ln*ASPWEST*; ln*AREA*; ln*SPRHOST*; ln*SAAR*; ln*FARL*; *RESHOST*
7-var	1	0.907	ln*ASPWEST*; ln*AREA*; ln*SPRHOST*; ln*SAAR*; ln*FARL*; *RESHOST*; ln*AREAsq*
	2	0.907	ln*AREA*; ln*ALTBAR*; ln*SPRHOST*; ln*SAAR*; ln*FARL*; *RESHOST*; ln*AREAsq*
	3	0.907	*a17*; ln*AREA*; ln*SPRHOST*; ln*SAAR*; ln*FARL*; *RESHOST*; ln*AREAsq*
8-var	1	0.908	ln*ASPWEST*; ln*AREA*; ln*ALTBAR*; ln*SPRHOST*; ln*SAAR*; ln*FARL*; *RESHOST*; ln*AREAsq*
	2	0.908	*a17*; ln*ASPWEST*; ln*AREA*; ln*SPRHOST*; ln*SAAR*; ln*FARL*; *RESHOST*; ln*AREAsq*
	3	0.908	*a16*; ln*ASPWEST*; ln*AREA*; ln*SPRHOST*; ln*SAAR*; ln*FARL*; *RESHOST*; ln*AREAsq*

13.6 Investigating and refining the model

This section presents the results when the model identified in §13.5 is recalibrated using an extended dataset (§13.6.1). Diagnostic plots and summary statistics are then used to assess the fit of this model (§13.6.2). Section 13.6.3 introduces a modification that improves the representation of non-linear effects in *AREA*. This refinement is used in the final model (§13.7).

13.6.1 Recalibration using an extended dataset

Section 13.5 resulted in the preliminary selection of a model containing the variables ln*AREA*, ln*SAAR*, ln*SPRHOST*, *RESHOST*, ln*FARL* and ln*AREAsq*. Here, this model is recalibrated using an extended dataset that includes 41 sites in Northern Ireland. The additional data could not be used for selecting variables, because not all catchment descriptors were available for the Northern Ireland sites.

The model is recalibrated using the GLS techniques described in §13.4 giving

$$\ln QMED = 0.0773 + 1.025 \ln AREA - 0.0185 \ln AREAsq + 1.580 \ln\left(\frac{SAAR}{1000}\right)$$

$$+ 2.671 \ln FARL + 1.213 \ln\left(\frac{SPRHOST}{100}\right) - 3.929\, RESHOST \tag{13.18}$$

The r^2 value is 0.905 (GLS scale), equating to $r^2 = 0.917$ on the log-residual scale (see below for further details).

13.6.2 Examining the fit of the model

To evaluate the suitability of a regression model requires investigation of the residuals. The GLS model is obtained by transforming the problem into OLS form and searching for an optimal model. The residuals on the transformed scale are referred to here as the *GLS residuals*; residuals on the original (log) scale are referred to as *log residuals*. It is the GLS residuals that form the basis of the r^2 and other summary statistics presented in §13.5. The log residuals are useful for further understanding model performance and uncertainty (e.g. §13.8).

The GLS residuals are checked for normality and homoscedacity (i.e. constant variance) and for further outlying and/or influential points (e.g. Figure 13.6). In general the model fit appears good. Slight non-normality is seen in the largest residuals. The residuals also show slightly less variability for higher fitted values, but this is not too worrying. Highly influential and outlying points had already been investigated prior to this final stage and the sites with abnormal characteristics dropped from the analysis (see Additional Note 13.1). No justification for exclusion of further sites was found. Figure 13.7 shows the fitted values and residuals viewed

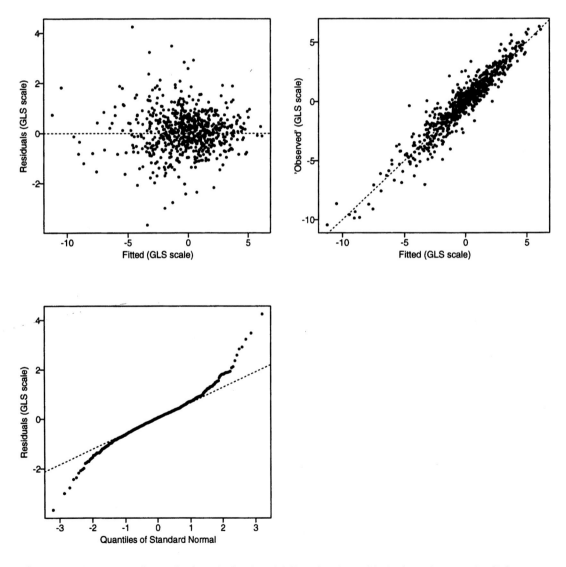

Figure 13.6 *Regression diagnostics from the fitted model. Note that the residuals shown here are the GLS residuals. The top two graphs show the fitted values versus the residual and observed values. The lower graph is used to examine the normality of the residuals. There is deviation in the extremes from the Normal case (the straight line).*

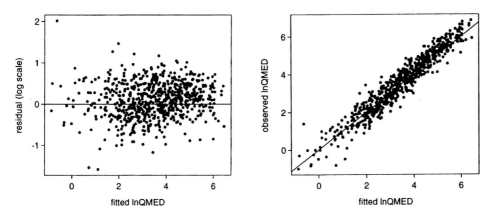

Figure 13.7 *Fitted values and residuals for the fitted model (log scale)*

on the log scale. Variation in model residuals shows little dependency on either the fitted ln*QMED* or the individual explanatory variables (Figure 13.8).

Summary information regarding the model coefficients is shown in Tables 13.6-3.8. The *analysis of variance* table (Table 13.6) shows the relative importance

Table 13.6 *Analysis of variance table for lnQMED for the fitted model (GLS scale). Df is the number of degrees of freedom. Sum of Squares and Mean Squares show the portion of the overall variability explained by each variable. The F-value is the F-test statistic: the significance level of the F-value is given in the final column (all values are highly significant).*

	Df	Sum of Sq	Mean Sq	F Value	Pr(F)
Intercept	1	196.4	196.4	308.3	0.000
ln*AREA*	1	3718.2	3718.2	5836.1	0.000
ln(*SPRHOST*/100)	1	331.4	331.4	520.1	0.000
ln(*SAAR*/1000)	1	35.6	35.6	55.8	0.000
ln*FARL*	1	39.3	39.3	61.6	0.000
RESHOST	1	41.2	41.2	64.7	0.000
ln*AREAsq*	1	10.1	10.1	15.8	0.000
Residuals	721	459.4	0.64		

Table 13.7 *Fitted model coefficients showing standard errors and t-test results. All coefficients except the intercept are significantly different from zero.*

	Coefficient	Standard error	*t* value	Pr(>|*t*|)
Intercept	0.077	0.228	0.339	0.734
ln*AREA*	1.025	0.046	22.327	0.000
ln*AREAsq*	−0.018	0.005	−3.975	0.000
ln(*SAAR*/1000)	1.580	0.150	10.497	0.000
ln*FARL*	2.671	0.319	8.363	0.000
ln(*SPRHOST*/100)	1.213	0.060	20.081	0.000
RESHOST	−3.929	0.490	−8.025	0.000

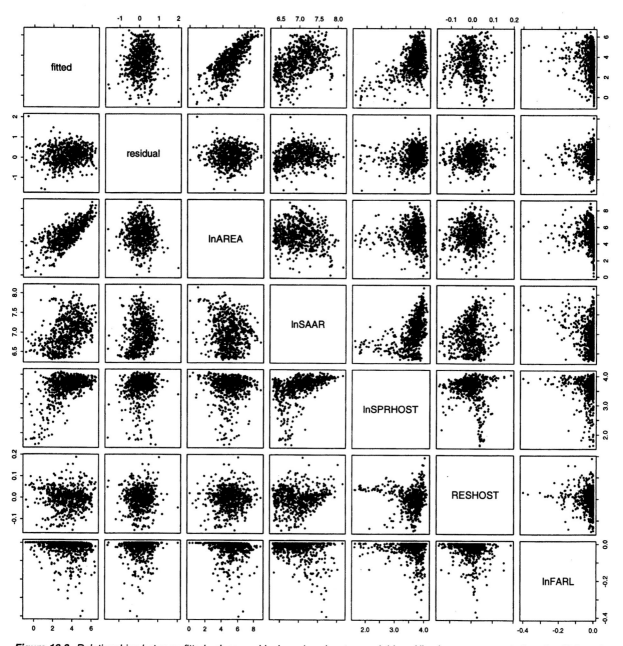

Figure 13.8 *Relationships between fitted values, residuals and explanatory variables. All values are presented on the GLS scale.*

of each of the descriptors to the overall fit; *AREA* and *SPRHOST* are the two most important variables. The fitted values and standard errors of the coefficients are shown in Table 13.7. All coefficients, except the intercept, are highly significant. The coefficient for ln*AREA* is very close to, and not significantly different from, 1.0. Table 13.8 shows the correlations between fitted coefficients. Low correlations tend to mean that coefficients are well defined; high correlations mean coefficients are less well defined. Table 13.8 shows moderate correlations between the intercept,

Table 13.8 Correlation between coefficients

	Intercept	lnAREA	lnAREAsq	lnSAAR	lnFARL	lnSPRHOST
lnAREA	−0.47					
lnAREAsq	0.43	−0.97				
lnSAAR	−0.20	0.17	−0.12			
lnFARL	−0.05	0.12	−0.06	0.12		
lnSPRHOST	0.29	0.04	−0.04	−0.18	−0.02	
RESHOST	0.08	−0.02	−0.01	−0.26	−0.04	0.14

ln*AREA* and ln*AREA*sq. Correlations for all other variables are relatively low. Overall the model appears to give a satisfactory fit to the data.

The *spatial distribution* of residuals (log scale) is examined in Figure 13.9 and shows clustering to be present at this scale. *QMED* tends to be overestimated in the Thames, Lee and Essex region and in North Wales and Ireland, and underestimated in the North East, near the South Coast and in South Wales. Note that using further variables in the model did not eliminate these spatial patterns. The equivalent plot for the GLS residuals (Figure 13.9) shows relatively little clustering. This seems to confirm the need to allow for spatial correlation in the model, thus vindicating the GLS approach.

The observed spatial clustering has a further important implication. It indicates that a *QMED* estimate may be improved using data from nearby sites. If such data are available, *QMED* is estimated at the nearby site using (i) flood data and (ii) the catchment descriptor equation. If the catchment descriptor equation overestimates for this site then it is likely that it will also overestimate for the subject site. This finding forms the basis for the data transfer techniques detailed in Chapter 4.

The spatial correlation in *QMED* residuals implies that *QMED* estimates can be improved by incorporating information from nearby sites using a data transfer process.

13.6.3 Modifying the AREA terms in the model

This section presents a minor modification to the model described in the previous two sections. The modification is made in order to improve the physical interpretability of the *AREA* terms but does not make a significant difference to the fitted values obtained for the available gauging stations (the refinement mainly affects very small catchments).

Considering only the contributions made by *AREA*, the *QMED* equation can be expressed as

$$\ln QMED = 1.025 \ln AREA - 0.0185 \ln AREAsq + ... \qquad (13.19)$$

which can be rewritten as

$$QMED = AREA^{1.025 - 0.0185 \ln AREA} ...$$
$$= AREA^{AE} ... \qquad (13.20)$$

where *AE* represents the *area exponent*. Physical considerations suggest that *AE* should always be less than 1.0. If *AE* is greater than 1.0, it would imply that doubling the catchment size, and keeping all other factors equal, would more

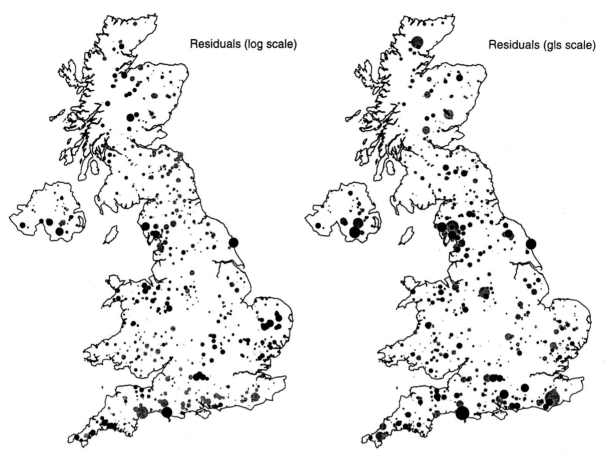

Figure 13.9 *Mapped residuals for the catchment descriptor equation on a log scale and a GLS scale. Black shows that the model overestimates QMED; grey shows underestimation. Spatial correlations are seen for the log scale residuals but not for the GLS residuals.*

than double *QMED*. Using Equation 13.20, it can be shown that *AE* is less than one for catchments of at least 2.1 km², but greater than 1.0 for smaller catchments. Such behaviour would defy the known effect that extreme rainfall is less readily sustained over large catchments than small catchments: the *areal-reduction* effect. To ensure that *AE* is always less than 1.0 for catchments greater than 0.5 km² – the lower limit to which FEH methods are applicable – the following form of model is refitted:

$$QMED = AREA^{1 + c\ln(AREA/0.5)}$$

(13.21)

where *c* is a positive constant.

Fitting this equation to the data marginally alters the model coefficients and makes only slight differences to the r^2 and fse. The modification mainly affects how *QMED* is estimated for very small catchments and there are few of these in the FEH dataset. This modification is incorporated into the final *QMED* model (see below).

13.7 Interpreting the final model

13.7.1 Model summary

The final fitted model is given by

$$\ln QMED = 0.159 + \ln AREA - 0.015 \ln AREA \ln\left(\frac{AREA}{0.5}\right) + 1.560 \ln\left(\frac{SAAR}{1000}\right)$$

$$+ 2.642 \ln FARL + 1.211 \ln\left(\frac{SPRHOST}{100}\right) - 3.923\ RESHOST \tag{13.22}$$

i.e.

$$QMED = 1.172 AREA^{1-0.015\ln(AREA/0.5)}\left(\frac{SAAR}{1000}\right)^{1.560} FARL^{2.642}\left(\frac{SPRHOST}{100}\right)^{1.211} 0.0198^{RESHOST} \tag{13.23}$$

where *RESHOST* is the soil variable defined in Section 13.3.4.

For this model, $r^2 = 0.905$ (GLS scale) and 0.916 (log scale). The fse is 1.546. Information on the final model coefficients is summarised in Table 13.9.

Table 13.9 *Final model coefficients showing standard errors and t-test results. All coefficients except the intercept are significantly different from zero.*

	Coefficient	Standard error	t value	Pr(>|t|)
Intercept	0.159	0.201	0.8	0.430
ln(*SAAR*/1000)	1.560	0.148	10.5	0.000
ln*FARL*	2.642	0.317	8.3	0.000
ln(*SPRHOST*/100)	1.211	0.060	20.1	0.000
RESHOST	−3.923	0.489	−8.0	0.000
AREA coeff	−0.015	0.001	−14.4	0.000

13.7.2 Hydrological interpretation

> For the *QMED* catchment descriptor model:
> - *QMED* increases with catchment area;
> - *QMED* increases with average annual rainfall;
> - *QMED* is higher for more impermeable catchments;
> - *QMED* tends to be higher for a relatively responsive flow regime;
> - *QMED* is moderated by reservoirs and lakes.

The catchment descriptor equation for rural catchments builds in the following aspects:

(i) *QMED* increases with increasing catchment size. The *QMED* equation allows for non-linearity due to catchment-size via the area exponent, *AE*.

$$AE = \text{area exponent} = 1 - 0.015 \ln\left(\frac{AREA}{0.5}\right) \tag{13.24}$$

For a small catchment, the exponent is close to 1.0, so that if catchment *AREA* is doubled, *QMED* is expected to double. For large catchments (up to 7000 km²), the exponent decreases towards 0.85. This can be interpreted as saying that, as catchment size increases, it becomes less likely that the flood-producing rainfall event will span the entire catchment (the 'areal reduction' effect). For an exponent of 0.85, doubling the catchment *AREA* results in *QMED* increasing by a factor of $2^{0.85} = 1.8$. Note that the *QMED* catchment descriptor equation is not designed for use with catchments smaller than 0.5 km². In these cases, the area exponent exceeds 1.0, which is physically unrealistic.

(**ii**) *QMED* increases with increasing average annual rainfall: the wetter the catchment the higher *QMED* is likely to be.

(**iii**) *QMED* is moderated by flood attenuation due to reservoirs and lakes, *FARL*. Catchments with significant lakes/reservoirs will have correspondingly lower *QMED* values than similar catchments without water-bodies.

(**iv**) *QMED* increases with *SPRHOST*: *QMED* is higher for impermeable catchments.

(**v**) *QMED* tends to be higher on catchments where the flow regime is relatively responsive, indicated by *BFIHOST* being lower than that expected from *SPRHOST*. This corresponds to the case when *RESHOST* is negative.

13.7.3 Local adjustments

In some circumstances it may be preferable to use locally derived values of some of the variables in the catchment descriptor equation. This section discusses how gauged values of *SPR* and *BFI* might be used in the catchment descriptor equation.

In general the value of *RESHOST* should never be recalculated, even if local values of *SPR* and BFI are available locally. This is because *RESHOST* is a measure of the relative difference in responsiveness. *RESHOST* has been calibrated using HOST data, and the behaviour of *RESHOST* using gauged estimates of *SPR* and *BFI* is not known. Since the model responds to quite small changes in *RESHOST*, incorrect use of this variable could give misleading results. However, use of two techniques might be considered.

Using a gauged estimate of *SPR*

It is unlikely that *QMED* would need to be estimated from catchment descriptors if an event based SPR were available, because *QMED* could presumably be estimated from the flood data (see Chapter 12). However, if necessary, the *SPRHOST* value in the catchment descriptor equation can be directly replaced by the local *SPR* value (leaving *RESHOST* unchanged).

Using a gauged estimate of *BFI*

If *BFI* is available, the recommended approach to incorporating this value into the *QMED* catchment descriptor equation is to estimate *SPR* from the gauged *BFI* value using

$$SPR = 100\left(\frac{RESHOST - BFI + 0.987}{1.30}\right) \tag{13.25}$$

and to use this in place of *SPRHOST*, leaving the value of *RESHOST* unchanged.

13.7.4 Cautionary notes

The catchment descriptor equation is a highly generalised model applicable across the whole UK, and describes only broad variations in *QMED*. It is not designed to capture all aspects of every catchment. The equation is a valuable tool when there are no data, or very few data, at the subject site. However, given a record as short as two years, an estimate of *QMED* from gauged data will typically provide a much better estimate of *QMED* than one based on catchment descriptors.

Warning

The catchment descriptor model should be used with caution, remembering that

- The model only applies to rural UK catchments;
- The model should not be applied to unusual catchments;
- The model should not be relied on if there are strongly influential lakes and reservoirs (*FARL* < 0.9);
- *QMED* may be poorly estimated on permeable catchments;
- Estimating *QMED* using two years of flood data provides a better estimate of *QMED* than the catchment descriptor equation.

The *QMED* equation is empirically derived rather than physically based. This means that the *QMED* equation is not suited to extrapolation outside the range of conditions on which it was developed. For example, it would be inappropriate to apply the model outside the UK. It is unreasonable to expect the generalised model to take account of an unusual and hydrologically important catchment feature that is not explicitly represented by the catchment descriptors appearing in the model. Thus, for example, the model should only be used with caution where a catchment is predominantly artificially drained. In some cases, it may be possible to make reasonable adjustments to the estimated *QMED* value to allow for the specific features in the catchment. Alternatively, it will be necessary to obtain flood peak data for the site or to seek a gauged catchment with similar features that can be used as an analogue for the subject site.

The catchment descriptor model does not provide very accurate *QMED* predictions for permeable catchments; this is to be expected since most hydrological models struggle to perform well on permeable catchments.

Although the catchment descriptor model recognises the important influence of lakes and reservoirs in a catchment it would be unwise to rely on the method when the *FARL* index is less than about 0.9 and represents an impounding reservoir that exerts a strong unnatural effect on the catchment flood regime.

The *QMED* catchment descriptor equation applies to rural catchments. For urban catchments *QMED* can be estimated by making an adjustment to the rural *QMED* value (see Chapter 18).

13.8 Uncertainty

This section investigates uncertainty in *QMED* estimates obtained using the catchment descriptor equation. This uncertainty is compared with *QMED* estimates obtained from flood peak data. Even a very short flood record provides a much better *QMED* estimate than does the catchment descriptor equation.

13.8.1 Uncertainty in the catchment descriptor equation

A confidence interval expresses the uncertainty in an estimate (see §12.5.1). For *QMED* it is appropriate to express a confidence interval in terms of the multiplicative error, known as the factorial standard error, fse (§12.5.1).

The fse of *QMED* is estimated here from the estimate of standard error obtained from the fitted model. This is the root mean square error (*rmse*) of the fitted model measured on the log scale:

$$rmse = \left\{ \frac{\sum (observed\ lnQMED\ -\ predicted\ lnQMED)^2}{df} \right\}^{1/2} = \left(\frac{138.1}{721} \right)^{1/2} = 0.438$$

$$(13.26)$$

where *df* is the number of degrees of freedom (721 in this case), and 138.1 is calculated from the observed and predicted ln*QMED* values. The rmse is an estimate of the standard error. The fse is estimated as $e^{rmse} = 1.549$.

Note that the above fse provides a slight overestimate of the true fse. This is because the rmse is based on the overall regression error which incorporates both model and sample errors; in prediction mode there are no sample errors (see §13.4.3). In practice any overestimation will be very small because sample errors on ln*QMED* are generally much smaller than the overall regression error (§13.4).

The fse is used to construct approximate confidence intervals as described in §12.5.1. These are

68% confidence limit for *QMED* = (*QMED*/fse, fse *QMED*) = (0.65 *QMED*, 1.55 *QMED*)
95% confidence limit for *QMED* = (*QMED*/fse^2, fse^2*QMED*) = (0.42 *QMED*, 2.40 *QMED*)

The confidence intervals for *QMED* estimates by the catchment descriptor equation are seen to be very wide. Narrower confidence intervals may be obtained by using catchment flood data (see below). Data transfer techniques (see Chapter 4) are likely to provide estimates of intermediate accuracy.

Example 13.1
Estimate QMED for the Yealm at Puslinch (47007) and assess its uncertainty

The catchment descriptors for station 47007 are

AREA = 56.4 km^2; *SAAR* = 1427 mm; *SPRHOST* = 33.2%; *FARL* = 0.992;
BFIHOST = 0.549

These yield *QMED* = 22.8 m^3 s^{-1} with a factorial standard error of 1.55.

Thus the 68% confidence limits for *QMED* are (22.8/1.55, 22.8×1.55) = (15, 35) m^3 s^{-1}, and the 95% confidence limits for *QMED* are (22.8/1.55^2, 22.8×1.55^2) = (9, 55) m^3 s^{-1}.

Note that the data-derived *QMED* estimate for this site is 22.7 m^3 s^{-1}.

13.8.2 Comparison with other QMED estimates

In Chapter 12, the factorial standard error (fse) is estimated for *QMED* values obtained by direct analysis of gauged flood data (§12.4). Table 13.10 summarises this information and compares it with the catchment descriptor equation.

Table 13.10 shows that it is almost always preferable to obtain *QMED* from flood data if at all possible. The confidence intervals for *QMED* calculated using the catchment descriptor equation are similar to those estimated from just one year of POT or annual maximum data. Using two or three years of data gives a much better estimate of *QMED* than the catchment descriptor equation.

Table 13.10 *A comparison of (factorial) confidence intervals for different QMED estimation methods. AM denotes an estimate based on annual maximum data and POT an estimate based on peaks-over-threshold data (see Table 12.3). The top row shows confidence intervals for the catchment descriptor equation. Lines shown in bold indicate the preferred estimation method for the given record length.*

Record length	Method	68% confidence limits (factorial)		95% confidence limits (factorial)	
		lower	upper	lower	upper
	Catchment descriptors:	0.647	1.55	0.418	2.39
1	AM	0.657	1.52	0.432	2.32
1	POT	0.674	1.48	0.454	2.20
2	AM	0.745	1.34	0.555	1.80
2	**POT**	**0.760**	**1.31**	**0.573**	**1.73**
3	AM	0.773	1.29	0.597	1.67
3	**POT**	**0.801**	**1.25**	**0.642**	**1.56**
5	AM	0.821	1.22	0.674	1.48
5	**POT**	**0.848**	**1.18**	**0.719**	**1.39**
10	AM	0.879	1.14	0.772	1.30
10	**POT**	**0.887**	**1.13**	**0.786**	**1.27**
15	**AM**	**0.902**	**1.11**	**0.813**	**1.23**

13.9 Model comparisons

13.9.1 Comparison with ordinary least-squares

This section compares the generalised least-squares approach, which was used in obtaining the final catchment descriptor equation, with the simpler alternative of ordinary least squares.

The equivalent OLS model takes the form

$$\ln QMED = 0.325 + \ln AREA - 0.0135 \ln AREA \ln\left(\frac{AREA}{0.5}\right) + 1.768 \ln\left(\frac{SAAR}{1000}\right)$$

$$+ 3.865 \ln FARL + 1.194 \ln\left(\frac{SPRHOST}{100}\right) - 3.726\ RESHOST$$

$$(13.27)$$

There are differences in the coefficients, although most OLS coefficients lie within two standard errors of the GLS coefficients. Figure 13.10 compares the OLS and

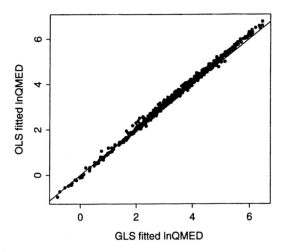

Figure 13.10 *Predicted lnQMED values for OLS and GLS 6-variable models*

GLS predicted values. The OLS model tends to predict higher *QMED* values than the GLS approach. Differences between the two models primarily relate to the different way in which the available information is weighted.

13.9.2 Comparison with the Flood Studies Report

The catchment descriptor equation is compared here with the six-variable equation of the Flood Studies Report (FSR). The FSR equation was fitted by regression and was designed to be used in much the same way as the FEH catchment descriptor equation. There are, however, some significant differences between the FSR and FEH equations, including the following:

- The index flood used in the FSR is *QBAR*, the *mean* annual maximum flood. In the FEH, the index flood is *QMED*.

- A different set of catchment descriptor variables was available for the FSR. For the FEH, all variables are derived digitally, eliminating the need for labour-intensive map-work. This has allowed rather more variables to be considered. However, digital data do not yet provide equivalent information to the 'blue line' at the 1:25 000 map scale. Thus, measures used in the FSR such as *STMFRQ* (stream frequency) and *S1085* (main stream slope) are not replicated in the FEH analysis.

- The number of available catchments for model calibration has increased considerably since the FSR. In the FSR, both urban and rural catchments were used to derive the equations. However, the FSR treated the most heavily urbanised region separately (see below). In this chapter, only rural catchments are used.

- For the FSR, different equations were used for different regions. For all areas except the Thames, Lee and Essex, a 6-variable equation was recommended together with fitted regional multipliers. For the Thames, Lee and Essex region a separate distinctive 3-variable equation was used, allowing for urban effects. In the FEH, a single equation is used to describe all rural catchments throughout the UK. Both the FEH and FSR recommended models contain a similar number of variables. Rather more fitted coefficients are required for the overall FSR model because of the use of regional multipliers.

Given the many differences, a direct comparison of the two equations is not really possible. A qualitative comparison of model fit and overall error suggests that the two models have broadly similar levels of performance. The FSR 6-variable model gives a factorial standard error (fse) of 1.46 and $r^2 = 0.92$, and the Thames-Lee-Essex region model has fse = 1.77 and $r^2 = 0.77$. The equivalent figures for the FEH are fse = 1.55 and $r^2 = 0.92$.

A comparison of the variables contributing to the FSR and FEH equations shows no major discrepancies. In the FSR, the six variables were *AREA*, *STMFRQ* (stream frequency), *S1085* (stream slope), *SOIL* (a soil index), *RSMD* (net 1-day rainfall with 5-year return period – a measure of wetness) and *LAKE* (an index of lake effects). Thus both models include terms for catchment size, wetness, soils and lakes. The FSR uses stream frequency and stream slope variables. The FEH model includes an additional soil variable and a non-linear catchment-size term.

Additional Note 13.1   Stations identified as unsuitable for use in building the catchment descriptor model for QMED

Station 27032, Hebden Beck at Hebden

This small upland catchment in North Yorkshire is highly unusual. The central part lies on Magnesian Limestone and the flow regime is strongly karstic, with swallowholes and no defined surface water channel. Stream flow occurs only occasionally. Consequently, flow measured at the gauging station derives only from the lower third of the catchment. This applies also in most flood conditions. Thus, the *QMED* value estimated from annual maximum gauged flows is very much smaller than that expected from catchment descriptors. Such geological conditions, though locally important in parts of northern England and in Somerset/Avon (notably the Mendips), are too infrequent and site-specific to be represented within a generalised model for *QMED*.

Station 27033, Sea Cut at Scarborough

This 33 km^2 catchment is augmented by flood flows diverted from the (larger) upper Derwent catchment (see station 27048 below). This represents an unnatural effect on the flood regime. Its catchment descriptors pertain only to the natural drainage area and therefore under-represent the actual flood potential.

Station 27048, Derwent at West Ayton

This is the farthest upstream gauging station on the Yorkshire Derwent. Its flood regime is strongly affected by a major drainage diversion, the Sea Cut, which intercepts flood flows from 119 km^2 of the 126 km^2 drainage area to West Ayton (see station 27033 above). Initial analysis revealed station 27048 to be both a notable outlier and an influential observation: the residual error from the model is consistent with a gauged *QMED* value that has been artificially reduced.

Station 42007, Alre at Drove Lane

This very highly permeable catchment has a gauged baseflow index of 0.98. The DTM-derived drainage area of 57 km² agrees well with the nominal area quoted for the catchment. However, the effective groundwater catchment is very much larger. The index of flood attenuation that is due to reservoirs and lakes shows a strong effect (*FARL* = 0.88) because the extensive watercress beds are treated as on-line lakes. The catchment was found to be highly influential.

Station 95801, Little Gruinard at Little Gruinard

According to the *FARL* index, this catchment in north-west Scotland is the gauged catchment that is most strongly affected by flood attenuation due to reservoirs and lakes (*FARL* = 0.55). The gauging station is about 15 km downstream of Fionn Loch, which dominates the flood regime of this 82 km² Highland catchment. Initial analysis revealed the station to be highly influential. The combination of a short record (the *QMED* estimate is based on just four years of data) and the very high leverage (i.e. influence) gave grounds for omitting the station from the main analysis.

Station 39027, Pang at Pangbourne

Runoff from this relatively permeable catchment (*BFI* = 0.86) is substantially diminished by groundwater abstraction; abstraction has been sufficiently large for it to be likely that depressed groundwater levels have reduced flood magnitudes also. The Pang proves to be a highly influential site in the regression, with *QMED* being badly overestimated. Including the Pang in the regression changes parameter values and the selected variables. The site is excluded on the grounds that question marks over the effect of abstractions do not justify allowing it to exert such an influence over the analyses.

Station 39033, Winterbourne Stream at Bagnor

Like the Pang, this catchment is substantially affected by groundwater abstraction. The Winterbourne is a highly permeable catchment (*BFI* = 0.96). The site is excluded because of the unknown effect of abstraction on *QMED* and because of the high influence that this site would otherwise exert on the fitted model.

Chapter 14 L-moments for flood frequency analysis

14.1 Introduction

L-moments and L-moment ratios are used in the FEH to estimate the parameters of the flood growth curve. L-moments provide a linear analogue of quantities such as the variance, CV and skewness of a distribution. L-moments are preferred for flood frequency estimation because of their robust properties in the presence of unusually small or large values (outliers).

14.2 Background

The method of L-moments is one of a number of methods available for estimating parameters of a probability distribution from a data sample. This section provides a brief background to these methods.

14.2.1 Methods for distribution fitting

A fundamental component of flood frequency analysis is to fit a flood frequency distribution to either site or pooled data. Common approaches to distribution fitting include the following:

Method of moments

The method of moments involves fitting a distribution so that the distribution mean, variance etc. match the sample mean, variance, etc. (see §14.2.2). The method of moments is best suited to symmetric distributions; it can give poor results when data are strongly skewed because sample estimates of skewness become unreliable (Hosking and Wallis, 1997). Since strong skewness is a feature of many flood series, L-moments are preferred over conventional moments in flood frequency analysis.

Maximum likelihood estimation

Maximum likelihood methods provide a flexible approach to estimation but can require either the solution of complex equations or use of numerical optimisation schemes. It is not uncommon for numerical problems to arise during the search for a maximum, preventing a solution being found. The L-moment approach has been shown to equal or out-perform maximum likelihood for flood estimation purposes in small to medium sized samples (Hosking et al., 1985; Hosking and Wallis, 1987).

L-moment approach

The L-moment approach is similar to the method of moments but is based on L-moments rather than conventional moments (§14.2.2). It is a development of probability weighted moments (§14.3.4) and is computationally convenient. Here an adaptation of the methods presented in Hosking and Wallis (1997) is used. Further details on the L-moment approach to distribution fitting are given in §14.4 and §15.2.

Note that, for pooled analyses, the sample L-moments effectively index the shape of a distribution; L-moment ratios of sites in the pooling group are averaged to give pooled L-moment values. An equivalent approach is possible with the conventional moment-based approach, but could not easily be achieved with maximum likelihood techniques.

14.2.2 Conventional moments and the method of moments

L-moments provide a linear analogue of conventional moments. A background summary of conventional moments and the method of moments is provided in this section.

A distribution is often described in terms of the mean, variance and skewness (and occasionally the kurtosis). The mean locates the 'middle' of the distribution. The variance measures the spread in the distribution. The skewness summarises any asymmetry in the distribution and the kurtosis says whether the distribution is peaky or flat.

Suppose the mean, variance and skewness are calculated for a data sample (more formally the sample mean, sample variance and sample skewness). A simple method of fitting a statistical distribution to the data involves choosing a distribution for which the *distribution* (or population) mean, variance and skewness match the *sample* mean, variance and skewness.

This is, in essence, the *method of moments*, where 'moments' refers to the conventional moments of the distribution. Here, we define the central moments:

$$
\begin{aligned}
1^{st} \text{ moment} &= E[X] = \mu \\
2^{nd} \text{ moment} &= E[(X-\mu)^2] \\
3^{rd} \text{ moment} &= E[(X-\mu)^3] \\
4^{th} \text{ moment} &= E[(X-\mu)^4]
\end{aligned}
\tag{14.1}
$$

where X is a variable and E denotes expected (or average) value. In fact the mean, variance and skewness of a distribution are defined directly in terms of the moments. So if a distribution is fitted by matching the mean, variance and skewness, this gives the same results as if the 1st, 2nd and 3rd moments had been matched.

The method of moments is a common way of estimating the parameters of a distribution. It is a good method to use in situations when the data are fairly symmetrical. Where data are skewed the L-moment approach is more robust.

14.3 Understanding L-moments

14.3.1 An introduction to L-moments

L-moments are a robust way of summarising a distribution. They are calculated from linear combinations of the data.

L-moments are based on linear combinations of the data: the L in L-moments emphasises this linearity. Just as the mean, variance and skewness are defined in terms of the moments, the L-mean, L-scale and L-skewness, are defined in terms of the L-moments.

The first L-moment l_1 is identical to the usual mean. It is a measure of location and is sometimes referred to as the L-mean.

The second L-moment l_2 is a measure of the spread or dispersion of the data, and is sometimes referred to as the L-scale. It is based on the differences between observations in a sample (see Figure 14.1).

The third L-moment l_3 is a measure of the symmetry of the data. Suppose there are three sample points: $x_1 < x_2 < x_3$. If x_1 and x_3 are symmetrical about the central point then $x_3 - x_2 = x_2 - x_1$, and thus $x_3 - 2x_2 + x_1 = 0$. If x_3 is further away from x_2 than x_1, then the distribution has positive skewness and $x_3 - 2x_2 + x_1$ will be greater than zero. Similarly if there is negative skewness then this quantity will take a negative value. The linear combination, $x_3 - 2x_2 + x_1$, is called the second-order difference of the ordered sample. The third L-moment is determined from the average of linear combinations of this type.

The fourth L-moment l_4 can be thought of as a measure of the peakiness of the data. It distinguishes between a distribution that is fairly flat-topped and a distribution with a high central peak and long tails (see Figure 14.1). It is based on the third-order difference of the ordered sample. For a sample $x_1 < x_2 < x_3 < x_4$, the third-order difference is $x_4 - 3x_3 + 3x_2 - x_1$.

14.3.2 L-moment definitions

In general, the L-moments of a distribution are derived from the expected values of the rth-order difference of an ordered sample of independent observations.

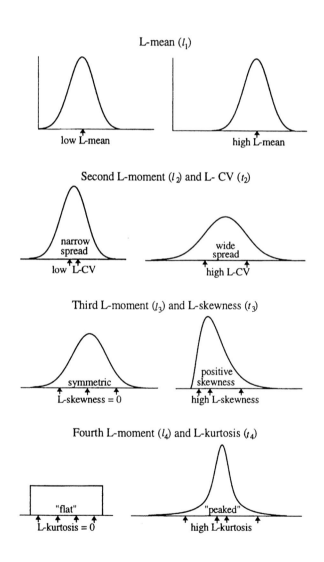

Figure 14.1 A sketch illustration of L-moments (based on Hosking and Wallis, 1997)

Thus, the L-moments of a random variable X are formally defined as follows:

$$\lambda_1 = E[X_{1:1}]$$
$$\lambda_2 = \tfrac{1}{2} E[X_{2:2} - X_{1:2}]$$
$$\lambda_3 = \tfrac{1}{3} E[X_{3:3} - 2X_{2:3} + X_{1:3}]$$
$$\lambda_4 = \tfrac{1}{4} E[X_{4:4} - 3X_{3:4} + 3X_{2:4} - X_{1:4}]$$

(14.2)

Here λ_1, λ_2, .. are the theoretical L-moments and $X_{i:n}$ denotes the ith observation from an ordered sample of size n. Thus $E[X_{2:2} - X_{1:2}]$ is the expected value of the difference between the largest and 2nd largest observations in a sample of size two.

Note that λ_r is used to denote a theoretical L-moment of a distribution. Sample estimates of the L-moments are written l_1, l_2, etc. The L-moments each take the units of the original data, e.g. $m^3 s^{-1}$ for flood peaks.

14.3.3 L-moment ratios

The L-CV, L-skewness and L-kurtosis help to characterise the flood frequency distribution. They are known as the L-moment ratios.

The estimation procedures for obtaining growth curves mainly work with the *L-moment ratios*. These are dimensionless versions of the above L-moments scaled either by the L-mean or the L-scale. The L-moment ratios are the L-CV, L-skewness and L-kurtosis. Notationally they are written τ_2, τ_3 and τ_4 and defined by

L-CV: $\tau_2 = \lambda_2 / \lambda_1$

L-skewness: $\tau_3 = \lambda_3 / \lambda_2$ (14.3)

L-kurtosis: $\tau_4 = \lambda_4 / \lambda_2$

Note that L-skewness and L-kurtosis are both defined relative to the L-scale, λ_2. Sample estimates of L-moment ratios are written as t_2, t_3 and t_4. The L-CV is known as the coefficient of L-variation. The L-skewness is sometimes referred to as a *shape* parameter. Example 14.1 shows how the L-moment ratios are found from the L-moments.

14.3.4 Calculating sample L-moments

This section summarises how sample L-moments are calculated from flood data. A detailed description of the calculation of L-moments is available in the book by Hosking and Wallis (1997).

The L-moment calculation proceeds via estimation of *probability weighted moments* (Greenwood et al., 1979). Probability weighted moments are another way of estimating the parameters of a distribution. For the L-moment calculation, the following unbiased probability weighted moment estimators (Landwehr et al., 1979) are used:

$$b_0 = n^{-1} \sum_{j=1}^{n} x_{(j)}$$

$$b_1 = n^{-1} \sum_{j=2}^{n} \frac{(j-1)}{(n-1)} x_{(j)}$$ (14.4)

$$b_2 = n^{-1} \sum_{j=3}^{n} \frac{(j-1)(j-2)}{(n-1)(n-2)} x_{(j)}$$

$$b_3 = n^{-1} \sum_{j=4}^{n} \frac{(j-1)(j-2)(j-3)}{(n-1)(n-2)(n-3)} x_{(j)} \qquad \text{(14.4 cont'd)}$$

where n is the sample size and $x_{(j)}$ denotes the jth element of a sample of size n sorted into *ascending* order.

The sample *L-moments* are then estimated by

$$l_1 = b_0$$

$$l_2 = 2b_1 - b_0$$

$$l_3 = 6b_2 - 6b_1 + b_0$$

$$l_4 = 20b_3 - 30b_2 + 12b_1 - b_0 \qquad \text{(14.5)}$$

An alternative (equivalent) calculation scheme for sample L-moments is presented by Wang (1996a).

Example 14.1
Calculate the L-moments and L-moment ratios for the Wye at Cadora (55001).

Station 55001 has a 32-year annual maximum record (1937 to 1968).

The L-moments of the annual maxima are calculated using the methods of §14.3.4, giving

$l_1 = 539.49$ (the mean)
$l_2 = 71.91$
$l_3 = 14.20$
$l_4 = 10.47$

From these the L-moment ratios are obtained:

L-CV: $\quad t_2 = l_2 \div l_1 = 71.91 / 539.49 = 0.133$
L-skewness: $t_3 = l_3 \div l_2 = 14.20 / 71.91 = 0.197$
L-kurtosis: $t_4 = l_4 \div l_2 = 10.47 / 71.91 = 0.146$

14.3.5 Properties of L-moments and L-moment ratios

The L-mean l_1 is identical to the mean: it can take any value. The L-scale is always greater than or equal to zero: $l_2 \geq 0$. The L-CV t_2 satisfies $0 \leq t_2 < 1$ for a distribution that takes only positive values. The L-skewness t_3 and L-kurtosis t_4 always lie between −1 and +1.

The L-CV, L-skewness and L-kurtosis are dimensionless and independent of scale. This means that scaling the data by a constant value does not affect the L-moment ratios. Thus, the L-moment ratios for a flood frequency distribution are identical to the L-moment ratios of the corresponding growth curve.

14.3.6 Adjusting L-moments for permeable catchments

Permeable catchments can pose a particular problem for flood frequency analysis. This is because in some years there may be no flood event: the annual maximum value then represents a non-flood flow. Chapter 19 presents methods in which a correction for the non-flood flows is made. The 'corrected' L-moments are referred to as the *adjusted L-moments* and are used for single-site and pooled analysis in the same way as the ordinary L-moments. It is recommended that the permeable adjustment be applied to all catchments with $SPRHOST \leq 20\%$.

14.3.7 L-moment ratio diagram

The L-moment ratio diagram illustrates the possible combinations of L-skewness and L-kurtosis for various distributions. It can be used to help identify useful distributions.

An L-moment ratio diagram is simply a plot of one L-moment ratio against another. Figure 14.2 is an L-kurtosis:L-skewness L-moment ratio plot, showing relationships between L-moment ratios for some common distributions (see also Chapter 15). For each distribution, it shows the possible combinations of L-skewness and L-kurtosis. A 3-parameter distribution plots as a line and a two-parameter distribution is shown as a point (L-skewness and L-kurtosis are fixed for these distributions). The 2-parameter Logistic distribution provides a typical example; it is a special case of the Generalised Logistic (GL) distribution, so it is represented as a point on the GL line. A 4-parameter distribution would be represented by an area on an L-moment ratio diagram.

A simple method of selecting a distribution for flood frequency analysis is to plot the sample L-moment ratios onto the L-moment ratio diagram. Since sample L-moment ratios are only estimates of the true L-moments, they will be scattered about the theoretical line (or point). The nearest line or point on the L-moment diagram provides a good indication of a likely choice of a distribution.

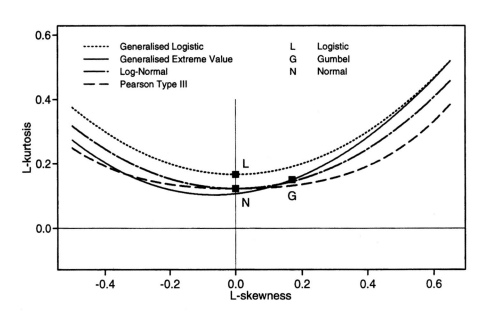

Figure 14.2 *L-moment ratio diagram showing the possible L-moment ratio values for a selection of distributions. Lines show three-parameter distributions; points show two-parameter distributions.*

14.4 Fitting distributions using L-moments

14.4.1 L-moment approach to distribution fitting

In the classical L-moment approach, the distribution L-moments are matched to the sample L-moments. This is directly analogous to the conventional method of moments (§14.2.2), in which the distribution moments are matched to the sample moments.

The FEH L-moment fitting approach is a variation on the classical L-moment approach. The sample L-moment ratios are used to obtain the growth curve (i.e. growth curve L-moment ratios are matched to the sample L-moment ratios). The flood frequency curve is then obtained by multiplying the growth curve by *QMED*. This procedure is equivalent to fitting a flood frequency curve by matching the median and the L-moment ratios.

14.4.2 Comparison of the FEH and classical L-moment methods

The classical L-moment approach is to fit a distribution by matching the L-moments, which is equivalent to matching the mean and the L-moment ratios. The classical L-moment approach corresponds to using *QBAR* as the index flood and is thus a mean-based approach. In the FEH, a median-based approach is required because of the use of *QMED* as the index flood. This section examines the differences between the median (*QMED*) and mean (*QBAR*) based L-moment approaches, i.e. between the FEH approach and the classical approach.

In the FEH, distributions are fitted by choosing parameters so that the median, L-CV and L-skewness of the fitted distribution match the sample median, L-CV and L-skewness.

In the FEH methodology, the growth curve is defined so that the 2-year growth factor equals 1 (i.e. the median of the growth curve distribution is 1). The flood frequency curve is *QMED* times the growth curve. Thus, for a flood frequency curve obtained by FEH methods, the *median* of the fitted flood frequency distribution equals *QMED* at the subject site: the fitted median equals the sample median.

In the classical approach, a slightly different growth curve is used. In this case, the definition of the growth curve distribution is that it has a mean of 1. The flood frequency curve is then obtained by scaling the growth curve by the observed *QBAR*. For the classical approach, the *mean* of the flood frequency distribution equals *QBAR* at the subject site: the fitted mean equals the sample mean.

The two approaches give flood frequency curves that are identical except for a scaling factor. This scaling factor corresponds to the ratio of the fitted median (under the classical approach) to *QMED*, or equivalently, as the ratio of *QBAR* to the fitted mean (under the FEH approach).

14.4.3 Implications of the FEH approach for single-site analysis

For single-site analyses, it is possible to compare the flood frequency curves obtained under the FEH and classical L-moment approaches. As described above, the two curves are identical except for a scaling factor, which is due to the FEH curve passing through the median of the data and the classical curve passing through the mean.

Flood data for the 421 rural FEH gauging stations with records of at least 20 years of data were used to evaluate the differences. Of these, there are 11 sites where the FEH and classically derived curves differ by more than 10%. Figure 14.3 shows one example where the two curves differ by 14%, and another where there is very little difference between the two approaches.

In general, the recommended methodology is to use the FEH approach to construct single-site flood frequency curves. In some cases, however, the FEH

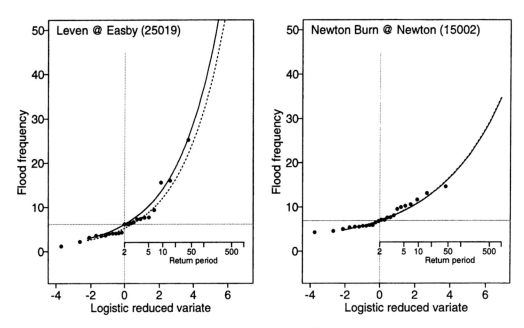

Figure 14.3 *Flood frequency curves fitted using the FEH QMED approach (solid line) and the classical QBAR approach (dotted line). The left hand graph shows an example where differences are apparent; the right hand graph shows a case where the two approaches give near identical results.*

flood frequency curve does not give a good visual fit to the data. In such situations, it may be preferable to use the flood frequency curve derived by the classical approach.

Particular care must be taken that the FEH site growth curve is always multiplied by *QMED* when calculating the flood frequency curve. Multiplying the FEH site growth curve by *QBAR* does not give the classical flood frequency curve, and would be meaningless.

14.4.4 Implications of the FEH approach for pooled analysis

As with single-site analysis, a flood frequency curve obtained by FEH methods will not be identical to that from a classical analysis. However, it is not advised that any *QBAR*-based fitting be attempted within a pooled FEH analysis. Many of the techniques presented in this volume are specifically tailored for use with *QMED* and are not directly applicable to *QBAR*.

14.5 L-moments of UK annual maxima

Site L-moments have been calculated for all FEH annual maximum series. For permeable catchments an adjustment has been applied to allow for non-flood values (Chapter 19).

In Figure 14.4, the UK data are shown plotted on an L-moment ratio diagram along with the theoretical curves of the GEV and GL distributions. The GEV and GL lines pass fairly centrally through the data, but the data are highly scattered about them. Urban and rural sites are shown separately (a site is rural if the urban index *URBEXT* ≤ 0.025). In a pooled analysis, L-moment ratios from a pool of rural sites are averaged.

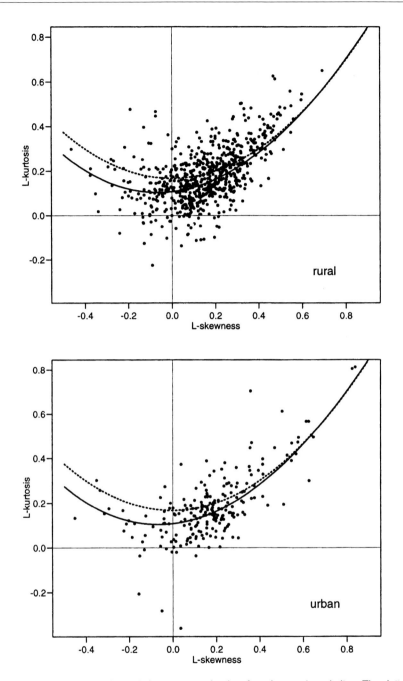

Figure 14.4 *L-skewness:L-kurtosis L-moment ratio plots for urban and rural sites. The dotted line shows the theoretical GL line; the solid line shows the GEV line. See Figure 14.2 for positions of other distributions.*

Figure 14.5 shows the geographical distribution of L-moment ratios. Rural sites show some regional patterns. There is a tendency for L-CV to show lower values to the North-West, and higher values in the South and East. Low L-skewness values are most common towards the South. The maps suggest that urban catchments tend to have higher L-CV and L-skewness than their rural counterparts.

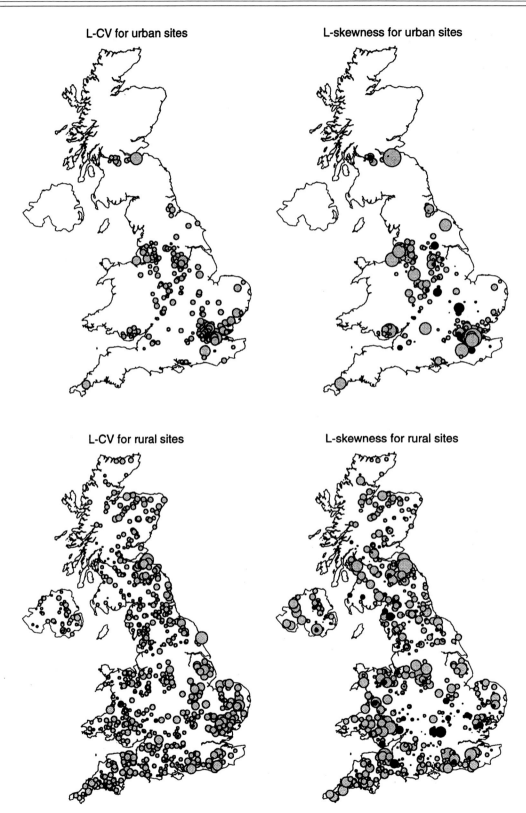

Figure 14.5 *Maps of site L-moment ratios for urban and rural sites. Adjusted L-moment ratios are used for permeable catchments (§14.3.6). Grey circles show positive values, black circles negative. Note that L-CV is always positive.*

Chapter 15 Distributions for flood frequency analysis

15.1 Introduction

15.1.1 Chapter overview

This chapter provides important background material on distributions used for flood frequency analysis. In the FEH, distributions are fitted using an L-moment approach (Chapter 14; §15.2). The recommended distribution for UK flood frequency analysis, the Generalised Logistic (GL), is detailed in §15.3, which also presents methods for producing flood frequency diagrams and extreme value plots for the GL distribution. Section 15.4 provides a similar exposition of the Generalised Extreme Value (GEV) distribution, comparing it with the GL. Special attention is paid to the GEV because of its theoretical and historical importance. Some other potentially useful distributions are summarised in §15.5.

15.1.2 Brief statistical review

This section recaps on the main concepts required for understanding extreme value distributions. Many of these concepts are discussed in detail in Chapter 11.

A *statistical distribution* describes the properties of an underlying population. It provides information about the values that observations (past, present or future) are likely to have. Flood peak behaviour is best described using a *continuous distribution*, i.e. a distribution that can take any value within a range (possibly infinite). If a distribution has a maximum possible value, it is said to be *bounded above*; if it has a minimum value, it is *bounded below*. A distribution that has no maximum value is said to be *unbounded above*.

A continuous distribution is usually defined in terms of either the probability density function or the cumulative distribution function. The *probability density function*, f(x), can be thought of as a continuous analogue of the probability of observing a value; if f(x) is high at x, then there is a relatively high probability of observing a value close to x. The *cumulative distribution function*, F(x), gives the probability of observing a value less than or equal to x: it takes a value between 0 and 1 and is often referred to as the *non-exceedance probability*. In this chapter, most distributions are presented in terms of F. The notation Q is used here to denote a peak flow, and corresponding probability density functions and non-exceedance probabilities are written as f(Q) and F(Q) respectively.

The return period T is the expected time interval between years with annual maxima exceeding a given flow (§11.3.1). T is usefully related to the non-exceedance probability F by

$$T = \frac{1}{1-F} \tag{15.1}$$

The annual maximum and peaks-over-threshold (POT) series are examples of *extreme value series*; they include only the extremes of the entire flow series. For these series it is inappropriate to describe them using standard distributions such as the Normal distribution; such distributions provide insufficient chance of a large event occurring. Many other distributions are available to describe such series; these tend to be characterised by an appreciable chance of a very large value occurring. Such distributions will be loosely referred to here as *extreme value distributions*. Sometimes the term extreme value distribution is reserved for members of the Generalised Extreme Value (GEV) family because of its theoretical justification (§15.4).

A *flood frequency distribution* is a distribution used to describe flood peak sizes and gives rise to the *flood frequency curve* (§11.3.2), relating flood size to flood frequency. In the FEH, the *growth curve* (§11.3.4), is a flood frequency curve scaled to take a value of 1 at the 2-year flood (*QMED*). The growth curve also corresponds to a distribution. For any site, the growth curve distribution and the flood frequency distribution come from the same family of distributions. If the flood frequency distribution is GEV, the growth curve will also be a GEV distribution. A growth curve distribution effectively has one parameter fewer than the corresponding flood frequency distribution, because of the constraint at *QMED*. The flood frequency and growth curves, written as Q_T and x_T, can be expressed either in terms of the return period or in terms of the non-exceedance probability F, written as $Q(F)$ and $x(F)$. Equation 15.1 can be used to convert between the two forms.

Sites with different *QMED* values (and hence different flood frequency curves) may nevertheless have similar growth curves. This is of fundamental importance for pooled frequency analysis. Similar growth curves may be pooled together to produce a *pooled growth curve*. The pooled growth curve is usually rescaled by the site *QMED* to obtain the required flood frequency curve at the subject site.

The growth curve is a scaled version of the flood frequency curve. All FEH growth curves take a value of 1 at the 2-year flood. Working with flood growth curves allows data from sites with differing QMED values to be combined to give an 'average' growth curve, called the pooled growth curve.

15.2 Fitting extreme value distributions

15.2.1 Selecting an extreme value distribution

When selecting a distribution, it is best to choose the one with the fewest parameters that gives an adequate fit. Because of the record lengths that are typically available, two- or three-parameter distributions are most commonly used for flood frequency estimation. Four- and five-parameter distributions are rarely used directly as flood frequency curves, but they have other important uses (see the Kappa distribution below, §15.5.7).

Table 15.1 Distributions used for describing flood frequency

2-parameter:	Gumbel	(G)
	Logistic	(L)
	Log-Normal	(LN2)
3-parameter:	Generalised Extreme Value	(GEV)
	Generalised Logistic	(GL)
	Pearson Type 3	(PE3)
	Log-Normal	(LN3)
	Generalised Pareto	(GP)
4-parameter:	Kappa	
5-parameter:	Wakeby	

Subsection 14.3.7 and Section 17.3 provide more information on how to choose between different distributions. In the FEH, the default recommended distribution is the Generalised Logistic.

15.2.2 Fitting distributions using L-moment ratios

The fundamental idea of the L-moment method of fitting a distribution (Chapter 14) is that the parameters of a fitted distribution are calibrated so that its L-moments equal those of the sample data. In the FEH, an adaptation of this approach is used. The sample median is matched to the distribution median and the sample L-moment ratios are matched to the distribution L-moment ratios. Essentially this differs from the L-moment approach only in the use of the median instead of the mean (§14.4).

For most distributions, formulae can be obtained that link distribution parameters to distribution L-moment ratios. Substituting the sample L-moment ratios into these relationships gives estimates of the parameters.

For single-site analysis, the sample L-moment ratios are calculated directly from the site annual maxima (Chapter 14). For pooled analysis, the sample L-moment ratios are found by taking a weighted average of the site L-moment ratios in the pooling group; these are the pooled L-moment ratios (§17.2.1).

In the FEH, 3-parameter distributions are normally used for flood frequency analysis. The three parameters describe the *location* (ξ), *scale* (α) and *shape* (k). The location is broadly equivalent to specifying the mean, the scale is equivalent to specifying the variance or L-CV, and the shape is related to the L-skewness. Note that, if $k=0$, most 3-parameter distributions are either not defined or take an alternative form. If the sample value of k is very close to zero, then the 2-parameter form of the distribution should normally be used.

Recall that a growth curve distribution requires specification of one fewer parameter than the corresponding flood frequency distribution. So, for a 3-parameter frequency distribution, the corresponding growth curve distribution requires only two parameters. In this case, the growth curve parameters are a modified scale parameter, β, together with the flood frequency shape parameter, k. Subsection 15.3.3 presents equations for β and k for the GL distribution. These equations allow the GL growth curve parameters to be estimated from the sample L-CV and sample L-skewness. Relationships for other distributions are summarised in subsequent sections.

15.3 The Generalised Logistic distribution

15.3.1 Introduction

The Generalised Logistic distribution is recommended for use with UK flood data. Details of the goodness-of-fit tests and other analyses leading to this recommendation are given in §17.3. An appealing trait of the GL distribution is that it is unbounded above (i.e. has no maximum value) unless the L-skewness is negative. Having an upper limit to a flood frequency distribution that is close to the maximum observed flow is often unrealistic except in special situations (such as downstream of a large lake). Other commonly used distributions such as the GEV are bounded above for a much larger proportion of UK catchments (see also §15.4).

The Generalised Logistic distribution is a generalisation of the 2-parameter Logistic distribution (§15.5.1). It is also a special case of the Kappa distribution (§15.5.7). The generalisation used here is based on Hosking and Wallis (1997). Note that it is a reparameterised version of the Log-Logistic distribution (Ahmad *et al.*, 1988) and differs from other published generalisations.

The Generalised Logistic (GL) distribution is the recommended distribution for UK flood growth and flood frequency curves.

15.3.2 Definition of flood frequency and growth curve

The Generalised Logistic distribution is a 3-parameter distribution defined by

$$Q(F) = \xi + \frac{\alpha}{k}\left\{1-\left(\frac{1-F}{F}\right)^{k}\right\} \qquad (k \neq 0) \tag{15.2}$$

where ξ is the location parameter, α the scale parameter and k the shape parameter. In the special case $k = 0$, the GL distribution reduces to the 2-parameter Logistic distribution, described in §15.5.1.

The range of possible values for the GL distribution is:

$$-\infty < Q \leq \xi + \frac{\alpha}{k} \qquad \text{if } k > 0$$
$$\xi + \frac{\alpha}{k} \leq Q < \infty \qquad \text{if } k < 0 \tag{15.3}$$

Thus, the GL is bounded above for $k > 0$, and bounded below for $k < 0$.

The median value of a distribution is the value of Q for which $F = 0.5$ (there is an equal chance of observing a value above or below the median). Substituting $F = 0.5$ in Equation 15.2 gives:

$$QMED = \xi \tag{15.4}$$

The Generalised Logistic *growth curve* is obtained from the flood frequency curve by substituting $x = Q/QMED = Q/\xi$ into Equation 15.2 and rearranging:

$$x(F) = 1 + \frac{\beta}{k}\left\{1-\left(\frac{1-F}{F}\right)^{k}\right\} \qquad (k \neq 0) \tag{15.5}$$

where $\beta = \alpha/\xi$.

Using Equation 15.1, the growth curve can also be written in terms of the return period T:

$$x_{T} = 1 + \frac{\beta}{k}\left\{1-(T-1)^{-k}\right\} \qquad (k \neq 0) \tag{15.6}$$

Observe that the growth curve takes a value of 1 for $F = 0.5$: this corresponds to the 2-year return period, $T = 2$. The range of values for the growth curve is

$$-\infty < x \leq 1 + \frac{\beta}{k} \qquad \text{if } k > 0$$
$$1 + \frac{\beta}{k} \leq x < \infty \qquad \text{if } k < 0 \tag{15.7}$$

i.e. it is bounded above for $k > 0$.

15.3.3 Growth curve estimation

The growth curve parameters of the GL distribution can be calculated directly from the observed L-CV and L-skewness.

The parameters k and β can be calculated from the sample L-moment ratios, t_2 and t_3, as

$$k = -t_3 \qquad \beta = \frac{t_2 k \sin\pi k}{k\pi(k+t_2)-t_2\sin\pi k} \tag{15.8}$$

Note that the distribution is bounded above if the L-skewness t_3 is negative. If the observed value of k is very small (near zero), then the Logistic distribution should be fitted instead of the GL.

15.3.4 Flood frequency and growth curve diagrams

A flood frequency diagram shows the relationship between flood magnitude and flood frequency (§11.3.2). The diagram is sometimes referred to as a *variate versus reduced-variate* plot. By convention, the frequency axis (usually the x-axis) is selected so that the distribution's 2-parameter special case plots as a straight line. Here, the 2-parameter special case is the Logistic distribution. Choosing the frequency scale in this way means that unbounded-above distributions curve upwards, whilst bounded-above distributions curve down and away from a straight line. For the GL distribution, the appropriate frequency scale is the *Logistic reduced-variate* y_L, defined by

$$y_L = -\ln\left(\frac{1-F}{F}\right) \tag{15.9}$$

which can also be written as

$$y_L = \ln(T-1) \tag{15.10}$$

where T is the return period.

A *growth curve diagram* is plotted in the same way as the flood frequency diagram. The sole difference is that the vertical axis is scaled by dividing by QMED, and shows the *growth factor*, $x = Q/QMED$ (see Example 15.1).

15.3.5 Logistic plotting positions

Adding observed flood data to the flood frequency or growth curve diagram is valuable for examining fit. When data are included on the flood frequency diagram it is usually referred to as an *extreme value plot*. This section provides brief details of the *plotting positions* for use with the GL distribution. The plotting positions specify the positions at which particular data points are to be plotted on the frequency axis.

To use the plotting positions, the data are ranked in ascending order, i.e. from smallest to largest and then the observation with the ith rank, Q_i, is plotted on the flood frequency plot at an assigned frequency, F_i (the plotting position). The recommended plotting positions for the n ordered flows $Q_1 \leq Q_2 \leq Q_3 \leq ... \leq Q_n$ are

$$F_i = i^{th} \text{ plotting position} = \frac{i-0.44}{n+0.12} \tag{15.11}$$

Plotting positions are used to show flood data on the flood frequency diagram. They specify where the data are plotted on the frequency axis.

This is the so-called Gringorten formula (Gringorten, 1963). Gringorten plotting positions are commonly used when plotting GEV distributions. An analysis of suitable plotting positions for the GEV distribution indicated that these plotting positions are also suitable for the Generalised Logistic distribution, although, as with the GEV, others might be used. Example 15.2 shows an example of an extreme value plot.

Example 15.1
Calculate the parameters of the site and pooled growth curves for the Blackwater at Stisted (37017).

Site L-moment ratios are calculated from the gauged annual maxima using the methods of Chapter 14. The regional L-CV and L-skewness are for a pooling group size corresponding to a 50-year return period (obtaining the pooling group and the pooled L-moments is described in Chapters 16 and 17). This gives

site L-CV:	0.212	site L-skewness:	− 0.273
pooled L-CV:	0.248	pooled L-skewness:	− 0.037

The growth curve parameters for the GL distribution are obtained from Equation 15.8:

Site growth curve parameters:

k = − L-skewness $\qquad\qquad\qquad\qquad$ = 0.273
$\beta = 0.212\,k\,\sin k\pi\,/\,(k\pi\,(k+0.212) - 0.212\,\sin k\pi\,)$ = 0.171

Pooled growth curve parameters:

k = − L-skewness $\qquad\qquad\qquad\qquad$ = 0.037
$\beta = 0.248\,k\,\sin k\pi\,/\,(\,k\pi\,(k+0.248) - 0.248\,\sin k\pi\,)$ = 0.244

The resulting growth curves calculated using Equation 15.5 are shown below. Note that, in this case, the site growth curve is bounded above. The pooled growth is also bounded above but much less strongly.

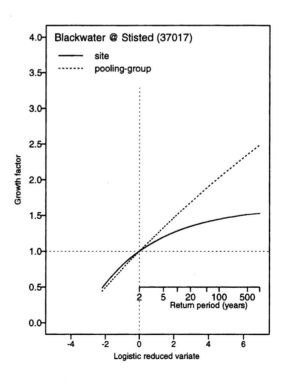

Example 15.2
Construct an extreme value plot for the Elwy at Pont-y-gwyddel (66006)

First, the site and pooled growth curves are obtained from the L-moment ratios. For this catchment, site L-CV = 0.195, site L-skewness = 0.269. Using a 50-year region size, pooled L-CV= 0.188 and pooled L-skewness= 0.259. The growth curve parameters are calculated to be $k = -0.269$, $\beta = 0.188$ (site) and $k = -0.259$, $\beta = 0.182$ (pooled).

To produce the flood frequency diagram, the growth curves are multiplied by $QMED = 63.2 \ m^3 s^{-1}$. This produces the site and pooled flood frequency curves shown below.

To add the flood data onto the flood frequency diagram, the F_i values are calculated from Equation 15.11 and the corresponding logistic reduced-variate value, y_L, is then determined from Equation 15.9. There are 24 annual maxima.

#	Q	F_i	y_L
1	42.9	0.023	−3.74
2	44.6	0.065	−2.67
3	46.9	0.106	−2.13
...	...	...	...
22	102.6	0.894	2.13
23	119.1	0.935	2.67
24	135.2	0.977	3.74

Using the y_L positions, the flood data are added to give the extreme value plot shown below.

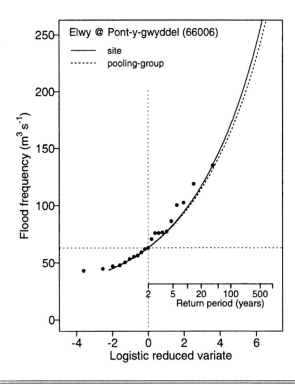

Statistical procedures for flood frequency estimation

The Generalised Extreme
Value distribution is an
important 3-parameter
distribution with strong
theoretical justification.

15.4 The Generalised Extreme Value distribution

15.4.1 Introduction

The Generalised Extreme Value (GEV) distribution is a particularly important 3-parameter distribution. Historically, GEV distributions have been widely used for UK flood frequency analyses. The *Flood Studies Report* used the GEV distribution to describe regional flood growth.

There are strong theoretical reasons for using a GEV distribution to describe extreme events. Statistically, the limiting form of a distribution that describes maximum values must be a GEV distribution (assuming a limit exists). This result holds providing that there are a large number of nearly independent peaks within a year, all coming from the same underlying process (from the same statistical distribution). Assuming these conditions hold for a flow peak series, the annual maxima should follow a GEV distribution.

15.4.2 Definition of flood frequency and growth curve

The GEV distribution is defined by

$$Q(F) = \xi + \frac{\alpha}{k}\left\{1-(-\ln F)^k\right\} \qquad (k \neq 0) \qquad (15.12)$$

where ξ is the location parameter, α the scale parameter and k the shape parameter. The special case corresponding to $k = 0$ is the Gumbel (GEV type I) distribution (§15.5.2). If $k > 0$ the distribution is known as a type II GEV distribution. If $k < 0$, the distribution is known as a type III GEV distribution and is closely related to the Weibull distribution. The range of possible values for the GEV distribution is:

$$-\infty < Q \leq \xi + \frac{\alpha}{k} \qquad \text{if } k > 0 \qquad (15.13)$$

$$\xi + \frac{\alpha}{k} \leq Q < \infty \qquad \text{if } k < 0 \qquad (15.14)$$

Thus the GEV is bounded above if $k > 0$.

The median of the GEV is found by substituting $F = 0.5$ in Equation 15.12. This gives

$$QMED = \xi + \frac{\alpha}{k}\left\{1-(\ln 2)^k\right\} \qquad (15.15)$$

The growth curve is obtained from the flood frequency curve by substituting $x = Q/QMED$ and rearranging to give:

$$x(F) = 1 + \frac{\beta}{k}\left\{(\ln 2)^k-(-\ln F)^k\right\} \qquad (15.16)$$

where

$$\beta = \frac{\alpha}{\xi + \frac{\alpha}{k}\left\{1-(\ln 2)^k\right\}} \qquad (15.17)$$

The growth curve can also be written in terms of the return period T:

$$x_T = 1 + \frac{\beta}{k} \left\{ (\ln 2)^k - \left(\ln \frac{T}{T-1} \right)^k \right\}$$ (15.18)

The range of possible values for the growth curve is

$$-\infty < x \leq 1 + \frac{\beta}{k} (\ln 2)^k \qquad \text{if } k > 0$$ (15.19)

$$1 + \frac{\beta}{k} (\ln 2)^k \leq x < \infty \qquad \text{if } k < 0$$ (15.20)

15.4.3 Growth curve estimation

The parameter k is estimated from the L-skewness via an approximation (Hosking et al., 1985) that has an accuracy better than 9×10^{-4} for $-0.5 \leq \tau_3 \leq 0.5$. Using this approximation, k is found thus:

$$k \approx 7.8590 c + 2.9554 c^2$$ (15.21)

$$c = \frac{2}{3 + t_3} - \frac{\ln 2}{\ln 3}$$ (15.22)

Note that these equations give $k < 0$ for $t_3 > 0.17$, and hence the GEV is unbounded above for L-skewness ≥ 0.17.

The parameter β is estimated using

$$\beta = \frac{k t_2}{t_2 \left\{ \Gamma(1+k) - (\ln 2)^k \right\} + \Gamma(1+k)(1-2^{-k})}$$ (15.23)

where Γ denotes the gamma function

$$\Gamma(x) = \int_0^\infty t^{x-1} e^{-t} \, dt$$ (15.24)

15.4.4 Flood frequency and growth curve diagram

Subsection 15.3.4 describes the flood frequency diagram and growth curves for the Generalised Logistic distribution. For the GEV distribution, the approach is the same, but the frequency axis is chosen to correspond to the Gumbel distribution. This means that a GEV distribution which is unbounded-above curves upwards, whilst a bounded-above GEV distribution curves down and away from a straight line. The appropriate frequency scale is the *Gumbel reduced-variate*, y_G, defined by

$$y_G = -\ln(-\ln F)$$ (15.25)

15.4.5 Gumbel plotting positions

The recommended plotting positions for the Gumbel distribution are the Gringorten plotting positions (FSR **I** 1.3.2; Cunnane, 1978). These are identical to the plotting positions used for the GL case and are described in §15.3.5 (Equation 15.11).

15.4.6 Comparison of the GEV and GL distributions

The GL and GEV distributions belong to a wider family of distribution functions represented by the 4-parameter Kappa distribution (§15.5.7). They are both 3-parameter special cases of the Kappa distribution.

In practical terms, use of the GL results in fewer bounded-above growth curves being fitted than would be the case for the GEV. This difference occurs because the GEV is bounded above for L-skewness values less than 0.17, whereas the GL is only bounded above for negative L-skewness. This is of considerable practical advantage in modelling flood peaks. Fitted distributions that have an upper bound close to the highest observed data value are rarely realistic in flood applications. Many factors affect flood formation and it is physically unreasonable to expect to have experienced something approaching the upper limit flood in an observation period of only a few decades.

For the GEV distribution, there is a theoretical link between POT and annual maximum data: the GEV arises as the maximum of a Poisson number of Generalised Pareto variates. A similar relationship holds for the GL; it arises as the maximum of a Geometric number of Generalised Pareto variates.

15.5 Other extreme value distributions

15.5.1 Logistic

The Logistic distribution is a 2-parameter special case of the Generalised Logistic distribution (§15.3). It is an unbounded distribution and is defined by

$$Q(F) = \xi + \alpha \ln\left(\frac{F}{1-F}\right) \tag{15.26}$$

where ξ is the location parameter and α the scale parameter. The median of the Logistic distribution is

$$QMED = \xi \tag{15.27}$$

and the growth curve is defined by

$$x(F) = 1 + \beta \ln\left(\frac{F}{1-F}\right) \tag{15.28}$$

where $\beta = \alpha/\xi$. The parameter β is estimated from the L-CV,

$$\beta = t_2 \tag{15.29}$$

For the Logistic distribution, L-skewness = 0 and L-kurtosis = 1/6.

15.5.2 Gumbel

The Gumbel distribution is a 2-parameter special case of the GEV distribution, and is also known as the type I GEV distribution. It is an unbounded distribution defined by

$$Q(F) = \xi + \alpha\{-\ln(-\ln F)\} \tag{15.30}$$

where ξ is the location parameter and α the scale parameter.

It has median

$$QMED = \xi - \alpha \ln(\ln 2)$$ (15.31)

and growth curve

$$x(F) = 1 + \beta \{\ln(\ln 2) - \ln(-\ln F)\}$$ (15.32)

where

$$\beta = \frac{\alpha}{\xi - \alpha \ln(\ln 2)}$$ (15.33)

The parameter β is estimated using

$$\beta = \frac{t_2}{\ln 2 - t_2 \{\gamma + \ln(\ln 2)\}}$$ (15.34)

where γ = Euler's constant ≈ 0.5772.
For the Gumbel distribution, L-skewness = 0.1699 and L-kurtosis = 0.1504.

15.5.3 2-parameter Log-Normal

The 2-parameter Log-Normal distribution is a special case of the 3-parameter Log-Normal distribution (§15.5.4). It is defined by

$$Q(F) = \xi \exp\{-k\,\Phi^{-1}(F)\}$$ (15.35)

for non-zero k and ξ, where $\Phi^{-1}(F)$ is the inverse of the cumulative distribution function of the Normal distribution.
The 2-parameter Log-Normal distribution is bounded below by zero if $k < 0$ and bounded above by zero if $k > 0$. The median is

$$QMED = \xi$$ (15.36)

and the growth curve is defined by

$$x(F) = \exp\{-k\,\Phi^{-1}(F)\}$$ (15.37)

The parameter k is estimated from the L-CV using

$$k = -\sqrt{2}\,\Phi^{-1}\left(\frac{1+t_2}{2}\right)$$ (15.38)

15.5.4 3-parameter Log-Normal

The 3-parameter Log-Normal distribution (LN3) can be defined as

$$Q(F) = \begin{cases} \xi + \dfrac{\alpha}{k}[1 - \exp\{-k\,\Phi^{-1}(F)\}] & k \neq 0 \\ \xi + \alpha\,\Phi^{-1}(F) & k = 0 \end{cases}$$ (15.39)

where $\Phi^{-1}(F)$ is the inverse of the cumulative distribution function of the Normal distribution. This is not the standard parameterisation of the 3-parameter Log-

Normal, but is a generalised form of the Log-Normal distribution (Hosking and Wallis, 1997).

The special case $k = 0$ gives rise to the Normal distribution; $k = -\alpha/\xi$ gives rise to the 2-parameter Log-Normal distribution (§15.5.3).

For this distribution,

$$QMED = \xi \tag{15.40}$$

The growth curve is

$$x(F) = 1 + \frac{\beta}{k}\left[1 - \exp\{-k\,\Phi^{-1}(F)\}\right] \tag{15.41}$$

where $\beta = \alpha/\xi$. For $k \neq 0$, the growth curve has the following bounds:

$$-\infty < x \leq 1 + \frac{\beta}{k} \qquad \text{if } k > 0 \text{ (bounded above)} \tag{15.42}$$

$$1 + \frac{\beta}{k} \leq x < \infty \qquad \text{if } k < 0 \text{ (bounded below)} \tag{15.43}$$

The parameter k may be calculated from the L-moment ratios using an approximation given by Hosking and Wallis (1997):

$$k \approx t_3\left[\frac{E_0 + E_1 t_3^2 + E_2 t_3^4 + E_3 t_3^6}{1 + F_1 t_3^2 + F_2 t_3^4 + F_3 t_3^6}\right] \tag{15.44}$$

where the constants E_0 to E_3 and F_1 to F_3 are as shown in Table 15.1. This has a relative accuracy better than 2.5×10^{-6} for $|\tau_3| \leq 0.94$ (this condition corresponds to $|k| \leq 3$). β is then given by

$$\beta = \frac{\tau_2 k \exp(-k^2/2)}{1 - 2\Phi(-k/\sqrt{2}) - \tau_2 \exp(-k^2/2)\{1 - \exp(-k^2/2)\}} \tag{15.45}$$

Table 15.1 *Numerical constants for estimation of k for the 3-parameter Log-Normal distribution*

E_0 =	2.0466534	F_1 =	−2.0182173
E_1 =	−3.6544371	F_2 =	1.2420401
E_2 =	1.8396733	F_3 =	−0.21741801
E_3 =	−0.20360244		

15.5.6 Generalised Pareto

The Generalised Pareto (GP) distribution is useful for describing peaks-over-threshold (POT) data but is not normally used for annual maximum data. It is defined by

$$Q(F) = \xi + \frac{\alpha}{k}\left\{1 - (1-F)^k\right\} \qquad (k \neq 0) \tag{15.46}$$

and has the following bounds:

$$\xi < Q \le \xi + \frac{\alpha}{k} \qquad k > 0 \text{ (bounded above and below)}$$
$$\xi \le Q \qquad\qquad k \le 0 \text{ (bounded below)} \tag{15.47}$$

Special cases of the GP are $k = 0$, the exponential distribution, and $k = 1$, the uniform distribution on the interval $\xi \le x \le \xi + \alpha$.

The median of the GP distribution is

$$QMED = \xi + \frac{\alpha}{k}(1-2^{-k}) \tag{15.48}$$

and the growth curve is

$$x(F) = 1 + \frac{\beta}{k}\{2^{-k} - (1-F)^{k}\} \tag{15.49}$$

where

$$\beta = \frac{\alpha}{\xi + \frac{\alpha}{k}(1-2^{-k})} \tag{15.50}$$

If the bounds of the distribution are unknown (i.e. ξ is unknown), then the parameters β, k may be estimated from the L-moment ratios using

$$k = \frac{1-3t_3}{1+t_3} \tag{15.51}$$

$$\beta = \frac{t_2 k(1+k)(2+k)}{k - t_2(2+k)\{2^{-k}(1+k)-1\}} \tag{15.52}$$

In the case where the lower bound is known to be zero,

$$k = \frac{1}{t_2} - 2 \tag{15.53}$$

$$\beta = \frac{k}{1-2^{-k}} \tag{15.54}$$

15.5.7 Kappa

The 4-parameter Kappa distribution is of particular note because many of the common 2- and 3-parameter distribution functions are special cases of it (Table 15.2). This makes the Kappa distribution useful for simulating artificial data. In the FEH, the Kappa distribution is used in calculating the heterogeneity measure H_2 (§16.3.2) and in obtaining the goodness-of-fit measure (§17.3.1).

The Kappa distribution is defined by

$$Q(F) = \xi + \frac{\alpha}{k}\left\{1 - \left(\frac{1-F^h}{h}\right)^k\right\} \tag{15.55}$$

where the parameters are ξ, α, k and h.

Table 15.2 *Some common distributions that derive from the Kappa distribution*

4-parameter ξ, α, k, h	3-parameter ξ, α, k		2-parameter ξ, α	
	$h = -1$	Generalised Logistic (GL)	$k = 0$	Logistic
Kappa distribution	$h = 0$	Generalised Extreme Value (GEV)	$k = 0$	Gumbel
	$h = 1$	Generalised Pareto	$k = 0$	Exponential

The bounds for the Kappa distribution are as follows:

$$\xi + \frac{\alpha}{k}(1-h^{-k}) \leq Q \leq \xi + \frac{\alpha}{k} \qquad k > 0,\ h > 0$$

$$\xi + \frac{\alpha}{k}(1-h^{-k}) \leq Q \leq \infty \qquad k \leq 0,\ h > 0$$

$$-\infty \leq Q \leq \xi + \frac{\alpha}{k} \qquad k > 0,\ h \leq 0 \qquad\qquad (15.56)$$

$$-\infty \leq Q \leq \infty \qquad k = 0,\ h \leq 0$$

$$\xi + \frac{\alpha}{k} \leq Q \leq \infty \qquad k < 0,\ h \leq 0$$

There are no simple expressions for obtaining the parameters from the L-moment ratios. Values of k and h can be obtained by Newton-Raphson iteration (Hosking and Wallis, 1997; Hosking, 1996).

Chapter 16 Selecting a pooling-group (B)

16.1 Introduction

16.1.1 What is a pooling-group?

In the FEH, a *pooling-group* consists of catchments that have similar hydrological characteristics. Members of the pooling-group need not be close to one another in geographical space. A pooling-group is formed by choosing catchments with similar

- area (*AREA*);
- average rainfall (*SAAR*);
- soil type (*BFIHOST*).

This chapter details the methods for selecting a suitable pooling-group and the analyses on which these methods are based.

A pooling-group contains sites that are hydrologically similar to the subject site.

16.1.2 Why pooling is necessary

For most gauging stations, flood records are too short to allow reliable estimation of long return-period floods. By using a pooling approach, more flood data become available for use in the analysis. Pooling methods combine flood data from several sites to obtain reliable estimates of long return-period floods. Pooling methods are essential for ungauged catchments. For gauged sites, they compensate for the lack of a long record at the subject site.

The main use of the pooling-group is to derive the *pooled growth curve* (see §11.3.4). This curve is multiplied by the site *index flood* (*QMED*) to give the pooled estimate of the flood frequency curve.

When to use pooled analysis

- Pooled analysis is *essential* for flood estimation if the catchment is ungauged or has only a short record.

- Pooled analysis is *recommended* if the record length is less than twice the target return period.

16.1.3 How to form a pooling-group

The method used in the FEH for forming the pooling-group is based on a *region-of-influence* approach, one of a number of possible *pooling methods*. The region-of-influence approach, pioneered by Burn (1990), is a flexible method in which the pooling-group is specifically tailored to the site of interest.

The fundamental idea in obtaining the pooling-group is to select a group of sites that are hydrologically similar to the subject site. A different group of sites is selected for each subject site. The hydrological characteristics of a pooling-group can be thought of as being centred on the subject site.

There are two main issues involved in forming pooling-groups: finding similar sites and choosing how many sites to include.

D. Jakob, D.W. Reed & A.J. Robson **153**

How to identify a pooling group

To find a pooling-group:

- Specify the target return period;
- Identify gauged catchments with similar *AREA*, *BFIHOST* and *SAAR* values (§16.2);
- Select the gauges that are most like the subject site, so that the total record length reaches approximately 5 times the target return period (§16.5);
- Consider whether adaptations are needed (§16.6).

Finding similar sites

The ideal pooling-group will contain catchments that have very similar hydrological behaviour to the subject site. In the FEH, this is achieved by selecting catchments with similar size (*AREA*), wetness (*SAAR*) and soils (*BFIHOST*). To do this a 'distance' measure, calculated in size-wetness-soil space, is used (§16.2): sites with a small 'distance' between them are similar to one another. Further details on selecting similar catchments are presented in §16.2.

Choosing an appropriate size of pooling-group

The optimal size depends on the target return period. The longer the target return period, the greater the need for a large pool of data. If more than one return period is to be investigated, the pooling-group should be sized according to the longest return period.

The 5*T* rule: as a rule of thumb, it is recommended that the pooling-group should contain about five times as many station-years as the target return period, *T*.

The FEH rule of thumb is that a pooling-group should include about five times as many station-years as the target return period (the 5*T* rule: §16.5.4). The number of *station-years* in a pooling-group is just the total record length of all the sites in the pooling-group (as if the records had occurred consecutively). The 5*T* rule offers general guidance on a suitable pooling-group size and it can be varied if necessary (§16.5.4).

16.1.4 What does a pooling-group look like?

In the FEH, pooling-groups are groups of catchments that have similar size, wetness and soil characteristics. Because of this, FEH pooling-groups tend to be geographically dispersed. Conceptually this makes sense, since a catchment with comparable catchment area, wetness and soils can validly contribute to pooled estimation even if it is some distance away. Indeed, geographical dispersion holds advantages, in that observed floods will show greater independence, thus providing a more effective pool of information. As the size of the pooling-group is increased (for longer return periods), the geographical spread tends to increase. Figure 16.1 shows a comparatively dispersed 50-year pooling-group for the Isla at Forter (15001) and a compact 50-year pooling-group for the Brett at Hadleigh (36005). For the Isla, most sites are on the western side of the UK. The 200-year pooling-groups are similar to the 50-year pooling-groups but they are larger and more spread out.

Catchments in a pooling-group are similar in size, wetness and soils, but often geographically dispersed.

Figure 16.1 *50-year and 200-year pooling-groups for the Isla at Forter and Brett at Hadleigh. In each case, the subject site is marked with an X.*

16.1.5 Chapter structure

The remainder of this chapter presents further details about how a pooling-group is selected and the analyses on which the recommended pooling strategy is based. Sections 16.2 and 16.3 describe the distance measure used for evaluating site similarity and present some useful tools for comparing, evaluating and adapting pooling-groups. Sections 16.4 and 16.5 summarise the analyses used to select the pooling variables and the size of the pooling-group. Once a pooling-group has been identified, the user may need to modify the pooling-group, and Section 16.6 considers how this is achieved. Finally, Section 16.7 discusses other pooling approaches and compares the FEH pooling approach with the fixed geographical regions used in the Flood Studies Report.

16.2 Finding similar sites

16.2.1 Overview

This section describes how similar sites are selected. It gives details of the variables used to form the pooling-group, of the gauges that may be used for pooling, and of the measure that is used to determine how similar two sites are.

In the rural case, forming the pooling-group involves choosing gauged sites that are likely to have similar hydrological behaviour to the subject site. In the urban case, it involves choosing rural sites that would have a similar hydrological behaviour to the subject site if it had remained rural.

To form a pooling-group centred on the subject site, a 'distance' measure is calculated to each suitable rural site (§16.2.3). The most similar sites are those with the smallest 'distance' values.

16.2.2 Variables for pooling

The observed flood statistics cannot be used as the primary basis for selecting a pooling-group; this would result in pooling-groups consisting of sites that have experienced similar floods. For example, a pooling-group might only include sites that have not experienced any big floods in recent history. Pooling such sites would badly underestimate future rare floods. For pooling to be useful, sites must be hydrologically similar but must also have experienced a variety of conditions. Achieving a pooling-group with these properties is best accomplished by examining information that is related to the catchment but is distinct from the flood statistics.

The information that can be used to form the pooling-groups includes catchment descriptors, flood seasonality information and geographic location (see §16.4.1). The variables used to choose sites similar to the subject site are referred to as the *pooling variables*. In the FEH, the recommended pooling variables are *AREA* (catchment area, km^2), *SAAR* (standard average annual rainfall, mm) and *BFIHOST* (base flow index, as derived from the HOST soils database, which ranges from 0 to 1). These have been selected from a much larger set of variables (see §16.4). Figure 16.2 summarises the range and interrelationships between these three pooling variables.

In the FEH, the recommended pooling variables are *AREA, SAAR* and *BFIHOST.*

16.2.3 Sites for pooling

Not all FEH stations are suitable for use in forming a pooling-group. Stations are considered for inclusion if the record is at least eight years long, if the station is essentially rural and larger than 0.5 km^2, and if catchment descriptors are known.

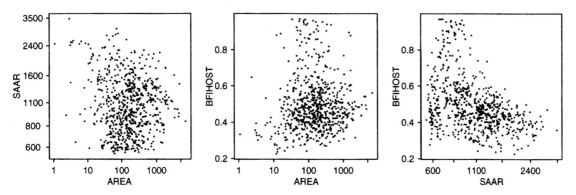

Figure 16.2 *AREA, SAAR and BFIHOST values for rural FEH gauging stations and their interrelationships. A logarithmic axis is used to display AREA and SAAR values.*

It is necessary to impose a minimum length of record because variability in the sample L-moment ratios is large when the record length is short. Only rural sites are used for pooling because urbanisation has a marked unnatural effect on flood regimes (Chapter 18). Growth curve derivation for urban sites is approached by estimating the as-rural behaviour and then making an urban adjustment.

Where further gauges are to be added to the set of catchments available for use in forming pooling-groups, screening for global discordancy is recommended, because this can help identify data problems. A site is said to be globally discordant if its flood data are unusual relative to other gauges (§16.3.1). If a site is found to be globally discordant, it is important to establish that all the floods are genuine and to confirm that the discordancy does not arise from errors in the data. Globally discordant records should generally be retained unless discordancy is caused by data problems. Such records may well prove to contain some of the rarest and most informative floods. Exclusion of these sites would be detrimental to flood frequency estimation: one of the main objectives of pooling is to obtain better estimates of the rare events.

Checks for global discordancy have been made for all FEH sites. The 4% of rural sites that are globally discordant have no known data quality problems and have been retained in the pool of sites available for pooling-group formation. There are currently 698 FEH stations available for use in forming pooling-groups.

Selection of stations for pooling-groups

Stations can be used to form pooling-groups if

- There are at least eight years of annual maxima;
- Catchment descriptors (*AREA, SAAR, BFIHOST*) are known;
- The catchment is essentially rural (*URBEXT*<0.025);
- Catchment area > 0.5 km^2.

16.2.4 Similarity distance measure

The *similarity distance measure* is used to judge the similarity of two catchments. It is defined in terms of the pooling variables. If there are n such variables then the distance between sites i and j is defined as

$$dist_{ij} = \sqrt{\sum_{k=1}^{n} (VAR_{k,\,i} - VAR_{k,\,j})^2} \qquad (16.1)$$

where $VAR_{k,\,i}$ is the value of kth variable at the ith site. The above distance, $dist_{ij}$, is the Euclidean distance in the n-dimensional space defined by the variables.

In practice, variables need to be standardised because they may have very different ranges. In the analyses used to select the pooling variables, each variable was standardised by dividing by its standard deviation (thus giving equal opportunity to each variable). This procedure was refined once the final selection of variables had been made. Preliminary application of pooling-group methods indicated that *AREA* was exerting too large an influence on the final selection of sites. The weight given to *AREA* in the recommended distance measure has been halved, thus allowing *SAAR* and *BFIHOST* to play a slightly more significant role in forming the pooling-groups.

The distance measure used in the FEH is

$$dist_{ij} = \sqrt{\frac{1}{2}\left(\frac{(lnAREA_i - lnAREA_j)}{\sigma(lnAREA)}\right)^2 + \left(\frac{lnSAAR_i - lnSAAR_j}{\sigma(lnSAAR)}\right)^2 + \left(\frac{BFIHOST_i - BFIHOST_j}{\sigma(BFIHOST)}\right)^2} \qquad (16.2)$$

where σ denotes the standard deviation of a variable. Here log transformations have been applied to the *AREA* and *SAAR* variables, partly to make their distribution more symmetrical, but also so that the distance measure is based on ratios of these quantities rather than on differences.

The distance measure, using the standard deviations evaluated on the 698 rural sites, is then

$$dist_{ij} = \sqrt{\frac{1}{2}\left(\frac{lnAREA_i - lnAREA_j}{1.34}\right)^2 + \left(\frac{lnSAAR_i - lnSAAR_j}{0.38}\right)^2 + \left(\frac{BFIHOST_i - BFIHOST_j}{0.15}\right)^2} \qquad (16.3)$$

For FEH gauging stations, the distance measure ranges from 0 to 6, but is typically about 0.5 for stations within a pooling-group. Example 16.1 shows how the distance measure is calculated.

16.3 Tools for evaluating pooling-groups

Three tools are used here for assessing pooling-groups and evaluating their homogeneity. The discordancy measure D and the heterogeneity measure H_2 are used only after the pooling-group has been identified. They provide the user with a means of examining a specific pooling-group with a view to possible modification. They are aimed at assessing whether the sites in the pooling-group genuinely appear to be derived from the same underlying flood growth curve. The pooled uncertainty measure *PUM* is not used in identifying the pooling-group, but is used as an analytical tool for evaluating how different pooling approaches perform.

Example 16.1
Find the similarity distance between the Cherwell at Enslow Mill (39021) and (a) the gauge upstream at Banbury (39026), (b) the Tern at Walcot (54012).

The *AREA*, *SAAR* and *BFIHOST* values for the three catchments are

	Cherwell at Enslow Mill (39021)	Cherwell at Banbury (39026)	Tern at Walcot (54012)
AREA	558 km^2	205 km^2	852 km^2
SAAR	664 mm	664 mm	694 mm
BFIHOST	0.590	0.416	0.616

(a) Using Equation 16.3, for the two sites on the Cherwell, first calculate the three terms contributing to the distance:

$AREA$ term $= 0.5\{(\ln AREA_1 - \ln AREA_2)/1.34\}^2 = 0.5 \times \{(6.324 - 5.323)/1.34\}^2 = 0.28$
$SAAR$ term $= 0$ (the *SAAR* values are identical)
$BFIHOST$ term $= \{(BFIHOST_1 - BFIHOST_2)/0.15\}^2 = \{(0.590 - 0.416)/0.15\}^2 = 1.35$

distance $= \sqrt{(0.28 + 0 + 1.35)} = 1.28$

(b) The Tern at Walcot is illustrated here because it is the first selected site in the pooling-group for the Cherwell at Enslow Mill. The distance measure can be calculated in the same way as shown above and is found to be

distance $= \sqrt{(0.050 + 0.014 + 0.030)} = 0.307$

Thus, although the Cherwell at Banbury is upstream of the Cherwell at Enslow Mill, notable differences in soils and in size mean that Enslow Mill is judged to be much less similar to the Banbury catchment than to the Tern. For a 50-year return period, the Banbury site is not automatically selected as part of the pooling-group for the Cherwell at Enslow Mill.

For example, it is used in selecting the pooling variables and in assessing the optimal pooling-group size (see §16.3.3).

16.3.1 Discordancy measure, D

A site is *discordant* if it has a growth curve distribution that is radically different from the group average. It is *group-discordant* if it is discordant relative to the sites in a particular pooling-group that contains it. It is *globally-discordant* if it is discordant relative to the set of all available gauging stations. The *discordancy measure* was developed by Hosking and Wallis (1997) for testing if a site is discordant. A high value of the discordancy measure indicates that a site may be discordant and not belong in the pooling-group. However, this must be weighed against the possibility that the site appears discordant because of one or two unusually extreme floods.

The discordancy measure works by comparing the L-moment ratios of a site with those of the pooling-group as a whole (see Chapter 14 for an introduction

> A site is discordant if it has a flood growth curve that is atypical of the pooling-group. The discordancy measure is used to test whether a site is discordant.

to L-moments). It identifies sites with L-moment ratios that are unusual relative to the pooling-group.

The discordancy is formally defined as follows. Let M be the number of sites in the pooling-group and let $\boldsymbol{u}_i$ be a vector of the L-moment ratios at site i,

$$\boldsymbol{u}_i = (t_2, t_3, t_4)^T \tag{16.4}$$

where superscript T denotes the transpose of a vector. Defining

$$U = \frac{1}{M} \sum_{i=1}^{M} \boldsymbol{u}_i \tag{16.5}$$

$$A = \sum_{i=1}^{M} (\boldsymbol{u}_i - U)(\boldsymbol{u}_i - U)^T \tag{16.6}$$

then the discordancy measure D_i for site i is given by

$$D_i = \frac{1}{3} M (\boldsymbol{u}_i - U)^T A^{-1} (\boldsymbol{u}_i - U) \tag{16.7}$$

where A^{-1} is the inverse of matrix A.

The discordancy measure D_i is calculated for each site in the pooling-group. Large values of D_i suggest that a site may be group-discordant. Critical values of D_i for various pooling-group sizes are shown in Table 16.1. These are based on a 10% significance level. For pooling-groups of 15 sites or more, $D = 3.0$ is used as the critical value. Note that the discordancy measure is only useful when there are at least seven sites in the pooling-group.

Discordancy in FEH data

For the FEH data, about 4% of sites (31 out of 698) are globally discordant once sites with data problems have been removed (this is somewhat less than the 10% proportion expected from a 10% significance level). In the process of investigating discordancy, two sites (33020 and 56015) were identified as showing data problems and were excluded from further analysis in Volume 3. In the remaining 29 cases, a high discordancy value arises from one of the following: (i) a single flood event that is substantially bigger than any other flood on the catchment (Figure 16.3a; Example 16.2); (ii) the existence of some *flood-free* years (i.e. years with a very small annual maximum); (iii) a catchment with floodplain storage or bypassing (Figure 16.3b), or (iv) short records. The presence of flood-free years is a particular feature of highly permeable catchments (Chapter 19). Short records seem to be particularly prone to high discordancy values. For example, 15 out of 29 of the globally discordant records are less than 15 years long: a disproportionately large fraction compared to the non-discordant data (Figure 16.4).

Table 16.1 *Critical values for the largest discordancy statistic D_i in a pooling-group (Hosking & Wallis, 1997). Values higher than the critical value show possible discordancy.*

Sites in pooling-group	7	8	9	10	11	12	13	14	≥15
Critical value of D_i	1.917	2.140	2.329	2.491	2.632	2.757	2.869	2.971	3.0

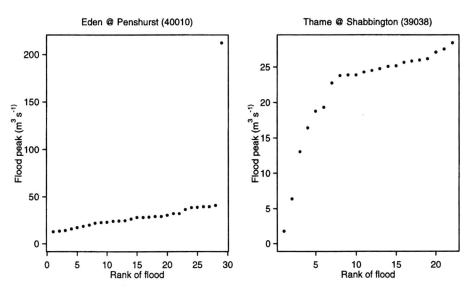

Figure 16.3 *Examples of two globally discordant sites. The Eden at Penshurst appears discordant because of an unusual but genuine flood; the Thame at Shabbington is discordant because of floodplain storage (with possible bypassing). At each site, floods are ordered from smallest to largest.*

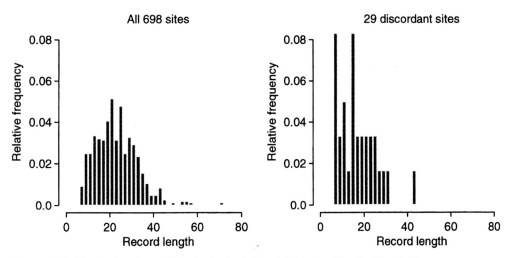

Figure 16.4 *Distribution of record lengths for the full rural dataset and for the 29 globally discordant sites. A higher proportion of shorter records show discordancy.*

16.3.2 Heterogeneity measure, H_2

A pooling-group is *homogeneous* if all sites in it have the same growth curve, i.e. the same distribution once standardised by *QMED*. It is *heterogeneous* if sites have significantly different growth distributions. A heterogeneity measure is used to test whether a pooling-group is homogeneous or heterogeneous. Heterogeneity is evaluated using the L-moment ratios (Chapter 14) and can be based on

- L-CV alone (H_1 statistic)
- L-CV and L-skewness (H_2 statistic)
- L-skewness and L-kurtosis (H_3 statistic)

The heterogeneity measure H_2 indicates whether sites in the pooling-group might have the same growth curve. High values suggest that sites may have different growth curves.

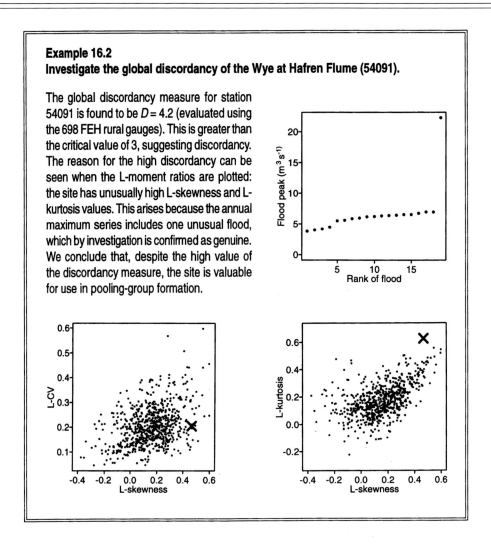

Example 16.2
Investigate the global discordancy of the Wye at Hafren Flume (54091).

The global discordancy measure for station 54091 is found to be $D = 4.2$ (evaluated using the 698 FEH rural gauges). This is greater than the critical value of 3, suggesting discordancy. The reason for the high discordancy can be seen when the L-moment ratios are plotted: the site has unusually high L-skewness and L-kurtosis values. This arises because the annual maximum series includes one unusual flood, which by investigation is confirmed as genuine. We conclude that, despite the high value of the discordancy measure, the site is valuable for use in pooling-group formation.

Hosking and Wallis (1997) provide further details on heterogeneity. In the FEH, heterogeneity is tested using H_2 because the L-CV and L-skewness are required for fitting pooled growth curves with a Generalised Logistic or Generalised Extreme Value distribution. Note, however, that Hosking and Wallis (1997) found that H_2 is a weaker test of heterogeneity than H_1.

The heterogeneity measure H_2 is determined using a simulation approach: the pooling-group is assumed to be homogeneous and multiple random samples are generated (Hosking and Wallis, 1997). If the real pooling-group is homogeneous, it should have similar properties to the randomly created data. For the random sampling, the underlying growth distribution is assumed to be a very general 4-parameter distribution known as the Kappa distribution (§15.5.7). The parameters of the Kappa distribution are found from the pooled L-moments.

Here, 500 simulations are used to determine H_2. Each simulation generates a new set of L-moment ratios for the sites in the pooling-group and represents a typical example of what would be expected if it were truly homogeneous. The heterogeneity is determined by comparing the variability of the observed pooling-group L-moments with the variability of the simulated L-moments. The variability in the observed values, V_2, is measured by

$$V_2 = \left\{ \frac{\displaystyle\sum_{i=1}^{M} n_i \{ (t_2^{(i)} - t_2^R)^2 + (t_3^{(i)} - t_3^R)^2 \}}{\displaystyle\sum_{i=1}^{M} n_i} \right\}^{\frac{1}{2}} \qquad (16.8)$$

where n_i is the record length of the ith site, M is the number of sites in the pooling-group, $t_2^{(i)}$ and $t_3^{(i)}$ are the L-CV and L-skewness of the ith site, and t_2^P and t_3^P are the average L-moment ratios for the pooling-group, weighted according to record length.

For each simulation, V_2 is recalculated. After 500 simulations, μ_{V_2} and σ_{V_2}, the mean and the standard deviation of V_2, are found. The heterogeneity measure H_2 is then defined as

$$H_2 = \frac{(V_2 - \mu_{V_2})}{\sigma_{V_2}} \qquad (16.9)$$

H_2 is used to assess whether all sites in a pooling-group could have the same flood growth curve. A pooling-group is said to be heterogeneous if $2 < H_2 \leq 4$; it is described as strongly heterogeneous if H_2 is greater than 4. Example 16.3 shows how H_2 is used to assess heterogeneity.

The FEH recommendation is that it is *essential* that strongly heterogeneous pooling-groups be reviewed, and *desirable* that heterogeneous ones are reviewed. In some cases, review of the pooling-group (§6.3; §16.6) may lead to inappropriate sites being identified and removed. Sometimes this will improve the homogeneity of a pooling-group. Equally, investigation may reveal an acceptable cause for H_2 being high (e.g. the pooling-group includes a useful discordant site at which a very large flood occurred).

In general, it is anticipated that a significant proportion of pooling-groups will remain heterogeneous, even after review. Although a homogeneous group is the ideal, a representative heterogeneous pooling-group is better than one that has been made homogeneous by removing similar sites with unusual floods. A heterogeneous pooling-group is also better than none at all.

Sometimes the observed heterogeneity in a pooling-group may occur because H_2 does not fully reflect the way that the pooled L-moments are obtained. The H_2 measure was developed for use in a fixed pooling method (§16.7.3; Hosking & Wallis, 1997) and is a measure of the heterogeneity of the pooling-group as a whole, weighting all sites equally. However, when the pooled L-moment ratios are calculated (Chapter 17), a weighting scheme places more emphasis on the most similar sites and only a small weight on the last few sites to be included in the pooling-group. H_2 does not incorporate this special weighting, and so, for FEH pooling-groups, H_2 values can sometimes be misleading. For example, a site on the 'fringe' of a pooling-group can trigger a high H_2 value, but may have only a marginal effect on the pooled analysis.

Summary details of heterogeneity measures for UK sites are shown in Table 16.2 and Figure 16.5. High values of H_2 show that a pooling-group is heterogeneous. Table 16.2 suggests that a significant proportion of pooling-groups are heterogeneous ($2 < H_2 \leq 4$), but that only a limited number are strongly heterogeneous ($H_2 > 4$).

The ideal pooling-group is homogeneous. However, a representative but heterogeneous pooling-group gives better flood frequency estimates than *either* single-site data *or* a pooling-group that has been made homogeneous by inappropriately removing sites.

Example 16.3
Determine whether these pooling-groups are homogeneous or heterogeneous

a) Little Avon at Berkeley Kennels (54088)

For a 50-year return period, the pooling-group contains 11 sites (including the subject-site) and 274 station-years. H_2 is calculated to be 4.08. This pooling-group is strongly heterogeneous.

b) Dove at Marston on Dove (28018)

For a 50-year return period, the pooling-group contains 9 sites (including the subject-site) and 258 station-years of record. H_2 is -0.98. This appears to be a particularly homogeneous pooling-group.

The following figure shows the L-CV and L-skewness values for the two pooling-groups (large dots) against a backdrop of the 698 rural gauges (small dots). The subject site is denoted by a cross. The greater scatter in L-moment values for the Little Avon is clear.

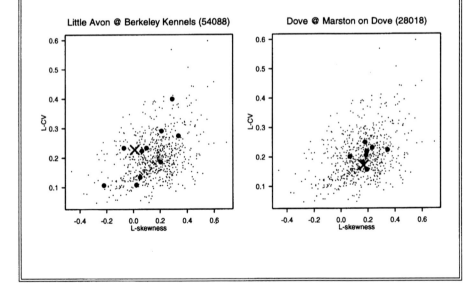

Table 16.2 *Summary of pooling-group sizes and heterogeneity measures H_2 for 50 and 100-year return periods.*

Pooling-group	Average no. of sites in group	Mean H_2	Groups with H_2>2	Groups with H_2>4
50-year FEH	11.3	1.58	36%	6%
100-year FEH	21.9	2.19	53%	10%

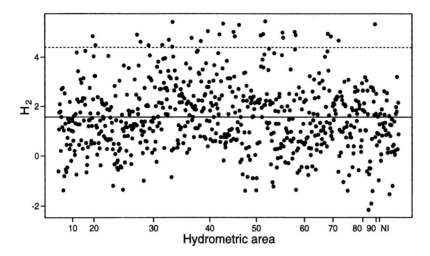

Figure 16.5 *Heterogeneity values for pooling-groups formed at rural sites for a 50-year return period. The average H_2 value is marked by the solid line. The sites are ordered by station number, with hydrometric areas shown on the horizontal axis (e.g. station 55001 would lie in the part of the graph between 50 and 60). The graph indicates some regional variation in heterogeneity. The dotted line shows the average H_2 value of the FSR regions (see also §16.7.4).*

16.3.3 Pooled uncertainty measure, PUM

In developing the pooling approach, it is important to be able to evaluate how well different pooling methods perform. Different schemes result in different pooling-groups, some of them better than others, and there are several ways in which one might judge which is best. An estimate of the uncertainty in the resulting pooled growth curves is used here.

A good pooling method will, on average, provide pooled growth curves close to the true growth curve. The true growth curve is unknown, but if a record is long enough, the site growth curve will approximate to the true growth curve. The pooled uncertainty measure *PUM* summarises the average difference between pooled and site growth factors at the target return period. Unlike the heterogeneity and discordancy, the pooled uncertainty measure is obtained by averaging over the sites with long records: it is not a site-specific value.

To calculate *PUM* for a target return period *T*, the *T*-year site and pooled growth factors are obtained for all the FEH long-record stations. The difference between these growth factors is used as a measure of the associated error in the pooled growth curve (Figure 16.6). *PUM* is a weighted average of these differences measured on a logarithmic scale, where the average is taken over all available long-record sites.

The pooled uncertainty measure for return period *T*, PUM_T, is defined by

> The pooled uncertainty measure *PUM* provides a measure of the average uncertainty associated with pooled growth curves for a particular pooling approach. It is used to compare pooling methods.

$$PUM_T = \sqrt{\frac{\sum_{i=1}^{M_{long}} n_i (lnx_{T_i} - lnx^{P}_{T_i})^2}{\sum_{i=1}^{M_{long}} n_i}} \qquad (16.10)$$

where M_{long} is the number of long-record sites, n_i is the record length of the ith site, x_{T_i} is the T-year site growth factor for the ith site, and $x^P_{T_i}$ is the T-year pooled growth factor for the ith site. A good pooling method will yield low values of PUM.

For the analyses presented in this chapter, PUM is evaluated using the rural FEH gauges with at least 20 years of data (i.e. a record is considered long if there are 20 years of data: M_{long} is the number of these records). The use of 20-year records represents a compromise between using as many sites as possible to determine PUM, and using only the best-defined site growth curves to find PUM. Pooled and single-site growth factors are fitted using the Generalised Logistic distribution (Chapters 15 and 17). Note that the subject-site is not included in its own pooling-group when PUM is evaluated. In the FEH, PUM is evaluated for two target return periods (20 and 50 years). It has not been calculated for longer return periods because 20-year records do not provide sensible estimates of the corresponding growth factors.

The pooled uncertainty measure has been used to help select a suitable pooling scheme and to assess optimal pooling-group size. It is also used to provide approximate uncertainty estimates for pooled growth curves.

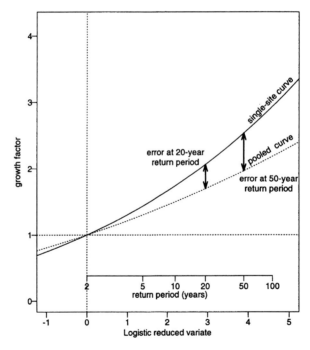

Figure 16.6 *Uncertainty measures for pooled growth curves. The differences between the site and pooled growth curves can be used as a measure of error.*

16.4 Selecting variables for pooling

This section summarises the analyses used to determine which variables give the best pooling-groups. The analysis was approached in two stages. First, linear regression techniques were used to screen the variables and to select a subset of variables for more detailed investigation. Then six candidate variables were compared in detail: from these, *AREA*, *SAAR* and *BFIHOST* were identified as the most suitable.

16.4.1 Available variables

The pooling variables were selected from the following:

Catchment descriptors

Around 30 catchment descriptors were considered. These include measures of catchment size and topography, wetness, soils, lakes and urban extent. Full listings and details of the more useful catchment descriptors can be found in Volume 5; brief definitions are given in Appendix C.

Flood seasonality variables

Two flood seasonality measures were considered. The first is a vector quantity (*XFLOOD*, *YFLOOD*), which describes the seasonal timing and concentration of floods, for example whether winter or summer flooding is more prevalent. The second variable, *CVRI*, is a measure of the irregularity of flood occurrences. Details of the seasonality variables and their derivation are given in Additional Note 16.1.

Geographical location

Geographical location was included because it can act as a surrogate for catchment properties (e.g. climate, soils and topography). Using geographical location as a pooling variable gives the nearest equivalent to the fixed geographical regions used in the FSR.

16.4.2 Pre-selection of possible variables

Linear regression was used to help identify the variables that might best explain the observed variation in site L-CV and L-skewness values. It was used to screen the variables and to select a smaller subset for more detailed investigation (§16.4.3). Five hundred stations were used in the regression analyses.

The linear regression model for L-CV identified ln*AREA*, ln*SAAR*, *BFIHOST*, ln*CVRI* and the seasonality vector (*XFLOOD*, *YFLOOD*). Together these account for around 37% of the variation in L-CV values.

The linear regression model for L-skewness identified ln*AREA* and ln*NWET* as the most useful variables. *NWET* is derived from MORECS data and describes the number of periods of soil saturation over a 30-year standard period. It is useful in distinguishing drier catchments in the east from regularly wet catchments in the north and west. Further details of *NWET* are given in Volume 5. L-skewness proved difficult to model: 8% of the variation was explained by these variables.

From these regressions, the following six variables were identified as candidates for inclusion in the pooling scheme: ln*AREA*, ln*SAAR*, *BFIHOST*, ln*CVRI*, ln*NWET* and the seasonality vector (*XFLOOD*, *YFLOOD*).

16.4.3 Final variable selection

The six variables above were examined in more detail using the pooled uncertainty measure (§16.3.3). *PUM* was evaluated at 20-year and 50-year return periods: these were assessed using a target pooling-group size of 100 and 250 station-years respectively. For this stage of the study, there were 422 rural gauges with 20 or more years of data. For each of these catchments, the pooling-group was selected from 672 rural sites.

All possible combinations of the six variables were tested, with from one to six variables being used. The (*XFLOOD, YFLOOD*) vector was treated as a single variable. The results for the 50-year return period are summarised in Table 16.3; similar results were obtained for the 20-year return period.

The best set of three variables comprised ln*AREA*, ln*SAAR* and *BFIHOST*. The next most useful variable was ln*NWET*, but the improvement over the 3-variable set was marginal and the simpler model is preferred.

Table 16.3   *Changes in the 50-year pooled uncertainty measure PUM as the number of pooling variables increases*

Variables used in model	PUM	Size
lnAREA	0.217	1
lnAREA,lnSAAR	0.210	2
lnAREA,lnSAAR,BFIHOST	0.201	3
lnAREA,lnSAAR,BFIHOST,lnNWET	0.199	4
lnAREA,lnSAAR,BFIHOST,lnNWET,lnCVRI	0.202	5
lnAREA,lnSAAR,BFIHOST,lnNWET,lnCVRI,(XFLOOD,YFLOOD)	0.206	6

16.5 Selecting the size of the pooling-group

16.5.1 Introduction

Choosing an appropriate size of pooling-group requires compromise. If the pooling-group is too small, then the pooled L-moments could be highly variable and predictions of rare floods uncertain. If it is too large, it could include sites that are rather different from the subject site.

In this section, analyses are undertaken to determine an optimal pooling-group size for a target return period. Pooling-group size is defined in terms of the number of station-years of data rather than the number of stations. This is necessary because of the large variation in site record lengths (see also §16.5.4).

Two approaches to evaluating pooling-group size were considered: (i) how PUM varies with size, and (ii) how the heterogeneity measure varies with size. The main conclusion from the analyses is that no pooling-group size is optimal. This perhaps shows that optimal pooling-group size is, in reality, site-dependent. Since no optimum was achieved, a pooling-group size of $5T$ station years is recommended. This is discussed in §16.5.4.

16.5.2 Using the pooled uncertainty measure

The pooled uncertainty measure was used to assess the uncertainty in the 20- and 50-year flood growth factors for a range of pooling-group sizes.

Figure 16.7 shows how *PUM* changes with pooling-group size. An optimum size is shown by a minimum *PUM* value. The resulting curve proves to be rather flat for pooling-groups larger than 100 station-years. *PUM* only begins to increase slightly for pooling-group sizes in excess of 1000 station-years. The curve can be interpreted as saying that the measure is relatively insensitive to pooling-group size.

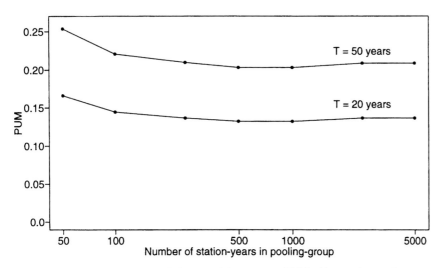

Figure 16.7 *The effect on the pooled uncertainty measure, PUM, of increasing pooling-group size*

16.5.3 How heterogeneity changes with pooling-group size

At selected sites, H_2 has been calculated incrementally for pooling-groups of 2 to 50 sites. On average, heterogeneity increases with pooling-group size (Figure 16.8), in accordance with expectations. However, H_2 also tends to show a varied and occasionally erratic behaviour. At some locations, a very wide range of pooling-group sizes is homogeneous. At other sites, virtually all pooling-groups are heterogeneous. H_2 is often non-monotone and inclusion of a single extra site can cause a marked jump in H_2 (Figure 16.8). The observed behaviour of H_2 discourages automatic selection of pooling-group size to minimise H_2. Alteration of the pooling-group requires detailed knowledge about the candidate sites.

16.5.4 Recommended pooling-group size: the 5T rule

The above analyses suggest that no one pooling-group size is optimal. The FEH recommendation is that the number of station-years in the pooling-group should be set at approximately five times the return period: the 5*T* rule. This is a 'rule of thumb' selected as a compromise between large indiscriminately pooled regions and excessive reliance on a small number of station-years of data.

    The 5*T* rule of thumb is given for general guidance and consistency; it may be varied if circumstances dictate. An example of when it may be appropriate to depart from the 5*T* rule is where a catchment has few hydrologically comparable gauges and hence it may be necessary to use a smaller pooling-group. If the pooling-group is modified, e.g. by removing a hydrologically anomalous site, it is not always necessary to compensate (by adding an extra site) unless the number of station-years has reduced markedly.

    To achieve a pooling-group containing 5*T* station-years, sites are added into the pooling-group (starting with the most similar) until the guide size has been reached. For the last site, the full record is used, even if this takes the pool size over the limit.

    Two examples of pooling-groups obtained using the 5*T* rule are given in Example 16.4. In these examples, the numbers of sites used in the pooling-group

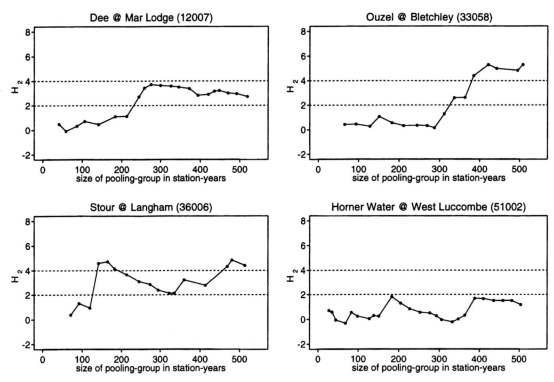

Figure 16.8 *Some examples of variable behaviour in the heterogeneity as pooling-group size is increased. The upper graphs show sites where heterogeneity increases with size. For the Horner Water, homogeneity is low for all pooling-groups. For the Stour, the heterogeneity appears large and variable.*

are quite different because of variations in the site record lengths, even though the target return period is the same.

16.6 Reviewing and adapting the pooling-group

This section discusses how a user can check the suitability of a pooling-group and gives guidelines on how a pooling-group may be modified.

16.6.1 When should the pooling-group be modified?

In the FEH, a pooling-group is normally selected automatically, but is then examined to establish whether the selected pooling-group is appropriate.

In some circumstances it may be necessary to modify the pooling-group. This may include some or all of the following:

- Removal of undesirable sites;
- Adding in other useful sites;
- Reordering of the sites to give greater emphasis to particular sites (see Chapter 17).

Reasons for modifying the pooling-group include

(1) The pooling-group is heterogeneous and particular sites are found to have catchment decriptors that suggest their expected hydrological regime is very different from that of the subject site (§16.6.2). Such sites may need to be removed from the pooling-group.

Example 16.4
Find the pooling-groups for estimating the 50-year flood for the St Neot at Craigshill Wood (48009) and the Torridge at Torrington (50002).

The recommended pooling-group size for estimating the 50-year flood is

$$5\,T \; = \; 5 \times 50 \; = \; 250 \text{ station-years.}$$

For the St Neot, the catchment characteristics for finding similar sites are $AREA$= 22.9 km^2, $SAAR$= 1512 mm, and $BFIHOST$ = 0.46. For the Torridge, these are $AREA$ = 664 km^2, $SAAR$ = 1185 mm and $BFIHOST$ = 0.425.

The following tables show the sites included in the two pooling-groups, in order of selection. In each case the subject site is included as the first site in the pooling-group. $Dist$ shows the similarity distance measure from the subject-site to each site (see §16.2.4).

St Neot at Craigshill Wood (48009)

Similarity rank	Station included	Record length	Dist
1	48009	12	0.000
2	65005	13	0.187
3	61003	15	0.281
4	48004	24	0.283
5	60012	13	0.304
6	57010	26	0.336
7	48001	25	0.347
8	59002	16	0.375
9	45006	9	0.389
10	64006	11	0.474
11	46006	16	0.475
12	73803	12	0.518
13	51002	15	0.530
14	75010	8	0.531
15	67013	12	0.540
16	21017	28	0.540
	Total	255 years	

Torridge at Torrington (50002)

Similarity rank	Station included	Record length	Dist
1	50002	33	0.000
2	27007	39	0.226
3	54014	35	0.237
4	203093	10	0.244
5	12003	19	0.247
6	84004	38	0.247
7	84019	13	0.262
8	8004	43	0.271
9	27002	57	0.285
	Total	287 years	

For the St Neot at Craigshill Wood (48009), 16 sites with short or moderate length records are required to reach the target of 250 station-years.

For the Torridge at Torrington (50002), just 9 sites are required, the majority with over 30 years of record.

(2) The subject catchment has distinguishing features that are not adequately represented in the size-wetness-soils selection process. In this case, it may be necessary to edit the pooling-group to ensure that the selected sites are relevant; this may entail removing some sites and adding other sites.

(3) There are upstream/downstream sites, or other key donor sites (see §4.3). It may be desirable to include these sites explicitly in the pooling-group, or, if they are already included, to give them greater weight when calculating the pooled growth curve (§17.2.1).

Statistical procedures for flood frequency estimation

The aim of modifying the pooling-group is to make it more representative of the subject site. Catchments should not be removed from the pooling-group just because they reduce the heterogeneity.

16.6.2 Modifying a heterogeneous pooling-group

Pooling-groups that are heterogeneous should be investigated with a view to possible modification. The greater the heterogeneity, the greater the need for the pooling-group to be reviewed. It is essential that pooling-groups with H_2 values higher than 4 should be investigated; for the FEH gauged catchments, this is likely to be required for around 10% of sites. Investigation is desirable where H_2 is between 2 and 4, and can be considered optional for H_2 between 2 and 1. If H_2 is less than 1 then the pooling-group does not justify investigation on the basis of heterogeneity.

The object of investigating a heterogeneous pooling-group is to determine whether particular sites in the selected pooling-group are unsuitable. For example, if one of the sites is dominated by a large reservoir ($FARL < 0.9$), then it is likely that its hydrological behaviour will be strongly dissimilar to that of a reservoir-free subject site. Unsuitable sites should be removed from the pooling-group.

Elimination of unsuitable sites will often reduce the heterogeneity and may sometimes result in the pooling-group becoming homogeneous. However, it is very important that *sites should not be removed from the pooling-group just because they reduce the heterogeneity*. Sites must only be removed if there are good grounds for expecting their hydrological regime to be very different to the subject site. Some sites cause apparent heterogeneity in a pooling-group because they have experienced particularly extreme events. These sites need to be retained because they contain valuable information.

A heterogeneous pooling-group is acceptable for flood frequency estimation as long as it has been thoroughly investigated and any unsuitable sites removed. A representative heterogeneous pooling-group will give better flood estimates than a non-representative homogeneous pooling-group. For the return periods typically of interest, a heterogeneous pooling-group is likely to give better results than single-site analysis.

Note that, although modification of the pooling-group may alter the heterogeneity, it does not always have a significant effect on the pooled growth curve. This is because the least-similar sites in the pooling-group (§16.2.4) have low weights applied in the growth curve derivation (Chapter 17). This situation arises because the weighting scheme used in obtaining the pooled growth curve differs from that used in the heterogeneity measure H_2 (§16.3.2).

To investigate a heterogeneous pooling-group, it is generally necessary to consider whether the subject catchment has any special qualities that need to be taken into account. It is then necessary to check whether any of the pooled sites has catchment descriptors that are particularly different from the subject site. It is advisable to pay particular attention to group-discordant sites (§16.3.1). In some cases, it may be necessary to check for possible problems with the flood data. The example given below illustrates the general approach. More advice on how to review the pooling-group can be found in Chapter 6.

16.6.3 A worked example to investigate a heterogeneous pooling-group

This section considers modification of the 100-year pooling-group for the Teise at Stone Bridge (40009). The 100-year pooling-group contains 23 sites and is strongly heterogeneous ($H_2 = 4.21$).

The sites in the pooling-group are listed in Table 16.4. Sites are investigated with the help of diagnostic plots that show the subject-site in the context of the pooling-group (Figure 16.9). The plots present information on catchment descriptors such as catchment size, wetness, soils, lakes and reservoirs, and urban extent. For

Table 16.4 *Site L-moments and the similarity distance (dist$_{ij}$) for a 100-year pooling-group for the Teise at Stone Bridge (40009)*

	No. of years	Gauge	t_2	t_3	t_4	$dist_{ij}$	Location	River
1	14	40009	0.173	−0.026	0.135	0.00	Stone Bridge	Teise
2	15	28002	0.134	0.116	0.277	0.20	Hamstall Ridware	Blithe
3	22	41003	0.307	0.303	0.136	0.23	Sherman Bridge	Cuckmere
4	18	41006	0.208	0.219	0.205	0.24	Isfield	Uck
5	17	27055	0.177	−0.143	0.078	0.26	Broadway Foot	Rye
6	22	21032	0.252	0.144	0.234	0.29	Kirknewton	Glen
7	18	42014	0.205	0.212	0.047	0.30	Ower	Blackwater
8	19	22004	0.286	0.147	0.215	0.30	Hawkhill	Aln
9	17	21024	0.233	0.384	0.274	0.32	Jedburgh	Jed Water
10	24	40007	0.202	0.378	0.284	0.34	Chafford Weir	Medway
11	26	9003	0.240	0.189	0.101	0.37	Grange	Isla
12	29	40010	0.329	0.545	0.559	0.38	Penshurst	Eden
13	31	41005	0.274	0.336	0.166	0.38	Gold Bridge	Ouse
14	16	39025	0.107	0.022	0.177	0.40	Brimpton	Enborne
15	30	68007	0.185	0.205	0.204	0.45	Lostock Graham	Wincham Brook
16	29	40004	0.202	-0.033	0.018	0.46	Udiam	Rother
17	21	206002	0.193	0.088	0.273	0.46	Jerretspass	Jerretspass
18	30	54018	0.134	0.050	0.164	0.47	Hookagate	Rea Brook
19	16	28061	0.100	0.017	0.310	0.48	Basford Bridge	Churnet
20	13	205011	0.123	0.088	0.015	0.49	Kilmore	Annacloy
21	21	54036	0.261	-0.060	0.149	0.49	Hinton on the Green	Isbourne
22	32	52004	0.077	-0.374	0.211	0.51	Ashford Mill	Isle
23	20	21025	0.205	0.169	0.133	0.51	Ancrum	Ale Water

each of these descriptors, the distribution of values for sites in the pooling-group is shown against a backdrop of the relative distribution of all rural sites. This helps to identify any particularly unusual sites. The exploratory plots also present the site growth curves and L-moment ratios together with information on flood seasonality, period of record and site location.

An initial examination of the Teise at Stone Bridge for notable catchment features (other than size-wetness-soils) reveals the presence of a major reservoir (Bewl Bridge) on one of the tributaries. This reservoir was constructed in 1976 effectively cutting off part of the catchment. The flood attenuation for the Teise catchment that is due to Bewl Bridge is marked (*FARL* = 0.905). Thus, some use of a rainfall-runoff method may be appropriate (see **1** 5.5). The selected pooling-group includes a number of other catchments with a strong reservoir/lake effect, notably station 28002 (Blithe at Hamstall Ridware).

The following sites were identified, with the aid of Figure 16.9, as worthy of further investigation:

Blithe at Hamstall Ridware (28002): the first selected site after the subject site. This site is picked out from the exploratory graphs because it is slightly unusual: it has an early record and a marked reservoir/lake attenuation effect (*FARL* = 0.876). Since this is the first selected site in the pooling-group, a high weight will be placed upon the information contained in it. Although the record is from an early period (1937-1951), Blithfield reservoir had already been built and

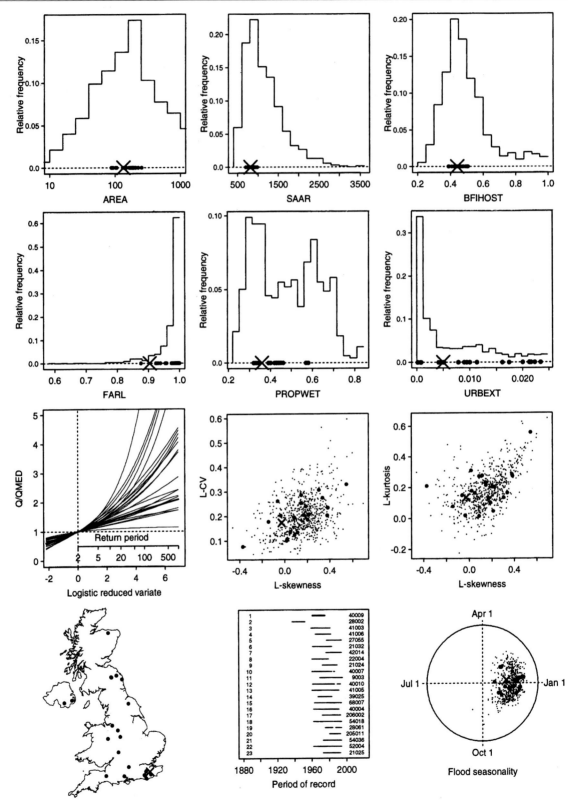

Figure 16.9 *Diagnostic plots for evaluating and adapting a pooling-group. The subject site is marked with an X or a bold line. Large dots denote sites included in the pooling-group, small dots mark other sites. The underlying distribution of each catchment descriptor is shown in the top six graphs. (See text.)*

the modern-day *FARL* value can be considered representative. Given the presence of a reservoir in the subject catchment, there are no strong grounds for leaving this site out. The L-moments for this site are fairly similar to the subject site.

Eden at Penshurst (40010): the 12th selected site. This site is selected for investigation because it has a high group-discordancy ($D = 4.01$). In fact it is also globally discordant, and the discordancy is due to an extreme event (Figure 16.3a). This site potentially contains important information and should be retained.

Isle at Ashford Hill (52004): the 22nd and penultimate selected site. This site is again chosen for investigation because it is group-discordant. Again, it is also globally discordant. It is possible that the discordancy arises because of floodplain storage or because flows bypass the gauge; either might give grounds for removing the site. Removal of site 52004 from the pooling-group brings H_2 down from 4.21 to 2.02, but the effect on the resultant L-moments and growth curve is minimal (Figure 16.10). This is mainly because only a small weight is placed on the 22nd site. In this instance, it makes little difference whether the site is included or not (Figure 16.10). Here, we choose to remove the site, leaving a homogeneous pooling-group of 22 sites, but noting that the 23-site pooling-group would have given very similar answers.

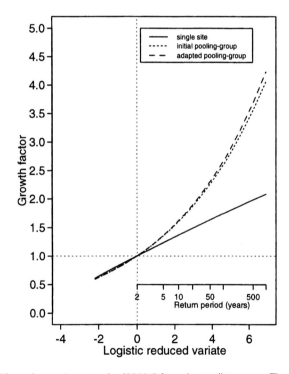

Figure 16.10 *Effect of removing one site (52004) from the pooling-group. The two pooled curves are only marginally different but are very different from the site growth curve.*

16.7 Other methods of pooling

The FEH recommends use of a pooling-group approach in which the sites are selected to be similar (as judged by *AREA*, *SAAR* and *BFIHOST*), and for which the pooling-group size is chosen to reflect the target return period. Other pooling methods were considered and are briefly reported here.

16.7.1 Similar-site pooling-groups with adjustable pooling-group sizes

This approach is very similar to that recommended in the FEH approach except in the choice of pooling-group size. Whereas the FEH sets the pooling-group size to be five times the return period, in the adjustable approach the pooling-group size is adjusted until the pooling-group becomes homogeneous. For example, one might start with a pooling-group size of 30 stations and remove sites until H becomes less than 2 (Burn, 1997). The advantage of using such an approach is that a small pooling-group can be used if there are only a few reasonably similar sites, and a large pooling-group if there are many similar sites. However, investigations using UK data highlight difficulties because of the unpredictable behaviour of the heterogeneity measure (§16.5.3).

16.7.2 Fixed geographical regions

This was the approach used in the Flood Studies Report (FSR), where 11 fixed geographical regions were delineated using hydrometric boundaries. Although simple to use, this suffers from grouping together catchments of very different sizes and soils. The FEH and FSR approaches are compared in §16.7.4.

16.7.3 Fixed non-geographic pooling-groups

This approach is intermediate to the FSR and FEH schemes. It involves use of catchment-descriptor variables and/or seasonality variables to form fixed clusters of sites that are used as the pooling-groups. This is the approach taken in Hosking and Wallis (1997), and the one for which the L-moment approach and the Hosking and Wallis tests for heterogeneity, discordancy and goodness-of-fit were developed. The main drawbacks of this approach for UK flood data are (1) assigning ungauged catchments to an appropriate pooling-group, (2) finding acceptably homogeneous pooling-groups, and (3) handling sites that are intermediate between pooling-groups. The method offered only a marginal improvement in performance over the FSR fixed regions.

16.7.4 Comparing FSR and FEH approaches

The Flood Studies Report regions and the FEH pooling-groups are compared using the heterogeneity and pooled uncertainty measures.

The results of the heterogeneity comparisons are summarised in Table 16.5 and Figure 16.11. In almost all cases, FEH pooling-groups are more homogeneous than the FSR region that they fall within. None of the FSR regions is fully homogeneous ($H_2 \leq 2$): Region 1 is closest with $H_2 = 2.13$. Eight of the eleven regions have a heterogeneity higher than 4; the average is 4.40. FEH pooling-

Table 16.5 *Summary of heterogeneity measure H_2 for FEH pooling-groups and FSR regions*

Pooling-group	Average no. of sites	Average H_2	Percentage of regions/groups with $H_2>2$	Percentage of regions/groups with $H_2<4$
50-year FEH	11.3	1.58	36%	94%
100-year FEH	21.9	2.19	53%	90%
300-year FEH	63.9	3.70	82%	58%
FSR regions	63.5	4.40	100%	27% (3 of 11)

groups generally show much lower levels of heterogeneity: for a 50-year return period, the average heterogeneity is 1.58 and, for the 100-year return period, it is 2.19 (Table 16.5).

Heterogeneity generally increases with pooling-group size. In part, this accounts for the higher heterogeneity values for the FSR regions. For a 50-year target return period, the FSR regions are about seven times larger than the FEH pooling-groups. The FEH 300-year pooling-group size provides a size-matched comparison with the FSR. Even with this size of pooling-group, the FEH pooling-groups perform better than the FSR regions. For shorter return periods, the improvement is still greater.

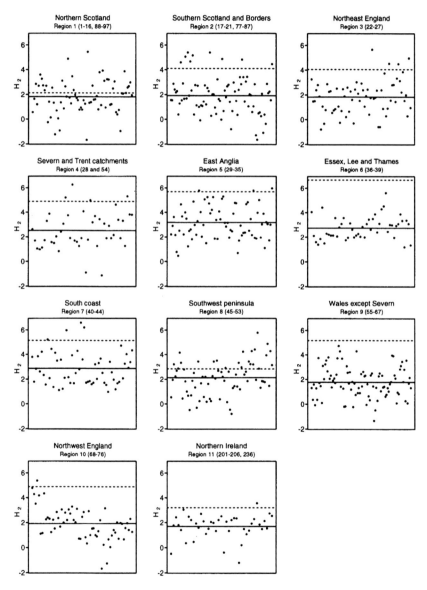

Figure 16.11 Heterogeneity comparisons for the FSR regions: the dotted line marks the FSR heterogeneity; the points are heterogeneity values for 100-year return-period FEH pooling-groups, for sites falling within each FSR geographic region; bracketed numbers show the hydrometric areas that fall in each FSR region.

The pooled uncertainty measure *PUM* also suggested that FEH pooling-groups perform better than FSR regions. In this case, differences in pooling-group size are of less concern because *PUM* tends to decrease as the pooling-group size increases.

Additional Note 16.1   *Flood seasonality variables*

Flood seasonality refers to the timing of flood events within the year. Flood seasonality variables are derived from flood date information contained in peaks-over-threshold (POT) records. Seasonality variables offer an important source of information about flood behaviour, reflecting the combined effect of rainfall regime and catchment properties. Similarity in flood seasonality suggests that flood-producing mechanisms may be correspondingly similar and that sites may share a common flood regime.

The flood seasonality variables are derived from date information. This is an integral part of a POT record yet can be considered independent from flood magnitudes. This means that it is reasonable to consider date information to help form pooling-groups. The date information provides evidence regarding the hydrological status of the catchment but does not compromise the process of forming and evaluating pooling-groups (Reed, 1994).

Three flood timing variables are considered. (*XFLOOD, YFLOOD*) should be thought of as a pair: jointly they summarise the seasonal distribution of flooding. *CVRI* summarises the irregularity of the timing of floods.

Variables describing the seasonality of flooding (*XFLOOD, YFLOOD*)

Seasonality is best described in terms of *circular statistics*. For this, a circle of unit radius is used, and the date is represented by the angle θ, measured anti-clockwise from the x-axis. One revolution of the circle (2π) corresponds to a whole year (Figure 16.12; Bayliss and Jones, 1993). θ is calculated from the day number (the number of days since the start of the calendar year) and is defined by

$$\theta = (\text{day no.} - 0.5) \frac{2\pi}{LENYR} \tag{16.12}$$

where *LENYR* is the number of days in the year (365 or 366), and the 0.5 term adjusts θ to represent the middle of the day.

The dates of POT events are represented on the unit circle by placing weights of unit mass on the circumference, with the angle θ corresponding to the event date. The centroid of these points (Figure 16.12) is used to summarise the seasonal behaviour. The centroid provides information about two things:

i The mean time of year at which flooding occurs: this is summarised by the angle $\bar{\theta}$ between the initial line and the radial line to the centroid.

ii The concentration of the seasonal distribution: this is summarised by $\bar{r}$, the distance from the origin to the centroid. If $\bar{r}$ is close to one, floods usually occur at the same time of year and seasonality is strong. If $\bar{r}$ is small, the timing of floods is more complex and seasonality is rather weak. When $\bar{r}$ is small, the direction $\bar{\theta}$ is less meaningful.

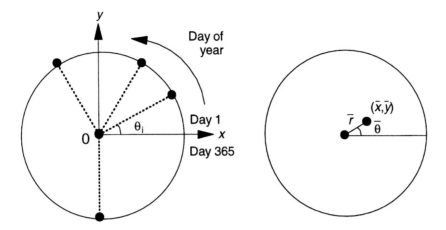

Figure 16.12 *Flood seasonality variables (assuming a non-leap year). The left-hand graph shows how each flood can be represented by a point on the circumference of a unit circle, where the angle represents the time of year. The right-hand graph shows the average time of flooding, found as the centroid of the flood points on the circle. The centroid can be described either in terms of an angle $\bar{\theta}$ and length $\bar{r}$, or by Cartesian coordinates XFLOOD = $\bar{x}$ and YFLOOD = $\bar{y}$.*

The centroid of the POT event dates can be represented either by the polar coordinates $\bar{r}$ and $\bar{\theta}$ (a length and an angle) or, equivalently, by the Cartesian coordinates *XFLOOD* and *YFLOOD* (see equations below). $\bar{r}$ and $\bar{\theta}$ are more readily interpreted but *XFLOOD* and *YFLOOD* are computationally much easier to work with. *XFLOOD* and *YFLOOD* are given by

$$XFLOOD = \bar{x} = \frac{1}{n}\sum_{i=1}^{n}\cos\theta_i \qquad YFLOOD = \bar{y} = \frac{1}{n}\sum_{i=1}^{n}\sin\theta_i \qquad (16.12)$$

The equations relating $\bar{r}$ and $\bar{\theta}$ to *XFLOOD* and *YFLOOD* are

$$\bar{\theta} = \begin{cases} \tan^{-1}\left(\frac{\bar{y}}{\bar{x}}\right) & \bar{x} \geq 0, \bar{y} \geq 0 \\ \tan^{-1}\left(\frac{\bar{y}}{\bar{x}}\right) + \pi & \bar{x} < 0 \\ \tan^{-1}\left(\frac{\bar{y}}{\bar{x}}\right) + 2\pi & \bar{x} \geq 0, \bar{y} < 0 \end{cases} \qquad (16.13)$$

$$\bar{r} = \sqrt{\bar{x}^2 + \bar{y}^2} \qquad (16.14)$$

Variable describing flood irregularity (*CVRI*)

The third seasonality variable provides a measure of the irregularity of event occurrence. The coefficient of variation of recurrence intervals (*CVRI*) is defined as the standard deviation of time intervals between floods divided by the mean time interval (Bayliss and Jones, 1994). Here, the *CVRI* is calculated using a POT3 series, i.e. a POT series containing an average of three events per year (§11.2). A low *CVRI* value means that POT events occur fairly regularly, whereas a high *CVRI* indicates highly irregular flooding behaviour: for instance long event-free periods followed by a succession of events.

The inclusion of *CVRI* is motivated by the striking differences between very irregular flood behaviour in eastern areas such as East Anglia (where large soil moisture deficits are common in summer) and flood behaviour in wetter western areas (where flooding tends to be much more regular; Figure 16.13). Note that *CVRI* provides a representation of variability in flood occurrences that is an alternative to the dispersion measure used in Chapter 12. The two variables show a correlation of about 0.6.

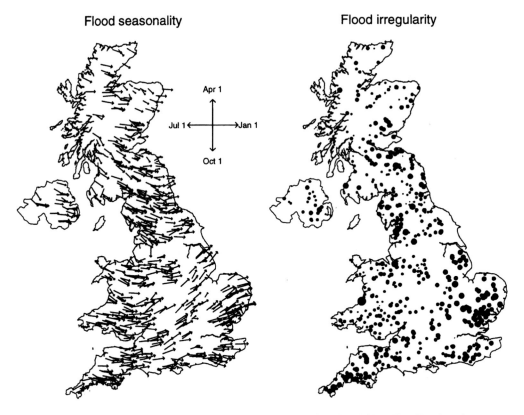

Figure 16.13 Maps of UK flood seasonality and flood irregularity (CVRI) variables. The direction of arrows on the left-hand graph shows the average timing of floods (see Figure 16.12). The right hand graph shows the CVRI values.

Chapter 17 Deriving the pooled growth curve (B)

17.1 Introduction

17.1.1 Pooled growth curve

The *pooled growth curve* is a growth curve obtained using information pooled from sites in the pooling-group (Chapter 16). It can be thought of as an average of the single-site growth curves in the pooling-group (see Chapter 11 for an introduction to growth curves). It is used because it enables flood frequency estimation at longer return periods.

The pooled growth curve x_T^P can be used to obtain the site flood frequency curve Q_T:

$$Q_T = x_T^P \; QMED \qquad\qquad (17.1)$$

where *QMED* is an estimate of the median annual maximum flood at the subject site and T denotes the return period.

As with single-site growth curves, the pooled growth curve x_T^P is fitted using L-moment ratios and takes a value of 1 for a return period of two years. The pooled growth curve results presented in this chapter are only suitable for use with the index *QMED*. In the FEH, the site and pooled growth curves are fitted using the L-moment ratios of the annual maximum data.

17.1.2 Overview of pooled growth curve derivation

The pooling-group must be found before the growth curve is derived. In the FEH, a pooling-group consists of hydrologically similar sites, with similarity being assessed using *AREA*, *SAAR* and *BFIHOST* (Chapter 16).

The pooled growth curve is a growth curve that is calculated using the sites in the pooling-group. It enables estimation of long return-period floods for catchments that do not have long flood data series.

The pooled growth curve is obtained by calculating the pooled L-moment ratios, and using these to estimate the growth curve parameters. The Generalised Logistic distribution is the recommended distribution for the pooled growth curve. There are three main steps to deriving a growth curve, once the pooling-group is known:

- Calculate the pooled L-moment ratios;
- Select a suitable form of distribution;
- Estimate the pooled growth curve parameters and then calculate x_T^P.

Section 17.2 details how the pooled L-moment ratios are calculated from the site L-moment ratios in the pooling-group. Section 17.3 considers various distributions for the growth curve and concludes by recommending that the Generalised Logistic distribution be the default choice for UK flood peak data. Section 17.4 summarises how the growth curve parameters are derived from the pooled L-moment ratios.

17.2 Calculating pooled L-moment ratios

17.2.1 Method

Pooled L-moment ratios are calculated by taking a weighted average of the site L-moment ratios for the sites in the pooling-group. If there are M sites in the pooling-group then the pooled L-CV, t_2^P, is calculated as

$$t_2^P = \text{pooled L-CV} = \frac{\sum_{i=1}^{M} w_i\, t_2^{(i)}}{\sum_{i=1}^{M} w_i} \tag{17.2}$$

The pooled L-moment ratios are weighted averages of the L-moment ratios of sites in the pooling-group. The weight can be thought of as an effective record length. It allows for length of record and similarity to the subject site.

where $t_2^{(i)}$ is the L-CV for the ith most similar site, and w_i is a weighting term. Pooled L-skewness, t_3^P, and pooled L-kurtosis, t_4^P, are obtained in the same way as the pooled L-CV, using the same weights.

A standard choice for w_i is to weight by record length, $w_i = n_i$ (Hosking and Wallis, 1997). This approach gives more emphasis to the longest records and is well suited to obtaining pooled L-moments for fixed pooling-groups. In the FEH, a weighting scheme tailored to catchment similarity is preferred.

The recommended weighting scheme allows for both record length and site similarity. Allowing for similarity means that more weight can be assigned to sites that are most similar to the subject site. A similarity ranking factor S_i is used to characterise similarity. For this, the sites in the pooling-group are ordered from most similar to least similar, as judged by the similarity distance measure (§16.2.4), based on AREA, SAAR and BFIHOST. If the subject-site is included in the pooling-group (see §6.6 and §8.1) then it is classed as the most-similar site. S_i assigns a weight of 1 to the most-similar site and decreasing weights to subsequent sites. S_i equals 1 minus the proportion of station-years that have already been assigned to the pooling-group:

$$S_i = \text{similarity ranking factor}$$
$$= 1 - \frac{1}{n_{total}} \sum_{j=1}^{i-1} n_j$$
$$= S_{i-1} - \frac{n_{i-1}}{n_{total}} \tag{17.3}$$

where n_i is the record length of the ith most-similar site and n_{total} is the total number of station-years in the pooling-group.

The similarity ranking factor depends only on the order in which the sites in the pooling-group are placed (usually in similarity order) and the lengths of the site records. This means that it is relatively straightforward to adjust the emphasis attached to certain sites. For example, if a local site is to be given higher prominence, it can be moved higher up the list of sites in the pooling-group and will then be weighted more heavily.

Record length and site-similarity are multiplied to give the *effective record length*, $e_i = n_i S_i$. This is then used as the weighting term in Equation 17.2. Thus

$$w_i = e_i = \text{effective record length} = n_i S_i \tag{17.4}$$

For the most-similar site, the effective record length equals the actual record length; the effective record length declines for less-similar sites. Thus, a site with a 20-year record whose similarity ranking is high could end up with an effective record length of 17 years, whereas a site with 20-year record that is not so similar might have an effective record length of only five years. Example 17.1 shows a calculation of the effective record lengths and the pooled L-moment ratios.

Example 17.1
For the Tamar at Gunnislake (47001), calculate pooled L-CV and pooled L-skewness for a 50-year return period.

For estimating the 50-year return period, the selected pooling-group comprises nine stations, providing 267 station-years of record. The site is included in its own pooling-group (see §8.1).

Calculating effective record lengths
The effective record length calculation is illustrated using the fourth most-similar station (84018). This site has a record length of 13 years. The number of station-years already in the pooling-group when 84018 is included is $38 + 36 + 38 = 112$. Using Equations 17.4 and 17.3,

$$
\begin{aligned}
\text{effective record length} &= \text{record length} \times \text{similarity ranking factor} \\
&= 13 \times (1 - 112/267) \\
&= 13 \times (1 - 0.419) \\
&= 7.5
\end{aligned}
$$

Calculating pooled L-CV and L-skewness
The site L-CV and L-skewness values are shown below. Effective record lengths e_i were found for each site as shown above.

	Site	L-CV	L-skewness	n_i	S_i	e_i	Dist
1	47001	0.188	0.236	38	1	38.0	0
2	50001	0.208	0.305	36	0.86	30.9	0.16
3	84004	0.172	0.236	38	0.72	27.4	0.19
4	84018	0.159	0.268	13	0.58	7.5	0.20
5	12003	0.182	0.138	19	0.53	10.1	0.22
6	8005	0.238	0.285	44	0.46	20.3	0.22
7	203093	0.104	0.200	10	0.30	3.0	0.25
8	84003	0.153	0.236	39	0.26	10.1	0.26
9	76005	0.109	0.110	30	0.11	3.4	0.27

The pooled L-CV and L-skewness are calculated as weighted averages of the L-CV and L-skewness for sites in the pooling-group, using Equation 17.2, and noting $w_i = e_i$:

Pooled L-CV   = 0.188
Pooled L-skewness = 0.248

Because the Tamar at Gunnislake is gauged, the pooled L-moment ratios can be compared with the site L-moment ratios. These are

Site L-CV   = 0.188
Site L-skewness = 0.236

17.2.2 Pooled L-moment ratios for UK flood data

Pooled L-moment values have been calculated for 698 rural catchments. The distributions of the pooled L-CV and pooled L-skewness for 50 and 100-year return periods are shown in Figure 17.1 and maps are shown in Figure 17.2. Where permeable catchments are included in a pooling-group, adjusted site L-moment ratios are used (see Chapter 19).

As might be expected, the pooled L-moments show considerably less scatter than the site L-moments. Pooled L-skewness tends to be low in East Anglia and the Midlands whilst L-CV is higher than average in this area. Pooled L-skewness values are rarely negative (less than 2% of cases for the 50-year return-period; only three sites for a 100-year return period). If the pooled L-skewness is non-negative, the fitted Generalised Logistic distribution is *unbounded above*: i.e. it does not imply a maximum value (§15.3).

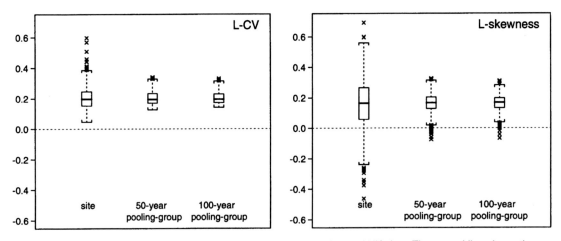

Figure 17.1 *Distributions of site and pooled L-CV and L-skewness for rural UK sites. The central line shows the mean; the box shows the interquartile range of the data. Outlying points are marked with an x.*

17.3 Selecting the pooled growth curve distribution

The recommended distribution for fitting pooled growth curves to UK flood data is the Generalised Logistic distribution.

This section describes how the Generalised Logistic distribution was selected. It introduces the goodness-of-fit measure, which can be used to compare the fit of different distributions. It presents an analysis of the fit of four distributions to the UK data, based on use of the L-moment ratio diagram and the goodness-of-fit measure. From this, the GL distribution is seen to give the best overall fit.

Note that the flood frequency curve is a scaled version of the growth curve and will therefore belong to the same distribution family as the growth curve.

17.3.1 Goodness-of-fit measure

The goodness-of-fit measure is used in two ways:
- To test whether a selected distribution is acceptable;
- To find the best-fitting distribution.

For some sites, many distributions are acceptable. For others, even the best-fitting distribution may not be considered acceptable.

The goodness-of-fit measure is used to identify the best-fitting distribution and to test for acceptability.

Figure 17.2 *Maps of site and pooled L-CV and L-skewness for rural UK sites (positive values in grey, negative in black: N.B. L-CV values are always positive). Site and pooled L-moment ratios are shown to the same scale.*

The goodness-of-fit measure was developed by Hosking and Wallis (1997) and is appropriate for evaluating and comparing 3-parameter distributions. Recall from Chapter 15, that the growth curve parameters are obtained using L-CV and L-skewness (Section 15.2.2). This leaves the L-kurtosis available as a check on how well the distribution fits. The goodness-of-fit test examines the difference between the pooled L-kurtosis, t_4^P, of the observed data and the theoretical L-kurtosis, t_4, of the growth curve distribution fitted to the pooled L-CV and L-skewness.

Let Z^{DIST} be the goodness-of-fit statistic for a specific distribution, defined by

$$Z^{DIST} = (\tau_4^{DIST} - t_4^P + B_4)/\sigma_4 \tag{17.5}$$

where t_4^P is the pooled L-kurtosis, τ_4^{DIST} is the L-kurtosis for the fitted distribution, B_4 is a bias correction term and σ_4 is an estimate of the sample variability of t_4^P.

B_4 and σ_4 are estimated using a simulation procedure. For this, random samples are drawn from a Kappa distribution, which is fitted to have L-moment ratios t_2^P, t_3^P, t_4^P (§15.5.7). In each simulation, the random samples provide new data for each site, and new pooled L-moment ratios are calculated. The process is repeated many times to create an artificial set of pooled L-moment ratios. From these, the bias and the sample variability are estimated:

$$B_4 = \frac{1}{N_s} \sum_{m=1}^{N_s} (t_4^{[m]} - t_4^P) \tag{17.6}$$

$$\sigma_4 = \sqrt{\frac{1}{N_s - 1} \sum_{m=1}^{N_s} (t_4^{[m]} - t_4^R - B_4)^2} \tag{17.7}$$

Here N_s is a large number of simulations (500 have been used here) and $t_4^{(m)}$ is the pooled L-kurtosis for the mth simulation.

Note that the bias term is important when the constituent record lengths are short (e.g. several $n_i \leq 20$ years), or the L-kurtosis is large ($t_4 \geq 0.4$).

The goodness-of-fit measure can be used to assess the suitability of different distributions. Values of Z^{DIST} that are near to zero indicate a good fit. A distribution is considered to give an acceptable fit if

A distribution fits the data well if the goodness-of-fit measure Z^{DIST} is close to zero.

$$-1.64 \leq Z^{DIST} \leq 1.64 \tag{17.8}$$

This gives significance levels of approximately 10%, except for the Generalised Logistic (see Table 5.2 and Section 5.2.4 in Hosking and Wallis, 1997). Trials indicate that the test is relatively harsh on the GL, i.e. more likely to reject even when it is the correct distribution (Hosking and Wallis, 1997). For small L-skewness values, the test is not very good at distinguishing between Generalised Extreme Value (GEV), Log Normal (LN3) and Pearson Type III (PE3). This is because their L-kurtosis values are all very similar in this range (see Figure 17.3).

17.3.2 Selecting a default distribution for UK flood data

This section summarises the results of analyses to select a suitable form of distribution to describe UK annual maximum floods. The conclusion is that the

Generalised Logistic (GL) distribution provides the best fit, with the Generalised Extreme Value (GEV) distribution as the second-best choice.

The first stage is to examine the pooled L-moment ratios and to use these to help identify a suitable frequency distribution. For this, sample and theoretical L-moment ratio values are plotted onto an L-skewness: L-kurtosis L-moment ratio diagram (Figure 17.3); Chapter 14 gives further details of L-moment ratio diagrams. For each catchment, the nearest line or point corresponding to a theoretical distribution provides a good indication of a likely choice of distribution. Since the pooled L-moment ratios are sample estimates of the true L-moments, some scatter about the theoretical line (or point) is to be expected. For the 698 UK sites, the points are scattered about the line corresponding to the GL. Some points fall close to the GEV distribution, but the majority are above the GEV line. Other standard 3-parameter distributions, such as the LN3, lie beneath the GEV curve and plot below the data (Figure 17.3). None of the 2-parameter distributions appears feasible. This initial analysis strongly suggests use of a Generalised Logistic distribution.

The second stage of the analysis was to use the goodness-of-fit measure (§17.3.1) to formally compare distributions. The goodness-of-fit measure was calculated for 698 rural sites and four 3-parameter distributions were considered:

- Generalised Logistic (GL);
- Generalised Extreme Value (GEV);
- Log-Normal (LN3);
- Pearson Type III (PE3).

> The Generalised Logistic distribution is found to give the best fit to UK flood data.

Chapter 15 gives further details of these distributions, and Example 17.2 shows how the goodness-of-fit measure is used.

The Generalised Logistic distribution gives the best overall fit to the UK data (Table 17.2). For 50-year return-period pooling-groups, it was the best distribution for 63% of cases, and was acceptable in 74% of cases. At least one acceptable distribution was found for 88% of sites and in 84% of these cases the Generalised Logistic was accepted. Of the 26% of sites for which the GL was not acceptable, only 55% had another alternative acceptable distribution available. Overall, the Generalised Logistic is either acceptable or the best (unacceptable) distribution in 86% of cases. The next most useful distribution is the GEV. This

---

Example 17.2
Select the best pooled growth distribution for the Coquet at Morwick (22001).

For the 50-year return-period pooling-group there are 12 sites, centred on station 22001, and the pooled L-moment ratios are 0.204 and 0.157. The goodness-of-fit measure is used to compare four 3-parameter distributions. The calculated values of Z^{DIST} are as follows

Distribution:	GL	GEV	LN3	PE3
Z^{DIST}:	0.35	−1.25	−1.26	−1.58

All four distributions have Z values less than 1.64 (in absolute value) and are therefore acceptable distributions to use. The best-fitting distribution is the GL (Z takes its smallest absolute value). The Generalised Logistic is an acceptable distribution and gives the best fit.

Statistical procedures for flood frequency estimation

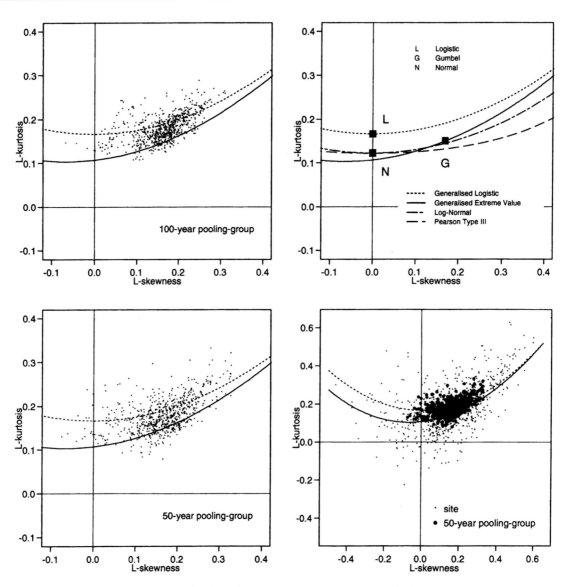

Figure 17.3 *L-moment ratio diagrams for site and pooled L-moments. The upper right-hand graph shows theoretical L-moment ratios for a selection of distributions. The curves corresponding to the GL (dotted) and GEV (solid) are shown on all graphs. The left-hand graphs show L-moment ratios for 50 and 100-year pooling-group sizes. The lower right-hand graph shows 50-year pooling-group L-moment ratios (large dots) on a backdrop of site L-moment ratios (small dots).*

Table 17.2 *Results of the goodness-of-fit measure applied to UK pooling-groups*

Pooling-group size	Criterion	Distribution			
		GL	GEV	LN3	PE3
50-year	acceptable	74%	66%	62%	46%
	best	63%	19%	12%	6%
100-year	acceptable	71%	45%	39%	22%
	best	72%	18%	10%	0%

was acceptable for 66% of sites but was the best distribution in only 19% of cases. For the larger 100-year pooling-group size, the performance of the GL distribution remains approximately constant but the performance of the other distributions weakens (Table 17.2). On the basis of this analysis, the Generalised Logistic distribution is recommended as the default distribution for flood frequency and growth curves for UK catchments.

17.4 Estimating pooled growth curve parameters

Once the form of the flood growth curve has been identified, the remaining step is to estimate the parameters of the growth curve from the pooled L-moments. Equations for obtaining growth curve parameters from L-moments are described for a selection of distributions in Chapter 15. The equations for the GL are restated for completeness.

The GL growth curve is defined by two parameters k and β :

$$x(F) = 1 + \frac{\beta}{k}\left\{1 - \left(\frac{1-F}{F}\right)^{k}\right\} \qquad (k \neq 0) \tag{17.9}$$

The two parameters may be calculated from the sample L-CV, t_2, and sample L-skewness, t_3, using

$$k = -t_3$$
$$\beta = \frac{t_2 k \sin\pi k}{k\pi(k+t_2) - t_2\sin\pi k} \tag{17.10}$$

It is recommended that the pooled growth curve be compared with the single-site growth curve, and its underlying data (e.g. Examples 17.3 and 17.4).

17.5 Uncertainty in the pooled growth curve

Uncertainty in the pooled growth curve can arise from a range of factors. For example, the final pooled growth curve is dependent on
- The pooling scheme;
- The size of the pooling-group;
- The set of sites available for pooling;
- The periods of record for sites in the pooling-group;
- Measurement error;
- Choice of distribution;
- The fitting method.

Assessing the uncertainty arising from all these aspects is beyond the scope of this handbook. It is hampered by lack of knowledge about the true form of the growth curve. Assessing uncertainty via a simulation approach would also be difficult and would itself require a large number of assumptions.

A general indication of the level of uncertainty associated with the growth curve is given by the pooled uncertainty measure, *PUM* (§16.3.3). For the recommended pooling method, the *PUM* values for the 20-year and 50-year growth factors are 0.14 and 0.21, which equate to factorial standard errors of 1.15 and 1.23 respectively (§12.5). These values will undoubtedly underestimate the true uncertainty in most pooled growth curves.

The pooled L-CV and pooled L-skewness are used to obtain the pooled growth curve parameters.

Example 17.3
Obtain the site and pooled growth curves for the Tamar at Gunnislake (47001) for a 50-year return period.

The site and pooled L-CV and L-skewness values are derived in Example 17.1. These values are used to obtain the growth curve parameters.

Site growth curve:

Site L-CV: $t_2 = 0.188$
Site L-skewness: $t_3 = 0.236$
$k = $ –L-skewness $= -0.236$
$\beta = 0.188\, k\, \sin\pi k\, /$
$\quad (k\pi(k+0.188)-0.188\,\sin\pi k)$
$\quad = 0.184$

Pooled growth curve:

Pooled L-CV: $t_2^{P} = 0.188$
Pooled L-skewness: $t_3^{P} = 0.248$
$k = $ –L-skewness $= -0.248$
$\beta = 0.188 k\, \sin\pi k\, /$
$\quad (k\pi(k+0.188)-0.188\,\sin\pi k)$
$\quad = 0.183$

These give the curves on the right (see also Chapter 15). In this example the single-site and pooled curves are very similar.

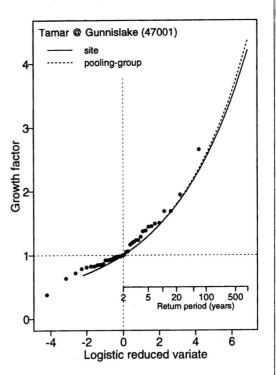

Example 17.4
Obtain the site and pooled growth curves for the Teise at Stone Bridge (40009) for a 100-year return-period pooling-group.

The 100-year pooling-group for the Teise is discussed in §16.6.3. For this station, appraisal of the automatically selected pooling-group led to one site being removed, leaving 22 (including the subject site) in the pooling-group. The L-moment ratios and growth curve parameters are as follows:

Site growth curve:

Site L-CV: $t_2 = 0.173$ Site L-skewness: $t_3 = -0.026$
$k = $ –L-skewness $= 0.026$ $\beta = 0.173 k\, \sin\pi k\, /(k\pi(k+0.173)-0.173\,\sin\pi k)= 0.172$

Pooled growth curve:

Pooled L-CV: $t_2^{P} = 0.223$ Pooled L-skewness: $t_3^{P} = 0.191$
$k = $ -L-skewness $= -0.191$ $\beta = 0.223 k\, \sin\pi k\, /(k\pi(k+0.188)-0.223\,\sin\pi k)= 0.225$

The resulting growth curves are shown in Figure 16.10. In this case the pooled growth curve is much steeper than the site growth curve.

Chapter 18 Adjusting for urbanisation (B)

18.1 Overview

In the FEH, a catchment is defined as urbanised if *URBEXT* is greater than 0.025. *URBEXT* is the proportion of urban land in the catchment as measured by satellite data.

18.1.1 Why an urban adjustment?

Urbanisation has a marked effect on the hydrological regime of a catchment. It tends to accelerate and magnify flood response and to change the seasonality of flooding (§18.2). The urban adjustments described in this chapter enable estimation of flood frequency for urbanised catchments. The term *adjustment* is used because urban development is viewed as causing a modification to the behaviour of the catchment in its rural state. It describes the net effect of urbanisation if a typical degree of flood alleviation has taken place.

> The urban adjustment describes how an urban catchment differs from its rural counterpart. It accounts for the unsuccessfully ameliorated effect of urbanisation, after a typical degree of flood alleviation has been provided.

18.1.2 When is the urban adjustment applied?

The urban adjustment is used to obtain the flood frequency curve for a catchment that is already urbanised. However, the urban adjustment is not appropriate for anticipating changes in the flood regime due to planned urbanisation. This is because the urban adjustment models the residual urban effect, after typical efforts have been made to control flooding. Section 18.5 discusses possible approaches to predicting the effects of increased urbanisation.

Urban adjustments are needed whenever a pooled estimation approach is used on an urbanised catchment; this will apply in almost all cases. The exception is for the unlikely case of an urban site with a very long flood record that covers a period when there has been little change in the degree of urbanisation. In such cases, a single-site analysis would be used (for which no urban adjustment is needed).

18.1.3 Overview of the urban adjustment procedure

The urban adjustment procedure uses the *urban adjustment factor UAF* to obtain the urban flood frequency curve. The urban adjustment factor is estimated by

$$UAF = (1 + URBEXT)^{0.83} \, PRUAF \qquad (18.1)$$

where

$$PRUAF = 1 + 0.615 \, URBEXT\left(\frac{70}{SPRHOST} - 1\right) \qquad (18.2)$$

Here *URBEXT* is the urban extent adjusted to the current-day level of urbanisation. Methods for adjusting *URBEXT* values are described in **1** 8.2 and **5** 6.5.8. *PRUAF* is a term describing the effect of urbanisation on percentage runoff (§18.3.2). The *UAF* and its derivation are further discussed in §18.3.

Two stages are used in estimation of the flood frequency curve, which is obtained as the product of *QMED* and the flood growth curve.

Stage 1: Obtaining *QMED*

If no flood peak data are available, *QMED* is estimated as

$$QMED = UAF \, QMED_{rural} \tag{18.3}$$

where $QMED_{rural}$ is the as-rural estimate of *QMED*, obtained by applying the *QMED* catchment-descriptor equation of Chapter 13. $QMED_{rural}$ can be thought of as the expected *QMED* for an otherwise identical but entirely rural catchment.

> The urban adjustment factor *UAF* can be used to estimate *QMED* for urban catchments and to obtain the urban growth curve.

If flood peak data are available at the subject site then *QMED* is estimated directly from the flood data using the methods of Chapter 12. For this case, the *QMED* estimation method is the same as for a rural catchment.

Stage 2: Obtaining the growth curve

The pooled growth curve for an urbanised catchment is obtained by applying an adjustment to the rural pooled growth curve. This adjustment takes the form

$$x_T = UAF^{-\left(\frac{\ln T - \ln 2}{\ln 1000 - \ln 2}\right)} xrural_T \qquad 2 \leq T \leq 1000 \tag{18.4}$$

where $xrural_T$ is the as-rural pooled growth curve, formed by treating the urban catchment as if it were rural, and *T* is the return period in years. The growth curve adjustment is further discussed in §18.4. The Volume 3 procedures should not be applied to return periods longer than 1000 years, irrespective of whether the catchment is rural or urbanised.

In the unlikely case where single-site analysis is appropriate (§18.1.2), no adjustments for urbanisation are required. The site growth curve is obtained from the site L-moments as described in Chapter 15.

18.2 The effects of urbanisation

18.2.1 Summary of direct effects of urbanisation

Urbanisation affects flooding in a variety of ways. It tends to cause

- Faster runoff because of improved drainage;
- Increased runoff because surfaces are less permeable;
- Reduced sensitivity to antecedent catchment wetness, because urban surfaces wet-up quickly.

These factors mean that urbanised catchments generally show increased flooding for most rainfall events relative to their rural counterparts. Urban effects tend to be particularly pronounced in response to short-duration rainfall events such as are typical of convective storms. Since such storms are relatively commonplace, particularly in the summer, this has the following implications:

- Urban catchments show an altered flood regime, with a greater tendency for all-year or summer flooding (rather than the winter flooding typical of rural catchments);
- The most noticeable effect of urbanisation is the increased frequency of floods.

For the most extreme (long return-period) rainfall events, the impact of urbanisation on flood response is likely to be small. Under such conditions, a catchment becomes fully saturated, with almost all water moving rapidly to the river by surface and near-surface routes. At such times, the catchment can be expected to behave much as it would in its original rural state.

Note also that highly permeable catchments tend to be the most affected by urbanisation. This is because of the more drastic alteration of the effective soil properties, i.e. from permeable soils to impermeable urban surfaces.

Further details on the effects of urbanisation are given in **1** 8.3 and **4** 9.3.2.

18.2.2 Summary of factors offsetting urbanisation effects

It is widely accepted that the direct effect of urbanisation is to cause faster and increased runoff. A consequence of this knowledge is that urban development often includes some form of flood mitigation works, designed to offset the effects of urbanisation. This is particularly true of modern developments: older ones may instead contain flood alleviation or flood defence structures that have been added at a later date.

Approaches to flood mitigation in urban areas include:

- Small-scale mitigation works that are an integral part of urbanisation: e.g. soakaways, combined sewers, tanks in storm-water sewers;
- Medium-scale storage-based mitigation works designed to reduce flood flows: e.g. balancing ponds;
- Flood defence works that are non-storage based (e.g. culverting, embankments, diversions): these alleviate the flood impact rather than the flood peaks;
- Strategic flood alleviation works that are storage-based: e.g. major flood storage areas.

The scale of flood mitigation works within a catchment can be difficult to assess because digital data are not widely available at a sufficient resolution. For example, small- and medium-scale works do not feature at the 1:50000 map scale. The most relevant digital information currently available is the index of flood attenuation due to reservoirs and lakes (*FARL*), which provides a general measure of open-water storage within the catchment (**5** 4.3). A comparison of the 60 most urbanised catchments with 60 rural catchments (selected to have similar size, wetness and soils) indicates that urban catchments typically contain significantly more water

> Urbanisation tends to cause increased flooding, but this is often partially offset by flood mitigation works.

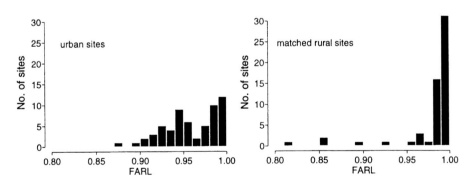

Figure 18.1 *A comparison of the flood attenuation by reservoirs and lakes (FARL) index for 60 urban and 60 rural catchments. Rural and urban catchments were selected to have similar size, wetness and soils. The urban catchments have much lower FARL values, showing greater water storage. A value of FARL between 1 and 0.98 shows a trivial storage effect; a value of less than 0.90 shows a marked storage effect.*

storage (Figure 18.1). Whilst some of this increased storage is due to reservoirs for urban water supply, it is likely that a proportion is linked to flood control and mitigation.

Note that, in the urban adjustment methods, the urban catchment is considered in relation to its rural counterpart. The latter should be viewed as containing the same surface lakes and reservoirs as are in the urban catchment. However, it does not incorporate water storage and drainage systems that are part of the urban infrastructure and that are not featured on a 1:50 000-scale map (i.e. water storage that is excluded from *FARL*: **5** 4).

18.2.3 Effects of urbanisation in FEH flood peak data

Direct analysis of how urbanisation has affected flood frequency is complex. However, a measure of the effect of urbanisation can be inferred by examining flood seasonality from the peaks-over-threshold (POT) flood series. As will be shown below, the POT data confirm that urbanisation strongly affects the flood regime. The data are consistent with the hypothesised effects of urbanisation described in §18.2.1.

The seasonality information is extracted from the POT flood dates and is represented using a flood seasonality plot (Figure 18.2; Additional Note 16.1 contains details of seasonality plots). It shows that urban catchments tend to produce all-year or summer flooding, whereas rural catchments mainly give winter flooding. Urban catchments also show wider flood seasonality than most rural catchments (Figure 18.2). A similar conclusion can be drawn from Figure 18.3 in which the 60 most urbanised catchments have been matched to 60 similar rural catchments. Again, urbanisation is seen to have a pronounced effect on flood seasonality.

> Urban catchments in the FEH datasets tend to show all-year or summer flooding, instead of the winter flooding that is characteristic of rural sites.

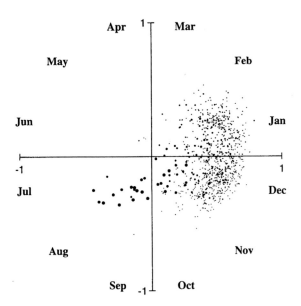

Figure 18.2 *The influence of urbanisation on flood seasonality. Circle size denotes the value of URBEXT (large circles are heavily urbanised; small points are rural). The position (angle) of each point marks the mean day of flooding. Points to the left-hand side of the graph indicate summer flooding; points to the right show winter flooding. Distance from the centre is a measure of the seasonal concentration in flooding: sites towards the edge of the circle show strongest flood seasonality.*

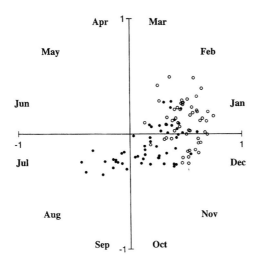

Figure 18.3 *Comparison of flood seasonality for matched urban (•) and rural (o) catchments. The rural catchments were selected to have similar size, wetness and soils to the urban ones.*

18.3 Deriving the urban adjustment factor

18.3.1 Introducing the urban adjustment factor

The *urban adjustment factor* (*UAF*) describes the proportional increase in *QMED* caused by urbanisation. It is a key component of the statistical procedure for flood frequency estimation on urban catchments. Thus, for an ungauged catchment, *QMED* is obtained by using *UAF* to scale up the estimated $QMED_{rural}$ value from the catchment-descriptor equation (Chapter 13). For both gauged and ungauged catchments, *UAF* is used in obtaining the urban growth curve; for this, the rural pooled growth curve is found and then adjusted using *UAF*.

> The urban adjustment factor describes how much *QMED* is proportionally increased by urbanisation, relative to the rural state.

It is recommended that the *UAF* is always estimated using Equation 18.1. The following sections describe the derivation and calibration of this equation.

18.3.2 Rationale for the urban adjustment factor model

In general the *UAF* is unknown, and a model is required so that the *UAF* can be estimated from catchment information.

The form of model used to estimate *UAF* is

$$UAF = (1 + URBEXT)^g \; PRUAF \qquad (18.5)$$

where

$$PRUAF = 1 + 0.615 \; URBEXT\left(\frac{70}{SPRHOST} - 1\right) \qquad (18.6)$$

and *g* is a coefficient to be estimated.

Here *URBEXT* is the proportion of the catchment that is urbanised, as estimated from satellite data (**5** 6.5), and *SPRHOST* is the standard percentage runoff, as estimated from HOST soils data (**5** 5.4).

The rationale for the *UAF* model (Equation 18.5) is as follows. The first term, $(1+URBEXT)^g$, represents the effect of urbanisation on runoff response times and the consequential sensitivity to shorter duration storms: the more urbanised the catchment, the faster the response and the more *QMED* is increased relative to the rural case. The second term is the *percentage runoff urban adjustment factor* (*PRUAF*) for the 2-year flood. It is an approximate estimate of the increase in percentage runoff that occurs due to urbanisation. The percentage runoff increases most when a highly permeable catchment (low *SPRHOST*) is urbanised (§18.2.1). The percentage runoff influences *UAF* because it represents the increase in the volume of water that is likely to reach the river during an event.

> The urban adjustment factor incorporates terms that reflect faster response times and increased percentage runoff.

The expression for calculating *PRUAF* (Equation 18.6) is a simplified form of the percentage runoff model (4 2.3). This model relates the percentage runoff from an urban catchment (*PR*) to the percentage runoff from its rural counterpart (*PR_rural*), and can be written (rearranging Equation 4 2.12) as

$$\frac{PR}{PR_{rural}} = 1 + 0.615 \; URBEXT\left(\frac{70}{PR_{rural}} - 1\right) \tag{18.7}$$

where

$$PR_{rural} = SPR + DPR_{CWI} + DPR_{rain} \tag{18.8}$$

Here, SPR is the standard percentage runoff, and DPR_{rain} and DPR_{CWI} are dynamic terms reflecting the rain depth (mm) and the pre-storm catchment wetness. For the 2-year flood, the dynamic terms in PR_{rural} are neglected and *SPR* is approximated by *SPRHOST*, giving *PRUAF* as

$$PRUAF = \frac{PR}{PR_{rural}} = 1 + 0.615 \; URBEXT\left(\frac{70}{SPRHOST} - 1\right) \tag{18.9}$$

18.3.3 Calibrating the urban adjustment

This section describes the results when the urban adjustment model

$$UAF = (1 + URBEXT)^g \; PRUAF \tag{18.10}$$

is calibrated to the flood data. For comparison, details are given of the fit of the simpler model:

$$UAF = (1 + URBEXT)^g \tag{18.11}$$

Other alternative models were evaluated but were either found to be unsuitable or to offer little improvement at the cost of added complexity.

Data for calibration

The model was fitted using flood data from 115 urban catchments for which *URBEXT* was 0.05 or greater (see **1** 8.2). The *URBEXT* values used in model calibration were adjusted to represent the urbanisation at the midpoint of each flood record. These values were found by backdating the satellite-derived values of *URBEXT*, which nominally correspond to 1990, using the method detailed in **5** 6.5.8.

For each of the 115 catchments, *UAF* was estimated by

$$UAF = \frac{QMED}{QMED_{rural}}$$ (18.12)

For this, the *QMED* value is found from the flood data using the methods of Chapter 12, whilst $QMED_{rural}$ is calculated from the rural catchment-descriptor equation (Chapter 13).

Checks were carried out to test whether the rural catchment-descriptor equation for *QMED* performs well on the type of catchment that is typically urbanised. This was required because the catchment characteristics of an average urban catchment are somewhat different to those of an average rural catchment (urban catchments are often smaller, lower lying and drier). Sixty rural catchments were selected that have similar size, wetness and soils to the 60 most urban catchments. For these rural catchments, $QMED_{rural}$ estimates from the catchment-descriptor model were compared with the *QMED* estimates from the gauged flood data. There appeared to be no bias in the $QMED_{rural}$ values and it was concluded that Equation 13.1 is suitable for estimation on these types of catchment.

The relationship between the *UAF* and catchment descriptors is explored in Figure 18.4. In general, *UAF* shows considerable scatter and only weak links with most variables.

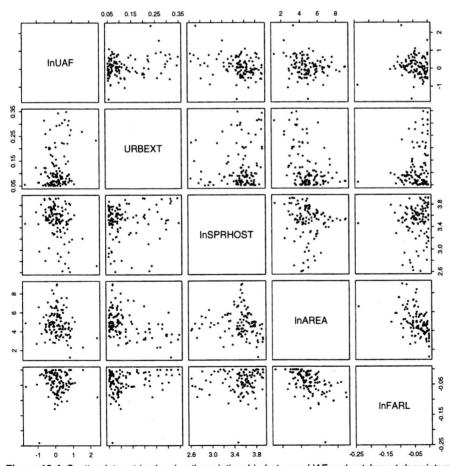

Figure 18.4 *Scatterplot matrix showing the relationship between UAF and catchment descriptors*

Model results

A logarithmic transformation was applied to Equation 18.5 to give the linear model structure:

$$\ln UAF = g \ln(1 + URBEXT) + PRUAF \qquad (18.13)$$

The model was fitted using weighted least-squares regression (§13.4.2) with the weights proportional to $URBEXT$, i.e. more weight was given to data from the more urbanised catchments. The resulting calibrated model is:

$$UAF = (1 + URBEXT)^{0.83} PRUAF \qquad (18.14)$$

A summary of the fit of this model, together with a comparison with the simpler model (Equation 18.11), is presented in Table 18.1. Here, r^2 of $\ln QMED$ is the r^2 judged on a log scale and includes the variance explained by the rural component of the model; r^2 of $\ln UAF$ is the r^2 for the fitted model on the weighted log scale. The results demonstrate that use of an urban adjustment factor gives a small but significant improvement in fit over the rural model. Inclusion of $PRUAF$ in the model is also clearly worthwhile (doubling the r^2). Nevertheless, only a moderate portion of the urban variation is explained by the urban model (the r^2 value is 0.19). In the main, this is because errors in the $QMED_{rural}$ model are rather large relative to the urban effect (Figure 18.5). For example, it is expected that urbanisation increases $QMED$, i.e. UAF should be greater than 1 for most urban catchments. In practice, 42% of the 123 urban sites have an 'observed' UAF less than 1. There appears to be considerable uncertainty attached to the derived values of UAF.

Table 18.1 *UAF model calibration results for 115 urbanised catchments, showing (in brackets) standard errors for the coefficients*

Model	fse	r^2 of ln*QMED*	r^2 of ln*UAF*	*g* (s.e.)
Rural model (Equation 13.1)	1.74	0.835		
Simplified urban model (Equation 18.11)	1.70	0.852	0.092	1.49 (0.30)
Urban model (Equation 18.10)	1.66	0.862	0.194	0.83 (0.28)

The fit of the calibrated model is indicated in Figure 18.6, again showing that only a small part of the variation in ln*UAF* is explained. It can be seen that the spread in the model residuals is larger than the spread in the predicted values and the uncertainty attached to the *UAF* model is rather large. However, at least part of this is because of the relatively poor estimates of *UAF* available from Equation 18.12. It is concluded that

- Incorporating an urban adjustment improves on the rural model;
- Allowing for soil permeability via *PRUAF* benefits modelling of urban effects;
- The overall urban effect, as modelled, is small compared to the residual error.

198

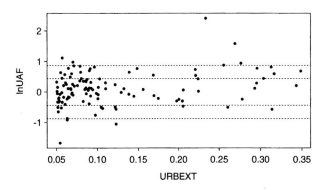

Figure 18.5 *Relationship between lnUAF and URBEXT. The horizontal lines show 1 and 2 standard errors for the catchment-descriptor equation for QMED$_{rural}$, indicating that the uncertainty linked to this model is substantial relative to observed UAF values.*

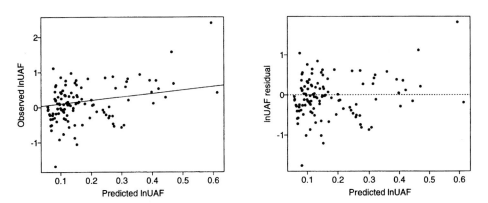

Figure 18.6 Predicted lnUAF values plotted against observed lnUAF and the model residuals.

18.3.4 Model interpretation

Typical effects of urbanisation

The fitted urban adjustment model suggests that urbanisation generally causes a relatively modest change in *QMED*. For example, for a heavily urbanised catchment with *URBEXT* = 0.20 and average soils (*SPRHOST* = 37), the model gives *UAF* = 1.31. Larger effects are predicted for permeable catchments with very small values of *SPRHOST* (Figure 18.7).

FEH data suggest that urbanisation has only a modest effect on *QMED* overall.

Comparison with experimental studies

The urban effect as modelled by the *UAF* is much smaller than that historically found from experimental studies. Such studies (e.g. Hollis, 1975; Walling, 1979) have typically indicated that heavy urbanisation can be expected to lead to a several-fold increase in flood peaks. This compares with the 31% increase for a catchment of typical soil permeability, as indicated by Equation 18.14.

The most likely explanation for the discrepancy is that the *UAF* includes the compensating effects of flood mitigation works, whereas experimental studies measure only the direct effect. Note that it is not possible, here, to develop a model describing the direct (unameliorated) effects of urbanisation; experimental data are currently too scarce for development of a generally applicable model. A

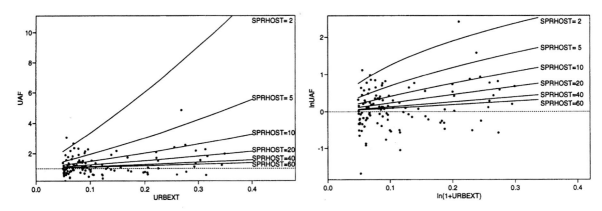

Figure 18.7 *Relationship between UAF and URBEXT for various values of SPRHOST, presented on both linear and log scales. The modelled urban effects are greatly enhanced when the catchment is permeable.*

further contributing factor might be that the urban catchments used here are larger than typical experimental catchments, and that the effects on smaller catchments are more pronounced.

If the compensating effect of flood mitigation is the main reason for the difference, it indicates that flood mitigation causes a marked reduction on short return-period flood peaks. It is therefore likely that local variations in the degree and type of flood amelioration are an important factor in determining the urban response of a catchment. Unfortunately, this type of information is not available for incorporation within an urban adjustment model.

Uncertainty in the UAF model

The fitted *UAF* model gives only a small r^2 value (0.19); the unexplained error is large relative to the fitted values (Figure 18.6). One source of uncertainty arises from the use of the rural *QMED* catchment-descriptor equation; the residual error from this model is comparable to the size of the observed urban effects (Figure 18.5). Further uncertainty arises from local variations in the type, age and nature of the urbanisation and the methods of flood control within a catchment that cannot be generally characterised through available digital information.

The error in the estimated *UAF* values is summarised by the factorial standard error (fse) of 1.64 (see §12.5.1 for further details on fse and confidence intervals).

18.4 The urban growth curve adjustment

The urban pooled growth curve is obtained by applying an adjustment to the rural pooled growth curve. The rural pooled growth curve is the growth curve formed when the urban catchment is treated as if it were rural. For this, rural catchments with similar size, wetness and soils to the urban site are found, and pooled L-moments are calculated. In contrast to rural catchment procedures, an urban catchment should never be included within its own pooling-group.

The urban adjustment that is applied to the rural pooled growth curve takes the form

$$x_T = UAF^{-\left(\frac{\ln T - \ln 2}{\ln 1000 - \ln 2}\right)} xrural_T \qquad 2 \le T \le 1000 \qquad (18.15)$$

where $xrural_T$ is the as-rural pooled growth curve, and T is the return period in years.

The adjustment to the rural pooled growth curve is based on the following perceptions (see §18.2.1):

- Urbanisation magnifies short return-period floods;
- Urbanisation has little impact on very long return-period floods.

The urban adjustment is designed so that (i) x_T takes a value of 1 for the 2-year flood (required for x_T to be a growth curve), and (ii) for long return periods, the flood frequency curve is similar to that for the catchment in its rural state. Observe that for a 1000-year return period, the growth factor is

$$x_{1000} = UAF^{-1} \, xrural_{1000} \qquad (18.16)$$

and the estimated 1000-year flood is therefore

$$
\begin{aligned}
Q_{1000} &= QMED \; x_{1000} \\
&= (UAF \; QMED_{rural}) \times (UAF^{-1} \; xrural_{1000}) \qquad (18.17) \\
&= QMED_{rural} \; xrural_{1000}
\end{aligned}
$$

i.e. the urban 1000-year flood estimate is the same as the anticipated rural 1000-year flood.

Note also that, in consequence of the above, the urban growth curve is always less steep than the rural growth curve (e.g. Examples 18.1, 18.2).

No formal statistical testing of the growth curve adjustment has been carried out. The level of scatter in UAF, combined with limited record lengths for many urban catchments, precluded a formal analysis.

> The modelled urban growth curve is always less steep than the corresponding rural growth curve.

18.5 Estimating the effect of future urban development

18.5.1 Possible approaches

The urban adjustments developed in this chapter are unsuitable for projecting the gross effect of urban development. In particular, the adjustment model must never be used as the sole basis for sizing remediation works for urban development.

In cases where an estimate of the direct effect of planned urbanisation is required, it is recommended that the rainfall-runoff method of flood frequency estimation (Volume 4) should be used. Typically, the rainfall-runoff method will show a stronger effect than use of the urban adjustment described here and will provide a better guide to the true (unameliorated) effect of catchment urbanisation. The rainfall-runoff method provides greater scope for the effect of urbanisation to be represented realistically although it is still not an ideal approach. One difficulty is that the rainfall-runoff method recommends that a different package of 'design inputs' is used when $URBEXT$ exceeds 0.125. This can lead to abrupt changes in flood frequency estimates when this threshold is crossed.

In cases where extensive flood peak data are available, use of hybrid methods may be appropriate. First, the urban flood frequency curve for the current day condition is calculated, as described in this chapter. This estimate is then combined with the flood frequency curve synthesised by the rainfall-runoff method (see 1 5). Finally, the $URBEXT$ value is projected forward, and the rainfall-runoff method rerun. Section 5.7 of Volume 1 provides guidance on transferring estimates from gauged to ungauged sites, when the subject catchment is urbanised.

Example 18.1
Find the flood growth and flood frequency curves for the Darwen at Ewood Bridge (71013).

The Darwen at Ewood Bridge has a 16-year annual maxima record. For this site, $URBEXT = 0.095$ and $SPRHOST = 37$. Using the annual maximum data, $QMED$ is calculated to be $30.6 \text{ m}^3\text{s}^{-1}$.

The urban adjustment factor is

$$UAF = (1 + URBEXT)^{0.83} \, PRUAF$$
$$= (1 + 0.095)^{0.83} \left\{1 + 0.615 \times 0.095 \times (70/37 - 1)\right\} = 1.13$$

The urban growth curve is therefore given by

$$x_T = 1.13^{-(\ln T - \ln 2)/(\ln 1000 - \ln 2)} \, xrural_T$$

To obtain the rural pooled growth curve $xrural_T$ a pooling-group of rural catchments is found. The Darwen has $AREA = 39.19 \text{ km}^2$, $SAAR = 1339$ mm and $BFIHOST = 0.423$; the pooling group for a 50-year target return period contains 14 essentially rural sites. The pooled L-moments for the rural growth curve are found to be L-CV = 0.182 and L-skewness = 0.115. The left-hand plot shows both the rural and urban growth curves. The right-hand one shows the urban flood frequency curve with the observed annual maximum flood data.

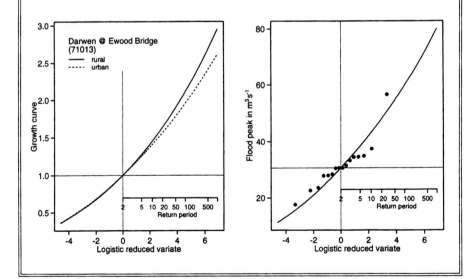

18.5.2 Discussion

The difficulty in providing a suitable method for predicting urban effects reflects a combination of factors. It is likely that models of urbanisation would benefit from further study of long-term paired-catchments in which the catchments differ only in their degree of urbanisation. In addition, more realistic rainfall-runoff

Example 18.2
Find the flood frequency curve for the ungauged catchment on the Pix Brook at Letchworth (GR 521000, 233650).

For the Pix, the following catchment descriptors apply: $AREA$ = 8.46 km^2, $SPRHOST$ = 33.8, $BFIHOST$ = 0.55, $URBEXT$ = 0.240, $FARL$= 1.0, $SAAR$ = 588 mm.

The first stage of the calculation is to estimate $QMED$. For this, Equation 13.1 and the UAF are used, giving $QMED_{rural}$ = 1.053 and UAF = 1.384. Hence,

$$QMED = UAF \times QMED_{rural} = 1.384 \times 1.053 = 1.46$$

N.B. in practice, $QMED$ should be refined using data from a local gauged catchment via a data transfer process (Chapter 4 and **1** Box 5.3).

The second stage is to calculate and then adjust the rural growth curve. The pooling group for a 50-year return period for this site contains 12 essentially rural sites, giving pooled L-CV = 0.319 and pooled L-skewness = 0.158. The rural growth curve is shown below. The urban growth curve is given by

$$x_T = 1.348^{-(\ln T - \ln 2)/(\ln 1000 - \ln 2)} \, xrural_T$$

and is seen to be less steep than the rural growth curve. The flood frequency curve is obtained by multiplying x_T by $QMED$.

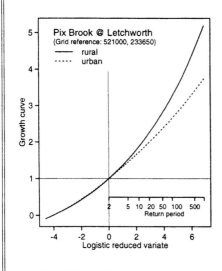
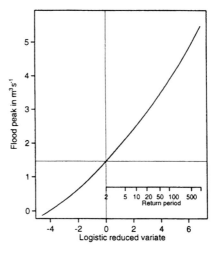

models in combination with a continuous simulation approach may be helpful in the longer term (see **1** 9.6 and **1** 12.6). Nevertheless, it is important to recognise that some factors will remain unquantifiable, and that aspects such as climatic variability (Chapter 20) make it difficult to detect the impact of urbanisation on flood frequency (Chapter 21).

Chapter 19 Adjusting for permeable catchments

19.1 Overview

19.1.1 Flood frequency estimation for permeable catchments

Permeable catchments tend to pose particular problems for flood frequency estimation, because there are some years in which the annual maximum flow is due to baseflow alone. Including non-flood annual maxima in a frequency analysis can result in an unrealistic growth curve.

The permeable adjustment allows for the presence of non-flood data in annual maximum series. It reduces the influence of these points on the L-moments and the growth curve.

This chapter describes a method that is suitable for growth curve estimation for permeable catchments. The method proceeds by applying an adjustment for non-flood data in the annual maximum series. The adjustment is applied to the L-moments (Chapter 14), rather than to the growth curve, to allow permeable catchments to be used in the pooling methods in the same way as any other rural catchment (Chapters 16, 17).

19.1.2 When should the permeable adjustment be used?

The permeable adjustment is recommended for all catchments that are permeable. For this purpose, a catchment is defined as permeable if *SPRHOST*, the standard percentage runoff estimated from HOST soils data, is less than 20%. *SPR* represents the percentage of rainfall that typically causes a short-term increase in flow.

The adjustment is appropriate whenever permeable catchments are included in a pooling-group and whenever single-site analysis is carried out for a permeable catchment.

19.1.3 Outline of the adjustment method

The adjustment allows for there being a proportion of years in which no flood occurs. All annual maxima that are smaller than *QMED*/2 are considered not to be floods, and are referred to as *non-floods*. The years with floods greater than *QMED*/2 are the *flood-years*.

There are three stages to the method:

- Identify the non-floods and estimate the probability of a year containing at least one flood;

- Obtain the *flood-years growth curve*, a hypothetical curve that would apply if all years contained a flood. It can be determined by calculating the L-moments for the annual maximum series corresponding to the flood-years;

- Obtain the *permeable-adjusted growth curve*, i.e. the required growth curve for the catchment, and the corresponding *permeable-adjusted L-moments*.

The permeable-adjusted growth curve is found by scaling the flood-years growth curve to allow for the proportion of years that do not contain a flood. The *permeable-adjusted L-moments* are also referred to simply as the *adjusted L-moments*; they differ from the L-moments of the full data series. Full details of the permeable adjustment are given in §19.3 and Additional Note 19.1.

19.2 Background

19.2.1 How floods occur in permeable catchments

Most of the rain falling on permeable catchments usually soaks rapidly into the ground and does not lead to rapid runoff. Thus, river-flows from such catchments are typically dominated by baseflow. A common mechanism that can lead to flooding on a permeable catchment is where prolonged winter rainfall elevates the groundwater table so that springs start to flow in what are usually dry valleys. As the catchment reaches saturation, any further rainfall leads to rapid runoff. Floods are thus most likely in winter or spring, and may be notable more for their volume and duration than for their peak flow (e.g. the Chichester flood in January 1994; Bradford and Faulkner, 1997). Snowmelt may also be a contributing factor since a frozen permeable catchment can act more like an impermeable catchment. In other cases, floods on permeable catchments may be caused by intense rainfall that exceeds the infiltration capacity of the ground, leading to rapid runoff. This mechanism is particularly likely on steep slopes such as the scarp slopes of the chalk in eastern and southern England. Such floods tend to rise quickly and can be devastating. A classic example was the flood on the Lud at Louth, Lincolnshire, in May 1920 (Robinson, 1995).

19.2.2 Nature of flooding in permeable catchments

There is often a sparsity of substantial floods on permeable catchments and a corresponding shortage of flow data (Bradford and Faulkner, 1997). For many permeable catchments there are some years in which the annual maximum flow is due to baseflow alone and cannot be considered a flood. In some cases, an ephemeral stream may be dry for an entire year, giving an annual maximum flow of zero. Including annual maxima from non-flood years in a frequency analysis can result in an unrealistic fitted growth curve that is bounded above (§15.1.2).

A further problem that sometimes arises with flood data from permeable catchments is the presence of many similar annual maximum floods. This can occur when the aquifer-characteristics of a catchment mean that there is a close relationship between annual maximum flows and groundwater level. As with the presence of small annual maxima, it can result in a growth curve that is bounded above.

Growth curves that are bounded above should be interpreted with caution: there is always the possibility of a much larger flood, e.g. if the groundwater level exceeds a critical elevation, or if there is an intense convective storm (Bradford and Faulkner, 1997). For example, the flood of 29th May 1920 on the Lud at Louth was estimated to be 31 times the median annual flood (NERC, 1975).

19.2.3 Flood frequency estimation methods

Most methods of flood estimation are designed with non-permeable catchments in mind, and may not necessarily be appropriate for permeable catchments, where floods tend to be different in character.

As seen above, use of annual maximum data for flood frequency estimation is not well suited to the estimation of floods on permeable catchments. Analysing 2 or even 5-year maxima would seem more natural, since this removes the influence of long periods of low flows. However, it is only a practical alternative if exceptionally long flood records are available. Another possibility would be to base the analysis on peaks-over-threshold (POT) data. Unfortunately, it is often problematic to derive POT data for baseflow-dominated streams. Independent flood peaks cannot usually be satisfactorily resolved because a threshold may not be exceeded at all one year, but then may be exceeded continuously for a large proportion of the following year.

The method described in this chapter is an adaptation of a conditional probability approach used by Bradford and Faulkner (1997) which was derived from the work of Guttman *et al.* (1993). It aims to reduce the influence of non-flood annual maxima, while making efficient use of the available data. Other techniques that suppress the influence of small annual maximum flows include: censored maximum likelihood methods (Leese, 1973), methods in which parameter estimation is applied to non-censored values with a subsequent conditional probability correction (e.g. US Water Resources Council, 1977, Appendix 5), partial probability-weighted moments (Wang, 1996b), and linear higher-order moments, or LH-moments, (Wang, 1997). Bradford and Faulkner (1997) found the method of partial probability-weighted moments to be unsatisfactory for UK permeable catchments.

19.3 Permeable-adjustment method

The methods described here assume that the flood growth curve follows a Generalised Logistic distribution (Chapter 17). Modifications to the method are required if another distribution is assumed, although similar principles apply.

In the following text ′ indicates that a quantity derives from the flood-years series, and * denotes one that relates to the permeable-adjusted growth curve.

19.3.1 Identifying flood-free years

For the adjustment, any annual maximum smaller than *QMED*/2 is considered not to be a flood. The *QMED*/2 threshold ensures that very small annual maxima are removed, but that the majority of annual maxima, assumed to represent floods, are retained. The threshold is appropriate for gauged permeable catchments in the UK, although not necessarily for more arid parts of the world. This is because the *QMED*/2 threshold will be too low if there are substantial floods in fewer than half of years.

Once the non-flood years have been identified, the probability of a year containing at least one flood, ω, is estimated by a ratio of counts:

$$\omega = \frac{\text{No. of years with floods}}{\text{No. of years of record}} \tag{19.1}$$

Note that if all floods are bigger than *QMED*/2 then ω = 1 and the adjustment process has no effect.

19.3.2 Obtaining the flood-years growth curve

The flood-years growth curve x_T' is obtained by treating the flood-years series (§19.1.3) as if it were the full series and calculating the L-CV, t_2', and the L-skewness, t_3'.

For the recommended Generalised Logistic distribution (§15.3), the growth curve parameters are related to the L-moments by Equations 15.8:

$$k = -t_3 \tag{19.2}$$

$$\beta = \frac{t_2 k \sin \pi k}{k \pi (k + t_2) - t_2 \sin \pi k} \tag{19.3}$$

The flood-years growth curve parameters, k' and β' are found by substituting t_2' and t_3' into these equations.

19.3.3 Obtaining the permeable-adjusted growth curve

The flood-years growth curve does not allow for there being some years in which no floods occur. The permeable-adjusted growth curve can be obtained from the flood-years growth curve by making an allowance for the non-flood years. This is done using ω, the probability of at least one flood occurring in a year (§19.3.1).

For example, suppose that there are 25 years of record at a site and that five of these years do not contain a true flood. For such a series, the probability of a year containing at least one flood is 20/25 = 0.8. Thus, out of every 100 years, typically 80 years will actually contain a flood. In other words, the 80-year flood for the flood-years will be equivalent to the 100-year flood for the full data. This can be thought of as requiring the flood-years growth curve to be stretched along the return period axis. In practice, a slight rescaling of the stretched curve is required to ensure that the resulting curve retains a growth factor of 1 at a return period of two years, to comply with the definition of a growth curve (§11.3.4).

A Generalised Logistic distribution is assumed for the permeable-adjusted growth curve, x_T^*. In general, the stretched and scaled flood-years growth curve does not quite follow a GL distribution, but is very close to being one. A GL curve is therefore fitted to the scaled curve using a numerical process that results in the fitted curve passing through the 2-year, 10-year and 50-year return period floods. This approximation is found to give a good fit, even for return periods much longer than 50 years.

The parameters for the permeable-adjusted growth curve are obtained numerically. Briefly, the shape parameter k^* is found as the solution to

$$\frac{1 - 9^{-k^*}}{1 - 49^{-k^*}} = \frac{1 - \left\{ \frac{10\omega - 1}{2\omega - 1} \right\}^{-k'}}{1 - \left\{ \frac{50\omega - 1}{2\omega - 1} \right\}^{-k'}} \tag{19.4}$$

β^* is then straightforwardly obtained as:

$$\beta^* = \frac{\beta' k^* A}{k' + \beta'(1 - B)} \tag{19.5}$$

where

$$A = \frac{(2\omega - 1)^{-k'} - (10\omega - 1)^{-k'}}{1 - 9^{-k^*}} \tag{19.6}$$

$$B = (2\omega - 1)^{-k'} \tag{19.7}$$

Details of the derivation of these equations are given in Additional Note 19.1.

19.3.4 Calculating the permeable-adjusted L-moments

The permeable-adjusted L-moments (t_2^*, t_3^*) can then be found using the inverted forms of Equations 19.2 and 19.3, i.e.

$$\text{L-skewness} = t_3 = -k \qquad\qquad (19.8)$$

$$\text{L-CV} = t_2 = \frac{\beta k^2 \pi}{(\beta + k)\sin k\pi - \beta k\pi} \qquad\qquad (19.9)$$

and substituting for k^* and β^*. These adjusted L-moments can be used in the same way as standard L-moments to derive a site growth curve or to form a pooled growth curve.

19.4 Application to UK sites

There are 60 catchments with *SPRHOST* less than 20% in the FEH flood peak dataset. The permeable-adjustment method was applied to each of these sites.

The effect of the adjustment on the L-moments is summarised in Figure 19.1. In general, L-CV values are decreased whilst L-skewness values increase. The increased values of L-skewness mean that growth curves are generally slightly steeper and that fewer growth curves are bounded above (§15.1.2). About 25% of the catchments are bounded above before the adjustment is applied. Half of these gain permeable-adjusted growth curves that are unbounded above. The others become less strongly bounded above. The permeable-adjustment method has no effect for around 1 in 10 sites; these are sites where none of the annual maxima is smaller than *QMED*/2.

Figure 19.2 shows some examples of the effect of the adjustment on the growth curve. The *QMED*/2 threshold is marked for reference. In some cases, elimination of a single small annual maximum causes a marked change in the growth curve (e.g. station 39020). In other cases, there is a group of small annual maxima that appear to belong to a different statistical population from the rest of

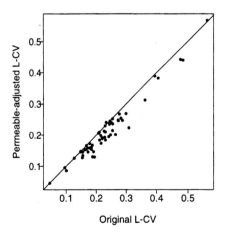
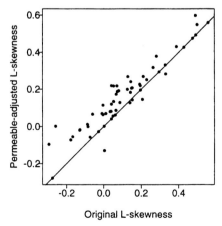

Figure 19.1 *Comparison of original and permeable-adjusted L-moments for 60 UK catchments with SPRHOST less than 20%.*

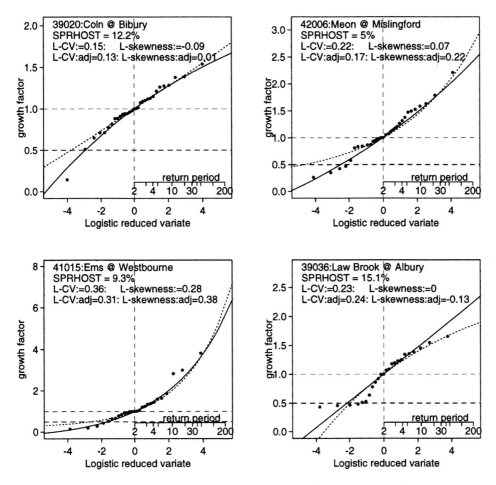

Figure 19.2 *Examples of the effect of the adjustment on flood growth curves for four permeable catchments. The solid lines show the original growth curve and the dotted lines the adjusted growth curve. The original and adjusted L-moment values are also marked. The horizontal dotted lines correspond to QMED and to QMED/2. Annual maxima smaller than QMED/2 are not used in deriving the adjusted L-moments.*

the data, and removing these gives a better fit to the main part of the data (e.g. station 42006). In a number of cases, removal of small annual maxima has a fairly minimal effect (e.g. station 41015).

The aim of the permeable-adjustment method is to reduce the effect of small annual maxima and the chance of an unrealistic growth curve resulting. There are a number of examples where the adjustment alters the growth curve from being bounded above to being unbounded (e.g. station 39020). An exception to this is for the Law Brook at Albury (station 39036). In this case, the adjustment causes the growth curve to change from an unbounded to a bounded distribution. This is an example where there is a more complex distribution of annual maximum floods, which is possibly due to a combination of several flood-generating processes. Neither the original nor the adjusted growth curve fits the data well.

Additional Note 19.1 Details of the permeable-adjustment method

This note describes the derivation of Equations 19.4 and 19.5, the equations that are used to find the permeable-adjusted growth curve parameters, which in turn are required for calculation of the permeable-adjusted L-moments.

As before, ′ is used to refer to the flood-years data and * to the permeable-adjusted growth curve. Thus k' and β' are the GL growth curve parameters derived from the L-moments of the flood-years, while k^*, β^* are the corresponding parameters for the required permeable-adjusted growth curve.

As explained in §19.3.3, the adjusted growth curve is obtained by stretching and scaling the flood-years growth curve by an amount depending on ω, the proportion of years in which a flood occurs (§19.3.1). This means that the permeable-adjusted growth curve at return period T, x_T^*, is proportional to $x_{\omega T}'$, the flood-years growth curve at a return period of ωT. Thus,

$$x_T^* = Cx_{\omega T}' \qquad (19.10)$$

where the constant C can be determined using the fact that x_T^* is a growth curve. An FEH growth curve must take a value of 1 for the 2-year return period (see §11.3.4). C is therefore given by

$$C^{-1} = x_{2\omega}' = 1 + \frac{\beta'}{k'}\{1 - (2\omega - 1)^{-k'}\} \qquad (19.11)$$

The objective is to find parameters β^* and k^* for which the corresponding growth curve x_T^* satisfies 19.10. Recall that the GL growth curve (§15.3.2) is defined by

$$x_T = 1 + \frac{\beta}{k}\{1 - (T - 1)^{-k}\} \qquad (19.12)$$

Substituting for x_T^*, x_T' in Equation 19.10 shows that values of k^* and β^* must be found that satisfy

$$1 + \frac{\beta^*}{k^*}\{1 - (T - 1)^{-k^*}\} = C\left[1 + \frac{\beta'}{k'}\{1 - (\omega T - 1)^{-k'}\}\right] \qquad (19.13)$$

To simplify the algebra, this equation is rewritten in the form

$$(\omega T - 1)^{-k'} = B - A\{1 - (T - 1)^{-k^*}\} \qquad (19.14)$$

where

$$A = C^{-1}\frac{k'\beta^*}{\beta' k^*} \qquad (19.15)$$

and

$$B = (1 - C^{-1})\frac{k'}{\beta'} + 1 \qquad (19.16)$$

In practice, it is not possible to find values of β^* and k^* that satisfy the above equations for all values of T. However, if the equations are fitted to go through the 2-year, 10-year and 50-year values, the resulting curve proves to be a well-behaved approximation, which gives a good fit for return periods much longer than 50 years. For a fit at return periods of 2, 10 and 50 years, Equation 19.14 gives

$$(2\omega - 1)^{-k'} = B$$
$$(10\omega - 1)^{-k'} = B - A(1 - 9^{-k^*})$$
$$(50\omega - 1)^{-k'} = B - A(1 - 49^{-k^*})$$

(19.17)

Eliminating the variables A and B from these simultaneous equations, gives k^* as the solution to

$$\frac{1 - 9^{-k^*}}{1 - 49^{-k^*}} = \frac{1 - \left\{\dfrac{10\omega - 1}{2\omega - 1}\right\}^{-k'}}{1 - \left\{\dfrac{50\omega - 1}{2\omega - 1}\right\}^{-k'}}$$

(19.18)

This can be solved using any standard numerical procedure for finding the root of an equation (e.g. using algorithms such as Bisection or the Newton Raphson method; Press *et al.*, 1992). Some software packages provide such a capability. Note that for small k^* or k' it may be necessary to use the approximation:

$$\frac{1 - a^{-k}}{1 - b^{-k}} \approx \frac{\ln a \left\{1 - \tfrac{1}{2}k \ln a\right\}}{\ln b \left\{1 - \tfrac{1}{2}k \ln b\right\}}$$

(19.19)

Once k^* is known, the solution is simply one of algebraic manipulation. First the constants A and B can be found as:

$$A = \frac{(2\omega - 1)^{-k'} - (10\omega - 1)^{-k'}}{1 - 9^{-k^*}}$$

(19.20)

and

$$B = (2\omega - 1)^{-k'}$$

(19.21)

β^* is then obtained from Equation 19.15 by substituting for C from 19.16 and rearranging. This gives

$$\beta^* = \frac{\beta' k^* A}{k' + \beta'(1 - B)}$$

(19.22)

where A and B are given by Equations 19.20 and 19.21 above.

Chapter 20 Adjusting QMED for climatic variation

20.1 Overview

20.1.1 Why an adjustment for climate is necessary

The UK tends to experience notable variations in climate from year to year. An important aspect of this variability is the tendency for there to be series of flood-rich years interspersed by series of flood-poor years (§20.2). These variations mean that a *QMED* estimate obtained from a short flood record can be unrepresentative of the long term. For example, *QMED* may be overestimated if a record from a flood-rich period is used. The adjustment described in this chapter provides *QMED* estimates that aim to be more representative of the long-term.

20.1.2 When to use the adjustment

An adjustment for the effects of climatic variation is recommended when *QMED* is estimated from short-record sites.

The adjustment is used when *QMED* is estimated from short flood records using either annual maxima or POT data. It does not apply if *QMED* is estimated from catchment descriptors.

It is recommended that the adjustment is used when estimating *QMED* for records with fewer than 14 years of data. It is optional for longer records, and is unlikely to be necessary for records of 30 or more years.

20.1.3 Summary of the adjustment method

The adjustment process enables transfer of information from long-record sites to short-record sites. For this, local sites with long records and similar flood behaviour are found and are used as the basis for a climatic adjustment. The sites from which information is taken are termed *donor* sites. The site at which the adjustment is made is referred to as the *subject* site.

There are three main steps to the method:

- Select one or more donors
- Calculate a *QMED* adjustment for the subject site based on each donor
- Combine the adjusted values

Step 1: Selecting the donor site(s)

The adjustment process uses information from one or more long-record donor sites to improve the estimate of *QMED*.

An ideal donor site should have a long record (30 years or more) that overlaps the subject-site's period of record. It should also be local to the subject-site and have comparable hydrological behaviour. If a good donor site can be found then one donor is usually sufficient. In other cases, two or three donors may be used. More details on selecting suitable donor sites are given in §20.3.1.

Step 2: Calculating the adjustment

The adjustment uses the ratio of *QMED* calculated at the donor site for (i) the full donor period, (ii) the part of the donor record that overlaps the subject site. The ratio of these *QMED* values is used to scale *QMED* at the subject site. The correlation between the donor and subject site is used to moderate the influence of the donor. Further background details are given in §20.3.2.

If the donor record *completely* overlaps the subject-site record then QS_{adj}, the adjusted *QMED*, is given by

$$QS_{adj} = QS \left(\frac{QD}{QD_o} \right)^{M(r)} \qquad (20.1)$$

using the notation in the box below. Here

$$M(r) = \frac{(n_o - 3)r^3}{(n_o - 4)r^2 + 1} \qquad (20.2)$$

where *r* is the Spearman's rank correlation between annual maxima at subject and donor sites, and n_o is the length of overlap between the subject and donor sites.

If the donor record only *partly* overlaps the subject site, then

$$QS_{adj} = \left(\frac{QD}{QD_o} \right)^{M(r) \frac{n_d}{n_t}} QS^{\frac{n_s}{n_t}} \; QS_o^{\frac{n_d - n_o}{n_t}} \qquad (20.3)$$

where the notation is given in the box below and $M(r)$ is given by Equation 20.2.

In each of the above cases, QS, QD, QS_o and QD_o are calculated for the relevant periods using the methods described in Chapter 12. This may mean that QD is estimated using annual maximum data, whilst QS_o and QD_o are found from *POT* data. Note that for very short records (under five years) the correlation is not well defined and it is not generally possible to allow for correlation in the adjustment process. In this case $M(r)$ is set at 1.

Step 3: Taking a weighted average of the adjusted QMED values

If more than one donor site is used, the final adjusted *QMED* is taken as a weighted geometric average of the individually adjusted *QMED* values (details are given in §20.3.3).

Notation used in the QMED adjustment

n_s	=	length of subject site record
n_d	=	length of donor site record
n_o	=	length of overlap period between subject and donor site
n_t	=	$n_s + n_d - n_o$ = total number of years with data for either subject or donor site

QS	=	QMED at the subject site
QS_{adj}	=	Adjusted QMED at the subject site
QS_o	=	QMED at the subject site for the overlap period
QS_d	=	QMED at the subject site for the donor period
QD	=	QMED at the donor site
QD_o	=	QMED at the donor site for the overlap period

r	=	Spearman's rank correlation between annual maxima at subject and donor sites
w	=	weighting measure

20.1.4 Chapter structure

The remainder of this chapter provides further details on the *QMED* adjustment method. Section 20.2 provides background information on the variability of the UK climate and why this affects *QMED* estimation. Further details and background to the adjustment procedure are given in §20.3; an automated approach to *QMED* adjustment is presented in §20.4. The approach is not intended for day-to-day use, but was developed to address the need to adjust *QMED* values consistently for use in deriving the catchment descriptor equation of Chapter 13. Manual selection of donors on this scale was not feasible. Section 20.4 summarises the results of the automated adjustment for rural UK sites.

20.2 Climatic variability in the UK

Climatic variability can be thought of as the year-to-year variation in the mix of weather systems that the UK experiences. The variability occurs over many time-scales, and in particular can give rise to groups of flood-rich years and groups of flood-poor years. This *grouping* means that a short record might only include flood-rich years and as a result is likely to overestimate *QMED*.

The variations in the number of floods and the average size of floods are summarised in Figure 20.1. This shows, for example, that floods tended to be larger and more frequent for 1965-1968 and 1978-1982, and smaller and less frequent between 1969 and 1973. Over a long enough period, variations in climate

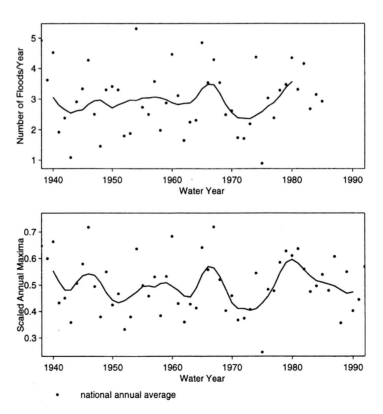

Figure 20.1 *Long-term fluctuations in the number of floods/year and in annual maxima. Points show national averages and a smoothed curve is fitted.*

even out (assuming no climate change) and do not affect *QMED*, but over short periods these climatic fluctuations may have a notable impact. A record needs to be considerably longer than 10 years for the effects of climatic variability to be safely neglected. The shorter the record, the more likely it is that the *QMED* estimate may differ significantly from the true (long-term) median.

Examination of UK records shows that there is a tendency for sites in close proximity to experience similar variations in flood frequency and flood magnitude (see §21.4.2 and Figure 21.2). Information from longer flood records at nearby sites can thus be used to improve a *QMED* estimate at a short-record site. The longer records *augment* the shorter records giving better estimates of *QMED*.

> Sites that are close to one another tend to experience similar variations in flood frequency and magnitude.

Example 20.1
Example of how QMED varies depending on the available period of record

The graph shows the annual maximum data for the Irk at Scotland Weir (69003).

The dotted line shows the *QMED* value for the full period (*QMED* = 39.6). Solid lines show four examples of *QMED* values calculated for seven-year sub-periods of the data. Some of the seven-year *QMED* values differ from the long-term median by more than 20%.

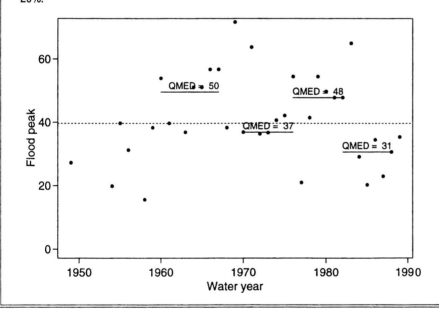

20.3 Details of the QMED adjustment

20.3.1 Selecting a donor site

Ideally, a donor site is chosen in the light of local knowledge and examination of data. The approach is similar to that used when *QMED* is transferred from a gauged to an ungauged catchment (Chapter 4). The following criteria need to be considered when selecting the donor site.

Period of record

For a donor site to be useful, the record at the donor site must be appreciably longer than that of the subject site, and should preferably be at least 30 years long. It must have a good overlap with the subject-site record.

Location

The donor site should be close enough so as to have experienced the same general climatic conditions as the subject site. An upstream or a downstream site, or an adjacent catchment, is a likely candidate.

Similar hydrological response

The donor site must be close by, have a long overlapping record and show comparable behaviour to the subject site.

The donor site should show similar hydrological response to the subject site. It should normally have a similar degree of urbanisation and comparable catchment characteristics. It is important to examine the correlation between the annual maxima of subject and donor sites. Ideally a donor site should show strong correlation; a donor site should not be used if negative correlation occurs. For very short records (under five years), examining the correlation is of little value unless monthly or other more frequent data can be obtained. In this case, correlation cannot be accounted for in the transfer process and extra care is required to ensure that the donor catchment is as similar as possible to the subject site.

Multiple donor sites are used if either no ideal donor site exists, or if two or more equally valuable donor sites are identified. If no suitable donor can be found then no adjustment is made to *QMED*.

20.3.2 Adjusting QMED by transfer of information from a donor

For each selected donor site, information must be transferred from the donor site to the subject site. For this, *QMED* is estimated at the donor site using all the donor's data, and is then re-estimated using only the data from the period overlapping with the subject site. The ratio of these two estimates provides a measure of how the subject site estimate of *QMED* is likely to differ from the long-term value.

The transfer process allows for the level of correlation between subject and donor sites. Full use of the donor site is only made if there is a very strong correlation between donor and subject sites. If the correlation is very poor then virtually no adjustment to the original *QMED* value will be made.

The transfer process proceeds in two stages, the second of these stages only being required if the donor site does not completely overlap the subject site. In the following text, the *donor period* refers to the period of record for the donor site, and the *total period* to the period with either donor or subject site data. The first stage adjusts the subject site *QMED* to the donor period, the second stage adjusts *QMED* to the total period. Without the second stage, no use would be made of data from the subject site that fell outside the donor period.

Stage 1: Adjusting QMED to the donor period

The stage 1 transfer equations use the ratio of (i) the donor *QMED* for the full donor period, and (ii) the donor *QMED* value for the period that overlaps the subject site, to scale QS_o (Example 20.2).

Example 20.2

Suppose we have the following periods of record:

```
          75    80    85
          [———————————]              subject site
65   70   75    80    85    90    95
[————————————————————————————]      donor site
```

In this case, the donor site overlaps the subject site completely. The overlap period is the same as the subject site period of record, i.e. 1975-1987. The donor period is the period 1965-1995. Suppose that the donor *QMED* values are as follows:

$$QD = QD_{65\text{-}95} = 21$$

$$QD_o = QD_{75\text{-}87} = 16$$

In this case the information from the donor site suggests that the *QMED* at the subject site needs to be scaled up by a factor of 21/16.

A power term $M(r)$ moderates the influence of the donor site. Thus QS_d, the subject-site *QMED* estimate adjusted to the donor period, is given by

$$QS_d = QS_o \left(\frac{QD}{QD_o}\right)^{M(r)} \tag{20.4}$$

with

$$M(r) = \frac{(n_o - 3)r^3}{(n_o - 4)r^2 + 1} \tag{20.5}$$

$M(r)$ takes a value close to 1 (full transfer of information) if there is perfect correlation and a long overlap; it decreases towards zero (no transfer of information) as correlation and record overlap decrease. $M(r)$ ensures that the transfer of information is conservative. The form of $M(r)$ is an adaptation based on an augmentation method developed by Vogel and Stedinger (1985) to improve estimates of the mean of a series. Note that for very short records it is impossible to derive a sensible measure of correlation from the annual maximum data. In this case, no allowance for correlation is made and $M(r)$ is set to 1. The transfer equation is then

$$QS_d = QS_o \left(\frac{QD}{QD_o}\right) \tag{20.6}$$

The correlation between subject and donor site annual maxima is used to moderate the transfer of information from donor site to subject site.

In the case where the donor site overlaps the subject site completely, $QS_o = QS$ and the donor period equals the total period. Thus the equation can be written

$$QS_{adj} = QS_d = QS \left(\frac{QD}{QD_o}\right)^{M(r)} \tag{20.7}$$

Stage 2: Adjusting for additional site data

The second stage is only necessary if there are additional data at the subject site that do not overlap with the donor site, as in the case depicted here:

```
                                   85    90    95
                                   [———————————]        subject site
  60    65    70    75    80    85    90
  [———————————————————————————————————]                donor site
```

Using this donor site, the adjustment described in stage 1 gives QS_d, the subject site $QMED$ value adjusted to the period 1960-1992. In fact, it is possible to obtain a $QMED$ value representing the total period 1960-1997.

    The adjustment to the total period is obtained by taking a geometric average of $QMED$ estimates for the subject-site period and the donor period. In fact, because these periods overlap, it is also necessary to use QS_o, the estimate of $QMED$ for the overlap period. The weighting used in the geometric average reflects the proportion of the total number of years that each estimate represents. This gives

$$QS_{adj} = QS_d^{\frac{n_d}{n_t}}\ QS^{\frac{n_s}{n_t}}\ QS_o^{-\frac{n_o}{n_t}} \tag{20.8}$$

The negative exponent to the QS_o term arises because this term compensates for the overlap between the subject and donor site (the geometric average would otherwise count the overlap period twice).

    Substituting for QS_d from Equation 20.4 gives

$$QS_{adj} = \left(\frac{QD}{QD_o}\right)^{M(r)\frac{n_d}{n_t}}\ QS^{\frac{n_s}{n_t}}\ QS_o^{\frac{n_d-n_o}{n_t}} \tag{20.9}$$

Observe that if the donor site fully overlaps the subject site record then $QS = QS_o$ and $n_s = n_o$; thus the first two terms in the above equation cancel out, leaving the adjusted estimate from stage 1 (Equation 20.7). Example 20.3 shows how such an adjustment is carried out.

20.3.3 Combining adjusted estimates from multiple donors

If more than one donor is used then it becomes necessary to average the adjusted $QMED$ values from the various donors. For this, a weighted geometric average should be used:

$$QS_{adj} = \prod_{i=1}^{n}(QS_{adj}^{i})^{\frac{w_i}{\Sigma w_j}} \tag{20.10}$$

where w_i is a weight for the ith donor and QS_{adj}^{i} is $QMED$ adjusted by the ith donor.

Example 20.3
Adjust the 8-year-record for the East Peffer Burn at Lochhouses (20004) for climatic variation.

For the East Peffer Burn, the annual maximum record extends from 1965-1972. There are also POT data, but data are missing during one water year. *QMED* is calculated using the annual maxima (because of the gap in the POT record) and is 4.42.

Selecting a donor
The West Peffer Burn (20002) is located adjacent to the East Peffer Burn (the catchment centroids lie just over 3 km apart). Both catchments drain flat arable land over boulder clay; their areas are similar (26 km² and 31 km²). The flood record at West Peffer Burn extends from 1966-1992, thus overlapping seven out of the eight years of record at the subject site, and providing an additional 20 years of data.

Comparison of the data from subject and donor sites shows a good correlation and suggests that the subject-site period of record may contain floods that are smaller than average.

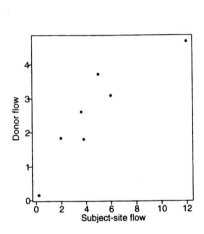

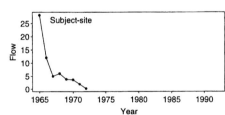

Adjusting QMED using station 20002
For this example, $n_s = 8$, $n_o = 7$, $n_d = 27$, $n_t = 28$.
The following *QMED* values are calculated for the donor site:

$QD = 3.5445$ $QD_o = QD_{1966\text{-}72} = 2.605$

And for the subject site:

$QS = 4.419$ $QS_o = QS_{1966\text{-}72} = 4.52$

Spearman's correlation between the annual maxima is $r = 0.857$.

$M(r)$ is calculated using Equation 20.5:

$M(r) = (7\text{-}3)\ 0.857^3 / \{(7\text{-}4)\ 0.857^2 + 1\} = 0.786$

The overlap between the donor (20002) and subject site is incomplete, so Equation 20.9 is used to obtain the adjusted *QMED* value:

$$QS_{adj} = (QD / QD_o)^{M \times 27/28}\ QS^{8/28}\ QS_o^{20/28}$$
$$= (3.5445 / 2.605)^{0.786 \times 27/28} \times 4.419^{8/28} \times 4.52^{20/28} = 5.304$$

QMED at the subject site is adjusted from 4.42 to 5.30.

The recommended weight takes account of

- The distance (d) in kilometres between the subject site and donor,
- The length of the overlap period (n_o),
- The additional years of data provided by the donor ($n_d - n_o$).

It takes the form

$$w = \left(1 - \frac{d}{120}\right) n_o (n_d - n_o)$$

(20.11)

20.4 An automated approach to adjusting for climate

20.4.1 Overview

This section describes an automated method of adjusting *QMED* for climate variation. The method is not expected to give as good results as if the donor sites had been hand-picked, but provides a standardised approach. The method was used to adjust *QMED* values for use in deriving the *QMED* catchment descriptor equation (Chapter 13). For this, two modifications are made to the method presented in §20.3. The first is that all sites are adjusted to a 30-year period that includes the site record whilst being as close as possible to the period 1961-1990 (§20.4.2). By standardising to similar periods, the effects of any climate variations are minimised. The second modification is to develop a method for selecting the donor sites automatically (§20.4.3).

> The automated approach is not recommended for use with individual sites. It was used in FEH analyses that required *QMED* values to be estimated for large numbers of sites.

20.4.2 Choosing a reference period

The aim of the automated adjustment process is to standardise *QMED* estimates so that they are representative of the long-term average. In practice, a 30-year period is likely to be long enough. For consistency between sites, a reference period is chosen for each site that

- Includes all the available subject-site data;
- Covers as many gaps in the subject-site record as possible;
- Is as close to the period 1961-1990 as possible.

For the majority of sites, this gives a reference period that is not very different from the 1961-1990 period.

In the automated methods for selecting donors and calculating adjustments, only donor data falling within the subject-site reference period are used.

20.4.3 Automatic selection of donors

Automatic selection of donors proceeds in two main stages. The first identifies potentially useful sites; the second refines this selection on the basis of the correlation. Note that because the automated procedure is only able to identify donors somewhat crudely, more donors are used in the adjustment process than when the donor sites are hand-selected. An example of the automated adjustment is given below (Example 20.4).

Stage 1: Selection of potentially useful and close sites

The objective of this stage is to pick out the sites that combine closeness, high correlation, and a period of record that is long and overlaps the subject site. Much of this information is already incorporated into the weighting measure described in Section 20.3.3 (Equation 20.11). The value of a donor v is defined by

$$v = wr = \left(1 - \frac{d}{120}\right) n_o (n_d - n_o)\, r \qquad (20.12)$$

where n_d is the length of donor site record falling within the reference period, n_o is the length of overlap period between subject site and donor, r is the correlation and d is the distance (km) between the sites.

All sites whose catchment centroids lie within 60 km of the subject-site catchment are considered as potential donors. Donors must also show positive correlation, must have some years additional to the subject site, and must overlap the subject-site record. Furthermore, to be retained as a donor, a site must also satisfy the equation

$$v \geq \frac{v_{max}}{2} \qquad (20.13)$$

where v_{max} is the maximum donor value amongst the candidate sites. Sites that are less than half as valuable as the most valuable site are eliminated. The above criteria were finely tuned by studying a number of examples and assessing 'by hand' which of the potential donors would be most suitable. Typically two to six donor sites are selected, with never more than 30 allowed.

Stage 2: Selection on the basis of correlation

Having selected potentially useful and close sites, the next stage is to examine correlations between the subject site and donors. A strong correlation means that transfer of information from a donor site is likely to help. A poor correlation is less useful, but may still be of value where the subject site has a very short record. Correlations are only assessed where the subject site has at least five years of data.

The basic approach is to remove sites that have correlations that are small compared with the highest observed correlation. For example, suppose there is a donor with a correlation of 0.92, a further donor with a correlation of 0.6 is then of comparatively limited value. However, a correlation of 0.6 may be worth considering if all the other correlations are small.

To remove the small correlations, the highest correlation r_{max} is found and an approximate 95% lower confidence limit is obtained for this correlation (Dixon and Massey, 1957):

$$r_l = \frac{e^{2z - \frac{2}{\sqrt{n-3}}} - 1}{e^{2z - \frac{2}{\sqrt{n-3}}} + 1} \qquad (20.14)$$

where

$$z = 0.5 \ln\left(\frac{1 + r_{max}}{1 - r_{max}}\right) \qquad (20.15)$$

Donor sites that have correlations smaller than the lower confidence bound r_i are removed. Finally, the donors with the highest correlations are selected. For this, donors are grouped according to the correlation significance level using the following divisions:

- 0.01 (highly significant)
- 0.05 (significant)
- 0.1
- 0.2
- Any positive correlation

Example 20.4
Obtain the adjusted QMED for the 10-year record for the Mole at Ifield Weir (39813).

The automated selection method identifies the following donor sites:

Donor	n_d	n_o	d	w	r (sig)		v	M(r)
41005	29	9	13.1	0.802	0.92	(0.010)	0.735	0.8885
40010	25	8	21.0	0.561	0.91	(0.018)	0.507	0.8664
40003	27	10	38.0	0.581	0.87	(0.010)	0.503	0.8275
40007	22	9	23.3	0.544	0.88	(0.013)	0.480	0.8437
40006	24	10	41.3	0.459	0.89	(0.008)	0.409	0.8590

Site details for these gauges are as follows:

Donor	River	Location	Area
40003	Medway	Teston	1256.1
40006	Bourne	Hadlow	50.3
40007	Medway	Chafford Weir	255.1
40010	Eden	Penshurst	224.3
41005	Ouse	Gold Bridge	180.9

The donor sites are all of larger area than the subject site (area 13 km²), but nevertheless they show a high level of correlation with station 39813.

Calculating the *QMED* adjustments for these five sites gives the following:

Donor	QS_{adj}	w
41005	2.75	0.802
40010	2.84	0.561
40003	2.97	0.581
40007	2.74	0.544
40006	3.20	0.459

The centre column of the table above shows the adjusted value based on the particular donor. These can be compared to the unadjusted *QMED* at the subject site (3.25). All the donors suggest that *QMED* at the subject site should be adjusted downwards.

Taking a weighted average of the above values gives QS_{adj} = 2.88, i.e. just over a 10% change in the *QMED* value.

The level of significance is gradually reduced until (1) there are at least three donor sites significant at the selected level, or (2) there is at least one site which is significant two levels 'above'.

20.4.4 Results of the automated adjustment for rural FEH sites

Adjusted *QMED* estimates have been used for derivation of the *QMED* catchment descriptor equation. The automated adjustment method was applied to all rural FEH sites with less than 30 years data.

Figure 20.2 compares the adjusted and original *QMED* values for FEH rural gauging stations. The largest adjustments to *QMED* values are generally made for the shortest records (Figure 20.2; Table 20.1). Adjustments made to records of 20 or more years in length are typically rather small (Table 20.1). Figure 20.3 shows a map illustrating the geographical spread of the *QMED* adjustments.

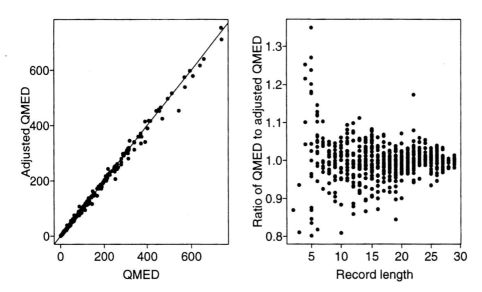

Figure 20.2 *Comparison of original and adjusted QMED estimates: the right-hand graph shows the ratio of the two estimates against record length.*

Table 20.1 *Proportion of sites changing by at least 5% and 10%, based on 718 UK gauges with records less than 30 years long. For a further 15 rural sites no donor site was found.*

Record length	Up to 5 years	6-10 years	11-15 years	16-20 years	Over 20 years
Total no. of sites	23	86	138	179	292
% of sites with ≥10% change	70	12	5	2	0.3
% of sites with ≥5% change	74	26	30	12	3

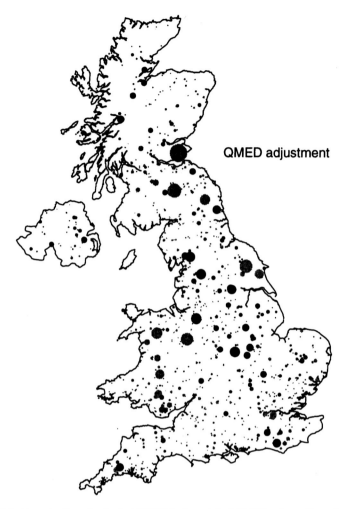

QMED adjustment

Figure 20.3 *Map of ratios of adjusted QMED to the original QMED values. Grey denotes an increased QMED value and black a decreased value. The larger the circle size the greater the adjustment to QMED.*

Chapter 21 Trend and other non-stationary behaviour

21.1 Introduction

21.1.1 Terminology

A data series is said to show *trend* if on average the series is progressively increasing or decreasing.

A data series is *non-stationary* if some of the underlying properties of the data change over time. A series with trend is one example of non-stationary data. Non-stationarity also arises if there is a sudden jump or *step change* in the data, or if there are marked fluctuations in the data. Trend, step change and fluctuation are the main forms of non-stationarity that will be discussed in this chapter.

A data series shows *fluctuation* if the average of the series changes noticeably through time but not in any consistent direction. Cycles in a data series are a special case of fluctuation. The main interest in fluctuation here is in relation to climatic variability, particularly when records are short (§21.2.3).

In practice it is often difficult to distinguish between step change, trend and fluctuation using only statistical tests. A data series that shows significant trend results often also shows significant step change, and *vice versa*. Similarly, fluctuations in flood series caused by climatic variability can be mistaken for trend, particularly for short records (Figure 21.1).

> A data series is said to be non-stationary if it shows trend or step change, or if there are marked fluctuations in the data.

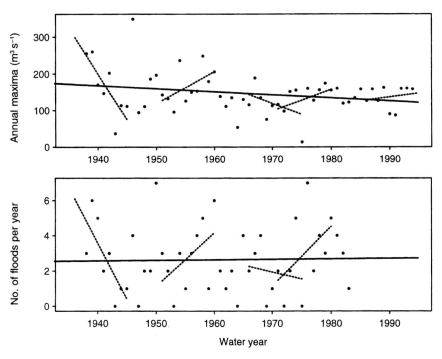

Figure 21.1 *Annual maxima and flood frequency data for the Thames at Day's Weir (39002). The solid line shows the regression line (trend) for the full data series (the slope is not significant). Dotted lines show trends associated with selected 10-year periods. If data had only been available for one of these periods, some highly varying conclusions could have been drawn. The different trends seen for each of the 10-year periods reflect the influence of climatic variability.*

A.J. Robson   **225**

Statistical procedures for flood frequency estimation

Climatic variability is variation in climate from one period to the next. It is not the same as climate change.

Climatic variability can be thought of as the natural variation in climate over time. It is not uncommon for wet and dry years to group together, for example, the 1960s and 1980s were generally rather wet in the UK and the 1970s were relatively dry. This can result in series of *flood-rich* and *flood-poor* years. Both flood frequency and flood magnitude vary noticeably across 5-10 year periods (see also §21.5; §20.2).

Climatic variability is not the same as climate change. Under *climate change*, a long-term alteration is occurring. Under climate variability, the climate differs from one period to the next but on average maintains a steady position, unless there is also climate change. Climatic variability can have a major influence on the appearance of plots of short flood records and an apparent trend may sometimes result. Such trends are likely to disappear as the record length is increased and the variations in climate are evened out (Figure 21.1). If trend is found in a short record it is important to consider whether the trend may reflect climatic variability rather than climate change or anthropogenic factors. Section 21.2.3 describes methods for helping to determine whether trends could be due to climatic variability.

Whenever trend or step-change is found in a short record it is important to consider whether this could be due to climatic variability.

Climate change cannot be clearly detected in the FEH datasets. In many instances the records are too short for reliable detection. For longer records, methods of data collection have changed over the years and most catchments have been subjected to human influences; thus any changes detected cannot be conclusively linked to climate.

21.1.2 Causes of non-stationarity

It is important to understand the origins of non-stationarity in a data series since the implications for flood frequency analysis differ (§21.1.3). Some standard causes of non-stationarity are as follows:

- Problems with the data records, e.g.:
  transcription/typographic errors
  abrupt changes in the rating equations
  rebuilding/relocation of weirs and recording stations
- Changes within the catchment, e.g.:
  land use change (notably urbanisation)
  drainage diversion
  reservoirs
  flood alleviation schemes
- Variations in the climate, e.g.:
  climatic variability
  climate change

To identify the most likely cause of non-stationary requires detailed investigation of the data record and historical information relating to the catchment (§21.4).

21.1.3 How to deal with non-stationary flood series

If a data series shows strong trend and is used for flood frequency analysis, then its flood frequency curve will, at best, represent the average response over the period of record. It may give poor results for the future. Depending on the cause of non-stationarity the following actions should be considered.

Non-stationarity due to data difficulties

The preferred action is to correct the data but if this is not possible, it may be necessary to use only part of the record, e.g. the record since the weir was rebuilt.

Non-stationarity due to changes in the catchment

In this case it may be preferable to use only the later, most relevant, part of the record. Alternatively, the full record can be used, but allowance for non-stationarity should be made in interpretation of the results.

Non-stationarity due to a short record

If the record is short then the possibility that trend reflects climatic variability should always be considered (§21.1.1). Section 21.2.3 presents methods to help assess whether a perceived trend may be due to climatic variation. If climatic variability is judged to be the cause, then a correction for climatic variation is required when calculating *QMED* (Chapter 20).

Non-stationarity with no obvious cause

If no obvious cause of non-stationarity is found then the full record should be used for flood frequency analysis, but consideration should be made in the interpretation of the results.

21.2 Methods for testing for non-stationarity

21.2.1 Statistical tests for trend

This section introduces four statistical tests for trend in flood series. It is recommended that more than one of these tests should be used. All four are used in the analyses presented in §21.3.

1 Linear regression

Linear regression is a commonly used statistical technique for evaluating whether two variables are related. It relies on assumptions of Normality: these are unlikely to hold for the annual maximum and POT magnitude series, for which the tests below may be more appropriate. As in the other three tests, the null hypothesis is that the gradient of the regression line is zero.

2 'Normal scores' linear regression

This is a robust but efficient distribution-free test. A *distribution-free* test is one that does not require assumptions to be made about the underlying distribution. A test is *robust* if its value is not strongly affected by the presence of one or two outlier values in the data, and *efficient* if it is good at detecting a trend when one is present. The approach is based on linear regression, but first the data are transformed to have a Normal structure: the transformation orders the data values and replaces them by *Normal score statistics*. Thus, the ith largest observation is replaced by the typical value of the ith largest observation from an equivalent sample with a Normal distribution.

3 Spearman's rank correlation

This is a standard distribution-free test for correlation between two variables (in this instance these are the flood-variable and time). It is analogous to the usual correlation coefficient (i.e. the Pearson product moment: Sprent, 1989) but uses the ranks of the data instead of the raw data (the rank of a data point is i if the data point is the ith value in a size-ordered sample). Another test of correlation based on ranks (the Mann-Kendall test: Kendall, 1970) was found to give almost identical significance levels and is therefore not included.

4 Linear regression using permutation

A permutation approach uses the data to determine a test's significance. It achieves this by permuting the data many times.

Permutation techniques use the observed data to test for significance (Lehmann, 1975; Maritz, 1981). Suppose that there is no trend in the data (the null hypothesis). If this is true, it is only by chance that the observed data values occurred in the order that they did: they could just as well have arrived in a different random order or *permutation*. The linear regression permutation test is carried out by permuting the data many times and calculating the regression gradient for each permutation. If the observed gradient lies in the middle of the gradients from the permutation distribution, then it seems unlikely that there is trend. If the observed gradient is rather different from most of the permutation gradients, then the observed gradient is unlikely to have arisen by chance and there is evidence of trend. The approach avoids making distributional assumptions but is computationally demanding because many permutations must be carried out for each station.

21.2.2 Statistical tests for step change

The tests described here are distribution-free methods that can be used to test for step change at individual stations. They assume that the *change-point times* (the times when an abrupt change occurs) are unknown. Again it is recommended that more than one test should be applied. All of the following were applied to the 1000 FEH records (§21.3).

1 Distribution-free CUSUM test

This is a rank-based test, in which successive observations are compared with the median of the series (Chiew and McMahon, 1993). The test statistic is the cumulative sum (CUSUM) of the sign of the difference from the median (the CUSUM of a series of plus or minus ones). Significance levels are determined using standard computational algorithms for the Kolmogorov-Smirnov test (Statistical Sciences, 1995; Kim and Jennrich, 1973; McGilchrist and Woodyer, 1975).

2 Buishand's Q test for normal scores

Buishand's Q test is based on the rescaled cumulative sum of deviations from the mean (Buishand, 1982). For a change-point which occurs towards the centre of a time series, the test is relatively powerful in comparison with other tests (e.g. Worsley's likelihood ratio test; Worsley, 1979; Buishand, 1982). Published significance levels are based on percentile points derived from Normally distributed simulation data (Buishand, 1982). A Normal scores transformation (see §21.2.1) is recommended so that Normal behaviour can be assumed.

3 Buishand's Q using permutation

For this test, Buishand's Q statistic was calculated from the raw data. For each station, significance levels can be calculated by generating a permutation distribution (see §21.2.1). This approach avoids any distributional assumptions.

4 Median change-point test using permutation

This is a distribution-free test for a change in the median of a series when the exact time of change is unknown (Siegel and Castellan, 1988; Pettit, 1979). The statistic is based on the ranks of the observations. The test is equivalent to a rank-based version of Buishand's Q test. Because of the lack of suitable large-sample approximations, it is recommended that the percentage points of the test statistic distributions are generated for each station using a permutation approach.

21.2.3 Statistical methods for assessing effects of climatic variability

It is important to consider whether non-stationarity in flood records arises from climatic variability. In this section, a climatically adjusted variable is derived. This can be tested for trend as described in §21.2.1 and the results compared with those from the original data. If the original variable shows significant trend, but the adjusted one does not, then it is likely that climatic variation or climate change is the cause.

> If a trend is caused by climate, it is likely that similar patterns will be seen at other sites nearby. Comparing flood data with neighbouring sites can indicate whether the trend is linked to climate or to other causes.

To obtain the climatically adjusted variable, data from nearby sites are used. Sites that are close together can be expected to experience similar climatic variation. (Ideally, the nearby sites should also be hydrologically similar, but in practice there are insufficient local sites for this to be possible.) If a site shows a trend and the average response of nearby sites for the identical period shows the same features, then it seems reasonable to conclude that the variations are due to climate. If a site shows a trend that is very different from the surrounding region, the trend is likely to be caused by anthropogenic factors. To obtain a climatically adjusted variable, the difference between the site data and the average behaviour of the surrounding region is found. Here, the region consists of all stations whose catchment centroids lie within a 50 km radius of the centroid of the subject site. (Other region sizes were considered but were found to give similar results.)

The climatic adjustment is most readily applied to annual data series. Here, the annual POT flood count series (the number of floods per year) and the annual maxima are adjusted. For POT flood counts, the region is used to determine the average number of floods in each year for the region. This background pattern is then subtracted from the site annual flood counts to give the adjusted series. For annual maxima, the adjustment is more complex because annual maximum sizes vary according to catchment size, wetness, etc.. As with the POT data, the objective is to examine the subject-site's annual maxima in relation to the region. For each site in the region, an annual rank-difference series is constructed: the annual maxima are replaced by their rank values and the difference between this series and the ranks of the subject-site annual maxima is found. Each of the rank difference series is standardised to have a variance of 1 (to compensate for differences in record length and overlap) and the adjusted annual maximum series is the regional average of the standardised series.

The results from trend tests on the adjusted variables are an aid to distinguishing between climatic and other sources of trend. They should not be considered to be definitive. If the climate is found to be the cause of trend, it may still be a matter of judgement whether this constitutes climate change or short-term fluctuation linked to climatic variation.

21.3 Application to UK floods data

One thousand FEH stations were tested for non-stationarity using the methods of §21.2. This section presents details of the analyses.

21.3.1 Data series used in the tests

Both annual maxima and POT records were investigated. For the POT series, two thresholds were used to standardise the data (§11.2). The POT3 series contains an average of three peaks per year at each station: this is the primary POT dataset. The POT1 series contains an average of one peak per year. The POT1 and POT3 series each provide (i) an irregular series of flood magnitudes (POT3m, POT1m) and (ii) a regular series of annual flood counts (the number of floods per year: POT3#, POT1#). Tests for non-stationarity in POT1 series highlight changes which occur in the very biggest floods. Tests on the POT3 series also allow for changes in medium-sized floods.

The following series were tested for trend:

- AM — annual maximum flows
- AMadj — climatically adjusted AM
- POT1m — magnitudes of POT1 events
- POT3m — magnitudes of POT3 events
- POT1# — the number of POT1 events/year (annual POT1 counts)
- POT3# — the number of POT3 floods/year (annual POT3 counts)
- POT3#adj — climatically adjusted POT3#

Step change tests were carried out for a more limited set of variables: the AM, POT3m and POT3# series.

21.3.2 General methodology

For each gauge, four tests (§21.2) for trend and/or step change were applied to the above variables, giving up to 40 tests per site. Trend tests were applied to all records with at least five years of data. Step change tests were applied to records with at least ten years of data.

In addition to the statistical tests, exploratory graphical techniques were used to examine the data. Time series plots of the data were studied and compared with data from other nearby stations. Smoothing curves were added to the plots to aid interpretation (Cleveland, 1979). The plots were used to help understand the data series, and to look for possible outliers and suspicious or interesting features.

In applying the permutation tests described in §21.2.1 and §21.2.2, annual series need to be treated differently to the irregular series. For the annual data series (e.g. annual maxima and POT counts) all data points are permuted. For the irregular series (POT magnitudes) the data are permuted in blocks of complete water years. This preserves the within-year structure of the data (notably seasonality). Two thousand permutations of the data were made in each test.

21.3.3 Summary of results

The full set of test results are presented in tabular form in Additional Note 21.1. Table 21.1 lists those stations where possible non-stationarity is detected. These are stations for which three out of four tests are significant for one or more variables (excluding adjusted variables). When using Table 21.1 it should be remembered that significant test results for shorter records may reflect climatic variation rather than genuine long-term trend: results for stations with less than 25 years of data need cautious interpretation (see §21.4). Records with less than 15 years of data are excluded from Table 21.1 (but are detailed in Additional Note 21.1).

It should also be remembered, when interpreting test results, that it is relatively common for significant results to be seen across a range of variables and in tests for both trend and step change. It is difficult to distinguish step change and trend purely on the basis of the statistical tests.

Flood frequency changes

Most of the annual POT flood count data showed no trend (or step-change). However, where a significant trend or step-change occurred it tended to be positive (i.e. a tendency to more frequent flood occurrences); this is particularly marked for the longer records. In the limited number of instances where a decrease in flood counts occurred, an associated gauging or rating change has usually been identified. The POT1 and POT3 annual flood count results are largely consistent with one another.

Flood magnitude changes

Where significant changes in annual maxima are detected they tend to be positive (i.e. towards larger floods) and they are often associated with a trend in flood counts. Trends in POT magnitudes are usually negative for longer records (>30 years) but tend to be positive for shorter records.

Climatic variability

The adjusted flood counts show fewer positive trends than the raw flood counts, though there is considerable site-to-site variation. For the shorter records, many apparent trends in annual flood counts disappear when placed in a regional context, suggesting period-dependent climatic conditions as the underlying cause. For the adjusted annual maxima, the difference in significance levels between raw and adjusted variables is yet more marked. This again suggests that, in many cases of trend, the cause is linked to climate.

General causes of non-stationarity

Some of the most strongly non-stationary sites were examined in more detail as part of the screening process for the main flood frequency analyses presented in this volume. It is not possible to give full details although §21.5 provides some illustrative examples. The main conclusions from the investigations are:

- For shorter records, climatic variability often appeared to be the most likely cause;
- For a sizeable proportion, no explanation of trend/step-change was found;
- The most commonly identified cause of trend/step-change was gauging problems;
- Urbanisation was implicated for a few sites;
- There were no obvious cases of effects from drainage diversion or other land-use change;
- There were no clear cases of climate change, except possibly in North West Scotland (see below).

> Climatic variability and gauging problems were the most commonly identified causes of non-stationarity in the FEH flood data.

Table 21.1 *Sites showing possible non-stationary behaviour. Sites are included here if three out of the four statistical tests give highly significant results for at least one variable. For further details on specific sites, refer to the full test tables in Additional Note 21.1, which show the test results and the direction of change for all variables and tests.*

Gauge	River	Location	Number of non-stationary variables	Record length
7001	Findhorn	Shenachie	4	33
8007	Spey	Invertruim	4	43
8009	Dulnain	Balnaan Bridge	2	43
9003	Isla	Grange	1	26
14001	Eden	Kemback	2	26
15001	Isla	Forter	1	26
15010	Isla	Wester Cardean	1	21
15016	Tay	Kenmore	1	18
17005	Avon	Polmonthill	2	22
18005	Allan Water	Bridge of Allan	2	21
18008	Leny	Anie	4	19
19002 *	Almond	Almond Weir	4	31
19003	Breich Water	Breich Weir	3	18
21012	Teviot	Hawick	1	30
21017	Ettrick Water	Brockhoperig	2	28
21021	Tweed	Sprouston	2	23
21025	Ale Water	Ancrum	1	20
21026	Tima Water	Deephope	2	19
22007 *	Wansbeck	Mitford	1	30
23011	Kielder Burn	Kielder	1	19
25002	Tees	Dent Bank	3	15
25018	Tees	Middleton in Teesdale	2	20
25020	Skerne	Preston Le Skerne	1	16
27002	Wharfe	Flint Mill Weir	1	57
27009	Ouse	Skelton	2	36
27021 *	Don	Doncaster	4	110
28021	Derwent	Draycott	3	16
28031	Manifold	Ilam	1	26
28804	Trent	Trent Bridge	1	82
30013	Heighington Beck	Heighington	1	18
32002	Willow Brook	Fotheringhay	2	53
32003 *	Harpers Brook	Old Mill Bridge	4	50
32006	Nene/Kislingbury	Upton	1	53
32008 *	Nene/Kislingbury	Dodford	3	47
33023	Lea Brook	Beck Bridge	1	29
33028	Flit	Shefford	2	27
33044	Thet	Bridgham	1	25
33054	Babingley	Castle Rising	1	17
35003	Alde	Farnham	2	26
37019	Beam	Bretons Farm	1	29
38001	Lea	Feildes Weir	1	121
38003	Mimram	Panshanger Park	3	41
38007	Canons Brook	Elizabeth Way	3	44
39001	Thames	Kingston	2	112
39002	Thames	Days Weir	1	57
39003	Wandle	Connollys Mill	1	46
39004	Wandle	Beddington Park	6	48
39006	Windrush	Newbridge	1	44
39007	Blackwater	Swallowfield	1	41
39036	Law Brook	Albury	1	25
39049	Silk Stream	Colindeep Lane	6	35
39093	Brent	Monks Park	4	54

Gauge	River	Location	Number of non-stationary variables	Record length
46005	East Dart	Bellever	2	30
46006	Erme	Ermington	1	16
47007	Yealm	Puslinch	2	32
49002	Hayle	St Erth	3	34
50007	Taw	Taw Bridge	1	21
52017	Congresbury Yeo	Iwood	1	19
53001 **	Avon	Melksham	3	49
54006 *	Stour	Kidderminster	1	40
54008	Teme	Tenbury	2	38
54018	Rea Brook	Hookagate	1	30
55002	Wye	Belmont	1	84
55003	Lugg	Lugwardine	1	46
55008	Wye	Cefn Brwyn	1	44
55012	Irfon	Cilmery	2	26
56019	Ebbw	Aberbeeg	1	18
57005	Taff	Pontypridd	2	26
57008	Rhymney	Llanedeyrn	1	21
57009	Ely	St Fagans	1	18
58009	Ewenny	Keepers Lodge	5	24
60004	Dewi Fawr	Glasfryn Ford	3	15
60006	Gwili	Glangwili	1	25
61001	Western Cleddau	Prendergast Mill	2	35
61002	Eastern Cleddau	Canaston Bridge	2	35
61003	Gwaun	Cilrhedyn Bridge	1	15
63002	Rheidol	Llanbadarn Fawr	1	19
67005 *	Ceiriog	Brynkinalt Weir	2	35
67018	Dee	New Inn	1	24
68005 *	Weaver	Audlem	2	58
68020	Gowy	Bridge Trafford	1	15
69006	Bollin	Dunham Massey	1	53
69015	Etherow	Compstall	1	25
69019	Worsley Brook	Eccles	1	16
70002	Douglas	Wanes Blades Bridge	2	27
70003	Douglas	Central Park Wigan	1	21
71004	Calder	Whalley Weir	1	22
72016	Wyre	Scorton Weir	1	23
76008	Irthing	Greenholme	2	27
78003	Annan	Brydekirk	3	26
78004	Kinnel Water	Redhall	3	31
79006	Nith	Drumlanrig	1	26
83802 **	Irvine	Kilmarnock	4	70
84001 *	Kelvin	Killermont	2	46
84006	Kelvin	Bridgend	5	26
84012	White Cart	Water Hawkhead	3	30
84015	Kelvin	Dryfield	1	41
84016	Luggie Water	Condorrat	2	20
203010	Blackwater	Maydown Bridge	5	23
203011	Main	Dromona	3	20
203012	Ballinderry	Ballinderry Bridge	2	23
203020	Moyola	Moyola New Bridge	1	22
203021	Kells Water	Currys Bridge	1	22
203022	Blackwater	Derrymeen Bridge	3	16

** denotes a record that has not been used in the main statistical analyses (Chapters 11-20).
* indicates that only part of the record has been used in the main analyses.
  Table 22.3 lists the reasons for removing the whole or part of a record.

It should be remembered that the gauged records used in the FEH are rarely located in catchments experiencing major land-use change. It is therefore not very surprising that land-use change effects are not evident in the FEH data, but this may well not be representative of the wider picture.

In some cases, the climatically adjusted variable was found to show significant trend and a climatic cause seems possible. For example, a number of stations in North West Scotland (mainly on the Spey, e.g. station 8009) show increases in both the raw and adjusted annual flood counts. Most of these records include data from the early 1990s, a flood-rich period for this area. It is possible that these sites are showing effects of climate change (see also Grew and Werritty, 1995; Green *et al.*, 1996).

Note that some of the 1000 FEH gauging stations are not used in the main analyses described in Chapters 11-20. Stations excluded from the analysis, or for which only part of the record is used, are listed in Table 22.3 and marked with an asterisk in Table 21.1 and Additional Note 21.1. Data were generally excluded where quality problems were uncovered (see Table 22.3 for details), a number of these being identified as a result of the non-stationarity analyses described here.

21.4 Investigating sites showing non-stationary behaviour

21.4.1 General principles

The recommended stages in an investigation are:

- Examine time series plots for the station and for similar nearby catchments;
- Use tests on climatically adjusted variables to check whether climate variation might be the cause (§21.2.3; Additional Note 21.1);
- Check out data quality, typographical errors, changes in rating equations, etc.;
- Examine background archive material in detail, looking for information on reservoirs, drainage diversion, urbanisation, etc.

21.4.2 Case studies

It is not possible here to investigate the causes of non-stationarity on all of the 104 FEH stations that show trend or step change. Instead a few illustrative examples are given.

Trends linked to climatic variation

For many medium to short records, observed trends may prove to be linked to climatic variation during the period of record. To illustrate this, the FEH sites in hydrometric areas 18 and 19 are investigated. Table 21.2 shows the statistical test results for the 15 gauged catchments in these two areas, of which four show trend in one or more variables: 18005, 18008, 19002 and 19003. (19005 shows some significant results but only in the climatically adjusted variable.) Figure 21.2 shows the POT flood counts for these four stations alongside the two longest records in the region (19001, 19004). From the figure, it seems that the whole region experienced more flooding in the early 1960s and in the 1980s and less flooding in the 1970s. Over the period 1960-1990 there is little overall evidence of trend, but records that cover only part of the period show trend. In the case of the relatively early record (1960-1979) for the Breich Water (19003), POT flood counts decrease, but for the later records on the Leny (18008) and Allan Water (18005)

Table 21.2 *Results of the statistical tests for non-stationarity for 15 sites in hydrometric areas 18 and 19. This table is extracted from Additional Note 21.1, where full details and a legend are provided. Large circles indicate a highly significant trend, and small circles a significant trend. Black circles represent an upward trend or change, and grey circles a downward one. The test results are shown in groups of four, each corresponding to a different flood variable.*

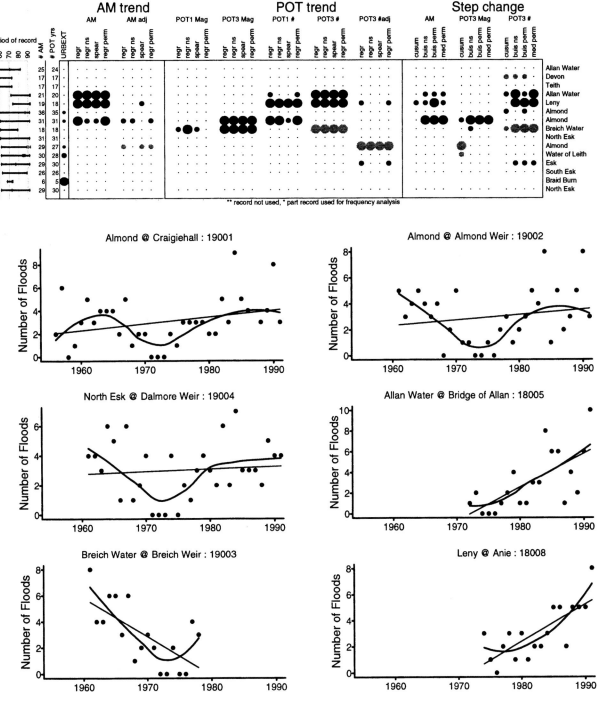

** record not used, * part record used for frequency analysis

Figure 21.2 *Changes in the number of floods per year (for the POT3 series) for six catchments in hydrometric areas 18 and 19. Records spanning 1960 to 1990 show no overall trend, but the sites with shorter records show a significant trend, which is unlikely to be representative of the longer-term picture. The graphs include the fitted regression line and a locally-weighted smoothing curve (Cleveland, 1979)*

the POT flood count trends are upwards. The test results for the climatically adjusted flood count variables are not significant, a further indication that the trend has its origin in climatic variability. Viewing the test results alongside the time series plots suggests that these are not trends that are likely to persist.

Tests on annual maxima for these sites show a similar picture to POT3 flood counts: the raw variable is significant, but the adjusted variable is not. The exception is for the Almond (19002) where the climatically adjusted variable shows slight significance. The Almond flood record is for a longer period than the other three sites with trend; it also shows significant step change for annual maxima and POT3 magnitudes. Further investigation of this catchment indicates that the rating curve changed notably in 1969 and this seems to have resulted in a step change in the flood series. For the main FEH analyses, only the data since October 1969 are used for this site.

Thus of the four sites in this region with strong non-stationarity, three appear to relate to climatic variability during a short period of record, while the fourth is the result of data quality problems.

Step change linked to gauging changes

The Weaver at Audlem (68005) has a 58-year annual maximum record that shows significant downwards trend and step change results (see Additional Note 21.1). A time series plot of the data shows a marked downwards jump in the series in the late 1960s (Figure 21.3), coinciding with the installation of a new recording station and the use of a new rating equation in 1969. The validity of the earlier rating curve seems suspect, and in consequence only the data from October 1969 have been retained in the main FEH analyses.

Trend linked to urbanisation

The Mimram at Panshanger Park (38003) has a 41-year annual maximum record and a 26-year POT record. Statistical tests show a strong positive trend in annual maxima and in POT1 and POT3 flood frequency (Figure 21.4; Additional Note 21.1). Since the tests on climatically adjusted annual maxima and POT3 flood counts are also significant it is unlikely that these trends are linked to climate change or climatic variability. The Mimram is a chalk catchment that contains small but influential areas of urbanisation. Investigation of archive material indicates that the quality of gauging is good. It seems reasonable that the observed trend could be genuine: the result of increasing urbanisation on a very permeable catchment (see §18.2.1).

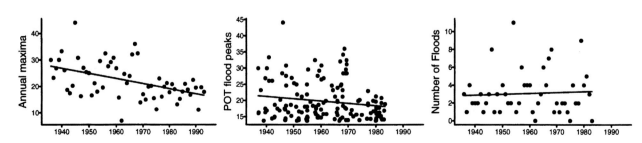

Figure 21.3 *Time series plot of annual maxima, POT flood magnitudes and POT flood counts for the Weaver at Audlem. A step change occurs in 1969.*

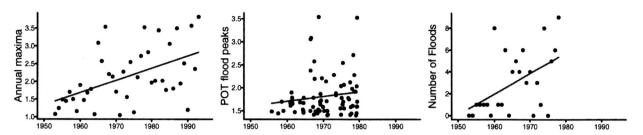

Figure 21.4 *Time series plot of annual maxima, POT flood magnitudes and POT flood counts for the Mimram at Panshanger Park. Increasing trends are seen for all three series.*

21.5 A national perspective on trend

The site-by-site analyses (Section 21.3) show a tendency for trend, where present, to be mainly towards increased flooding (both frequency of occurrence and magnitude). This raises the question of whether climate change and/or land-use change are causing increased flood risk in the UK. To help answer this question a national analysis of trend was undertaken (Robson *et al.*, 1998) and a summary is provided here.

21.5.1 Methodology

Testing for trend nationally requires very careful application of statistical tests. This is because there are strong spatial dependencies between the sites and these dependencies violate the usual assumptions of independence. To avoid these difficulties, a permutation approach has been used in which all data from the same water-year are permuted as a block. This allows spatial dependencies to be preserved. Under this approach, permutation tests of linear regression, normal scores regression and Spearman's correlation were applied. Two variables were tested, the number of POT3 floods per year, and a scaled version of the annual maxima. For the annual maxima, scaling is required because differences in catchment size and wetness mean that typical flood sizes vary considerably between catchments. The annual maximum data were therefore scaled by (i) replacing the data by the rank values and (ii) centring and standardising the ranks to have a mean of 0.5 and a variance of 1 (Robson *et al.*, 1998).

Two main analyses were undertaken. The first examined data since 1940: this dataset contains a large number of sites giving a good spatial coverage of the UK. The second analysis examined data from 1880: for this, there are very few data for the earlier part of the record and the spatial coverage is poor, but information is obtained for a much longer period.

21.5.2 Trends since 1940

For POT data, national trend was tested for the period 1941-1980. For annual maxima, more recent records exist and a 50-year period (1941-1990) was examined.

Three permutation-based trend tests (§21.2.1) were applied to the pooled UK annual flood counts and annual maximum series. For both series, the observed trends were generally rather small and were not significant. Figure 21.5 shows the fitted trends and a locally weighted smoothing curve. The smoothing curve shows notable fluctuations over periods of 5-10 years; the fitted trend appears insignificant relative to them.

21.5.3 Trends since 1870

Caution must be applied in interpreting the test results for this period: before 1930 there are data for only ten sites; from the mid-1970s the data extend to over 600 sites. The early data are inevitably less reliable and the few early sites are neither geographically nor hydrologically representative.

In addition to trend tests, a comparison is made with long-term total rainfall records. The annual rainfall totals are based on long series for England and Wales, and for Scotland (Woodley, 1996). Though not perfect, the rainfall series is probably more consistent than the flood data, since there were many more raingauges in the early years.

The flood and rainfall series show a close resemblance, despite the fact that annual rainfall is a crude measure of flood potential (Figure 21.6). The correlation between the series is 0.54 and is highly significant. Both the rainfall and flood series graphs suggest gradual increases since 1900 (Figure 21.6). Application of permutation tests to 1870-1990 and 1900-1990 rainfall series does not identify any clearly significant changes. For flood POT counts, some of the trend test results are significant (Table 21.3), but this may well relate to long-term change at just one or two sites since only three sites extend back to 1900.

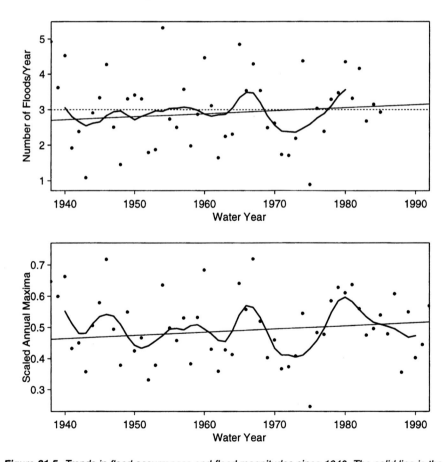

Figure 21.5 *Trends in flood occurrences and flood magnitudes since 1940. The solid line is the trend (non-significant). The upper graph shows the nationally averaged number of POT3 flood occurrences per year: the horizontal dotted line marks the average number of POT events per year for the POT3 series. The lower graph shows the nationally averaged values of the scaled annual maxima.*

The long-term flood series also help to put the more recent data into perspective. Examining the last 40 to 50 years of data might suggest that flood variability is on the increase: the fluctuations have become larger (Figure 21.5). However, judged against the longer series, 1941-1960 was relatively quiet in terms of flood fluctuation (Figure 21.6).

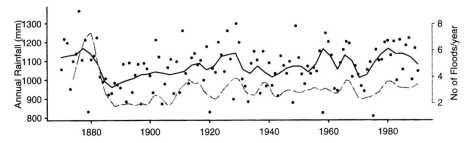

Figure 21.6 *Long-term series of rainfall and flood data. The points show the nationally averaged number of POT3 floods per year. The solid line is a smoothed curve fitted to annual rainfall totals; the dotted line is a smoothed curve fitted through the flood data. The two curves show quite similar behaviour.*

Table 21.3 *Permutation test results for trend in long-term time series of rainfall and floods data. There are very few sites for the early flood data, so the results should be interpreted cautiously. SL = significance level.*

	Regression gradient	Linear regression (SL)	Normal scores regression (SL)	Spearman's correlation (SL)
POT flood counts:				
(1870-1995)	0.009	0.07 *	0.03 **	0.21
(1900-1995)	0.010	0.12	0.05 **	0.17
Annual rainfall:				
(1870-1995)	0.38	0.18	0.24	0.10
(1900-1995)	0.62	0.13	0.17	0.07

* significant result; ** highly significant result

21.5.4 Summary

The main findings to emerge from the analysis of the national data are:

- Whilst there are few significant trends for the period to 1980/1990, the influence of climatic variation is clear. Its confounding effect means that trends associated with land-use change or climate change can neither be easily identified nor readily dismissed.
- The analyses do not show that climate change has affected UK flood behaviour. However, neither do they prove that it has not affected flood behaviour: the possibility of climate change affecting flood response, now or in the future, cannot be eliminated and should not be disregarded.
- Significant year-to-year fluctuations in flooding are observed. These have important consequences for flood design and trend analyses, especially when short records are used. This is part of the reason for favouring pooled analyses (Chapter 16), and why estimates of the index flood *QMED* from short records should be adjusted (Chapter 20).

Additional Note 21.1 Results of trend and step-change tests for FEH gauges

This note tabulates the non-stationarity test results for 1000 FEH gauging stations. Each line of the table shows results for a specific site. Circles are used to show where a statistical test is significant. Black circles indicate an upward trend or change; grey circles show a downward one. Details of the statistical tests are given in §21.2.

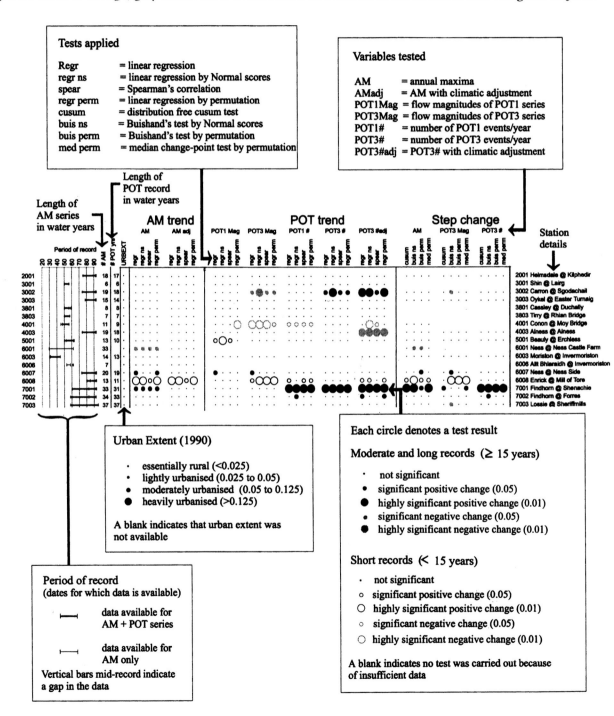

Tests applied

Regr	= linear regression
regr ns	= linear regression by Normal scores
spear	= Spearman's correlation
regr perm	= linear regression by permutation
cusum	= distribution free cusum test
buis ns	= Buishand's test by Normal scores
buis perm	= Buishand's test by permutation
med perm	= median change-point test by permutation

Variables tested

AM	= annual maxima
AMadj	= AM with climatic adjustment
POT1Mag	= flow magnitudes of POT1 series
POT3Mag	= flow magnitudes of POT3 series
POT1#	= number of POT1 events/year
POT3#	= number of POT3 events/year
POT3#adj	= POT3# with climatic adjustment

Urban Extent (1990)

- · essentially rural (<0.025)
- · lightly urbanised (0.025 to 0.05)
- ● moderately urbanised (0.05 to 0.125)
- ⬤ heavily urbanised (>0.125)

A blank indicates that urban extent was not available

Each circle denotes a test result

Moderate and long records (≥ 15 years)

- · not significant
- ● significant positive change (0.05)
- ⬤ highly significant positive change (0.01)
- significant negative change (0.05)
- ⬤ highly significant negative change (0.01)

Short records (< 15 years)

- · not significant
- ○ significant positive change (0.05)
- ○ highly significant positive change (0.01)
- ○ significant negative change (0.05)
- ○ highly significant negative change (0.01)

A blank indicates no test was carried out because of insufficient data

Period of record
(dates for which data is available)

⊢——⊣	data available for AM + POT series
⊢—⊣	data available for AM only

Vertical bars mid-record indicate a gap in the data

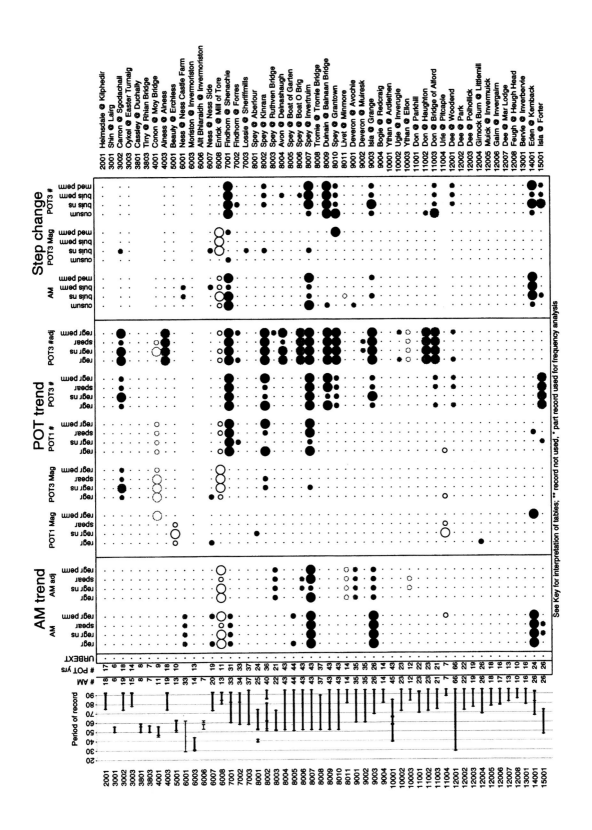

Trend and other non-stationary behaviour

See Key for interpretation of tables; ** record not used, * part record used for frequency analysis

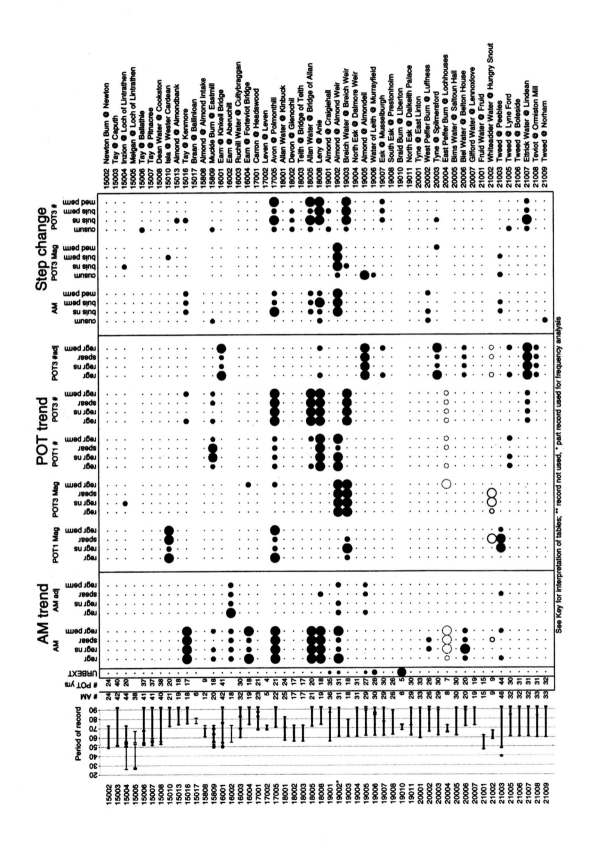

See Key for interpretation of tables; ** record not used; * part record used for frequency analysis

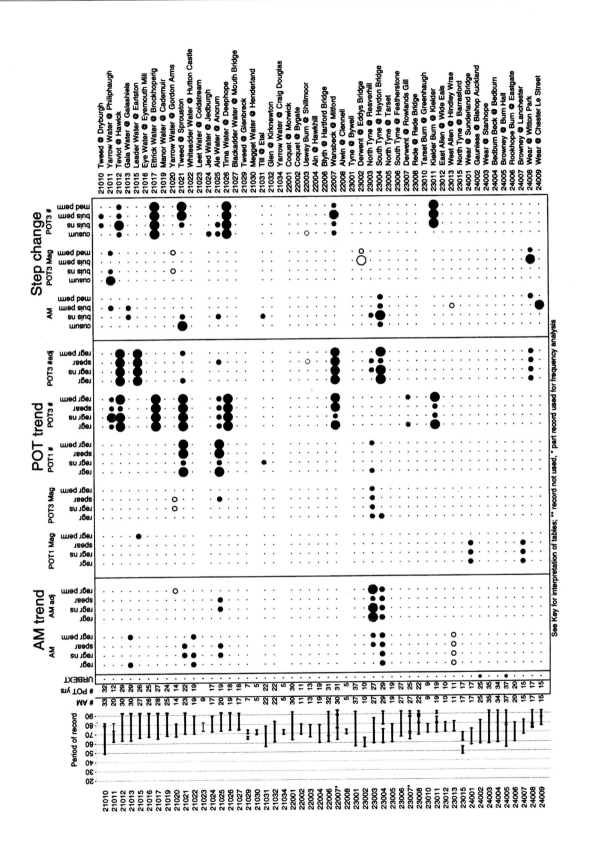

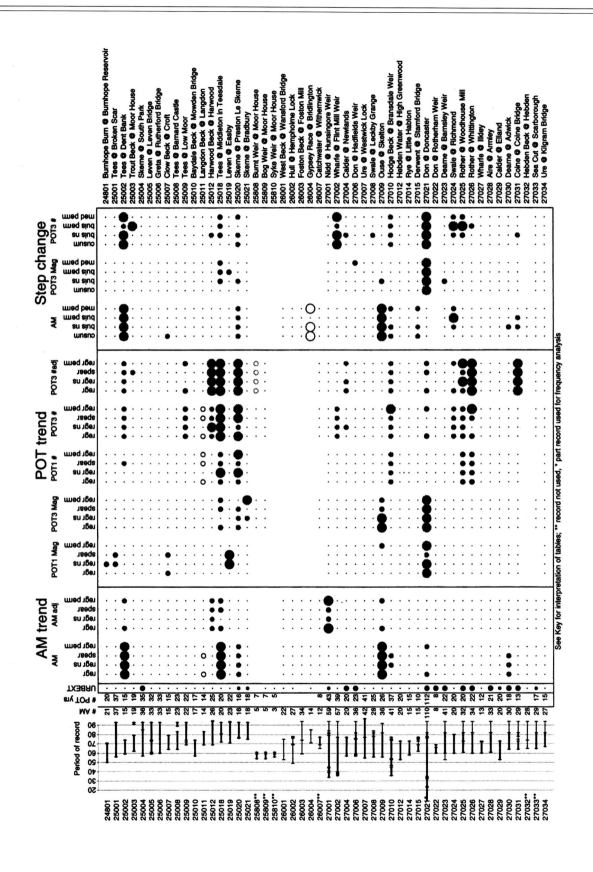

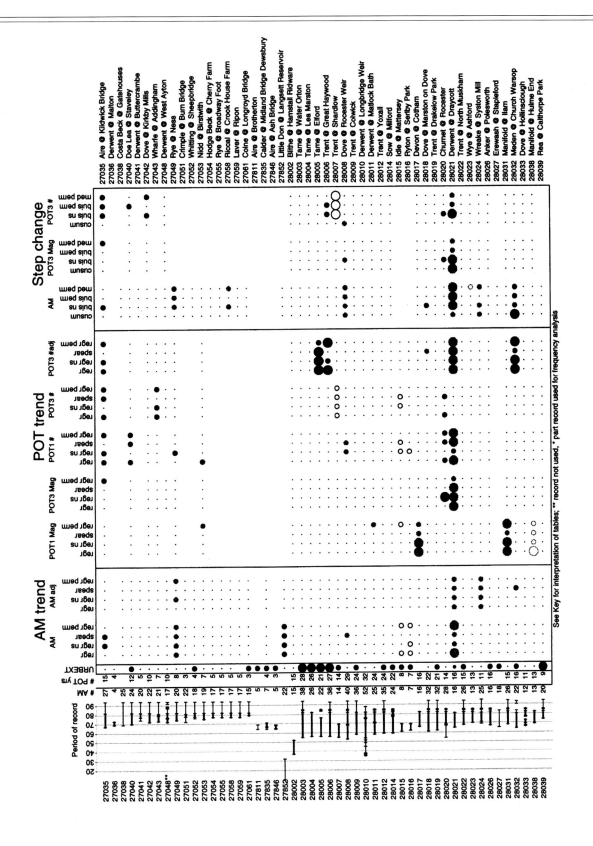

See Key for interpretation of tables; ** record not used; * part record used for frequency analysis

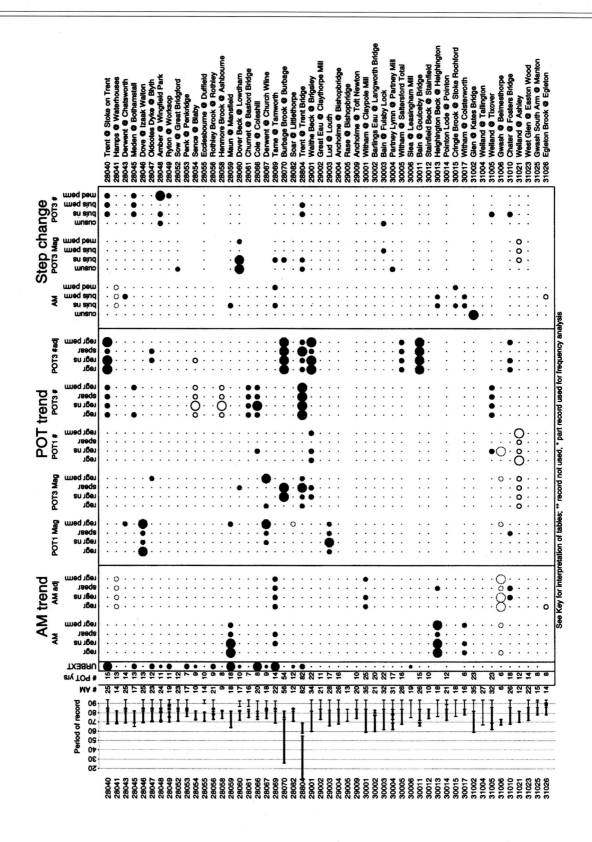

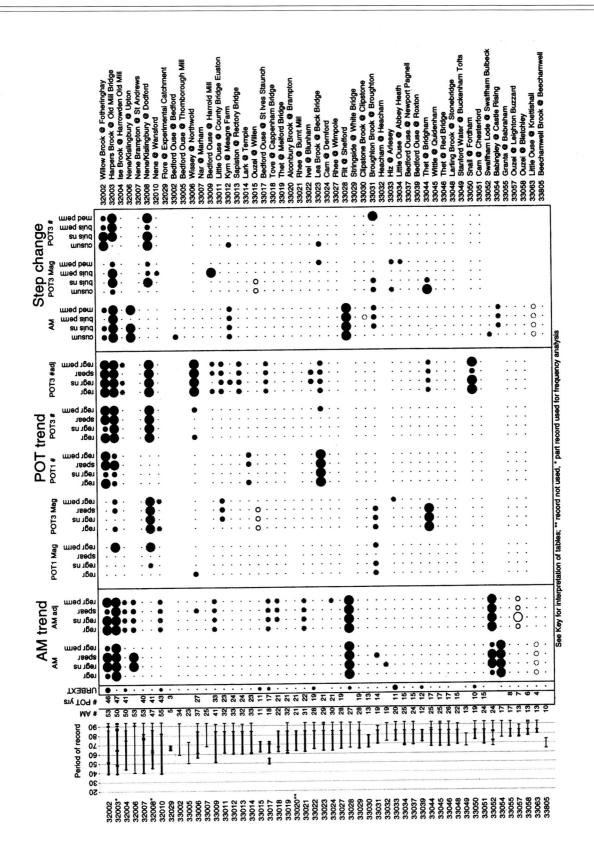

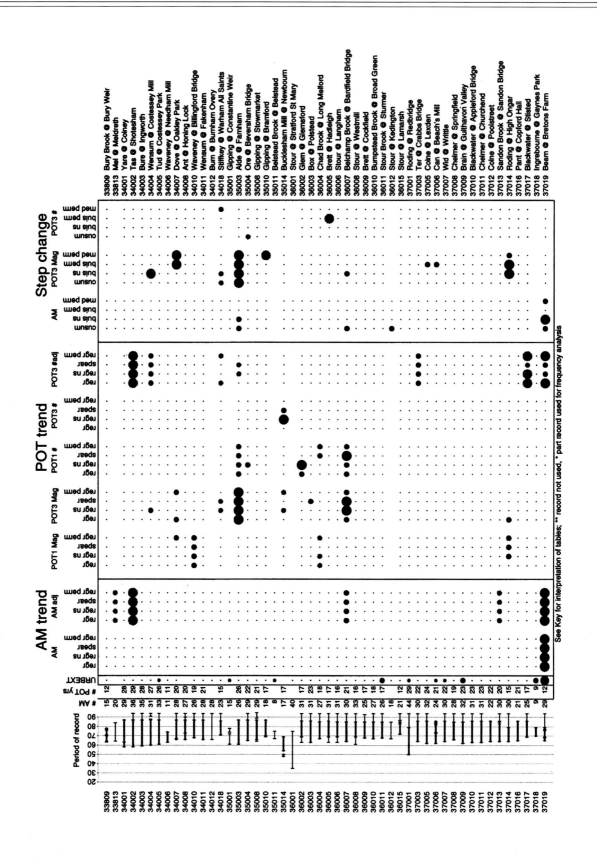

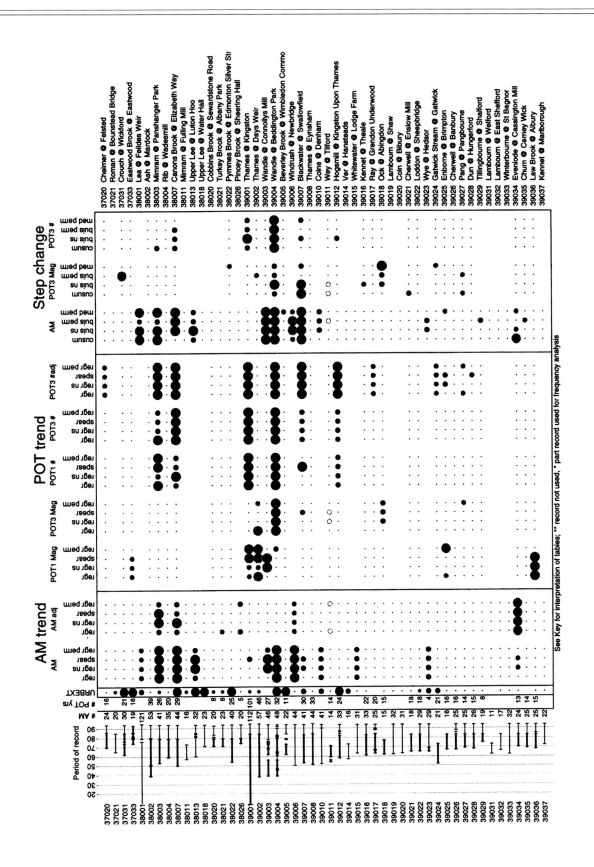

See Key for interpretation of tables; ** record not used, * part record used for frequency analysis

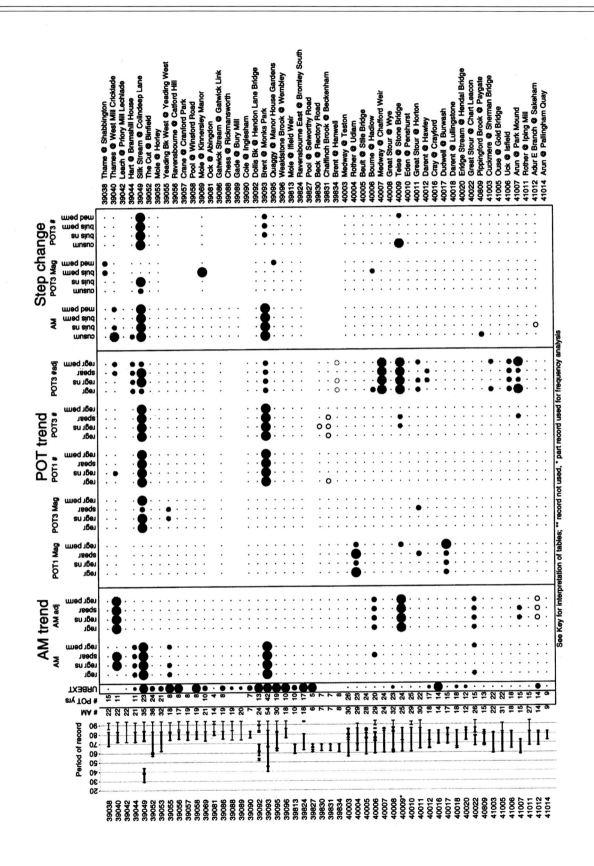

See Key for interpretation of tables; ** record not used, * part record used for frequency analysis

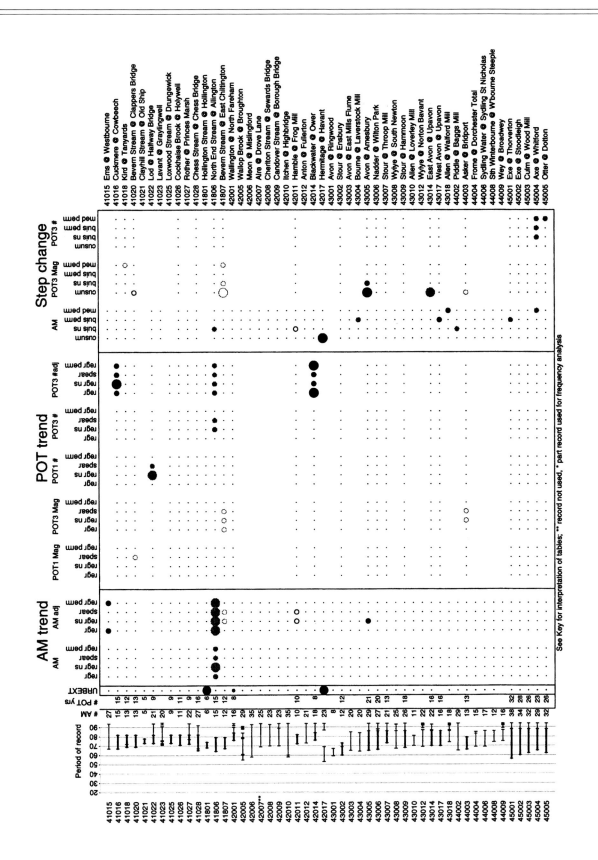

See Key for interpretation of tables; ** record not used, * part record used for frequency analysis

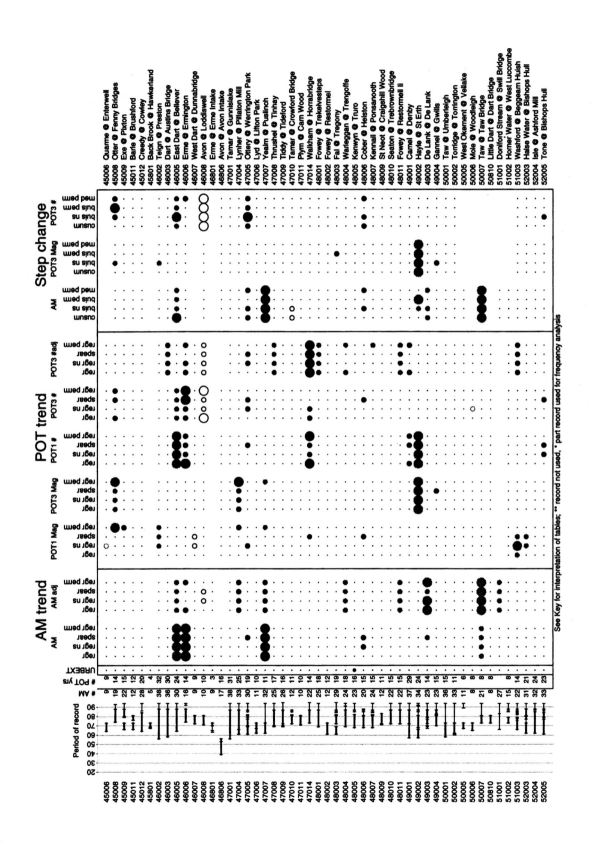

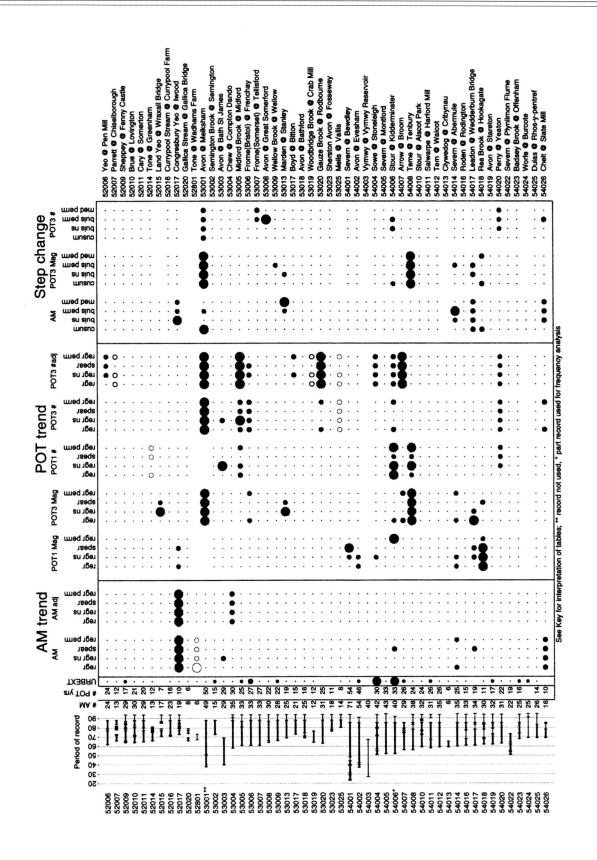

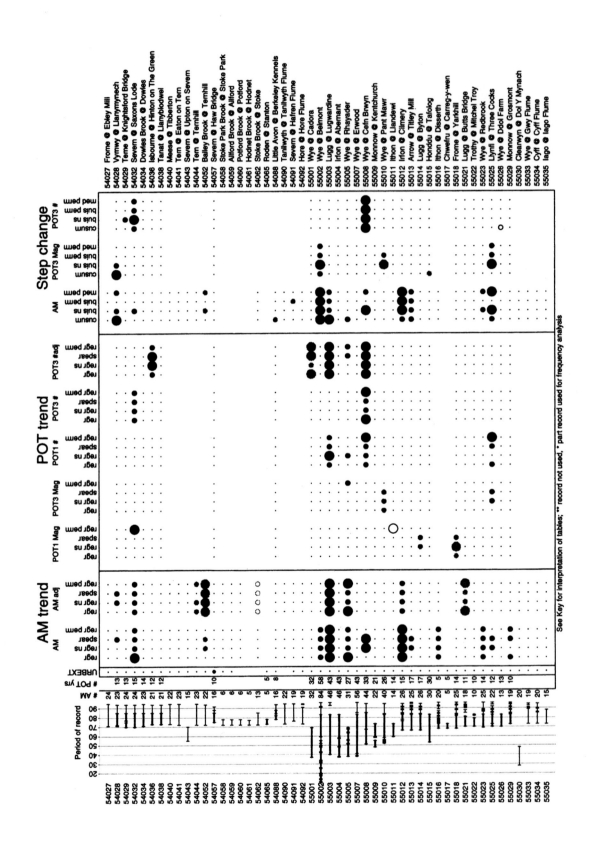

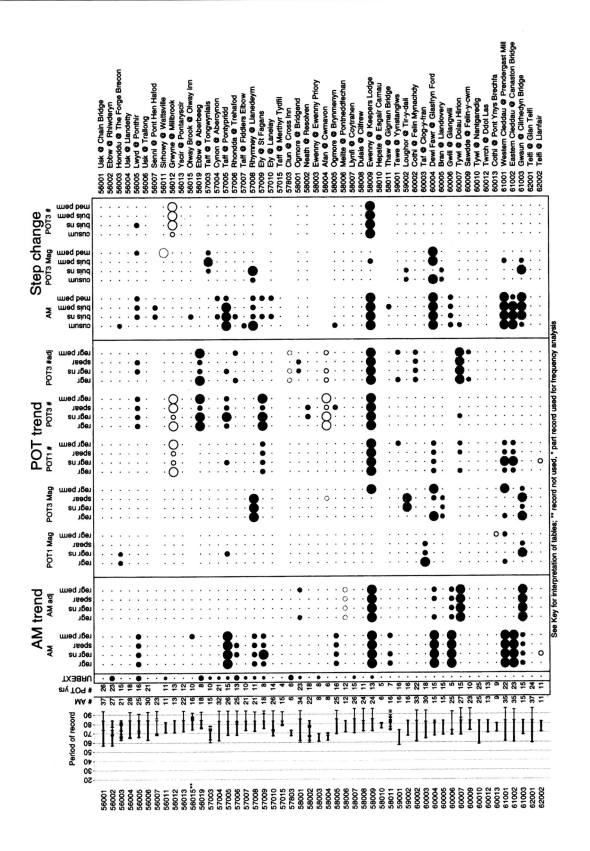

See Key for interpretation of tables; '**' record not used; '*' part record used for frequency analysis

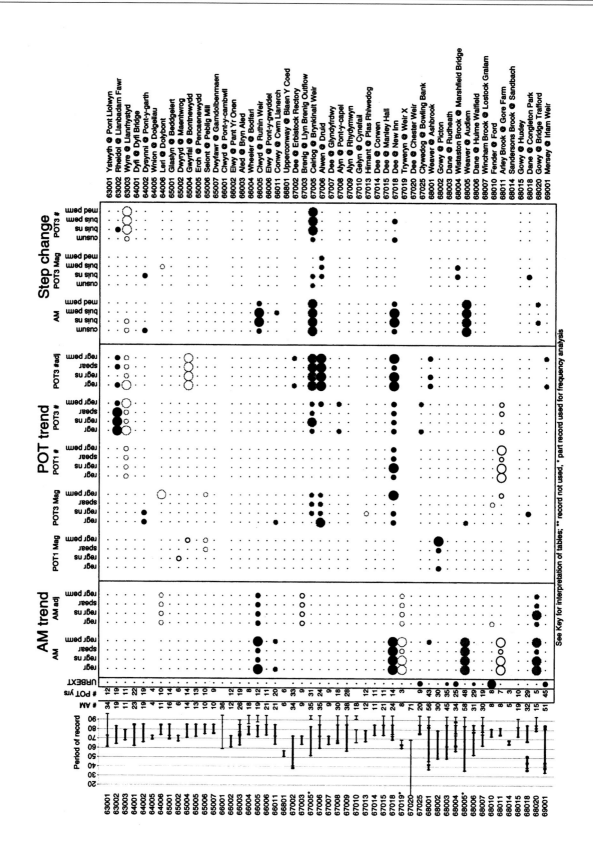

See Key for interpretation of tables; * record not used; ** record not used for frequency analysis

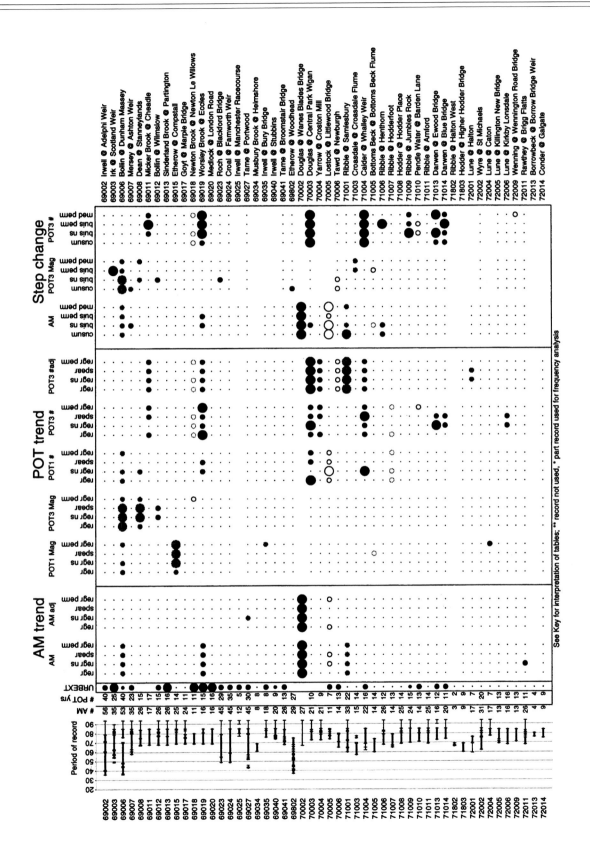

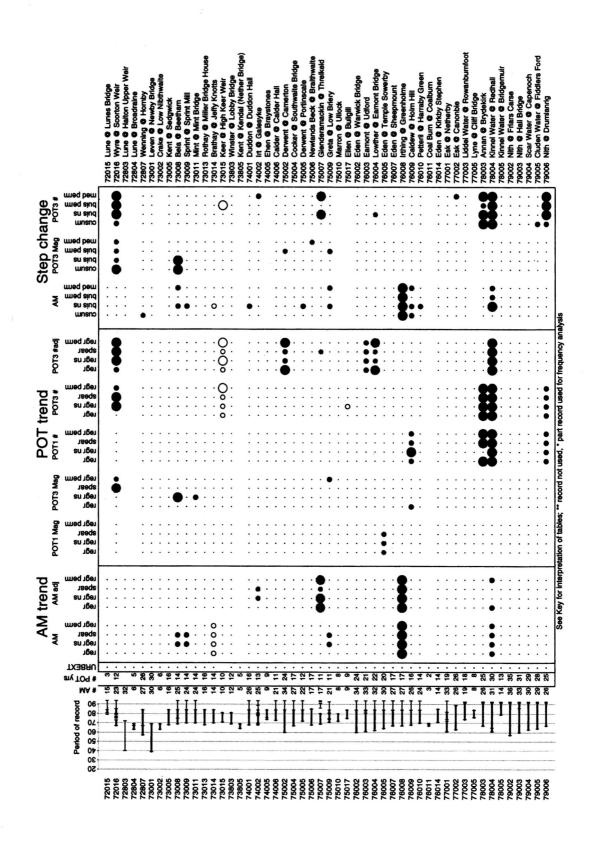

See Key for interpretation of tables; '' record not used; ' part record used for frequency analysis

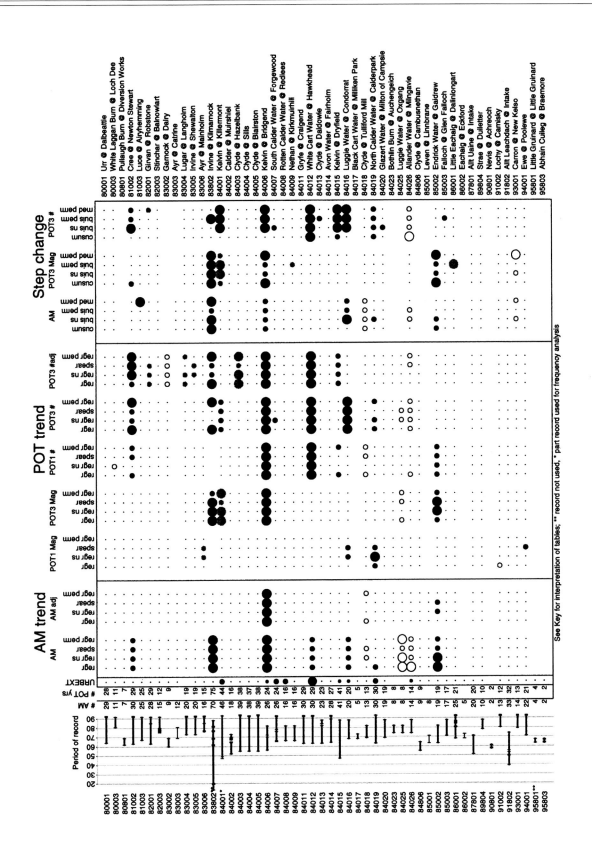

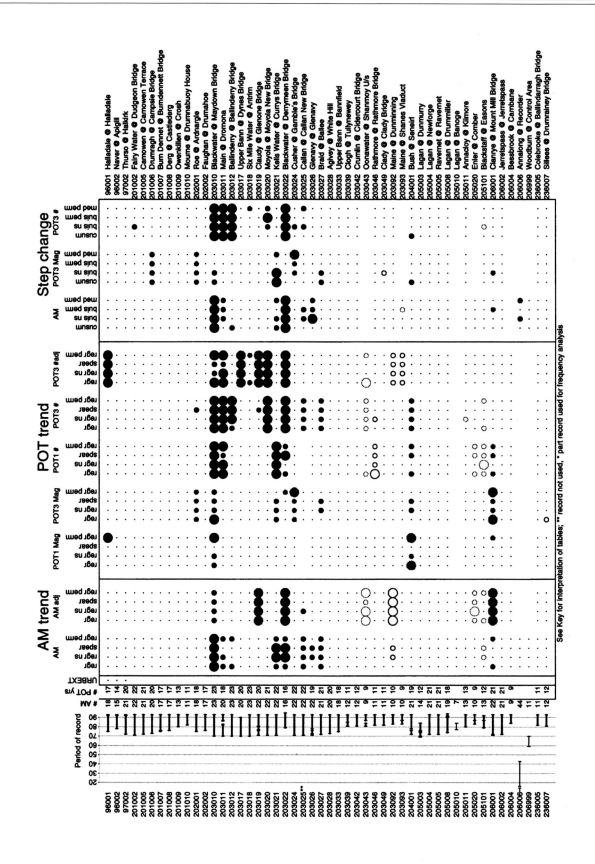

Chapter 22   Validation and update of flood peak data

22.1 Introduction

The publication of instantaneous flood peaks for over 550 gauging stations in Volume IV of the Flood Studies Report (NERC, 1975) was the culmination of a huge collation, appraisal, extraction and processing exercise by the research team.

A second phase of extraction, carried out at the Department of Environment's Water Data Unit (WDU), and further major updates to both peaks-over-threshold and annual maximum flood peak data at IH (Bayliss and Jones, 1993) meant that a significant extension to the original dataset had been achieved by 1991.

Plans to replace the FSR with the Flood Estimation Handbook recognised that maximising the use of available flood peak data, nearly 20 years on from the FSR, should be a primary concern. With many records ending in the early 1980s, there was a strong argument for extending records still further.

22.2 Approach

The approach taken to validating and updating the FEH flood peak dataset was a pragmatic one (Reed, 1994). With the agreement and support of senior management with water resource and flood defence responsibilities at Environment Agency (EA) headquarters, a package of material was sent to EA-nominated regional contacts. This included listings of current holdings of both POT and annual maximum data, and guidance on how these might be validated. Similar packages were sent to the other principal organisations concerned with river flow gauging in the UK: the regional offices of the Scottish Environment Protection Agency (SEPA) and the Department of Agriculture for Northern Ireland (DANI).

Where POT data had been extracted the FEH team was pleased to receive the data for review, although they were not requested specifically, since few authorities extracted POT data routinely. The request for information therefore focused on the need for the holdings of annual maximum data to be validated and updated.

22.3 Validation

22.3.1 Peaks-over-threshold data

Most of the EA regions were unable to check the POT series sent to them in their entirety but were able to comment on the authenticity of at least part of the record. The North East region had abstracted POT series for the Northumbria area and were able to compare IH values with those held locally.

Post-1973 POT data held at IH for Scottish catchments were in general derived by researchers at St Andrews University. These extractions were undertaken with the full cooperation of the gauging authorities in Scotland and it is understood that validation took place at the time.

In Northern Ireland, POT series for all good quality stations are routinely extracted from charts using FSR guidelines and exhaustive checking of the data held at IH was undertaken.

22.3.2 Annual maximum data

Annual maximum flood peaks are now routinely extracted by most gauging authorities in the UK. However, for most regions of the EA, these have typically only been stored on a computer database since the late 1970s. As a result, the validation of records prior to computerisation presented difficulties to some regions.

Generally, gauging authorities use 15-minute data in the derivation of annual maximum flood peaks. Although this means that annual maxima are not truly instantaneous, this is generally acceptable unless the catchment responds very quickly. In these cases there is a risk that the magnitude of the flood may be underestimated. For those catchments where flood peak data have been derived from charts (principally in Northern Ireland, Scotland and Northumbria), the annual maxima taken from these will be instantaneous and strictly comparable with data sent to them for validation.

The availability of these post-computerisation data allowed extensive checks to be made on both the date and magnitude of the annual maximum. The validation of pre-computerisation data has been less comprehensive since fewer values were available locally. The intention was that comparisons of the two datasets would always be made by experienced staff at the gauging authority. However, in some cases the checks had to be made by less experienced staff, or at IH using listings supplied by the measuring organisation, in order that the task did not delay the research programme unacceptably.

Where significant differences between IH and gauging authority values were found, checks were carried out in order to ascertain the reason for the discrepancies. First, if the authority was able to supply the relevant rating curves, these were compared with those used at IH. If the stage-discharge relationship used by IH was found to be inappropriate, the level data relating to the period of record concerned were reprocessed using the correct rating curve. In many cases this only occurred after discussion between the two parties since the choice of rating curve is often far from straightforward. Second, where the validity of the peak level, or the date on which the peak occurred, was in doubt, checks were made by referring to the original extraction notes and, where necessary, to microfilm copies of the charts.

Any corrections to annual maximum data were, of course, also applied to the appropriate events, or periods of record, in any peaks-over-threshold series held.

22.4 Update

22.4.1 Peaks-over-threshold data

Since POT data were not routinely extracted by many gauging authorities (§22.3.1), updates were principally in Northumbria, Scotland and Northern Ireland (Figure 22.1). Extensions to existing records were provided for 156 stations, and new POT records were received for a further 35 sites. With respect to the latter, 31 records were for stations completely new to the database, and four were POT series relating to sites where IH had previously held only annual maximum data. The North Region (East Division) of SEPA (formerly North East River Purification Board) extracted POT data from charts for 11 sites new to the database. The largest number of new records (19) was supplied by DANI's Rivers Agency, where the contemporary nature of the gauging network in the Province meant that these POT data were not previously included in the IH database.

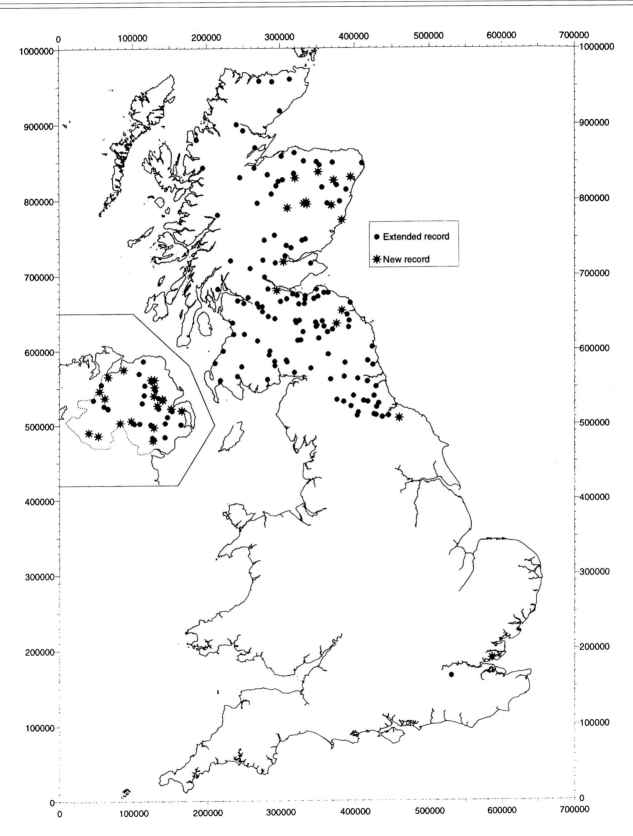

Figure 22.1 *Updates to peaks-over-threshold data*

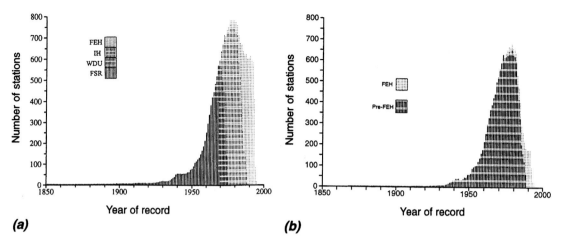

(a)   (b)

Figure 22.2 *Growth in holdings of (a) peaks-over-threshold and (b) annual maximum data*

The extraction of new POT records at IH was generally not practical within the timescale of the project. However, the offer of a long chart record by the Anglian Region of the EA provided the opportunity to obtain a flood series for a coastal urban catchment atypical of overall data holdings. Thus over 20 years of POT record were extracted for Eastwood Brook (37033) in Southend.

The time-consuming nature of extracting POT records from charts meant that a pragmatic approach had to be taken with regard to updating this part of the flood peak database. Nevertheless, Figure 22.2(a) illustrates that the overall holding of POT data was usefully extended.

22.4.2 Annual maximum data

The primary objective of the validation and updating programme, given the difficulties of obtaining good quality POT data, was to extend holdings of annual maximum flood data. Updates were received for 628 catchments. In addition, annual maximum data were derived from the 31 new POT records referred to above. Figure 22.3 shows that annual maximum updates were received for sites throughout the UK although difficulties were experienced in obtaining data for some regions.

Annual maximum flood peaks are now generally produced and stored routinely by the gauging authorities. However, because the data tend to be produced automatically there is a risk that spurious values will remain undetected unless the data are examined by personnel familiar with the gauging station concerned. In most cases data were reviewed by experienced staff before being sent to IH but, where this did not appear to be the case, additional checks were carried out by the FEH team before the data were accepted.

Although updates were provided for the majority of sites still in operation, data for about 150 sites were either not supplied by the gauging authority or were rejected before loading. Data were not loaded where the extraction appeared to be of poor quality or where level data were supplied and the gauging authority was unable to supply an appropriate stage-discharge relationship.

Updates were supplied in a number of different formats, from hand-written notes to data recorded in spreadsheets on floppy-disk. The wide variety of data formats made it difficult to set up standard 'review and load' procedures for

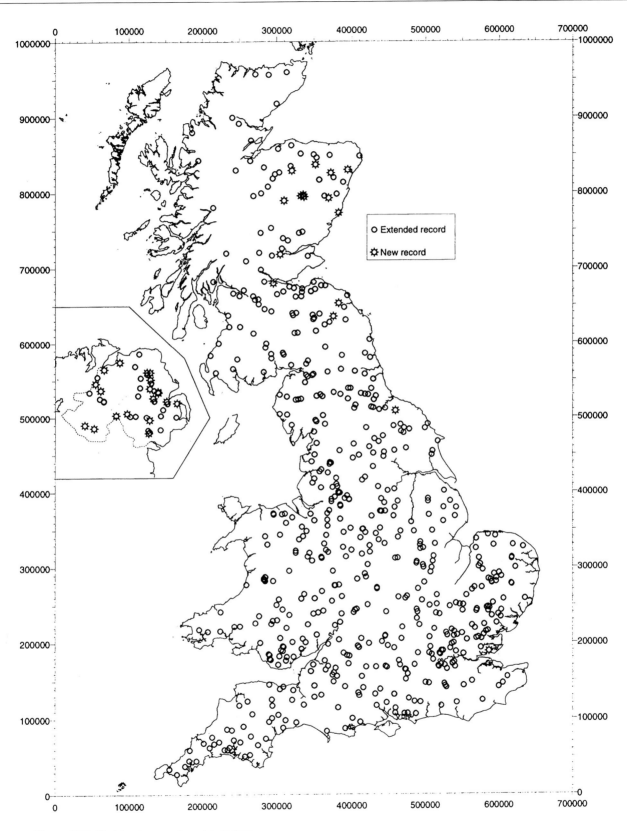

Figure 22.3 Updates to annual maximum data

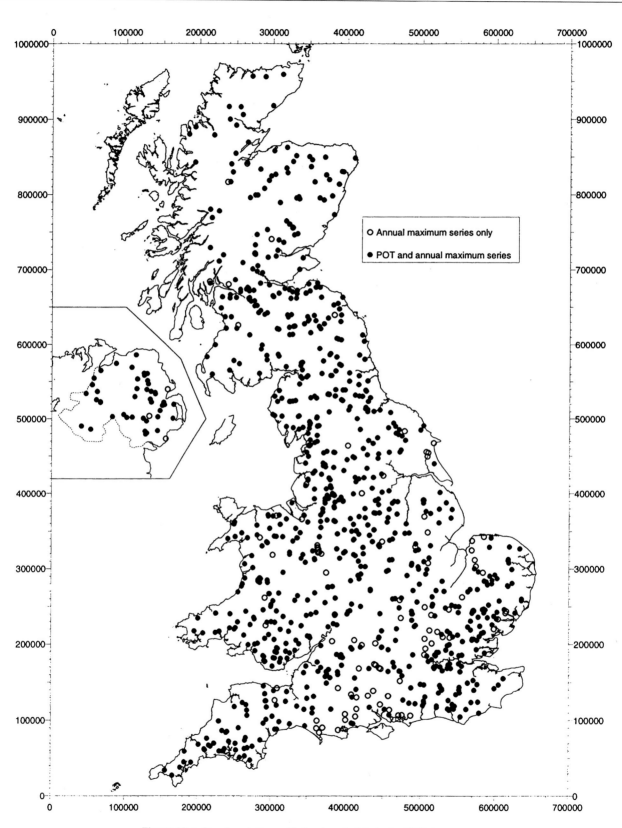

Figure 22.4 *Gauging stations with flood peak data in the FEH dataset*

incoming data. Although software was written to perform tasks where possible, a huge staff effort was needed to sift through updates comprising nearly 6000 years of record.

Despite these problems, the updating programme succeeded in significantly extending annual maximum flood peak records (Figure 22.2b) for a large number of catchments in a relatively short time. As a result the FEH flood peak dataset now comprises 1000 annual maximum flood records derived from gauges throughout the UK and peaks-over-threshold data for 890 of these sites (Figure 22.4). Annual maximum series only are held for 110 gauging stations, primarily where the permeable nature of the catchment results in few independent flood peaks and where the extraction of peaks-over-threshold data is impractical.

22.5 Summary

22.5.1 Peaks-over-threshold data

Nearly 88000 POT flood peaks are held with an average record length of almost 20 years. An examination of the number of *complete water years* (incomplete years are often excluded from analyses) held for each catchment, reveals that 79 per cent of sites have POT records longer than ten years and nearly 35 percent of catchments have more than 20 years of record (Figure 22.5). POT record lengths at seven sites exceed 50 years.

Figure 22.6 shows the geographical distribution of POT record lengths that occur within the dataset, ranging from 101 years for the Thames at Kingston (39001) to catchments with just two complete water years of data. Details about individual POT series can be found in Table A.1 (Appendix A).

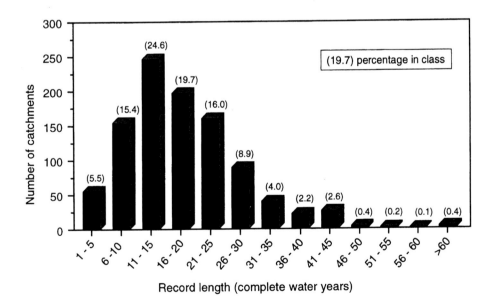

Figure 22.5 *Numerical distribution of catchment record lengths (peaks-over-threshold data) – complete water years*

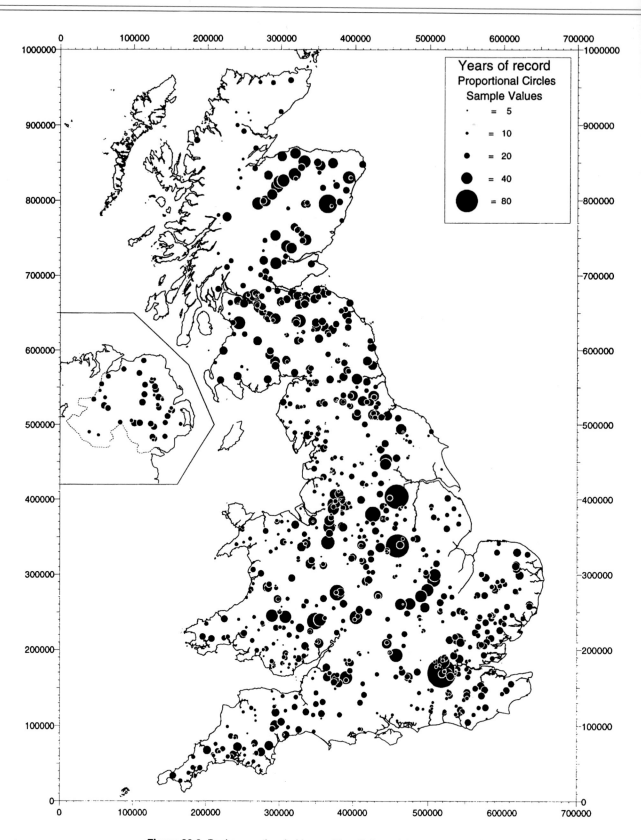

Figure 22.6 *Peaks-over-threshold record length (complete water years) for 890 catchments*

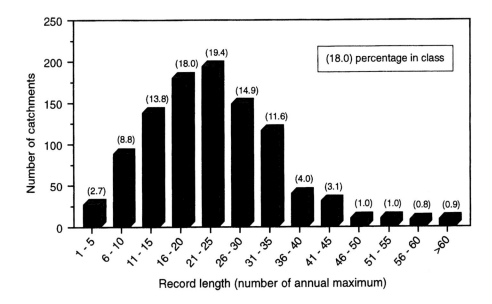

Figure 22.7 *Numerical distribution of catchment record lengths (annual maximum data)*

22.5.2 Annual maximum data

Holdings of annual maximum data now comprise over 23000 peaks with a mean record length of 23.4 years. Over 50 percent of catchments have records spanning more than 20 years and nearly 90 percent have annual maximum flood peaks for more than 10 years (Figure 22.7). Annual maximum record lengths exceed 50 years at 27 sites.

Figure 22.8 illustrates that, with the exception of sparsely gauged north-west Scotland, sites with medium to long records are reasonably well distributed. In Northern Ireland, records are relatively short, but there is a 44-year annual maximum series for the Annalong (206006). Table B.1 (Appendix B) gives details for individual catchments.

22.5.3 Comparison of FEH and FSR datasets

The validation and update of flood peak data have been successful in checking a large proportion of existing data, in usefully lengthening POT records in Scotland, Northern Ireland and Northumbria, and in significantly extending holdings of annual maximum data by over 32 percent. The average POT record length now available is double that used in FSR and with respect to annual maximum data has increased by a factor of 2.5.

22.6 Provision of flood peak data with the Handbook

The full flood peak dataset, described in this chapter and summarised in the Appendices, is provided in digital form on the accompanying CD-ROM. They are also supplied with the WINFAP-FEH software. It is important that users have access to *all* available flood data, and equally important that they are aware of limitations or problems that pertain to a particular flood series. Comments that

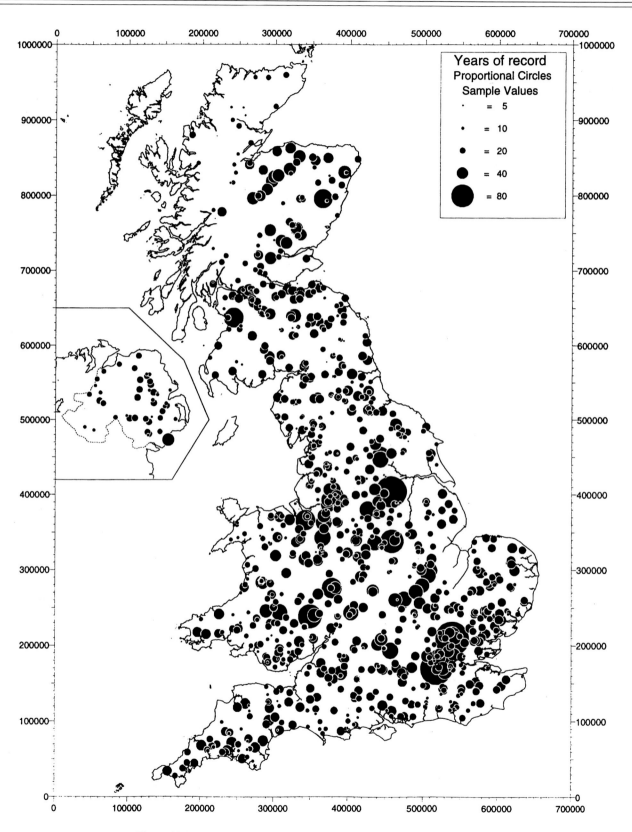

Figure 22.8 *Annual maximum record length for 1000 catchments*

have been recorded on data quality during work on the Handbook, are provided as "FEH comments" in WINFAP-FEH. Specifically, some records and part-records were not used after suspect data were highlighted during tests to identify non-stationarity, trends or discordancy (Chapter 21). A list of those rejected records and part-records is presented in Table 22.1. Although rejected from the FEH analyses, these data are included, marked with an asterisk, in the flood peak datasets accompanying WINFAP-FEH.

Table 22.1 *Rejected records and part-records*

Station No.	Name	Record rejected		FEH comments
		Annual maximum	POT	
19002	Almond at Almond Weir	1961 – 1968	09 Jun 1961 – 30 Sep 1969	Step change around 1970 thought to result from land use changes and new rating in 1969 – FEH uses data from 1 Oct 1969 only
22007	Wansbeck at Mitford	1963 – 1975	05 Feb 1963 – 30 Nov 1975	Record to 1 Nov 1966 from another site (Highford) is poor – FEH uses record from Mitford after new structure operative (1 Dec 1975 onwards)
23007	Derwent at Rowlands Gill	1963 – 1964	31 Oct 1962 – 30 Sep 1965	POT and ann max pre and post Derwent reservoir (1965). Short pre-reservoir record not used in FEH analyses.
25808	Burnt Weir at Moor House	**1954 – 1958**	**23 Nov 1953 – 17 May 1962**	Exceptionally small (0.05 square kilometres) experimental catchment at Moorhouse in Upper Teesdale. Not used in FEH analyses
25809	Bog Weir at Moor House	**1954 – 1958**	**03 Dec 1953 – 24 May 1962**	Exceptionally small (0.05 square kilometres) experimental catchment at Moorhouse in Upper Teesdale. Not used in FEH analyses
25810	Syke Weir at Moor House	**1956 – 1958**	**15 Aug 1956 – 24 May 1962**	Exceptionally small (0.04 square kilometres) experimental catchment at Moorhouse in Upper Teesdale. Not used in FEH analyses
26007	Catchwater at Withernwick	1965 – 1976	01 Oct 1969 – 30 Sep 1977	Bypassing of station and regular siltation of inlet pipe. No current meter confirmation of original calibration. Not used in FEH analyses
27021	Don at Doncaster	1868 – 1958	01 Oct 1868 – 13 Apr 1959	Ann max dates 1933–41 and 1955–56 arbitrary (01 Oct). Increase in POT frequency and decrease in magnitudes is evident after a large gap (1 Oct 1932 – 13 Apr 1959). FEH uses record from 14 Apr 1959
27032	Hebden Beck at Hebden	**1965 – 1993**	No POT data available	Unusual catchment – partly Karstic Limestone. Extreme event on 13 Aug 1975 estimated to be 27 cumecs. Rejected from ann max series since it was involved in a 'dam burst'. Series not used in FEH analyses
27033	Sea Cut at Scarborough	**1965 – 1993**	**22 Sep 1965 – 01 Jan 1983**	Flow regime augmented by flood flows diverted from Upper Derwent (see 27048). Not used in FEH analyses.
27048	Derwent at West Ayton	**1972 – 1993**	**01 May 1972 – 04 Jan 1983**	Flood regime strongly affected by a major drainage diversion, the Sea Cut (27033) which intercepts flood flows from 95% of the catchment. Not used in FEH analyses
32003	Harpers Brook at Old Mill Br.	1939 – 1965	07 Dec 1938 – 16 Sep 1965	An increase in POT frequency and magnitudes through the record is evident – FEH uses record from 17 Sept 1965 when new weir was built
32008	Nene/Kislingbury at Dodford	1945 – 1966	07 Dec 1944 – 30 Sep 1967	Step change in POT frequency evident in late 1960s. FEH uses record from 1 Oct 1967 when new weir built
33020	Alconbury Brook at Brampton	**1963 – 1983**	**07 Mar 1963 – 14 Jan 1985**	Poor quality station which suffers from ungauged out-of-bank flows and a structure that drowns. Not used for FEH analyses

[Continued on page 272]

Table 22.1 *continued*

Station No.	Name	Record rejected Annual maximum	POT	FEH comments
40009	Teise at Stone Bridge	1975 – 1985	01 Oct 1975 – 02 Jan 1987	POT and ann max are pre and post Bewl Bridge reservoir (1975). FEH analyses use pre-reservoir record to 30 Sep 1975
42007	Alre at Drove Lane	**1969 – 1993**	No POT data available	Ann max largely derived by taking highest stage on 2.5 m weir and using highest stage on corresponding day at 1.5 m weir. Groundwater catchment exceeds topographic catchment. Not used in FEH analyses
53001	Avon at Melksham	**1938 – 1987**	**03 Dec 1937 – 02 Dec 1988**	Gross step change in POT magnitudes evident in early 1970s. Poor quality record with complex rating and datum changes. Data not used for FEH analyses
54006	Stour at Kidderminster	1952 – 1978	23 Jul 1952 – 01 Jan 1979	Early level data appear to be suspect – FEH uses record from 2 Jan 1979
56015	Olway Brook at Olway Inn	**1974 – 1991**	**01 Oct 1974 – 31 Dec 1984**	Above 1.8 m there is considerable floodplain flow. Truncated annual maximum series almost certainly due to ungauged bypassing of station. Not used in FEH analyses
67005	Ceiriog at Brynkinalt Weir	1952 – 1968	01 Oct 1952 – 05 Oct 1969	A reduction in POT magnitudes and frequency coincided with building of new gauging structure – FEH uses data from 6 Oct 1969 when new weir became operative
67019	Tryweryn at Weir X	1964 – 1968	No POT data rejected	POT data are pre-reservoir. Ann max are pre and post-reservoir. Post-reservoir ann max (1964 – 1968) not used in FEH analyses
68005	Weaver at Audlem	1936 – 1968	19 Jun 1936 – 30 Sep 1969	Early rating is thought to be suspect – FEH uses data from 1 Oct 1969 when new rating applied
83802	Irvine at Kilmarnock	**1913 – 1987**	**29 Aug 1913 – 31 Dec 1988**	Increasing POT magnitudes and frequency. Data quality thought to be poor – data not used for FEH analyses
84001	Kelvin at Killermont	1947 – 1961	01 Jan 1949 – 28 Jun 1962	Early rating thought to be suspect – FEH uses data from 29 Jun 1962
95801	Little Gruinard at Lit. Gruinard	**1963 – 1966**	**15 Nov 1962 – 11 Feb 1968**	The gauging station is about 8 km downstream of a large lake (Fionn Loch) which dominates the flood regime (FARL = 0.557). Not used in FEH analyses
203025	Callan at Callan New Bridge	**1971 – 1992**	**31 Aug 1971 – 31 Dec 1993**	DANI advise that high flows are truncated by upstream bridge and ungauged out-of-bank flows. Not used in FEH analyses

Emboldened font denotes that the complete record was rejected.

Chapter 23 Deriving flood peak data

23.1 Introduction

Time series data, by their very nature, quickly become out-of-date. The effort required to update the large number of flood peak series used in the FEH was considerable (see Chapter 22). Inevitably the data provided with WINFAP-FEH are already out-of-date. Rightly, users will want to gain access to updated records across the UK, and to update particular records themselves.

This chapter seeks to give guidance to those who are new to deriving flood peak data by briefly summarising the procedures adopted at IH over a period of nearly thirty years. It is anticipated that gauging authorities will, in due course, take responsibility for overseeing these updates and revisions, and that users will gain access to UK flood peak datasets via the Internet.

23.2 Flood peak data

There are two types of flood peak data series used in statistical flood frequency estimation: the annual maximum and peaks-over-threshold (POT) series. The former comprises the largest flood peak in each year (usually a water year) and the latter consists of independent flood peaks above a defined threshold. Annual maxima are easier to derive but provide less information about the flood regime than a POT series, which typically comprises between three to five times more events. In addition, annual maximum series can contain a value that, because of its small magnitude, cannot be considered a true flood. It is included because it represents the highest flow recorded during the water year. Some annual maximum series may contain more than one such peak.

Many permeable catchments produce a relatively smooth hydrograph with few real flood peaks. Since the river flow may stay above the defined threshold for long periods, perhaps with no discernible peak, it can be inappropriate to try to extract a POT series. In these cases, only annual maximum data are derived.

23.3 Water level records

Early streamflow records were generally made using an autographic recorder where a continuous trace of water level was recorded on a chart (Figure 23.1). Digital recorders eventually supplemented or replaced the analogue recorders at many sites, with stage (i.e. water level above an established datum) typically recorded every 15 minutes. A comparison of the extraction of flood peak data from analogue charts with those from digital records can be found in Section 23.6.

23.4 Rating curves

The computation of river flow from river level, or stage, requires a relationship between the two to be established, with discharge measurements required over a range of river levels. Normally, measurements at low or medium flows are relatively easy to obtain, but those at high flows less so.

A simple approach to producing a stage-discharge curve is to plot the discharge measurements on arithmetic graph paper, with discharge on the abscissa and gauge height (i.e. river level relative to the gauge datum) on the ordinate scale. The curve is then drawn through the scatter of the plotted points. However, in most cases, the stage-discharge relationship, or rating curve, is defined by using

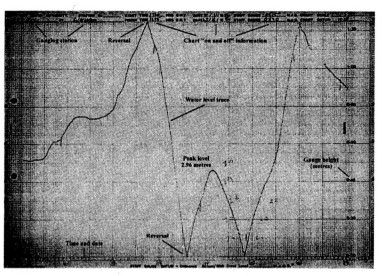

Figure 23.1 A weekly chart taken from an autographic recorder on the Avon at Evesham (54002)

the logarithmic method. This has the advantage of portraying the rating curve as a straight line, or a set of straight-line segments, by adding or subtracting a datum correction value to the gauge height (Figure 23.2). The stage-discharge relationship is then expressed as:

$$Q = C(h + a)^n$$

where Q is the discharge, h is the gauge height, a is the stage at zero flow (datum correction), and C and n are constants (Herschy, 1995).

Figure 23.2 provides an example where two rating segments are required for the calculation of flood flows. The lower segment is used for the production of flood flows up to bankfull and the upper segment when flows are out-of-bank (i.e. no longer confined to the river channel). Note that the gradient of the out-of-bank segment is less steep than that used for in-bank flows. Where flows exceed bankfull the cross-sectional area occupied by the river often increases dramatically, and, once this occurs, a relatively small rise in water level generally represents a significant increase in discharge.

Gauging station records which incorporate good estimates of flood peaks above bankfull level are relatively rare. The relative infrequency of such floods, their short duration on responsive catchments, and problems of access to the gauged section when the area is flooded, can mean that some opportunities to improve the high-flow calibration of the stage-discharge curve are lost. In addition, where there is ponding or storage on the floodplain, water returning to the channel from flooded areas may cause a backwater effect and discharge for a given stage is significantly decreased. In this situation, it is difficult to develop a single rating curve which is appropriate to all conditions (Herschy, 1995).

As a consequence, flood rating curves, particularly those that represent out-of-bank conditions, are often based on a small number of measurements, or on extrapolation from the highest calibration measurement. The accurate measurement of flood flows is problematical, but of great importance, if high-flow rating curves are to be used with confidence. Hydraulic modelling can

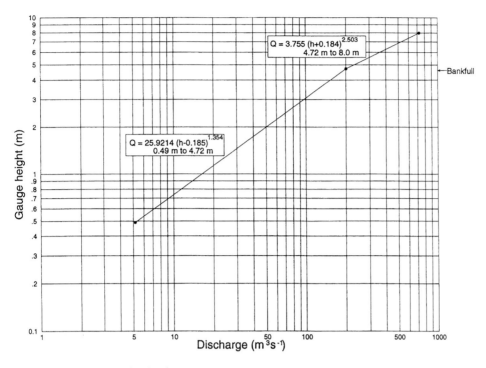

Figure 23.2 Compound flood rating curve

sometimes assist in rating curve extrapolation. However, it is a poor substitute for direct measurement of flood flows.

23.5 Definition of terms and procedures for data extraction

A set of rules and procedures was developed as part of the FSR (Volume IV) to promote the uniform extraction of flood peak data. This methodology was adopted in subsequent phases of extraction carried out at IH (Bayliss and Jones, 1993) and checks were made to ensure that data, contributed to the dataset by other organisations and individuals, conformed to these procedures. A brief description of the approach is given here.

23.5.1 Peaks-over-threshold series

Abstraction threshold

An abstraction threshold of river flow is chosen to give, on average, about five peaks a year. To achieve this average, a practical approach is to choose an initial threshold that is likely to be too low, by quickly reviewing all the major peaks for the period of record being analysed, and then progressively raising the threshold until the desired number of events is realised.

Where an extension to an existing POT series is being derived, the same threshold should be used to ensure consistency throughout the record. If, after extending the series, the threshold appears to have been set too low (i.e. too many peaks) then the threshold can be raised. This new threshold should then be applied retrospectively to the *complete* record for that site. The threshold can also be lowered, if the average number of peaks is too low, but this will require earlier extractions to be redone using the new threshold.

Setting the abstraction threshold low enough to produce an average of about five peaks a year means that, for analytical purposes, there is the flexibility to raise the threshold to exclude the smaller floods. For example, a POT series with an average of three events per year (POT3) contains only the medium and large floods, and a POT series with an average of one event per year (POT1) only the largest. Note that the POT1 series is not the same as the annual maximum series, since, with respect to the former, there may be some years with no POT1 event and other years with several events. When comparing POT series, it is often important that the average number of events per year should be the same for each site (e.g. standardising on the use of the POT3 series).

The threshold is specified in terms of river flow, rather than river level, since the latter is often defined relative to an arbitrary datum at the site (gauge height) that will be subject to change if the gauging site is altered (e.g. if a measuring structure is installed in a natural section). If charts are being used for the extraction, the trace is often one of river level. In this situation there is a requirement to convert the threshold flow to threshold level using the appropriate stage-discharge table or rating curve. If a new stage-discharge relationship is used part-way through the record, the threshold flow remains the same but the threshold level will usually change.

Date of flood peak

The day on which the flood peak occurred is defined by a 24-hour period starting from 0900 GMT, often referred to as the *water day*, to enable direct comparisons with most flow and meteorological data. The date format should include a four-digit year.

Independence of flood peaks

It is important, when identifying all peaks above the threshold, that they are subjected to independence tests before being recorded as a POT event, in order that multi-peaked events do not bias the resultant POT series. The FSR gives arbitrary, yet consistent, rules to determine the independence of adjacent flood peaks. When the time difference between two or more peaks is small, the highest is considered to be independent, while the independence of the others relative to this event is confirmed only if they satisfy the following criteria:

- The two peaks must be separated by at least three times the average time to rise. The time to rise is defined by calculating the time difference between the start of the rising limb and the peak, on the flood hydrograph. In order that the mean be representative, the time to rise should be calculated for at least five clean (i.e. not multi-peaked) events, whose peaks exceed the threshold.

- The minimum discharge in the trough between two peaks must be less than two-thirds of the discharge of the *first* of the two peaks. Where a river level record is being used, access to a stage-discharge table or rating curve is required (since the comparison is between *flows*), in order that this second test be applied. In practice many adjacent peaks fail the first test, so, in these cases, the second rather more time-consuming procedure need not be used.

An example illustrating the application of the independence tests to a number of adjacent peaks is given in Figure 23.3, where three times the average time to rise has been pre-calculated to be 15 hours.

Period of record

The first day of record examined should be noted. This defines the beginning (start date) of the POT period of record. In general this will be earlier than the first POT event, and it is important not to confuse the two dates. Similarly, the last day of record examined should be noted. This defines the end date of the POT period of record, not the date on which the last POT event occurred. Flood-free periods within the POT record are important in their own right, particularly if the temporal character of flood occurrences is being investigated.

Gaps in the POT series

When extracting a POT series, it is important to record any gaps in the record. If this is not done, periods when data are missing will simply be portrayed as

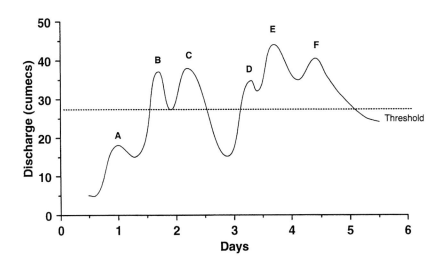

Three times the average time to rise = 15 hours.

Peak E is the largest and is therefore independent.

Peak D occurs less than 15 hours before peak E and is defined as dependent.

Peak F is defined as dependent since although it occurs more than 15 hours after peak E, the minimum discharge in the trough between the two peaks does not fall by more than two-thirds of the peak discharge for event E.

Peak C is larger than peaks A and B and is judged independent of peak E because (i) it occurs more than 15 hours beforehand and (ii) the minimum discharge in the trough between the two is less than two-thirds of the discharge for peak C.

Peak B occurs less than 15 hours before peak C and is therefore dependent.

Peak A is below the threshold and therefore not a POT event.

Figure 23.3 *Application of peaks-over-threshold independence rules*

flood-free, rather than what they are (i.e. gaps in the POT series). However, a POT series is devalued if there is a large number of gaps. If a missing period is thought likely to be flood-free, it is worth looking at records for neighbouring stations to determine if this is indeed the case. Where the gap is relatively short it is often possible to ascertain that no flood above the threshold occurred during the missing period. In this case, the gap need not be recorded. However, if there is doubt, a gap should be noted.

23.5.2 Annual maximum series

Water year

The calendar year begins and ends during the principal flood-producing period for many catchments in the UK, and as such tends to cut the flood series at an inappropriate time. The use of a water year seeks to avoid this by selecting a starting point that is coincident with the onset of a decline in soil moisture deficits: taken to be the start of the flood season. The choice is somewhat arbitrary however, since this turning point occurs at different times each year and will vary from one geographical region to another. Nevertheless, the use of a water year is more pertinent to flood data than the use of the calendar year, and the year used here begins on 1st October. The convention is that the annual maximum flood peak is recorded against the four-digit year in which the water year *begins*. For example, an annual maximum event occurring on 7th February 1990 will be recorded with the water year 1989.

Many gauging authorities, past and present, have routinely extracted annual maxima for calendar years rather than water years. In preference to discarding a long and valuable record which has been collated in calendar years (e.g. Lea at Feildes Weir, 1851-1994) the record can be held with an appropriate flag to distinguish the record from those which are defined using water years. However, there are only three such records in the FEH dataset (38001, 55030 and 72803), and the use of water years, rather than calendar years, is strongly encouraged.

Date of flood peak and gaps in record

The day on which the annual maximum flood peak occurred is defined by use of the water day (i.e. beginning at 0900 GMT), in keeping with the rules applied to the extraction of POT data.

It is important that any gaps in an annual maximum series are apparent (perhaps by allocating a null value or missing code against the relevant water year), but it is not usually necessary to record missing periods separately. The omission of an annual maximum value in a series implies there is a gap in the record, without recording the details in the way that is necessary for POT data.

23.6 Analogue or digital?

Extraction of flood peak data for the Floods Studies Report was largely undertaken using microfilmed copies of analogue charts (NERC, 1975). Although digital recorders were installed at most gauging sites in the early 1960s, the use of charts was seen to have a number of advantages:

- the flood peaks are truly instantaneous;
- independence rules for POT data can be applied more easily;
- spurious values and gaps in the record can be spotted quickly.

Subsequent updates to the flood peak dataset at IH, carried out in the 1980s (Bayliss and Jones, 1993), continued the procedure of collecting charts from the gauging authority and obtaining microfilm copies. The charts could then be returned, with the microfilm forming a valuable archive which could be revisited after extraction, if the need arose.

Incomplete or illegible chart annotation and, more commonly, a poorly defined trace, are problems associated with using analogue records, particularly those taken from the early recorders. Generally, deriving flood peak data from charts is labour intensive and the use of autographic charts at gauging stations likely to become less common. Any future collation of flood peak data, therefore, will almost certainly rely on the use of digital data. It is important that techniques be established which allow annual maximum and peaks-over-threshold data to be derived from digital data, and maintain the quality of extraction that can be achieved when using analogue charts.

23.7 Deriving flood peak data from digital records

23.7.1 Instantaneous flood peaks

Digital recorders typically log river level every 15 minutes. Flood peaks taken from these data are not, therefore, truly instantaneous, but are sufficiently accurate for all but the most responsive catchments. Where a 15-minute interval is inadequate, the use of programmable loggers allows the gauging authority to customise the recording interval of the instrument to the response characteristics of the catchment.

23.7.2 POT series

The automated production of a POT series from digital data requires a considered approach. Some database systems have the option to identify all peak levels or flows above a specified threshold, with the requirement that events do not occur on the same calendar day, acting as a crude test for independence. Extraction carried out in this way will inevitably include a number of dependent flood peaks in the resultant POT series. In addition, the need to record the start and finish points of the record being analysed, and any gaps that may occur, is often overlooked.

To produce a POT series of comparable quality, to that which can be derived manually from charts, requires that the independence tests are rigorously applied. The manual procedure adopted when using charts, could be simulated by producing a hydrograph from the digital data for the relevant period of record, to allow the independence tests to be applied manually. This would be time-consuming but reliable. The development of software to apply independence rules to digital river level or flow data automatically would greatly facilitate the derivation of POT records. However, to be successful the automated system will need to cope with all the variations in hydrograph shape that can occur. Manual checks using visualisation of the flood hydrographs, at least for a small number of flood events, are still likely to be necessary with an automated system, if the quality of the extraction is to be maintained.

23.7.3 Annual maximum series

The derivation of the annual maximum flood from digital data, for each water year, is relatively straightforward. Most database systems that store time-series data have software options that will report the maximum value for a specified period. The confidence with which this level or flow value can be accepted will depend on the extent to which the data have been subject to quality control procedures. Where possible it is well worth producing a hydrograph of the annual maximum flood event for visual inspection. In this way, peaks that are in fact spurious points on the hydrograph (perhaps from a flood-gate being opened or an inlet pipe to the stilling-well being flushed out) can be quickly identified.

Where an annual maximum at the end of a water year is followed closely by another annual maximum event at the start of the following water year, checks for independence should be made using the POT independence criteria (see §23.5.1).

Acknowledgements

Many individuals working for gauging authorities assisted in the supply of flood peak data, without which the validation and updating of flood series would have been much the poorer. Geraldene Wharton is thanked for stimulating the inclusion of a *QMED* estimation method based on channel dimensions (§5.2), and for supplying related data and advice. David Archer, Andrew Black, Dick Bradford and John Packman were amongst those who exchanged ideas on particular topics, including: historical floods, flood seasonality, permeable catchments, and the effect of urban development on flood runoff.

However, the main acknowledgement is to Don Burn, Con Cunnane, Jon Hosking and David Jones: for their important and generous contributions to the statistical flood frequency research presented here. Although remembered more generally in the Preface, it was to research related to this volume that Tanya Jones principally contributed before her illness.

References

Acreman, M.C. and Wiltshire, S.E. 1989. The regions are dead, long live the regions: methods of identifying and dispensing with regions for flood frequency analysis. In: Roald, L. et al. (eds), *FRIENDS in Hydrology Bolkesjø (Norway) (IAHS Publ. No. 187)*. 175-188. International Association of Hydrological Sciences Press, Wallingford.

Ahmad, M.I., Sinclair, C.D. and Werritty, A. 1988. Log-logistic flood frequency analysis, *J. Hydrol.* **98**, 215-24.

Allen, D.M. 1974. The relationship between variable selection and data augmentation and a method for prediction. *Technometrics* **16**, 125-127.

Arnell, N.W. 1988. Unbiased estimation of flood risk with the GEV distribution. *Stochastic Hydrol. Hydraul.* **2**, 201-212.

Bayliss A.C. and Jones R.C. 1993. Peaks-over-threshold flood database: summary statistics and seasonality. *Institute of Hydrology Report No. 121*.

Bradford, R.B. and Faulkner, D.S. 1997. Review of floods and flood frequency estimation in permeable catchments. Report to MAFF, Institute of Hydrology, Wallingford, UK.

Buckingham, E. 1914. On physically similar systems; illustrations of the use of dimensional equations. *Physical Review*, 1914, 4, 345-376.

Buishand, T.A. 1982. Some methods for testing the homogeneity of rainfall records. *J. Hydrol.* **58**, 11-27.

Burn, D.H. 1990. Evaluation of regional flood frequency analysis with a region of influence approach. *Water Res. Res.* **26**, 2257-2265.

Burn, D.H. 1997. Catchment similarity for regional flood frequency analysis using seasonality measures. *J. Hydrol.* **202**, 221-220.

Calver, A. and Lamb, R. 1996. Flood frequency estimation using continuous rainfall-runoff modelling. *Phys. Chem. Earth* **20**, 479-483.

Chiew, F.H.S. and McMahon, T.A. 1993. Detection of trend or change in annual flow of Australian rivers. *Int. J. Climatol.* **13**, 643-653.

Cleveland, W.S. 1979. Robust locally weighted regression and smoothing scatterplots. *J. Amer. Statist. Soc.* **74**, 829-836.

Cox, D.R. and Lewis, P.A.W. 1966. *The statistical analysis of series of events*. Methuen. 285pp.

Cunnane, C. 1978. Unbiassed plotting positions – a review. *J. Hydrol.* **37**, 205-22.

Dixon W.J. and Massey, F.J. 1957. *Introduction to statistical analysis*. McGraw Hill, 488pp.

Draper, N.R. and Smith, 1981. *Applied Regression Analysis*, 2nd Edn. John Wiley and Sons.

Fisher, N.I. 1993. *Statistical analysis of circular data*. Cambridge University Press.

Green, S., Sanderson, F.J. and Marsh, T.J. 1996. Evidence for recent instability in rainfall and runoff patterns in the Celtic regions of western Europe. In: *Hydrologie dans les pays celtiques*, Rennes (France). Ed INRA, Paris 1996 (Les Colloques, n° 79). 73-83.

Greenwood, J.A. Landwehr, J.M., Matalas, N.C, and Wallis, J.R. 1979. Probability weighted moments: definition and relation to parameters of several distributions expressible in reverse form. *Wat. Resour. Res.* **15**, 1049-54.

Grew, H. and Werrity, A. 1995. Changes in flood frequency and magnitude in Scotland. BHS 5th National Hydrology Symposium, Edinburgh, 3.1-3.9.

Gringorten, I.I. 1963. A plotting rule for extreme probability paper. *J. Geophys. Res.* **68**, 813-4.

Guttman, N.B., Hosking, J.R.M. and Wallis, J.R. 1993. Regional precipitation quantile values for the continental United States computed from L-moments. *J. Climate* **6**, 2236-2340.

Herschy, R.W. 1995. *Streamflow measurement* (2nd edn), E. & F.N. Spon.

Hirsh, D.M., Helsel, D.R., Cohn, T.A. and Gilroy, E.J. 1993. Statistical analysis of hydrological data. In: Maidment D. (ed.), *Handbook of Hydrology*, 17.1-17.55.

Holder, R.L. 1985. *Multiple regression in hydrology.* Institute of Hydrology, Wallingford.

Hollis, G.E. 1975. The effect of urbanisation on floods of different recurrence intervals. *Water Res. Res.* **11**, 431-435.

Hosking, J.R.M. 1996. Fortran routines for use with the method of L-moments, Version 3. Research Report RC 200525, IBM Research Division, Yorktown Heights, NY.

Hosking J.R.M. and Wallis, J.R. 1987. Parameter and quantile estimation for generalised Pareto distribution. *Technometrics* **29**, 339-49.

Hosking J.R.M. and Wallis, J.R. 1997. Regional frequency analysis: an approach based on L-moments. Cambridge University Press, 224 pp.

Hosking J.R.M., Wallis, J.R. and Wood, E.F. 1985. Estimation of the generalised extreme-value distribution by the method of probability-weighted moments. *Technometrics* **27**, 251-61.

ICE 1996. *Floods and Reservoir Safety: An Engineering Guide,* 3rd edn, Institution of Civil Engineers, Thomas Telford, London.

IE Australia 1987. *Australian rainfall and runoff: a guide to flood estimation,* edited by D.H. Pilgrim, Institution of Engineers, Australia.

IH/BGS 1998. *Hydrological Data UK: Hydrometric Register and Statistics 1991-1995.* Institute of Hydrology / British Geological Survey, Wallingford.

Kendall, M.G. 1970. *Rank correlation methods.* Griffin, London.

Kendall, M. and Stuart, A. 1979. *The advanced theory of statistics.* Oxford University Press, Oxford, England.

Kim, P.J. and Jennrich, R.I. 1973. Tables of the exact sampling distribution of the two sample Kolmogorov-Smirnov criteria. In: Harper, H.L. and Owen, D.B. (eds), *Selected tables in mathematical statistics,* Volume 1. Providence, Rhode Island: American Mathematical Society.

Kuczera, G. 1983. Effects of sampling uncertainty and spatial correlation on an empirical Bayes procedure for combining site and regional information. *J. Hydrol.* **65**, 373-398.

Kuczera, G. 1997. A generalised expected probability approach to design flood estimation. 24th Hydrology and Water symposium proceedings, Water/Land, 65-70.

Landwehr , J.M., Matalas, N.C. and Wallis J.R. 1979. Probability weighted moments compared with some traditional techniques in estimating Gumbel parameters and quantiles. *Wat. Resour. Res.* **15**, 1055-64

Langbein, W.B. 1949. Annual floods and the partial duration method. *Trans. Amer. Geophys. Union* **30**, 879-881.

Leese 1973. Use of censored data in the estimation of the Gumbel distribution parameters for annual maximum flood series. *Wat. Resour. Res.* **9**, 1534-42.

Lehmann, E.L. 1975. *Nonparametrics: statistical methods based on ranks.* McGraw-Hill, 457pp.

McGilchrist, C.A. and Woodyer, K.D. 1975. Note on a distribution-free CUSUM technique. *Technometrics* **17**, 321-325.

Mallow, C.L. 1973. Some comments on Cp. *Technometrics* **15**, 661-675.

Maritz, J.S. 1981. *Distribution-free statistical methods.* Chapman and Hall, 264pp.

Miller, A.J., 1984. Selection of subsets of regression variables (with discussion), *J. Royal Statist. Soc.* Ser. A, **147**, 389-425.

Naden, P.S., Calver, A.F., Samuels, P. and Ash, J. 1997. Whole catchment modelling: a basis for an integrated approach to catchment management. Report to MAFF. Institute of Hydrology, Wallingford.

NERC, 1975. *Flood Studies Report.* Natural Environment Research Council.

Pettit, A.N. 1979. A non-parametric approach to the change point problem. *Applied Statistics* **28**, 126-135.

Press, W.H., Flannery, B.P., Teukolsky, S.A. and Vetterly, W.T. 1992. *Numerical recipes in Fortran,* 2nd Edn. Cambridge University Press.

Reed, D.W. 1994. Plans for the Flood Estimation Handbook. Proc. Conf. of River & Coastal Engineers, Loughborough. MAFF, London. 8.3.1-8.3.8.

Reed, D.W. and Field, E.K. 1992. *Reservoir flood estimation: Another look.* IH Report No. 114. Institute of Hydrology, Wallingford.

Robinson, D.N. 1995. *The Louth Flood of 29th May 1920*. Louth Naturalists', Antiquarian and Literary Society, Louth, Lincolnshire. 36pp.

Robson, A.J., Jones, T.K., Reed, D.W. and Bayliss, A.C. 1998. A study of national trend and variation in UK floods. *Int. J. Climat.* **18**, 165-182.

Siegel, S. and Castellan, N.J. 1988. *Non parametric statistics for the behavioral sciences.* McGraw-Hill, 399pp.

Sprent, P. 1989. *Applied non-parametric statistical methods*. Chapman and Hall, 259pp.

Statistical Sciences, 1995. Splus Version 3.3 supplement, Seattle: StatSci, a division of MathSoft, Inc. Chapter 3.

Stedinger, J.R. 1983. Design events with a specified flood risk. *Wat. Resour. Res.* **19**, 511-522.

Stedinger, J.R. and Tasker, G.D. 1985. Regional Hydrologic analysis I. Ordinary, weighted and generalised least regression squares compared. *Wat. Resour. Res.* **31**, 1421-1432.

Stedinger, J.R., Vogel, R.M. and Foufoula-Georgiou, E. 1993. Frequency analysis of extreme events. In: Maidment D. (ed.), *Handbook of Hydrology*, 18.1-18.65.

Tasker, G.D. and Stedinger, J.R. 1989. An operational GLS model for hydrologic regression. *J. Hydrol.* **111**, 361-375.

US Water Resources Council, 1977. Guidelines for determining flood flow frequency. Bulletin 17A, Hydrology committee, Washington D.C.

Vogel, R.M. and Stedinger, J.R., 1985. Minimum variance streamflow augmentation procedures. *Wat. Resour. Res.* **21**, 715-723.

Walling, D.E. 1979. The hydrological impact of building activity: a study near Exeter. In: Hollis, G.E. (ed.), *Man's impact on the hydrological cycle in the United Kingdom*. Geo Abstracts Ltd., Norwich, 135-151.

Wang, Q.J. 1996a. Direct sample estimators of L-moments. *Wat. Resour. Res.* **32**, 3617-3619.

Wang, Q.J. 1996b. Using partial probability-weighted moments to fit the extreme value distributions to censored samples. *Wat. Resour. Res.* **32**, 1767-1771.

Wang, Q.J. 1997. LH-moments for statistical analysis of extreme events. *Wat. Resour. Res.* **33**, 2841-2848.

Weisberg, S. 1980. *Applied linear regression*. John Wiley and Sons, Chichester.

Wharton, G. 1989. River discharge estimated from channel dimensions in Britain. PhD thesis, University of Southampton, 378 pp.

Wharton, G. 1992. Flood estimation from channel size: guidelines for using the channel-geometry method. *Appl. Geog.* **12**, 339-359.

Wharton, G., Arnell, N.W., Gregory, K.J. and Gurnell, A.M. 1989. River discharge estimated from channel dimensions. *J. Hydrol.* **106**, 365-376.

Woodley, M. 1996. A review of two national rainfall series. *Int. J. Climatol.* **16**, 677-687.

Worsley, K.J. 1979. On the likelihood ratio test for a shift in location of normal populations. *J. Amer. Statist. Assoc.* **74**, 365-376.

Appendix A

Register of gauging stations and summary statistics: peaks-over-threshold flood data

Table A.1 gives, for 890 catchments, period of record details and summary statistics following the FEH update of peaks-over-threshold flood data. Catchments marked with an asterisk indicate that part of the record, or in some cases the complete record, has not been used in the Volume 3 analyses (see Table 22.1).

A brief description of some of the variables shown is given below.

Grid ref
Grid reference of the gauging station, taken from the National River Flow Archive. (For automatic generation of an IHDTM catchment boundary, a grid reference located exactly on the appropriate drainage path should be sought.)

NRFA area
Catchment area to the gauging station in km², taken from the National River Flow Archive.

THRESH
Abstraction threshold in $m^3 s^{-1}$.

NPOT
Number of peaks-over-threshold values held.

NYRS
Length of record in years (including incomplete water years but excluding gaps).

NWYRS
Length of record in years (complete water years only).

Ratio NPOT/NYRS
Average number of peaks per year taken over the whole record (including incomplete water years but excluding gaps).

Table A.1 *Period of record details and summary statistics – peaks-over-threshold flood data*

No.	Name	Grid ref	NRFA Area km²	Record starts	Record ends	THRESH	NPOT	NWYRS NYRS	NWYRS Ratio	No.
2001	Helmsdale at Kilphedir	2997 9181	551.4	01 01 1975	08 07 1993	97.00	98	18.5	17 5.3	2001
3001	Shin at Lairg	2581 9062	494.6	23 06 1950	31 12 1956	22.00	39	6.5	6 6.0	3001
3002	Carron at Sgodachail	2490 8921	241.1	01 01 1974	04 07 1993	106.00	108	19.5	18 5.5	3002
3003	Oykel at Easter Turnaig	2403 9001	330.7	01 01 1978	13 07 1993	210.00	73	15.5	14 4.7	3003
3801	Cassley at Duchally	2387 9168	72.3	08 09 1950	30 09 1959	42.00	51	8.6	8 6.0	3801
3803	Tirry at Rhian Bridge	2553 9167	64.2	29 06 1950	03 12 1958	32.54	38	8.4	7 4.5	3803
4001	Conon at Moy Bridge	2482 8547	961.8	09 07 1945	31 12 1956	191.00	79	11.3	9 7.0	4001
4003	Alness at Alness	2654 8695	201.0	01 01 1974	11 07 1993	30.00	107	19.5	18 5.5	4003
5001	Beauly at Erchless	2426 8406	849.5	09 12 1949	05 01 1964	180.00	68	14.0	10 4.9	5001
6003	Moriston at Invermoriston	2416 8169	391.0	19 03 1930	30 10 1944	164.00	83	14.6	13 5.7	6003
6007	Ness at Ness Side	2645 8427	1839.1	01 01 1973	11 07 1993	190.00	125	20.5	19 6.1	6007
6008	Enrick at Mill of Tore	2450 8300	105.9	01 01 1980	11 07 1993	14.58	126	13.5	11 9.3	6008
7001	Findhorn at Shenachie	2826 8337	415.6	01 08 1960	23 06 1993	107.00	245	32.9	31 7.5	7001
7002	Findhorn at Forres	3018 8583	781.9	19 06 1958	10 07 1993	145.00	195	35.0	33 5.6	7002
7003	Lossie at Sheriffmills	3194 8626	216.0	19 07 1958	31 12 1995	18.50	143	37.5	37 3.8	7003
8001	Spey at Aberlour	3278 8439	2654.7	01 01 1939	31 12 1974	242.00	116	26.0	24 4.5	8001
8002	Spey at Kinrara	2881 8082	1011.7	07 08 1951	31 12 1995	76.00	243	40.3	36 6.0	8002
8003	Spey at Ruthven Bridge	2759 7996	533.8	06 08 1951	31 12 1973	59.79	103	22.4	21 4.6	8003
8004	Avon at Delnashaugh	3186 8352	542.8	03 08 1952	31 12 1995	115.20	156	43.4	43 3.6	8004
8005	Spey at Boat of Garten	2946 8191	1267.8	29 08 1951	31 12 1995	90.00	256	44.3	44 5.8	8005
8006	Spey at Boat O Brig	3318 8518	2861.2	10 08 1952	31 12 1995	285.00	167	43.4	43 3.8	8006
8007	Spey at Invertruim	2687 7962	400.4	16 09 1952	31 12 1995	38.50	276	43.3	43 6.4	8007
8008	Tromie at Tromie Bridge	2789 7995	130.3	08 09 1952	03 02 1990	21.00	187	37.4	37 5.0	8008
8009	Dulnain at Balnaan Bridge	2977 8247	272.2	23 01 1952	31 12 1995	49.00	256	43.9	43 5.8	8009
8010	Spey at Grantown	3033 8268	1748.8	29 11 1951	31 12 1995	126.00	256	44.1	43 5.8	8010
8011	Livet at Minmore	3201 8291	104.0	25 03 1981	31 12 1995	11.00	119	14.8	14 8.1	8011
9001	Deveron at Avochie	3532 8464	441.6	04 11 1959	31 12 1995	68.00	127	36.2	35 3.5	9001
9002	Deveron at Muiresk	3705 8498	954.9	21 06 1960	31 12 1995	121.00	126	35.5	35 3.5	9002
9003	Isla at Grange	3494 8506	176.1	01 10 1969	31 12 1995	24.00	93	26.3	26 3.5	9003
9004	Bogie at Redcraig	3519 8373	179.0	01 12 1980	31 12 1995	12.00	71	15.1	14 4.7	9004
10001	Ythan at Ardlethen	3924 8308	448.1	01 08 1939	31 12 1984	26.00	209	45.2	43 4.6	10001
10002	Ugie at Inverugie	4101 8485	325.0	01 01 1972	31 12 1995	19.00	131	24.0	23 5.5	10002
10003	Ythan at Ellon	3947 8303	523.0	18 05 1983	31 12 1995	23.20	79	12.6	12 6.3	10003
11001	Don at Parkhill	3887 8141	1273.0	01 01 1970	10 05 1993	71.00	99	23.4	22 4.2	11001
11002	Don at Haughton	3756 8201	787.0	01 01 1972	31 12 1995	57.60	114	24.0	23 4.8	11002
11003	Don at Bridge of Alford	3566 8170	499.0	01 01 1974	31 12 1995	41.00	132	22.0	21 6.0	11003
11004	Urie at Pitcaple	3721 8260	198.0	30 12 1987	31 12 1995	8.50	38	8.0	7 4.7	11004
12001	Dee at Woodend	3635 7956	1370.0	01 10 1929	31 12 1995	195.00	354	66.3	66 5.3	12001
12002	Dee at Park	3798 7983	1844.0	01 01 1973	31 12 1995	234.00	130	23.0	22 5.7	12002
12003	Dee at Polhollick	3344 7965	690.0	01 01 1976	31 12 1995	140.00	130	20.0	19 6.5	12003
12004	Girnock Burn at Littlemill	3324 7956	30.3	25 06 1969	31 12 1995	5.56	191	26.5	26 7.2	12004
12005	Muick at Invermuick	3364 7947	110.0	10 03 1977	31 12 1995	19.60	159	18.8	18 8.5	12005
12006	Gairn at Invergairn	3353 7971	150.0	12 10 1978	31 12 1995	23.50	95	17.2	16 5.5	12006
12007	Dee at Mar Lodge	3098 7895	289.0	09 09 1982	31 12 1995	90.00	92	13.3	13 6.9	12007
12008	Feugh at Heugh Head	3687 7928	229.0	14 01 1985	31 12 1995	45.00	82	11.0	10 7.5	12008
13001	Bervie at Inverbervie	3826 7733	123.0	16 08 1979	31 12 1995	10.00	133	16.4	16 8.1	13001
14001	Eden at Kemback	3415 7158	307.4	29 09 1967	17 06 1993	18.50	118	25.7	24 4.6	14001
15001	Isla at Forter	3187 7647	70.7	26 08 1947	31 12 1973	25.00	112	26.4	26 4.3	15001
15002	Newton Burn at Newton	3230 7605	15.4	18 07 1949	31 12 1973	3.70	118	24.5	24 4.8	15002
15003	Tay at Caputh	3082 7395	3211.0	11 10 1951	18 05 1993	507.00	185	41.6	40 4.4	15003
15004	Inzion at Loch of Lintrathen	3280 7559	24.7	25 12 1950	31 12 1973	2.63	104	22.4	20 4.6	15004
15006	Tay at Ballathie	3147 7367	4587.1	03 10 1952	03 05 1993	575.30	233	40.5	37 5.8	15006
15007	Tay at Pitnacree	2924 7534	1149.4	02 11 1951	18 05 1993	210.00	206	41.5	37 5.0	15007
15008	Dean Water at Cookston	3340 7479	177.1	01 10 1953	06 07 1993	13.50	189	39.6	38 4.8	15008
15010	Isla at Wester Cardean	3295 7466	366.5	01 01 1972	19 07 1993	53.00	101	21.5	20 4.7	15010

No.	Name	Grid ref	NRFA Area km²	Record starts	Record ends	THRESH	NPOT	NWYRS NYRS	NWYRS Ratio	No.
15013	Almond at Almondbank	3067 7258	174.8	01 01 1974	31 05 1993	46.00	142	19.4 18	7.3	15013
15016	Tay at Kenmore	2782 7467	600.9	01 01 1975	19 07 1993	100.00	99	18.5 17	5.3	15016
15808	Almond at Almond Intake	2758 7332	31.0	02 05 1961	05 01 1971	8.40	40	9.7 9	4.1	15808
15809	Muckle Burn at Eastmill	3223 7604	16.5	10 05 1949	30 12 1973	4.23	90	24.0 18	3.8	15809
16001	Earn at Kinkell Bridge	2933 7167	590.5	09 11 1948	18 05 1993	122.20	265	44.3 41	6.0	16001
16003	Ruchill Water at Cultybraggan	2764 7204	99.5	01 06 1959	03 01 1993	80.10	184	32.8 30	5.6	16003
16004	Earn at Forteviot Bridge	3043 7184	782.2	01 01 1974	17 06 1993	138.10	128	19.5 18	6.6	16004
17001	Carron at Headswood	2832 6820	122.3	01 10 1968	01 04 1993	33.00	163	24.2 21	6.7	17001
17002	Leven at Leven	3369 7006	424.0	01 10 1968	02 10 1973	19.00	15	4.9 4	3.1	17002
17005	Avon at Polmonthill	2952 6797	195.3	01 01 1971	02 06 1993	30.00	134	22.4 21	6.0	17005
18001	Allan Water at Kinbuck	2792 7053	161.0	23 07 1957	31 12 1982	49.90	89	25.4 24	3.5	18001
18002	Devon at Glenochil	2858 6960	181.0	31 08 1956	01 10 1973	21.60	108	17.1 17	6.3	18002
18003	Teith at Bridge of Teith	2725 7011	518.0	11 06 1956	01 10 1973	112.00	81	17.3 17	4.7	18003
18005	Allan Water at Bridge of Allan	2786 6980	210.0	01 01 1972	20 05 1993	58.00	146	21.4 20	6.8	18005
18008	Leny at Anie	2585 7096	190.0	01 01 1974	01 06 1993	48.00	121	19.4 18	6.2	18008
19001	Almond at Craigiehall	3165 6752	369.0	31 08 1956	01 04 1993	56.50	176	36.6 35	4.8	19001
*19002	Almond at Almond Weir	3004 6652	43.8	09 06 1961	02 02 1993	9.00	151	31.7 31	4.8	19002*
19003	Breich Water at Breich Weir	3014 6639	51.8	28 06 1961	31 12 1979	11.30	73	18.5 18	3.9	19003
19004	North Esk at Dalmore Weir	3252 6616	81.6	28 03 1961	01 04 1993	9.65	178	32.0 31	5.6	19004
19005	Almond at Almondell	3086 6686	229.0	31 01 1962	05 07 1993	43.00	126	29.5 27	4.3	19005
19006	Water of Leith at Murrayfield	3228 6732	107.0	25 05 1962	01 04 1993	12.10	187	30.8 28	6.1	19006
19007	Esk at Musselburgh	3339 6723	330.0	19 12 1961	01 04 1993	29.30	161	31.3 30	5.1	19007
19008	South Esk at Prestonholm	3325 6623	112.0	01 10 1963	02 01 1990	9.50	93	26.3 26	3.5	19008
19010	Braid Burn at Liberton	3273 6707	16.2	01 10 1968	01 01 1974	0.46	18	5.3 5	3.4	19010
19011	North Esk at Dalkeith Palace	3333 6678	137.0	27 06 1962	01 04 1993	15.00	159	30.8 30	5.2	19011
20001	Tyne at East Linton	3591 6768	307.0	23 12 1958	16 06 1993	23.00	151	34.5 33	4.4	20001
20002	West Peffer Burn at Luffness	3489 6811	26.2	27 10 1965	05 07 1993	1.10	130	27.7 26	4.7	20002
20003	Tyne at Spilmersford	3456 6689	161.0	09 02 1962	01 04 1993	16.00	75	31.1 30	2.4	20003
20004	East Peffer Burn at Lochhouses	3610 6824	31.1	30 05 1966	31 12 1973	1.75	22	7.6 7	2.9	20004
20005	Birns Water at Saltoun Hall	3457 6688	93.0	09 02 1962	01 04 1993	9.80	123	31.1 30	3.9	20005
20006	Biel Water at Belton House	3645 6768	51.8	01 01 1972	05 07 1993	3.60	110	21.5 20	5.1	20006
20007	Gifford Water at Lennoxlove	3511 6717	64.0	01 01 1973	26 01 1993	3.20	135	20.1 19	6.7	20007
21001	Fruid Water at Fruid	3088 6205	23.7	01 10 1947	30 09 1962	10.52	83	15.0 15	5.5	21001
21002	Whiteadder W. at Hungry Snout	3663 6633	45.6	30 12 1957	16 06 1968	11.50	42	10.5 9	4.0	21002
21003	Tweed at Peebles	3257 6400	694.0	01 06 1939	04 05 1993	100.00	206	46.1 44	4.5	21003
21005	Tweed at Lyne Ford	3206 6397	373.0	13 03 1961	21 05 1993	64.40	147	32.2 30	4.6	21005
21006	Tweed at Boleside	3498 6334	1500.0	11 07 1961	10 05 1993	240.00	125	31.8 31	3.9	21006
21007	Ettrick Water at Lindean	3486 6315	499.0	29 09 1961	19 05 1993	118.50	161	31.6 31	5.1	21007
21008	Teviot at Ormiston Mill	3702 6280	1110.0	01 10 1960	27 04 1993	170.50	173	32.6 31	5.3	21008
21009	Tweed at Norham	3898 6477	4390.0	01 01 1960	05 05 1993	449.00	139	33.3 32	4.2	21009
21010	Tweed at Dryburgh	3588 6320	2080.0	25 02 1949	31 12 1982	260.00	161	33.8 32	4.8	21010
21011	Yarrow Water at Philiphaugh	3439 6277	231.0	28 08 1962	01 10 1974	34.00	59	12.1 12	4.9	21011
21012	Teviot at Hawick	3522 6159	323.0	18 09 1963	01 05 1993	98.00	154	29.6 29	5.2	21012
21013	Gala Water at Galashiels	3479 6374	207.0	30 09 1963	21 05 1993	27.00	99	29.6 29	3.3	21013
21015	Leader Water at Earlston	3565 6388	239.0	01 10 1966	01 05 1993	30.00	101	26.6 26	3.8	21015
21016	Eye Water at Eyemouth Mill	3942 6635	119.0	01 10 1967	07 05 1993	15.00	105	25.6 25	4.1	21016
21017	Ettrick Water at Brockhoperig	3234 6132	37.5	27 08 1965	24 05 1993	25.10	197	27.7 27	7.1	21017
21019	Manor Water at Cademuir	3217 6369	61.6	27 09 1968	21 05 1993	11.00	117	24.6 24	4.7	21019
21020	Yarrow Water at Gordon Arms	3309 6247	155.0	30 05 1967	31 12 1981	25.00	63	14.6 14	4.3	21020
21021	Tweed at Sprouston	3752 6354	3330.0	01 01 1970	05 05 1993	384.00	121	23.3 22	5.2	21021
21022	Whiteadder W. at Hutton Castle	3881 6550	503.0	01 01 1970	03 01 1990	50.00	78	20.0 19	3.9	21022
21024	Jed Water at Jedburgh	3655 6214	139.0	01 01 1972	03 01 1990	20.00	158	18.0 17	8.8	21024
21025	Ale Water at Ancrum	3634 6244	174.0	01 01 1973	27 04 1993	19.00	141	20.3 19	6.9	21025
21026	Tima Water at Deephope	3278 6138	31.0	01 01 1974	24 05 1993	25.00	154	19.4 18	7.9	21026
21027	Blackadder W. at Mouth Bridge	3826 6530	159.0	01 01 1974	05 05 1993	16.00	66	19.3 18	3.4	21027

No.	Name	Grid ref	NRFA Area km²	Record starts	Record ends	THRESH	NPOT	NWYRS NYRS		Ratio	No.
21029	Tweed at Glenbreck	3063 6215	34.0	04 02 1964	01 09 1975	18.70	51	9.9	7	5.2	21029
21030	Megget Water at Henderland	3231 6232	56.2	13 11 1968	07 01 1975	22.00	39	6.2	5	6.3	21030
21031	Till at Etal	3927 6396	648.0	07 12 1955	29 06 1980	43.20	109	24.4	22	4.5	21031
21032	Glen at Kirknewton	3919 6310	198.9	01 09 1961	31 10 1983	19.00	85	22.2	22	3.8	21032
21034	Yarrow Water at Craig Douglas	3288 6244	116.0	13 11 1968	07 01 1975	15.00	33	6.2	5	5.4	21034
22001	Coquet at Morwick	4234 6044	569.8	23 09 1963	30 04 1994	78.00	112	30.6	30	3.7	22001
22002	Coquet at Bygate	3870 6083	59.5	01 10 1969	03 03 1981	11.00	61	11.4	11	5.3	22002
22003	Usway Burn at Shillmoor	3886 6077	21.4	01 10 1966	01 07 1980	9.40	55	13.8	13	4.0	22003
22004	Aln at Hawkhill	4211 6129	205.0	13 04 1960	31 05 1980	28.00	91	20.1	19	4.5	22004
22006	Blyth at Hartford Bridge	4243 5800	269.4	09 11 1960	30 04 1994	19.20	160	33.1	31	4.8	22006
*22007	Wansbeck at Mitford	4175 5858	287.3	05 02 1963	30 04 1995	38.00	106	32.2	31	3.3	22007*
22008	Alwin at Clennell	3925 6063	27.7	01 10 1969	31 12 1974	4.50	23	5.3	5	4.4	22008
23001	Tyne at Bywell	4038 5617	2175.6	19 06 1956	30 04 1994	412.60	207	37.9	37	5.5	23001
23002	Derwent at Eddys Bridge	4041 5508	118.0	07 12 1954	14 10 1965	21.00	50	10.9	10	4.6	23002
23003	North Tyne at Reaverhill	3906 5732	1007.5	23 03 1959	30 11 1986	247.00	100	27.7	27	3.6	23003
23004	South Tyne at Haydon Bridge	3856 5647	751.1	17 07 1959	30 04 1994	226.00	176	30.5	29	5.8	23004
23005	North Tyne at Tarset	3776 5861	284.9	01 09 1960	27 12 1979	137.00	77	19.3	19	4.0	23005
23006	South Tyne at Featherstone	3672 5611	321.9	01 10 1966	30 04 1994	180.00	75	27.6	27	2.7	23006
*23007	Derwent at Rowlands Gill	4168 5581	242.1	31 10 1962	30 04 1994	26.00	80	30.1	25	2.7	23007*
23008	Rede at Rede Bridge	3868 5832	343.8	01 10 1968	30 04 1994	70.00	136	25.3	22	5.4	23008
23010	Tarset Burn at Greenhaugh	3789 5879	96.0	19 06 1970	30 06 1980	28.00	50	10.0	9	5.0	23010
23011	Kielder Burn at Kielder	3644 5946	58.8	19 06 1970	30 04 1994	30.00	123	22.4	19	5.5	23011
23012	East Allen at Wide Eals	3802 5583	88.0	13 05 1971	31 12 1981	32.00	56	10.6	10	5.3	23012
23013	West Allen at Hindley Wrae	3791 5583	75.1	11 05 1971	17 07 1983	28.00	63	12.2	11	5.2	23013
23015	North Tyne at Barrasford	3924 5721	1043.8	01 10 1947	27 02 1971	269.00	87	18.2	17	4.8	23015
24001	Wear at Sunderland Bridge	4264 5376	657.8	01 10 1957	01 01 1975	101.40	88	17.3	17	5.1	24001
24002	Gaunless at Bishop Auckland	4215 5306	93.0	26 09 1958	31 10 1983	8.80	93	25.1	25	3.7	24002
24003	Wear at Stanhope	3984 5391	171.9	01 10 1958	30 04 1994	63.00	132	35.6	35	3.7	24003
24004	Bedburn Beck at Bedburn	4118 5322	74.9	28 08 1959	30 04 1994	13.20	141	34.7	34	4.1	24004
24005	Browney at Burn Hall	4259 5387	178.5	01 10 1954	30 04 1994	16.00	200	39.4	37	5.1	24005
24006	Rookhope Burn at Eastgate	3952 5390	36.5	30 09 1960	31 10 1980	11.40	93	20.1	20	4.6	24006
24007	Browney at Lanchester	4165 5462	44.6	06 12 1967	31 10 1983	7.00	49	15.9	15	3.1	24007
24008	Wear at Witton Park	4174 5309	455.0	01 10 1974	30 04 1994	60.00	115	19.3	17	6.0	24008
24009	Wear at Chester Le Street	4283 5512	1008.3	01 09 1977	30 04 1994	150.00	69	16.6	15	4.2	24009
24801	Burnhope Burn at Burnhope Res.	3855 5395	21.0	01 07 1950	31 12 1970	13.20	85	20.5	20	4.1	24801
25001	Tees at Broken Scar	4259 5137	818.4	01 10 1956	30 04 1994	211.00	172	37.6	37	4.6	25001
25002	Tees at Dent Bank	3932 5260	217.3	20 06 1959	31 12 1974	163.00	60	15.5	15	3.9	25002
25003	Trout Beck at Moor House	3759 5336	11.4	01 10 1962	31 03 1994	9.50	114	20.5	19	5.6	25003
25004	Skerne at South Park	4284 5129	250.1	23 09 1957	30 04 1994	11.20	160	36.6	35	4.4	25004
25005	Leven at Leven Bridge	4445 5122	196.3	01 06 1959	30 04 1994	14.90	164	33.6	32	4.9	25005
25006	Greta at Rutherford Bridge	4034 5122	86.1	22 08 1960	30 04 1994	39.00	168	33.7	33	5.0	25006
25007	Clow Beck at Croft	4282 5101	78.2	01 10 1964	10 02 1980	9.00	39	15.4	15	2.5	25007
25008	Tees at Barnard Castle	4047 5166	509.2	29 07 1964	30 04 1994	155.00	91	23.8	23	3.8	25008
25009	Tees at Low Moor	4364 5105	1264.0	01 08 1969	30 04 1994	130.00	150	24.0	22	6.2	25009
25010	Baydale Beck at Mowden Bridge	4260 5156	31.1	25 09 1957	30 09 1974	2.90	93	17.0	17	5.5	25010
25011	Langdon Beck at Langdon	3852 5309	13.0	01 10 1969	09 10 1983	9.00	68	14.0	14	4.8	25011
25012	Harwood Beck at Harwood	3849 5309	25.1	16 08 1969	31 03 1995	22.00	87	25.6	25	3.4	25012
25018	Tees at Middleton In Teesdale	3950 5250	242.1	30 09 1972	30 04 1994	90.00	142	21.5	20	6.6	25018
25019	Leven at Easby	4585 5087	14.8	10 04 1971	30 04 1994	1.50	103	23.1	22	4.5	25019
25020	Skerne at Preston Le Skerne	4292 5238	147.0	10 09 1976	30 04 1994	10.00	77	17.5	16	4.4	25020
25021	Skerne at Bradbury	4318 5285	70.1	01 10 1975	30 04 1994	2.40	131	18.6	18	7.0	25021
*25808	Burnt Weir at Moor House	3752 5332	0.05	23 11 1953	17 05 1962	0.06	42	7.5	5	5.6	25808*
*25809	Bog Weir at Moor House	3773 5327	0.05	03 12 1953	24 05 1962	0.04	34	7.5	5	4.5	25809*
*25810	Syke Weir at Moor House	3772 5332	0.04	15 08 1956	24 05 1962	0.04	33	4.8	3	6.9	25810*
*26007	Catchwater at Withernwick	5171 4403	15.5	01 10 1969	30 09 1977	0.70	45	8.0	8	5.6	26007*

No.	Name	Grid ref	NRFA Area km²	Record starts	Record ends	THRESH	NPOT	NWYRS NYRS	Ratio	No.
27001	Nidd at Hunsingore Weir	4428 4530	484.3	15 05 1934	10 01 1983	66.50	197	48.5	43	4.1	27001
27002	Wharfe at Flint Mill Weir	4422 4473	758.9	09 06 1936	10 01 1978	146.00	185	41.5	39	4.5	27002
27004	Calder at Newlands	4365 4220	899.0	25 04 1957	01 06 1978	135.00	58	21.1	20	2.7	27004
27006	Don at Hadfields Weir	4390 3910	373.0	21 11 1956	06 01 1983	38.60	159	26.1	23	6.1	27006
27007	Ure at Westwick Lock	4356 4671	914.6	01 10 1955	06 11 1997	150.00	244	42.0	26	5.8	27007
27008	Swale at Leckby Grange	4415 4748	1345.6	20 10 1955	01 01 1983	118.80	132	27.2	25	4.9	27008
27009	Ouse at Skelton	4568 4554	3315.0	01 10 1956	01 01 1983	273.80	63	26.3	26	2.4	27009
27010	Hodge Beck at Bransdale Weir	4627 4944	18.9	09 04 1936	01 01 1978	5.25	137	41.6	37	3.3	27010
27012	Hebden W. at High Greenwood	3973 4309	36.0	23 03 1953	31 12 1973	7.36	83	20.8	20	4.0	27012
27014	Rye at Little Habton	4743 4771	679.0	26 02 1958	18 01 1974	49.00	79	15.9	15	5.0	27014
27015	Derwent at Stamford Bridge	4714 4557	1634.3	17 02 1962	01 10 1977	52.00	72	12.4	10	5.8	27015
*27021	Don at Doncaster	4569 4040	1256.2	01 10 1868	06 01 1983	73.00	235	87.3	85	2.7	27021*
27022	Don at Rotherham Weir	4427 3928	826.0	01 10 1960	06 10 1969	63.90	43	9.0	8	4.8	27022
27023	Dearne at Barnsley Weir	4350 4073	118.9	21 09 1960	01 01 1983	15.50	73	22.3	22	3.3	27023
27024	Swale at Richmond	4146 5006	381.0	24 05 1960	01 01 1981	146.00	93	20.6	20	4.5	27024
27025	Rother at Woodhouse Mill	4432 3857	352.2	20 05 1961	06 01 1983	21.50	114	21.2	20	5.4	27025
27026	Rother at Whittington	4394 3744	165.0	28 07 1960	06 01 1983	12.40	159	22.4	22	7.1	27026
27027	Wharfe at Ilkley	4112 4481	443.0	06 04 1960	31 12 1972	165.00	53	12.7	12	4.2	27027
27028	Aire at Armley	4281 4340	691.5	12 12 1960	01 01 1983	93.00	98	22.1	21	4.4	27028
27029	Calder at Elland	4124 4219	341.9	13 08 1953	01 01 1974	75.50	84	20.4	20	4.1	27029
27030	Dearne at Adwick	4477 4020	310.8	30 10 1963	06 01 1983	11.75	142	19.2	18	7.4	27030
27031	Colne at Colne Bridge	4174 4199	245.0	13 12 1963	07 01 1983	78.50	40	14.3	13	2.8	27031
*27033	Sea Cut at Scarborough	5028 4908	33.2	22 09 1965	01 01 1983	19.80	55	17.3	17	3.2	27033*
27034	Ure at Kilgram Bridge	4190 4860	510.2	05 07 1967	01 01 1983	165.00	64	15.5	15	4.1	27034
27035	Aire at Kildwick Bridge	4013 4457	282.3	01 10 1967	05 01 1983	44.00	95	15.3	15	6.2	27035
27036	Derwent at Malton	4789 4715	1421.0	10 01 1969	11 01 1974	62.20	20	5.0	4	4.0	27036
27040	Doe Lea at Staveley	4443 3746	67.9	01 07 1970	06 01 1983	4.46	66	12.5	12	5.3	27040
27041	Derwent at Buttercrambe	4731 4587	1586.0	01 10 1977	01 01 1983	52.00	40	5.3	5	7.6	27041
27042	Dove at Kirkby Mills	4705 4855	59.2	17 01 1972	01 01 1983	7.00	56	11.0	10	5.1	27042
27043	Wharfe at Addingham	4092 4494	427.0	01 01 1973	31 12 1982	165.00	32	9.9	7	3.2	27043
*27048	Derwent at West Ayton	4990 4853	127.0	01 05 1972	04 01 1983	0.76	65	10.1	8	6.4	27048*
27049	Rye at Ness	4696 4791	238.7	07 08 1974	06 01 1983	20.50	33	8.4	8	3.9	27049
27051	Crimple at Burn Bridge	4284 4519	8.1	07 12 1976	06 01 1983	1.95	39	6.0	3	6.5	27051
27052	Whitting at Sheepbridge	4376 3747	50.2	04 01 1978	06 01 1983	11.50	17	5.0	4	3.4	27052
27053	Nidd at Birstwith	4230 4603	217.6	01 10 1975	05 01 1983	45.00	30	7.3	7	4.1	27053
27054	Hodge Beck at Cherry Farm	4652 4902	37.1	11 01 1977	06 01 1983	7.00	26	6.0	5	4.3	27054
27055	Rye at Broadway Foot	4560 4883	131.7	23 08 1977	04 01 1983	34.50	18	5.4	5	3.4	27055
27058	Riccal at Crook House Farm	4661 4810	40.5	02 08 1977	06 01 1983	5.40	21	5.4	5	3.9	27058
27059	Laver at Ripon	4301 4710	87.5	01 10 1977	08 01 1983	14.00	21	5.3	5	4.0	27059
27061	Colne at Longroyd Bridge	4136 4161	72.3	01 11 1978	07 01 1983	15.20	30	4.2	3	7.2	27061
27835	Calder at Midland Br. Dewsbury	4243 4215	691.0	21 04 1964	20 07 1973	120.00	31	8.8	4	3.5	27835
27846	Aire at Ash Bridge	4472 4266	1880.0	09 12 1964	01 10 1969	210.00	30	4.5	3	6.6	27846
28002	Blithe at Hamstall Ridware	4109 3192	163.0	01 10 1937	01 10 1952	9.16	79	15.0	15	5.3	28002
28003	Tame at Water Orton	4169 2915	408.0	06 09 1955	02 01 1986	48.00	141	29.3	28	4.8	28003
28004	Tame at Lea Marston	4206 2935	795.0	28 09 1956	29 12 1982	49.90	141	26.3	26	5.4	28004
28005	Tame at Elford	4173 3105	1475.0	07 12 1955	03 01 1986	59.00	138	23.1	21	6.0	28005
28006	Trent at Great Haywood	3994 3231	325.0	07 12 1955	02 01 1986	16.80	161	29.1	27	5.5	28006
28007	Trent at Shardlow	4448 3299	4400.0	28 09 1955	01 10 1969	151.20	73	14.0	14	5.2	28007
28008	Dove at Rocester Weir	4112 3397	399.0	11 04 1953	02 01 1986	55.60	137	31.7	29	4.3	28008
28009	Trent at Colwick	4620 3399	7486.0	15 09 1958	29 12 1982	268.00	109	24.3	24	4.5	28009
28010	Derwent at Longbridge Weir	4356 3363	1054.0	07 06 1935	24 12 1982	95.00	188	45.9	32	4.1	28010
28011	Derwent at Matlock Bath	4296 3586	690.0	10 01 1958	30 12 1985	49.00	158	26.8	24	5.9	28011
28012	Trent at Yoxall	4131 3177	1229.0	23 09 1959	02 01 1986	40.60	123	25.3	24	4.9	28012
28014	Sow at Milford	3975 3215	591.0	01 10 1959	02 01 1986	17.60	113	25.1	22	4.5	28014
28015	Idle at Mattersey	4690 3895	529.0	26 04 1961	30 09 1969	6.15	53	8.4	8	6.3	28015

No.	Name	Grid ref	NRFA Area km²	Record starts	Record ends	THRESH	NPOT	NWYRS NYRS	Ratio	No.
28016	Ryton at Serlby Park	4641 3897	231.0	19 12 1961	30 09 1969	8.60	26	7.8 7	3.3	28016
28017	Devon at Cotham	4787 3476	284.0	30 09 1966	17 04 1984	13.60	54	16.6 16	3.3	28017
28018	Dove at Marston On Dove	4235 3288	883.2	28 07 1961	02 01 1986	71.40	116	23.4 22	4.9	28018
28019	Trent at Drakelow Park	4239 3204	3072.0	21 05 1959	02 01 1986	105.00	119	23.6 21	5.0	28019
28020	Churnet at Rocester	4103 3389	236.0	01 10 1969	27 12 1985	19.00	93	15.2 14	6.1	28020
28021	Derwent at Draycott	4443 3327	1175.0	26 04 1965	01 07 1982	80.00	64	17.2 16	3.7	28021
28022	Trent at North Muskham	4801 3601	8231.0	15 03 1968	02 01 1986	259.00	75	16.8 15	4.5	28022
28023	Wye at Ashford	4182 3696	154.0	01 10 1970	01 01 1986	9.00	63	14.3 13	4.4	28023
28024	Wreake at Syston Mill	4615 3124	413.8	01 10 1969	22 01 1986	20.00	67	14.7 11	4.6	28024
28026	Anker at Polesworth	4263 3034	368.0	05 07 1967	03 01 1986	20.00	62	17.5 16	3.5	28026
28031	Manifold at Ilam	4140 3507	148.5	11 04 1968	02 01 1986	30.00	115	16.8 15	6.9	28031
28032	Meden at Church Warsop	4558 3680	62.8	01 08 1964	05 04 1984	1.60	209	18.5 16	11.3	28032
28033	Dove at Hollinsclough	4063 3668	8.0	05 05 1966	01 01 1986	2.50	58	14.3 11	4.1	28033
28038	Manifold at Hulme End	4106 3595	46.0	23 12 1968	30 09 1982	23.00	74	13.8 13	5.4	28038
28039	Rea at Calthorpe Park	4071 2847	74.0	27 12 1973	03 01 1986	13.10	71	11.0 9	6.4	28039
28040	Trent at Stoke On Trent	3892 3467	53.2	29 03 1968	02 01 1986	5.50	87	16.8 15	5.2	28040
28041	Hamps at Waterhouses	4082 3502	35.1	29 03 1968	03 10 1982	10.00	82	14.5 13	5.7	28041
28043	Derwent at Chatsworth	4261 3683	335.0	13 02 1969	30 12 1985	35.00	67	15.9 14	4.2	28043
28045	Meden at Bothamstall	4681 3732	262.6	26 09 1969	03 04 1984	6.40	42	13.5 13	3.1	28045
28046	Dove at Izaak Walton	4146 3509	83.0	03 06 1969	02 01 1986	7.10	83	16.0 13	5.2	28046
28047	Oldcotes Dyke at Blyth	4615 3876	85.2	17 06 1970	02 01 1986	3.82	47	14.5 12	3.2	28047
28048	Amber at Wingfield Park	4376 3520	139.0	25 08 1970	30 12 1985	9.70	88	14.3 11	6.1	28048
28049	Ryton at Worksop	4575 3794	77.0	01 10 1970	02 01 1986	2.60	48	13.8 12	3.5	28049
28052	Sow at Great Bridgford	3883 3270	163.0	18 01 1971	02 01 1986	7.20	43	14.0 12	3.1	28052
28053	Penk at Penkridge	3923 3144	272.0	01 04 1976	02 01 1986	13.00	50	8.7 7	5.7	28053
28054	Sence at Blaby	4566 2985	133.0	22 12 1971	29 12 1982	10.00	57	11.0 9	5.2	28054
28055	Ecclesbourne at Duffield	4320 3447	50.4	11 08 1971	01 07 1982	6.80	56	10.9 10	5.1	28055
28056	Rothley Brook at Rothley	4580 3121	94.0	01 10 1973	06 01 1986	6.10	44	11.2 9	3.9	28056
28058	Henmore Brook at Ashbourne	4176 3463	42.0	31 01 1974	29 12 1982	6.50	35	8.9 8	3.9	28058
28059	Maun at Mansfield	4548 3623	28.8	01 06 1964	19 07 1984	5.00	165	19.1 18	8.6	28059
28060	Dover Beck at Lowdham	4653 3479	69.0	09 02 1972	11 04 1984	1.30	38	11.2 10	3.4	28060
28061	Churnet at Basford Bridge	3983 3520	139.0	30 12 1974	01 01 1983	15.00	51	8.0 7	6.4	28061
28066	Cole at Coleshill	4183 2874	130.0	01 10 1973	31 12 1982	11.00	46	9.2 8	5.0	28066
28067	Derwent at Church Wilne	4438 3316	1177.5	27 12 1973	03 01 1986	85.00	49	11.0 9	4.4	28067
28069	Tame at Tamworth	4206 3037	1407.0	24 09 1969	03 01 1986	67.00	73	15.3 14	4.8	28069
28070	Burbage Brook at Burbage	4259 3804	9.1	13 11 1925	30 09 1982	2.04	258	56.8 54	4.5	28070
28082	Soar at Littlethorpe	4542 2973	183.9	07 07 1971	06 01 1986	12.60	66	13.5 12	4.9	28082
28804	Trent at Trent Bridge	4582 3384	7490.0	28 09 1884	30 09 1969	150.00	455	82.0 82	5.5	28804
29001	Waithe Beck at Brigsley	5253 4016	108.3	19 08 1960	27 09 1983	1.13	114	23.1 22	4.9	29001
29002	Great Eau at Claythorpe Mill	5416 3793	77.4	03 05 1973	30 09 1984	2.00	49	11.4 11	4.3	29002
29003	Lud at Louth	5337 3879	55.2	10 05 1966	29 09 1984	1.52	78	18.4 17	4.2	29003
29004	Ancholme at Bishopbridge	5032 3911	54.7	13 03 1968	30 09 1984	3.00	89	16.6 16	5.4	29004
29009	Ancholme at Toft Newton	5033 3877	27.2	03 06 1974	30 10 1984	1.20	50	10.4 10	4.8	29009
30001	Witham at Claypole Mill	4842 3480	297.9	27 01 1959	01 10 1984	7.90	119	25.7 25	4.6	30001
30002	Barlings Eau at Langworth Bridge	5066 3766	210.1	21 09 1960	01 10 1984	10.00	105	22.3 20	4.7	30002
30003	Bain at Fulsby Lock	5241 3611	197.1	07 09 1962	01 10 1984	5.65	142	22.1 22	6.4	30003
30004	Partney Lymn at Partney Mill	5402 3676	61.6	04 05 1962	01 10 1984	2.83	115	18.3 17	6.3	30004
30005	Witham at Saltersford Total	4927 3335	126.1	13 03 1968	01 10 1984	2.40	97	16.6 16	5.9	30005
30011	Bain at Goulceby Bridge	5246 3795	62.5	17 06 1966	30 09 1984	1.63	67	15.7 15	4.3	30011
30012	Stainfield Beck at Stainfield	5127 3739	37.4	04 04 1974	30 09 1984	4.40	42	10.5 10	4.0	30012
30014	Pointon Lode at Pointon	5128 3313	11.9	01 05 1972	30 09 1984	0.85	58	12.4 12	4.7	30014
30017	Witham at Colsterworth	4929 3246	51.3	01 10 1978	30 09 1984	1.95	45	6.0 6	7.5	30017
31002	Glen at Kates Bridge	5106 3149	341.9	18 10 1958	01 10 1982	8.49	98	24.0 23	4.1	31002
31005	Welland at Tixover	4970 2997	417.0	24 04 1962	30 09 1986	11.50	136	24.4 23	5.6	31005
31006	Gwash at Belmesthorpe	5038 3097	150.0	31 03 1967	02 10 1973	6.29	27	6.5 6	4.1	31006

No.	Name	Grid ref	NRFA Area km²	Record starts	Record ends	THRESH	NPOT	NWYRS NYRS	NWYRS Ratio	No.
31010	Chater at Fosters Bridge	4961 3030	68.9	03 01 1968	30 09 1986	3.50	96	18.7	18	5.1	31010
31021	Welland at Ashley	4819 2915	250.7	01 10 1970	01 10 1982	12.68	66	12.0	12	5.5	31021
31023	West Glen at Easton Wood	4965 3258	4.4	26 01 1972	30 09 1986	0.56	81	14.7	14	5.5	31023
31025	Gwash South Arm at Manton	4875 3051	24.5	17 07 1978	30 09 1986	4.00	37	8.2	8	4.5	31025
31026	Egleton Brook at Egleton	4878 3073	2.5	01 10 1978	30 09 1986	0.30	31	8.0	8	3.9	31026
32002	Willow Brook at Fotheringhay	5067 2933	89.6	03 10 1938	30 09 1986	2.12	259	47.9	46	5.4	32002
*32003	Harpers Brook at Old Mill Bridge	4983 2799	74.3	07 12 1938	30 09 1986	3.60	194	47.3	43	4.1	32003*
32004	Ise Brook at Harrowden Old Mill	4898 2715	194.0	02 12 1943	30 09 1986	5.60	275	42.6	41	6.5	32004
32007	Nene Brampton at St Andrews	4747 2617	232.8	10 05 1940	01 10 1982	10.08	133	41.5	40	3.2	32007
*32008	Nene/kislingbury at Dodford	4627 2607	107.0	07 12 1944	30 09 1986	2.80	327	41.6	39	7.9	32008*
32010	Nene at Wansford	5081 2996	1530.0	23 05 1939	01 10 1982	39.00	161	43.4	43	3.7	32010
32029	Flore at Experimental Catchment	4660 2610	7.0	17 08 1964	30 09 1969	0.47	37	4.7	3	7.9	32029
33006	Wissey at Northwold	5771 2965	274.5	13 02 1956	02 01 1985	3.50	156	28.9	27	5.4	33006
33009	Bedford Ouse at Harrold Mill	4951 2565	1320.0	29 08 1951	10 01 1985	44.50	129	33.4	33	3.9	33009
33011	Little Ouse at County Br. Euston	5892 2801	128.7	02 10 1960	15 01 1985	0.98	150	24.3	23	6.2	33011
33012	Kym at Meagre Farm	5155 2631	137.5	14 09 1960	14 01 1985	6.80	135	24.3	24	5.5	33012
33013	Sapiston at Rectory Bridge	5896 2791	205.9	11 04 1960	09 01 1985	2.01	131	24.8	24	5.3	33013
33014	Lark at Temple	5758 2730	272.0	01 10 1960	09 01 1985	4.40	106	24.2	23	4.4	33014
33015	Ouzel at Willen	4882 2408	277.1	22 11 1961	01 10 1973	9.60	57	11.9	11	4.8	33015
33017	Bedford Ouse at St Ives Staunch	5314 2705	2860.0	01 02 1949	01 10 1973	56.50	78	18.5	17	4.2	33017
33018	Tove at Cappenham Bridge	4714 2488	138.1	25 01 1962	10 01 1985	8.40	108	22.8	21	4.7	33018
33019	Thet at Melford Bridge	5880 2830	316.0	01 10 1960	15 01 1985	3.80	117	23.6	21	5.0	33019
*33020	Alconbury Brook at Brampton	5208 2717	201.5	07 03 1963	14 01 1985	11.00	69	21.9	21	3.2	33020*
33021	Rhee at Burnt Mill	5415 2523	303.0	01 10 1962	04 01 1985	5.73	76	22.3	22	3.4	33021
33022	Ivel at Blunham	5153 2509	541.3	15 12 1964	14 01 1985	10.01	100	20.1	19	5.0	33022
33023	Lea Brook at Beck Bridge	5662 2733	101.8	08 11 1962	09 01 1985	1.30	107	22.2	21	4.8	33023
33024	Carn at Dernford	5466 2506	198.0	21 08 1963	10 01 1985	3.96	111	21.4	21	5.2	33024
33027	Rhee at Wimpole	5333 2485	119.1	01 10 1965	07 01 1985	2.94	77	19.3	19	4.0	33027
33029	Stringside at White Bridge	5716 3006	98.8	21 07 1965	30 09 1984	1.70	80	19.2	19	4.2	33029
33030	Clipstone Brook at Clipstone	4933 2255	40.2	01 10 1966	15 07 1980	4.30	50	13.8	13	3.6	33030
33031	Broughton Brook at Broughton	4889 2408	66.6	01 10 1970	02 01 1985	2.86	63	14.3	14	4.4	33031
33033	Hiz at Arlesey	5190 2379	108.0	01 10 1973	15 01 1985	1.97	56	11.3	11	5.0	33033
33034	Little Ouse at Abbey Heath	5851 2844	699.3	20 03 1968	02 01 1985	11.69	44	16.8	15	2.6	33034
33037	Bedford Ouse at Newport Pagnell	4877 2443	800.0	01 10 1969	10 01 1985	26.50	90	15.3	15	5.9	33037
33039	Bedford Ouse at Roxton	5160 2535	1660.0	01 10 1972	14 01 1985	42.00	59	12.3	12	4.8	33039
33044	Thet at Bridgham	5957 2855	277.8	01 06 1967	14 01 1985	5.70	52	17.6	17	3.0	33044
33045	Wittle at Quidenham	6027 2878	28.3	01 05 1967	14 01 1985	0.50	60	17.7	17	3.4	33045
33046	Thet at Red Bridge	5996 2923	145.3	14 02 1967	14 01 1985	3.75	62	17.9	17	3.5	33046
33048	Larling Brook at Stonebridge	5928 2907	21.4	01 10 1969	14 01 1985	0.14	76	15.3	15	5.0	33048
33050	Snail at Fordham	5631 2703	60.6	01 10 1974	29 01 1985	1.00	47	10.3	10	4.5	33050
33051	Carn at Chesterford	5505 2426	141.0	01 10 1969	04 01 1985	3.52	81	15.3	15	5.3	33051
33055	Granta at Babraham	5510 2504	98.7	29 07 1976	04 01 1985	2.20	35	8.4	8	4.1	33055
33057	Ouzel at Leighton Buzzard	4917 2241	119.0	08 01 1976	02 01 1985	4.35	36	9.0	7	4.0	33057
33058	Ouzel at Bletchley	4883 2322	215.0	10 05 1978	02 01 1985	10.07	30	6.7	6	4.5	33058
33063	Little Ouse at Knettishall	5955 2807	101.0	01 10 1980	15 01 1985	1.70	22	4.3	4	5.1	33063
33809	Bury Brook at Bury Weir	5286 2837	65.3	01 10 1963	30 10 1978	3.05	65	14.9	12	4.4	33809
34001	Yare at Colney	6182 3082	231.8	01 01 1958	02 11 1987	6.50	90	29.6	28	3.0	34001
34002	Tas at Shotesham	6226 2994	146.5	15 10 1957	30 09 1987	4.60	85	30.0	29	2.8	34002
34003	Bure at Ingworth	6192 3296	164.7	08 06 1959	01 11 1987	2.48	168	28.4	28	5.9	34003
34004	Wensum at Costessey Mill	6177 3128	570.9	27 01 1960	01 10 1987	15.00	64	27.7	27	2.3	34004
34005	Tud at Costessey Park	6170 3113	73.2	07 06 1961	01 10 1987	1.10	125	26.3	26	4.7	34005
34006	Waveney at Needham Mill	6229 2811	370.0	30 09 1963	07 04 1975	8.80	53	11.5	11	4.6	34006
34007	Dove at Oakley Park	6174 2772	133.9	21 06 1966	01 10 1987	4.10	88	21.2	20	4.1	34007
34008	Ant at Honing Lock	6331 3270	49.3	20 05 1966	30 09 1987	0.65	116	21.3	20	5.4	34008
34010	Waveney at Billingford Bridge	6168 2782	149.4	03 04 1968	30 09 1987	5.52	66	19.5	19	3.4	34010

No.	Name	Grid ref	NRFA Area km²	Record starts	Record ends	THRESH	NPOT	NWYRS NYRS	Ratio	No.
34011	Wensum at Fakenham	5919 3294	161.9	18 04 1966	03 10 1987	2.50	100	21.5 21	4.7	34011
34018	Stiffkey at Warham All Saints	5944 3414	87.8	01 10 1971	05 09 1987	1.84	50	15.9 15	3.1	34018
35003	Alde at Farnham	6360 2601	63.9	01 10 1961	30 09 1987	2.35	116	26.0 26	4.5	35003
35004	Ore at Beversham Bridge	6359 2583	54.9	01 03 1965	30 09 1987	2.44	112	22.6 22	5.0	35004
35008	Gipping at Stowmarket	6058 2578	128.9	17 02 1964	30 09 1987	3.90	156	23.0 21	6.8	35008
35010	Gipping at Bramford	6127 2465	298.0	01 10 1970	30 09 1987	6.20	91	17.0 17	5.4	35010
35014	Bucklesham Mill at Newbourn	6270 2420	27.1	01 01 1948	30 09 1969	0.28	128	20.3 17	6.3	35014
36002	Glem at Glemsford	5846 2472	87.3	30 09 1969	31 12 1986	3.90	105	17.3 17	6.1	36002
36003	Box at Polstead	5985 2378	53.9	01 10 1963	31 12 1986	0.88	133	23.3 23	5.7	36003
36004	Chad Brook at Long Melford	5868 2459	47.4	01 10 1967	31 12 1985	2.36	77	18.3 18	4.2	36004
36005	Brett at Hadleigh	6025 2429	156.0	01 10 1969	31 12 1986	4.60	76	17.3 17	4.4	36005
36006	Stour at Langham	6020 2344	578.0	01 10 1969	31 12 1985	12.60	123	16.3 16	7.6	36006
36007	Belchamp Brook at Bardfield Br.	5848 2421	58.6	01 10 1964	31 12 1985	1.40	113	21.3 21	5.3	36007
36008	Stour at Westmill	5827 2463	224.5	30 09 1969	31 12 1985	7.25	112	16.3 16	6.9	36008
36009	Brett at Cockfield	5914 2525	25.7	23 02 1968	31 12 1985	1.23	93	17.9 17	5.2	36009
36010	Bumpstead Brook at Broad Green	5689 2418	28.3	01 10 1967	02 01 1986	2.70	75	18.3 18	4.1	36010
36011	Stour Brook at Sturmer	5696 2441	34.5	28 05 1968	02 01 1986	2.20	113	17.6 17	6.4	36011
36015	Stour at Lamarsh	5897 2358	480.7	25 02 1972	30 12 1985	18.90	53	13.7 12	3.9	36015
37001	Roding at Redbridge	5415 1884	303.3	01 02 1950	08 01 1980	10.90	165	29.9 29	5.5	37001
37003	Ter at Crabbs Bridge	5786 2107	77.8	01 12 1963	29 12 1986	1.65	136	23.1 22	5.9	37003
37005	Colne at Lexden	5962 2261	238.2	01 10 1962	29 12 1986	5.70	127	24.2 24	5.2	37005
37006	Can at Beach's Mill	5690 2072	228.4	01 10 1962	31 12 1986	10.70	109	24.1 21	4.5	37006
37007	Wid at Writtle	5686 2060	136.3	01 10 1964	31 12 1986	7.00	117	22.3 22	5.3	37007
37008	Chelmer at Springfield	5713 2071	190.3	02 10 1965	06 01 1986	8.65	72	20.3 19	3.6	37008
37009	Brain at Guithavon Valley	5818 2147	60.7	01 06 1962	03 01 1986	1.71	113	23.6 23	4.8	37009
37010	Blackwater at Appleford Bridge	5845 2158	247.3	01 10 1963	29 12 1986	5.20	148	23.2 23	6.4	37010
37011	Chelmer at Churchend	5629 2233	72.6	01 10 1963	31 12 1986	3.40	115	23.3 23	4.9	37011
37012	Colne at Poolstreet	5771 2364	65.1	01 02 1964	31 12 1986	2.90	105	22.9 22	4.6	37012
37013	Sandon Brook at Sandon Bridge	5755 2055	75.1	01 01 1964	31 12 1986	3.40	107	22.9 20	4.7	37013
37014	Roding at High Ongar	5561 2040	95.1	11 02 1964	06 12 1979	4.29	80	15.8 15	5.1	37014
37016	Pant at Copford Hall	5668 2313	62.5	17 06 1965	31 12 1986	3.95	89	21.5 21	4.1	37016
37017	Blackwater at Stisted	5793 2243	139.2	01 10 1969	31 12 1986	6.40	63	17.3 17	3.7	37017
37018	Ingrebourne at Gaynes Park	5553 1862	47.9	01 10 1970	09 01 1980	3.50	36	9.3 9	3.9	37018
37019	Beam at Bretons Farm	5515 1853	49.7	01 07 1965	09 01 1980	4.90	71	14.5 12	4.9	37019
37020	Chelmer at Felsted	5670 2193	132.1	01 05 1970	30 12 1986	5.60	67	16.7 16	4.0	37020
37031	Crouch at Wickford	5748 1934	71.8	30 01 1962	31 12 1985	4.80	85	22.6 21	3.8	37031
37033	Eastwood Brook at Eastwood	5859 1888	10.4	26 03 1974	20 01 1994	1.86	120	19.4 16	6.2	37033
38002	Ash at Mardock	5393 2148	78.7	07 09 1939	01 10 1979	2.26	226	39.1 39	5.8	38002
38003	Mimram at Panshanger Park	5282 2133	133.9	01 12 1952	02 01 1980	1.30	100	27.1 26	3.7	38003
38004	Rib at Wadesmill	5360 2174	136.5	30 04 1959	03 01 1980	5.60	106	20.7 20	5.1	38004
38007	Canons Brook at Elizabeth Way	5431 2104	21.4	01 10 1950	07 01 1980	3.20	150	29.3 29	5.1	38007
38020	Cobbins Brook at Sewardstone Rd	5387 1999	38.4	24 05 1971	07 01 1980	3.40	40	8.6 8	4.6	38020
38021	Turkey Brook at Albany Park	5359 1985	42.2	01 10 1971	07 01 1980	3.80	41	8.3 8	5.0	38021
38022	Pymmes Bk at Edmonton Silver St	5340 1925	42.6	07 04 1954	31 12 1979	11.80	134	25.7 25	5.2	38022
38026	Pincey Brook at Sheering Hall	5495 2126	54.6	18 07 1974	08 01 1980	2.90	32	5.5 5	5.8	38026
39001	Thames at Kingston	5177 1698	9948.0	01 01 1883	31 12 1984	200.00	346	102.0 101	3.4	39001
39002	Thames at Days Weir	4568 1935	3444.7	01 10 1938	30 09 1984	100.00	121	46.0 46	2.6	39002
39003	Wandle at Connollys Mill	5265 1705	176.1	22 12 1938	31 12 1973	4.90	163	29.3 27	5.6	39003
39004	Wandle at Beddington Park	5296 1655	122.0	29 12 1938	20 12 1982	1.83	331	41.6 26	8.0	39004
39005	Beverley Bk at Wimbledon Cmn	5216 1717	43.6	27 09 1962	31 12 1973	7.08	53	11.3 11	4.7	39005
39007	Blackwater at Swallowfield	4731 1648	354.8	14 10 1952	30 09 1983	12.70	171	31.0 30	5.5	39007
39008	Thames at Eynsham	4445 2087	1616.2	01 10 1951	30 09 1984	39.65	151	33.0 33	4.6	39008
39011	Wey at Tilford	4874 1433	396.3	18 05 1954	20 01 1972	14.00	68	15.3 14	4.5	39011
39012	Hogsmill at Kingston upon Thames	5182 1688	69.1	04 09 1958	29 10 1982	9.40	66	24.2 24	2.7	39012
39016	Kennet at Theale	4649 1708	1033.4	11 09 1961	07 10 1983	22.00	120	22.1 22	5.4	39016

No.	Name	Grid ref	NRFA Area km²	Record starts	Record ends	THRESH	NPOT	NWYRS NYRS	Ratio	No.
39017	Ray at Grendon Underwood	4680 2211	18.6	20 09 1963	31 08 1985	1.95	99	21.7 20	4.6	39017
39018	Ock at Abingdon	4486 1969	234.0	01 02 1962	23 03 1978	6.40	88	16.1 15	5.5	39018
39021	Cherwell at Enslow Mill	4482 2183	551.7	06 01 1965	05 10 1983	13.50	106	18.7 18	5.7	39021
39022	Loddon at Sheepbridge	4720 1652	164.5	01 10 1965	07 10 1983	10.00	82	18.0 18	4.6	39022
39023	Wye at Hedsor	4896 1867	137.3	27 11 1964	30 09 1969	2.45	21	4.8 4	4.3	39023
39024	Gatwick Stream at Gatwick	5288 1402	31.1	30 07 1952	30 09 1973	3.90	99	21.2 21	4.7	39024
39025	Enborne at Brimpton	4568 1648	147.6	18 05 1967	30 09 1983	8.61	95	16.4 16	5.8	39025
39026	Cherwell at Banbury	4458 2411	199.4	30 11 1966	05 10 1983	8.20	78	16.8 16	4.6	39026
39027	Pang at Pangbourne	4634 1766	170.9	13 11 1968	05 10 1983	1.80	66	14.9 14	4.4	39027
39028	Dun at Hungerford	4321 1685	101.3	18 03 1968	01 10 1983	1.17	51	15.5 15	3.3	39028
39029	Tillingbourne at Shalford	5000 1478	59.0	01 10 1975	30 09 1983	1.39	21	8.0 8	2.6	39029
39034	Evenlode at Cassington Mill	4448 2099	430.0	01 10 1970	03 10 1983	13.00	49	13.0 13	3.8	39034
39035	Churn at Cerney Wick	4076 1963	124.3	01 10 1969	30 09 1983	2.00	78	14.0 14	5.6	39035
39036	Law Brook at Albury	5045 1468	16.0	26 09 1968	07 10 1983	0.25	83	15.0 15	5.5	39036
39038	Thame at Shabbington	4670 2055	443.0	08 03 1968	05 10 1983	11.19	74	15.6 15	4.8	39038
39040	Thames at West Mill Cricklade	4094 1942	185.0	23 06 1972	04 10 1983	7.10	57	11.3 11	5.1	39040
39044	Hart at Bramshill House	4755 1593	84.0	01 10 1972	07 10 1983	3.10	70	11.0 11	6.4	39044
39049	Silk Stream at Colindeep Lane	5217 1895	29.0	30 10 1928	31 12 1983	4.10	185	26.1 23	7.1	39049
39052	The Cut at Binfield	4853 1713	50.2	16 07 1957	07 10 1983	3.80	141	25.9 24	5.4	39052
39053	Mole at Horley	5271 1434	89.9	17 11 1961	07 10 1983	13.70	111	21.9 21	5.1	39053
39055	Yeading Bk West at Yeading W	5083 1846	17.6	08 03 1974	10 12 1982	2.00	56	8.8 8	6.4	39055
39056	Ravensbourne at Catford Hill	5372 1732	120.3	02 12 1974	22 12 1983	8.56	69	9.1 8	7.6	39056
39057	Crane at Cranford Park	5103 1778	61.7	24 01 1974	31 03 1983	6.95	55	9.2 8	6.0	39057
39058	Pool at Winsford Road	5371 1725	38.3	04 12 1974	31 12 1983	5.98	66	9.1 8	7.3	39058
39069	Mole at Kinnersley Manor	5262 1462	142.0	14 11 1972	07 10 1983	16.00	50	10.9 10	4.6	39069
39081	Ock at Abingdon	4481 1966	234.0	18 05 1979	03 10 1983	6.40	28	4.4 4	6.4	39081
39086	Gatwick Stream at Gatwick Link	5285 1417	33.6	02 09 1975	01 10 1983	6.00	30	8.1 8	3.7	39086
39090	Cole at Inglesham	4208 1970	140.0	01 10 1976	03 10 1983	5.80	42	7.0 7	6.0	39090
39092	Dollis Bk at Hendon Lane Bridge	5240 1895	25.1	14 02 1952	30 09 1969	3.90	80	16.6 13	4.8	39092
39093	Brent at Monks Park	5202 1850	117.6	02 01 1939	22 11 1984	11.17	290	45.5 42	6.4	39093
39095	Quaggy at Manor House Gdns	5394 1748	33.9	05 10 1961	31 12 1982	3.00	109	21.2 20	5.1	39095
39096	Wealdstone Brook at Wembley	5192 1862	21.7	22 09 1976	30 09 1986	4.49	105	10.0 10	10.5	39096
39813	Mole at Ifield Weir	5244 1364	12.7	19 12 1958	30 09 1969	1.50	52	10.8 10	4.8	39813
39824	Ravensbourne East at Bromley S	5405 1687	10.3	31 10 1962	30 09 1980	2.54	75	17.9 17	4.2	39824
39827	Pool at Selworthy Road	5369 1722	36.0	15 09 1961	05 01 1970	3.70	39	7.7 5	5.0	39827
39830	Beck at Rectory Road	5370 1697	10.0	27 09 1962	01 01 1970	1.20	41	7.3 7	5.6	39830
39831	Chaffinch Brook at Beckenham	5360 1685	7.0	04 09 1962	01 01 1970	1.40	42	7.3 7	5.7	39831
39834	Brent at Hanwell	5151 1801	132.0	21 02 1961	30 12 1969	14.40	45	8.9 8	5.1	39834
40003	Medway at Teston	5708 1530	1256.1	24 09 1956	02 01 1987	89.00	115	30.2 26	3.8	40003
40004	Rother at Udiam	5773 1245	206.0	01 09 1962	02 01 1987	24.48	61	24.3 23	2.5	40004
40005	Beult at Stile Bridge	5758 1478	277.1	30 09 1958	20 01 1987	18.80	108	28.1 24	3.8	40005
40006	Bourne at Hadlow	5632 1497	50.3	14 07 1959	20 01 1987	2.80	121	24.3 20	5.0	40006
40007	Medway at Chafford Weir	5517 1405	255.1	28 09 1960	29 12 1986	29.10	111	25.2 24	4.4	40007
40008	Great Stour at Wye	6049 1470	230.0	18 07 1960	29 12 1986	16.50	83	26.0 23	3.2	40008
*40009	Teise at Stone Bridge	5718 1399	136.2	16 06 1961	02 01 1987	17.02	90	25.3 24	3.6	40009*
40010	Eden at Penshurst	5520 1437	224.3	23 06 1961	21 11 1986	15.60	110	25.4 25	4.3	40010
40011	Great Stour at Horton	6116 1554	345.0	01 07 1964	02 01 1987	15.60	63	22.5 22	2.8	40011
40012	Darent at Hawley	5551 1718	191.4	12 11 1963	06 10 1983	2.30	59	19.4 17	3.0	40012
40016	Cray at Crayford	5511 1746	119.7	27 06 1969	06 10 1983	3.50	58	14.3 14	4.1	40016
40017	Dudwell at Burwash	5679 1240	27.5	20 05 1969	29 12 1986	11.70	66	17.5 15	3.8	40017
40018	Darent at Lullingstone	5530 1643	118.4	16 06 1964	06 10 1983	1.70	123	19.3 18	6.4	40018
40020	Eridge Stream at Hendal Bridge	5522 1367	53.7	01 10 1973	29 12 1986	15.90	75	13.0 12	5.8	40020
40022	Great Stour at Chart Leacon	5992 1423	72.5	20 03 1967	29 12 1986	3.05	93	18.3 15	5.1	40022
40809	Pippingford Brook at Paygate	5479 1343	24.0	24 04 1967	30 09 1983	3.26	123	15.9 13	7.8	40809
41003	Cuckmere at Sherman Bridge	5533 1051	134.7	16 09 1959	30 09 1981	19.10	72	22.0 22	3.3	41003

No.	Name	Grid ref	NRFA Area km²	Record starts	Record ends	THRESH	NPOT	NWYRS NYRS		Ratio	No.
41005	Ouse at Gold Bridge	5429 1214	180.9	22 02 1960	29 12 1982	15.00	133	22.9	22	5.8	41005
41006	Uck at Isfield	5459 1190	87.8	07 07 1964	29 12 1982	17.35	80	18.5	18	4.3	41006
41007	Arun at Park Mound	5033 1200	403.3	24 02 1958	01 10 1973	23.70	68	15.6	15	4.4	41007
41011	Rother at Iping Mill	4852 1229	154.0	27 10 1966	11 01 1983	15.50	81	16.2	15	5.0	41011
41012	Adur E Branch at Sakeham	5219 1190	93.3	01 10 1967	04 01 1983	8.00	98	15.2	14	6.4	41012
41014	Arun at Pallingham Quay	5047 1229	379.0	01 10 1973	04 01 1983	39.00	36	9.3	9	3.9	41014
41016	Cuckmere at Cowbeech	5611 1150	18.7	30 06 1967	05 01 1983	2.38	118	15.5	15	7.6	41016
41018	Kird at Tanyards	5044 1256	66.8	20 06 1969	29 12 1982	6.50	99	13.4	12	7.4	41018
41020	Bevern Stream at Clappers Br.	5423 1161	34.6	01 10 1969	06 01 1983	5.90	82	13.2	13	6.2	41020
41021	Clayhill Stream at Old Ship	5448 1153	7.1	01 10 1973	30 09 1978	1.50	28	5.0	5	5.6	41021
41022	Lod at Halfway Bridge	4931 1223	52.0	01 10 1973	03 01 1983	6.60	59	9.3	9	6.4	41022
41025	Loxwood Stream at Drungewick	5060 1309	91.6	01 10 1973	03 01 1983	17.00	44	9.3	9	4.8	41025
41026	Cockhaise Brook at Holywell	5376 1262	36.1	01 10 1971	05 01 1983	4.50	45	11.3	11	4.0	41026
41027	Rother at Princes Marsh	4772 1270	37.2	01 10 1972	11 01 1983	5.00	42	10.3	9	4.1	41027
41028	Chess Stream at Chess Bridge	5217 1173	24.0	13 11 1964	21 12 1982	4.50	59	18.1	16	3.3	41028
41801	Hollington Stream at Hollington	5788 1100	3.5	02 08 1968	30 12 1974	1.05	31	6.4	6	4.8	41801
41806	North End Stream at Allington	5385 1138	2.3	17 07 1964	29 05 1980	0.46	50	15.9	15	3.2	41806
41807	Bevern Stream at E Chiltington	5368 1153	5.6	23 12 1966	31 07 1980	1.30	86	13.6	12	6.3	41807
42001	Wallington at North Fareham	4587 1075	111.0	01 10 1976	01 01 1985	7.80	36	8.3	8	4.4	42001
42011	Hamble at Frog Mill	4523 1149	56.6	16 08 1972	31 12 1982	4.74	50	10.4	10	4.8	42011
42014	Blackwater at Ower	4328 1174	104.7	01 10 1976	01 01 1985	8.80	42	8.3	8	5.1	42014
43002	Stour at Ensbury	4089 964	1056.7	20 11 1959	30 09 1973	64.00	74	12.9	12	5.7	43002
43005	Avon at Amesbury	4151 1413	323.7	26 07 1965	09 02 1987	7.21	73	21.5	21	3.4	43005
43006	Nadder at Wilton Park	4098 1308	220.6	09 02 1966	09 02 1987	8.80	111	21.0	20	5.3	43006
43007	Stour at Throop Mill	4113 958	1073.0	01 10 1973	02 02 1987	64.00	47	13.3	13	3.5	43007
43009	Stour at Hammoon	3820 1147	523.1	25 04 1968	05 02 1987	44.00	97	18.8	18	5.2	43009
43014	East Avon at Upavon	4133 1559	86.2	01 10 1970	09 02 1987	1.97	84	16.4	16	5.1	43014
43017	West Avon at Upavon	4133 1559	76.0	01 10 1970	09 02 1987	2.40	89	16.4	16	5.4	43017
44003	Asker at Bridport	3470 928	49.1	01 10 1966	13 02 1980	7.00	58	13.4	13	4.3	44003
45001	Exe at Thorverton	2936 1016	600.9	13 04 1956	09 10 1988	97.70	156	32.5	32	4.8	45001
45002	Exe at Stoodleigh	2943 1178	421.7	01 04 1960	09 10 1988	79.15	122	28.5	28	4.3	45002
45003	Culm at Wood Mill	3021 1058	226.1	29 01 1962	09 10 1988	30.00	127	26.7	26	4.8	45003
45004	Axe at Whitford	3262 953	288.5	05 11 1964	09 10 1988	49.10	91	23.9	23	3.8	45004
45005	Otter at Dotton	3087 885	202.5	29 09 1962	11 10 1988	33.60	118	26.0	26	4.5	45005
45006	Quarme at Enterwell	2919 1356	20.4	02 07 1964	04 10 1973	4.50	34	9.3	9	3.7	45006
45008	Otter at Fenny Bridges	3115 986	104.2	01 10 1974	11 10 1988	23.50	59	14.0	14	4.2	45008
45009	Exe at Pixton	2935 1260	147.6	28 04 1966	09 10 1988	22.40	112	16.5	15	6.8	45009
45011	Barle at Brushford	2927 1258	128.0	01 04 1966	01 10 1981	43.82	47	13.1	12	3.6	45011
45012	Creedy at Cowley	2901 967	261.6	23 03 1964	01 10 1987	49.00	79	21.5	20	3.7	45012
45801	Back Brook at Hawkerland	3058 887	2.5	19 08 1967	04 10 1973	0.68	31	4.9	4	6.3	45801
46002	Teign at Preston	2856 746	380.0	13 04 1956	12 10 1988	83.50	93	32.5	32	2.9	46002
46003	Dart at Austins Bridge	2751 659	247.6	19 09 1958	12 10 1988	109.00	170	30.1	30	5.7	46003
46005	East Dart at Bellever	2657 775	21.5	06 03 1964	06 10 1988	26.00	62	24.6	24	2.5	46005
46006	Erme at Ermington	2642 532	43.5	01 10 1974	01 10 1988	34.60	21	14.0	14	1.5	46006
46007	West Dart at Dunnabridge	2643 742	47.9	01 10 1972	30 09 1981	43.40	32	9.0	9	3.6	46007
46008	Avon at Loddiswell	2719 476	102.3	01 10 1971	01 10 1981	30.00	26	10.0	10	2.6	46008
46801	Erme at Erme Intake	2640 632	14.9	01 09 1970	30 09 1973	15.50	13	3.1	3	4.2	46801
46806	Avon at Avon Intake	2681 641	14.0	01 10 1939	31 03 1957	15.78	80	17.4	16	4.6	46806
47001	Tamar at Gunnislake	2426 725	916.9	26 06 1956	26 11 1987	166.00	163	31.4	31	5.2	47001
47004	Lynher at Pillaton Mill	2369 626	135.5	10 05 1961	17 10 1987	23.70	150	26.4	25	5.7	47004
47005	Ottery at Werrington Park	2336 866	120.7	14 04 1961	15 01 1988	23.35	154	22.7	19	6.8	47005
47006	Lyd at Lifton Park	2388 842	218.1	08 08 1962	30 09 1973	57.30	52	10.7	10	4.9	47006
47007	Yealm at Puslinch	2574 511	54.9	17 05 1962	30 09 1973	16.50	48	11.4	11	4.2	47007
47008	Thrushel at Tinhay	2398 856	112.7	28 11 1969	05 01 1988	30.00	92	18.1	17	5.1	47008
47009	Tiddy at Tideford	2343 595	37.2	05 12 1969	06 01 1988	3.60	138	18.1	16	7.6	47009

No.	Name	Grid ref	NRFA Area km²	Record starts	Record ends	THRESH	NPOT	NWYRS NYRS		Ratio	No.
47010	Tamar at Crowford Bridge	2290 991	76.7	01 07 1972	05 01 1988	36.00	82	13.0	11	6.3	47010
47011	Plym at Carn Wood	2522 613	79.2	01 06 1971	30 09 1981	22.40	50	10.3	10	4.8	47011
47014	Walkham at Horrabridge	2513 699	43.2	01 10 1973	29 12 1987	15.60	67	14.2	14	4.7	47014
48001	Fowey at Trekeivesteps	2227 698	36.8	23 09 1969	17 10 1987	10.30	97	18.1	18	5.4	48001
48002	Fowey at Restormel	2108 613	171.2	07 04 1961	30 09 1973	27.70	62	12.5	12	5.0	48002
48003	Fal at Tregony	1921 447	87.0	10 04 1961	07 01 1988	6.38	141	22.2	19	6.3	48003
48004	Warleggan at Trengoffe	2159 674	25.3	22 09 1969	31 12 1987	4.90	85	18.3	18	4.7	48004
48005	Kenwyn at Truro	1820 450	19.1	01 10 1968	07 01 1988	2.50	81	16.9	16	4.8	48005
48006	Cober at Helston	1654 273	40.1	01 10 1968	31 12 1987	3.05	124	16.8	15	7.4	48006
48007	Kennall at Ponsanooth	1762 377	26.6	01 10 1968	07 01 1988	2.80	77	17.0	15	4.5	48007
48009	St Neot at Craigshill Wood	2184 662	22.7	10 03 1971	01 10 1983	5.00	42	12.5	11	3.3	48009
48010	Seaton at Trebrownbridge	2299 596	38.1	02 08 1972	06 01 1988	4.50	58	15.4	15	3.8	48010
48011	Fowey at Restormell Ii	2098 624	169.1	01 10 1972	07 01 1988	27.70	58	15.3	15	3.8	48011
49001	Camel at Denby	2017 682	208.8	03 04 1957	02 01 1988	29.40	159	30.7	29	5.2	49001
49002	Hayle at St Erth	1549 342	48.9	26 02 1957	31 12 1987	3.00	103	27.9	24	3.7	49002
49003	De Lank at De Lank	2132 765	21.7	23 11 1966	07 01 1988	8.00	86	19.2	14	4.5	49003
49004	Gannel at Gwills	1829 593	41.0	15 12 1969	24 12 1987	6.00	89	16.8	15	5.3	49004
50001	Taw at Umberleigh	2608 1237	826.2	26 09 1958	02 10 1973	125.00	67	15.0	15	4.5	50001
50002	Torridge at Torrington	2500 1185	663.0	06 07 1960	02 10 1973	158.80	41	12.1	11	3.4	50002
50005	West Okement at Vellake	2557 903	13.3	23 07 1967	04 10 1973	13.30	31	6.2	6	5.0	50005
50006	Mole at Woodleigh	2660 1211	327.5	11 01 1965	30 09 1973	112.00	33	8.7	8	3.8	50006
50007	Taw at Taw Bridge	2673 1068	71.4	01 10 1973	31 12 1981	26.00	47	8.3	8	5.7	50007
50810	Little Dart at Dart Bridge	2669 1137	125.6	01 10 1973	06 10 1981	14.00	78	8.0	8	9.7	50810
51002	Horner Water at West Luccombe	2898 1458	20.8	16 03 1973	09 12 1988	2.43	46	10.1	8	4.6	51002
51003	Washford at Beggearn Huish	3040 1395	36.3	01 10 1966	09 12 1988	2.40	95	18.0	14	5.3	51003
52003	Halse Water at Bishops Hull	3206 1253	87.8	07 11 1961	09 12 1988	5.00	136	24.7	21	5.5	52003
52004	Isle at Ashford Mill	3361 1188	90.1	17 09 1962	28 12 1988	17.80	118	25.8	24	4.6	52004
52005	Tone at Bishops Hull	3206 1250	202.0	06 01 1961	09 12 1988	21.10	153	26.2	23	5.8	52005
52006	Yeo at Pen Mill	3573 1162	213.1	18 05 1962	06 12 1988	30.80	81	25.5	24	3.2	52006
52007	Parrett at Chiselborough	3461 1144	74.8	01 10 1966	06 12 1988	11.70	68	16.1	15	4.2	52007
52009	Sheppey at Fenny Castle	3498 1439	59.6	31 12 1963	07 12 1988	4.20	90	23.2	17	3.9	52009
52010	Brue at Lovington	3590 1318	135.2	01 10 1964	06 12 1988	20.40	112	23.8	21	4.7	52010
52011	Cary at Somerton	3498 1291	82.4	02 09 1965	30 09 1988	6.70	88	22.0	20	4.0	52011
52014	Tone at Greenham	3078 1202	57.2	13 05 1966	30 09 1981	7.50	45	14.0	12	3.2	52014
52015	Land Yeo at Wraxall Bridge	3483 1716	23.3	29 12 1970	12 12 1988	1.08	60	11.4	7	5.3	52015
52016	Currypool Stream at Currypool Fm	3221 1382	15.7	30 04 1971	05 12 1988	1.30	73	17.5	16	4.2	52016
52017	Congresbury Yeo at Iwood	3452 1631	66.6	01 10 1973	12 12 1988	5.30	73	14.0	10	5.2	52017
52020	Gallica Stream at Gallica Bridge	3571 1100	16.4	01 10 1966	30 09 1979	9.20	40	7.4	6	5.4	52020
*53001	Avon at Melksham	3903 1641	665.6	03 12 1937	02 12 1988	35.00	259	50.3	44	5.1	53001*
53002	Semington Brook at Semington	3907 1605	157.7	01 10 1973	19 12 1988	14.70	73	15.2	15	4.8	53002
53003	Avon at Bath St James	3753 1645	1595.0	25 11 1939	06 10 1969	77.00	147	29.9	29	4.9	53003
53004	Chew at Compton Dando	3648 1647	129.5	26 02 1958	31 12 1988	7.07	164	30.8	30	5.3	53004
53005	Midford Brook at Midford	3763 1611	147.4	21 04 1961	20 12 1988	11.50	159	27.5	25	5.8	53005
53006	Frome(bristol) at Frenchay	3637 1772	148.9	07 07 1961	31 12 1988	12.87	147	27.5	27	5.3	53006
53007	Frome(somerset) at Tellisford	3805 1564	261.6	21 04 1961	20 12 1988	30.86	118	27.7	27	4.3	53007
53008	Avon at Great Somerford	3966 1832	303.0	16 12 1963	04 12 1987	17.60	127	23.9	22	5.3	53008
53009	Wellow Brook at Wellow	3741 1581	72.6	01 01 1966	20 12 1988	6.20	115	23.0	22	5.0	53009
53013	Marden at Stanley	3955 1729	99.2	01 10 1969	19 12 1988	7.60	102	19.2	19	5.3	53013
53017	Boyd at Bitton	3681 1698	48.0	01 10 1973	20 12 1988	6.10	68	15.2	15	4.5	53017
53018	Avon at Bathford	3786 1671	1552.0	01 10 1969	02 12 1988	77.00	95	16.4	16	5.8	53018
53019	Woodbridge Brook at Crab Mill	3949 1866	46.6	13 04 1964	31 12 1976	5.20	60	12.7	12	4.7	53019
53020	Gauze Brook at Rodbourne	3937 1840	28.2	28 03 1963	19 12 1988	2.30	79	25.7	25	3.1	53020
53023	Sherston Avon at Fosseway	3891 1870	89.7	01 10 1976	19 12 1988	4.25	45	12.0	11	3.8	53023
53025	Mells at Vallis	3757 1491	119.0	31 12 1979	20 12 1988	10.00	53	9.0	8	5.9	53025
54001	Severn at Bewdley	3782 2762	4325.0	23 06 1923	02 01 1986	210.00	313	59.5	54	5.3	54001

Statistical procedures for flood frequency estimation

No.	Name	Grid ref	NRFA Area km²	Record starts	Record ends	THRESH	NPOT	NYRS	NWYRS	Ratio	No.
54002	Avon at Evesham	4040 2438	2210.0	13 09 1937	07 01 1986	65.80	213	48.3	46	4.4	54002
54004	Sowe at Stoneleigh	4332 2731	262.0	19 03 1951	02 01 1986	12.80	218	34.2	30	6.4	54004
54005	Severn at Montford	3412 3144	2025.0	28 04 1952	02 01 1986	200.00	150	33.7	33	4.5	54005
*54006	Stour at Kidderminster	3829 2768	324.0	23 07 1952	31 12 1985	9.00	191	28.2	26	6.8	54006*
54007	Arrow at Broom	4086 2536	319.0	19 03 1956	01 01 1986	30.00	102	29.7	26	3.4	54007
54008	Teme at Tenbury	3597 2686	1134.4	22 08 1956	24 12 1985	63.00	118	25.3	24	4.7	54008
54010	Stour at Alscot Park	4208 2507	319.0	15 12 1958	08 01 1986	18.00	116	26.2	24	4.4	54010
54011	Salwarpe at Harford Mill	3868 2618	184.0	28 07 1958	02 01 1986	8.40	127	27.3	26	4.7	54011
54012	Tern at Walcot	3592 3123	852.0	11 05 1959	02 01 1986	17.30	200	26.7	26	7.5	54012
54013	Clywedog at Cribynau	2944 2855	57.0	01 01 1959	30 09 1965	25.00	33	6.7	6	4.9	54013
54014	Severn at Abermule	3164 2958	580.0	15 06 1960	02 01 1986	105.00	110	25.6	25	4.3	54014
54016	Roden at Rodington	3589 3141	259.0	02 03 1961	02 01 1986	8.80	77	16.8	15	4.6	54016
54017	Leadon at Wedderburn Bridge	3777 2234	293.0	14 08 1961	02 01 1986	15.20	80	19.7	19	4.1	54017
54018	Rea Brook at Hookagate	3466 3092	178.0	01 10 1962	06 01 1986	15.60	63	13.7	11	4.6	54018
54019	Avon at Stareton	4333 2715	347.0	26 09 1962	02 01 1986	13.40	83	18.0	17	4.6	54019
54020	Perry at Yeaton	3434 3192	180.8	25 09 1963	03 01 1986	6.40	82	22.3	22	3.7	54020
54022	Severn at Plynlimon Flume	2853 2872	8.7	27 04 1951	02 12 1973	6.80	120	22.1	19	5.4	54022
54023	Badsey Brook at Offenham	4063 2449	95.8	02 05 1968	07 01 1986	5.40	103	17.6	16	5.8	54023
54025	Dulas at Rhos-y-pentref	2950 2824	52.7	01 10 1969	05 01 1984	11.60	77	14.3	14	5.4	54025
54026	Chelt at Slate Mill	3892 2264	34.5	01 10 1969	10 01 1986	4.26	64	11.3	10	5.7	54026
54028	Vyrnwy at Llanymynech	3252 3195	778.0	01 10 1972	02 01 1986	146.20	72	13.3	13	5.4	54028
54029	Teme at Knightsford Bridge	3735 2557	1480.0	01 10 1970	30 12 1985	110.00	37	13.2	13	2.8	54029
54032	Severn at Saxons Lode	3863 2390	6850.0	01 10 1970	27 12 1985	271.00	74	15.2	15	4.9	54032
54034	Dowles Brook at Dowles	3768 2764	40.8	01 10 1971	30 09 1985	3.75	62	14.0	14	4.4	54034
54036	Isbourne at Hinton on the Green	4023 2408	90.7	26 12 1972	07 01 1986	6.40	52	13.0	12	4.0	54036
54038	Tanat at Llanyblodwel	3252 3225	229.0	11 05 1973	03 01 1986	41.00	72	12.7	12	5.7	54038
54057	Severn at Haw Bridge	3844 2279	9895.0	01 10 1975	27 12 1985	315.00	57	10.2	10	5.6	54057
54065	Roden at Stanton	3565 3241	210.0	01 10 1973	30 09 1978	6.13	24	5.0	5	4.8	54065
54088	Little Avon at Berkeley Kennels	3683 1988	134.0	07 08 1978	21 12 1988	7.70	50	9.4	8	5.3	54088
55001	Wye at Cadora	3535 2090	4040.0	29 10 1936	01 10 1969	354.00	145	32.9	32	4.4	55001
55002	Wye at Belmont	3485 2388	1895.9	07 01 1908	29 12 1983	235.00	448	71.2	58	6.3	55002
55003	Lugg at Lugwardine	3548 2405	885.8	01 12 1939	29 12 1983	35.80	233	44.1	43	5.3	55003
55004	Irfon at Abernant	2892 2460	72.8	01 10 1937	28 12 1983	35.00	215	46.1	43	4.7	55004
55005	Wye at Rhayader	2969 2676	166.8	09 11 1937	06 10 1969	59.00	131	31.7	27	4.1	55005
55007	Wye at Erwood	3076 2445	1282.1	02 11 1937	28 12 1983	255.00	253	45.9	43	5.5	55007
55008	Wye at Cefn Brwyn	2829 2838	10.6	20 07 1951	31 12 1985	8.20	249	34.1	33	7.3	55008
55009	Monnow at Kentchurch	3419 2251	357.4	01 10 1948	07 10 1973	62.00	102	21.8	21	4.7	55009
55010	Wye at Pant Mawr	2843 2825	27.2	26 08 1952	03 01 1984	25.00	178	30.4	26	5.9	55010
55011	Ithon at Llandewi	3105 2683	111.4	09 09 1959	12 11 1973	30.00	66	14.2	14	4.7	55011
55012	Irfon at Cilmery	2995 2507	244.2	30 09 1966	28 12 1983	110.00	61	17.0	15	3.6	55012
55013	Arrow at Titley Mill	3328 2585	126.4	23 06 1966	31 12 1983	13.00	90	17.5	17	5.1	55013
55014	Lugg at Byton	3364 2647	203.3	01 10 1966	29 12 1983	17.00	49	17.2	17	2.8	55014
55015	Honddu at Tafolog	3277 2294	25.1	29 03 1953	28 12 1983	9.60	126	30.8	30	4.1	55015
55016	Ithon at Disserth	3024 2578	358.0	29 07 1968	01 10 1973	55.00	21	5.2	5	4.1	55016
55017	Chwefru at Carreg-y-wen	2998 2531	29.0	01 07 1968	05 11 1973	10.00	24	5.3	5	4.5	55017
55018	Frome at Yarkhill	3615 2428	144.0	14 06 1968	29 12 1983	13.20	57	15.5	14	3.7	55018
55021	Lugg at Butts Bridge	3502 2589	371.0	06 10 1969	27 05 1982	24.00	50	12.6	11	4.0	55021
55022	Trothy at Mitchel Troy	3503 2112	142.0	06 10 1969	28 12 1983	17.00	62	14.0	10	4.4	55022
55023	Wye at Redbrook	3528 2110	4010.0	24 09 1969	28 12 1983	354.00	67	14.3	14	4.7	55023
55025	Llynfi at Three Cocks	3166 2373	132.0	30 07 1970	19 12 1983	16.50	74	13.4	12	5.5	55025
55026	Wye at Ddol Farm	2976 2676	174.0	06 10 1969	28 12 1983	59.00	91	14.2	13	6.4	55026
55029	Monnow at Grosmont	3415 2249	354.0	01 10 1973	28 12 1983	62.00	55	10.2	10	5.4	55029
56001	Usk at Chain Bridge	3345 2056	911.7	12 02 1957	02 01 1985	198.00	127	27.8	26	4.6	56001
56002	Ebbw at Rhiwderyn	3259 1889	216.5	24 04 1957	02 01 1985	38.00	188	26.5	23	7.1	56002
56003	Honddu at The Forge Brecon	3051 2297	62.1	01 10 1963	30 09 1984	11.00	105	20.6	15	5.1	56003

No.	Name	Grid ref	NRFA Area km²	Record starts	Record ends	THRESH	NPOT	NWYRS NYRS	NWYRS Ratio	No.
56004	Usk at Llandetty	3127 2203	543.9	05 11 1965	27 12 1984	179.00	78	19.1	18	4.1	56004
56005	Lwyd at Ponthir	3330 1924	98.1	15 06 1966	27 12 1984	24.00	97	17.8	16	5.4	56005
56006	Usk at Trallong	2947 2295	183.8	01 10 1963	27 12 1984	72.00	114	21.2	21	5.4	56006
56011	Sirhowy at Wattsville	3206 1912	76.1	01 10 1971	22 06 1983	18.80	66	11.7	11	5.6	56011
56012	Grwyne at Millbrook	3241 2176	82.2	01 10 1971	31 12 1984	10.40	67	13.3	13	5.1	56012
56013	Yscir at Pontaryscir	3003 2304	62.8	01 10 1972	31 12 1984	19.00	48	12.3	12	3.9	56013
*56015	Olway Brook at Olway Inn	3384 2010	105.1	01 10 1974	31 12 1984	16.90	51	10.2	9	5.0	56015*
56019	Ebbw at Aberbeeg	3210 2015	77.0	01 10 1975	02 01 1985	23.00	48	9.2	8	5.2	56019
57003	Taff at Tongwynlais	3132 1818	486.9	01 10 1960	30 09 1973	159.90	48	12.7	10	3.8	57003
57004	Cynon at Abercynon	3079 1956	106.0	26 12 1960	04 01 1984	38.00	120	22.9	21	5.2	57004
57005	Taff at Pontypridd	3079 1897	454.8	12 03 1968	04 01 1984	145.50	85	15.8	15	5.4	57005
57006	Rhondda at Trehafod	3054 1909	100.5	28 06 1968	04 01 1984	46.00	103	14.7	13	7.0	57006
57007	Taff at Fiddlers Elbow	3089 1951	194.5	18 04 1973	04 01 1984	55.00	49	10.7	10	4.6	57007
57008	Rhymney at Llanedeyrn	3225 1821	178.7	08 09 1972	04 01 1984	52.00	64	11.3	11	5.7	57008
57009	Ely at St Fagans	3121 1770	145.0	22 10 1974	04 01 1984	32.00	44	9.2	8	4.8	57009
57010	Ely at Lanelay	3034 1827	39.4	31 07 1967	04 01 1984	18.99	73	15.8	14	4.6	57010
57015	Taff at Merthyr Tydfil	3043 2068	104.1	05 12 1978	04 01 1984	39.00	31	5.0	4	6.1	57015
57803	Clun at Cross Inn	3053 1824	25.9	27 01 1967	30 09 1973	10.50	37	6.7	6	5.5	57803
58001	Ogmore at Bridgend	2904 1794	158.0	01 10 1960	30 09 1985	56.00	128	24.5	23	5.2	58001
58002	Neath at Resolven	2815 2017	190.9	01 10 1960	31 12 1983	96.00	130	21.9	18	5.9	58002
58003	Ewenny at Ewenny Priory	2914 1780	62.9	28 12 1960	20 03 1970	13.30	49	9.2	8	5.3	58003
58004	Afan at Cwmavon	2781 1919	85.7	08 12 1961	27 01 1971	27.00	72	8.8	6	8.2	58004
58005	Ogmore at Brynmenyn	2904 1844	74.3	01 10 1969	30 10 1985	20.20	102	16.1	16	6.3	58005
58006	Mellte at Pontneddfechan	2915 2082	65.8	10 02 1971	31 12 1983	36.00	57	12.9	12	4.4	58006
58007	Llynfi at Coytrahen	2891 1855	50.2	01 10 1970	30 09 1985	22.50	84	15.0	15	5.6	58007
58008	Dulais at Cilfrew	2778 2008	43.0	08 12 1971	31 12 1983	25.77	64	12.1	11	5.3	58008
58009	Ewenny at Keepers Lodge	2920 1782	62.5	01 11 1971	06 11 1985	17.00	69	14.0	13	4.9	58009
58010	Hepste at Esgair Carnau	2969 2134	11.0	03 09 1975	31 12 1981	8.19	40	6.3	5	6.4	58010
58011	Thaw at Gigman Bridge	3017 1716	49.2	01 10 1973	31 12 1983	4.20	54	10.2	7	5.3	58011
59001	Tawe at Ynystanglws	2685 1998	227.7	18 10 1956	02 10 1973	122.00	90	17.0	16	5.3	59001
59002	Loughor at Tir-y-dail	2623 2127	46.4	12 09 1967	31 12 1983	31.00	75	16.3	16	4.6	59002
60002	Cothi at Felin Mynachdy	2508 2225	297.8	30 08 1961	01 01 1984	76.70	112	22.3	22	5.0	60002
60003	Taf at Clog-y-fran	2238 2160	217.3	31 07 1964	18 11 1982	38.20	81	18.3	18	4.4	60003
60004	Dewi Fawr at Glasfryn Ford	2290 2175	40.1	21 02 1967	06 01 1984	11.00	63	16.4	15	3.8	60004
60005	Bran at Llandovery	2771 2343	66.8	08 04 1968	01 01 1984	15.50	98	15.7	15	6.2	60005
60006	Gwili at Glangwili	2431 2220	129.5	02 05 1968	04 10 1973	39.50	19	5.4	5	3.5	60006
60007	Tywi at Dolau Hirion	2762 2362	231.8	25 04 1968	01 01 1984	92.97	40	15.7	15	2.5	60007
60009	Sawdde at Felin-y-cwm	2712 2266	81.1	01 01 1973	01 01 1984	70.73	31	11.0	10	2.8	60009
60010	Tywi at Nantgaredig	2491 2204	1090.4	01 01 1958	03 01 1984	200.00	121	26.0	25	4.7	60010
60012	Twrch at Ddol Las	2650 2440	20.7	10 09 1970	01 01 1984	8.00	61	13.3	13	4.6	60012
60013	Cothi at Pont Ynys Brechfa	2537 2301	261.6	27 07 1971	10 07 1981	65.00	54	10.0	9	5.4	60013
61001	W Cleddau at Prendergast Mill	1954 2177	197.6	28 07 1961	01 01 1984	32.00	142	22.4	22	6.3	61001
61002	Eastern Cleddau at Canaston Br.	2072 2153	183.1	30 11 1959	01 01 1984	41.06	127	24.1	23	5.3	61002
61003	Gwaun at Cilrhedyn Bridge	2005 2349	31.3	17 09 1968	01 01 1984	8.90	69	15.3	15	4.5	61003
62001	Teifi at Glan Teifi	2244 2416	893.6	05 06 1959	01 01 1984	118.05	107	24.6	24	4.4	62001
62002	Teifi at Llanfair	2433 2406	510.0	01 12 1970	03 02 1983	65.00	64	12.2	11	5.3	62002
63001	Ystwyth at Pont Llolwyn	2591 2774	169.6	29 06 1961	01 10 1973	51.75	68	12.3	12	5.5	63001
63002	Rheidol at Llanbadarn Fawr	2601 2804	182.1	22 10 1963	03 01 1984	40.00	133	20.2	19	6.6	63002
63003	Wyre at Llanrhystyd	2542 2698	40.6	01 10 1968	03 12 1979	16.00	40	11.2	11	3.6	63003
64001	Dyfi at Dyfi Bridge	2745 3019	471.3	27 09 1962	02 01 1986	164.00	159	23.2	22	6.8	64001
64002	Dysynni at Pont-y-garth	2632 3066	75.1	03 11 1965	02 01 1986	36.00	96	20.1	19	4.8	64002
64005	Wnion at Dolgellau	2730 3179	110.8	18 05 1969	30 01 1974	80.00	14	4.7	4	3.0	64005
64006	Leri at Dolybont	2635 2882	47.2	30 01 1974	02 01 1986	8.50	61	11.9	10	5.1	64006
65001	Glaslyn at Beddgelert	2592 3478	68.6	06 10 1969	02 01 1986	65.00	61	16.1	14	3.8	65001
65002	Dwyryd at Maentwrog	2670 3415	78.2	04 05 1967	30 01 1974	63.00	38	6.7	6	5.6	65002

No.	Name	Grid ref	NRFA Area km²	Record starts	Record ends	THRESH	NPOT	NWYRS NYRS	Ratio	No.
65004	Gwyrfai at Bontnewydd	2484 3599	47.9	13 03 1971	02 01 1986	13.00	60	14.8	14	4.1	65004
65005	Erch at Pencaenewydd	2400 3404	18.1	05 09 1972	02 01 1986	6.20	75	13.3	13	5.6	65005
65006	Seiont at Peblig Mill	2493 3623	74.4	01 10 1975	02 01 1986	24.00	51	10.3	10	5.0	65006
65007	Dwyfawr at Garndolbenmaen	2499 3429	52.4	19 02 1975	02 01 1986	21.00	61	10.9	9	5.6	65007
66002	Elwy at Pant Yr Onen	3021 3704	220.0	26 07 1961	24 12 1973	35.40	67	12.4	12	5.4	66002
66003	Aled at Bryn Aled	2957 3703	70.0	24 07 1963	07 01 1986	12.60	91	21.8	19	4.2	66003
66004	Wheeler at Bodfari	3105 3714	62.9	31 12 1973	13 01 1986	2.00	42	10.5	8	4.0	66004
66005	Clwyd at Ruthin Weir	3122 3592	95.3	01 10 1972	18 10 1984	6.00	62	12.0	12	5.1	66005
66006	Elwy at Pont-y-gwyddel	2952 3718	194.0	31 12 1973	07 01 1986	39.00	44	12.0	11	3.7	66006
66011	Conwy at Cwm Llanerch	2802 3581	344.5	29 05 1964	07 01 1986	272.00	81	21.6	20	3.8	66011
66801	Upperconway at Blaen Y Coed	2804 3452	10.4	17 11 1950	04 06 1958	9.10	35	7.5	6	4.6	66801
67002	Dee at Erbistock Rectory	3357 3413	1040.0	29 12 1937	31 12 1973	134.00	161	35.9	33	4.5	67002
67003	Brenig at Llyn Brenig Outflow	2974 3539	20.2	29 09 1964	31 12 1973	7.80	39	9.3	9	4.2	67003
*67005	Ceiriog at Brynkinalt Weir	3295 3373	113.7	01 10 1952	03 11 1983	15.20	142	31.1	31	4.6	67005*
67006	Alwen at Druid	3042 3436	184.7	12 01 1960	03 01 1986	33.60	143	26.0	24	5.5	67006
67007	Dee at Glyndyfrdwy	3155 3428	728.0	20 01 1964	31 12 1973	93.00	64	9.9	9	6.4	67007
67008	Alyn at Pont-y-capel	3336 3541	227.1	29 05 1965	08 01 1986	13.00	94	20.5	18	4.6	67008
67009	Alyn at Rhydymwyn	3206 3667	77.8	17 08 1957	06 01 1986	4.10	104	28.4	28	3.7	67009
67013	Himant at Plas Rhiwedog	2946 3349	33.9	10 07 1967	02 01 1980	10.30	68	12.5	12	5.4	67013
67014	Dee at Corwen	3069 3433	655.4	31 12 1973	17 01 1986	93.00	79	12.0	11	6.6	67014
67015	Dee at Manley Hall	3348 3415	1019.3	01 01 1974	31 12 1985	134.00	47	12.0	11	3.9	67015
67018	Dee at New Inn	2874 3308	53.9	24 12 1968	31 12 1985	39.00	109	16.0	14	6.8	67018
67019	Tryweryn at Weir X	2932 3360	111.2	28 07 1960	30 09 1964	30.40	32	4.2	3	7.7	67019
67025	Clywedog at Bowling Bank	3396 3483	98.6	01 10 1975	13 01 1986	9.20	32	9.3	9	3.4	67025
68001	Weaver at Ashbrook	3670 3633	622.0	27 05 1937	02 01 1986	25.00	278	47.7	43	5.8	68001
68002	Gowy at Picton	3443 3714	156.2	26 05 1949	04 01 1980	10.10	156	30.6	30	5.1	68002
68003	Dane at Rudheath	3668 3718	407.1	16 05 1949	02 01 1986	34.90	154	36.5	35	4.2	68003
68004	Wistaston Brook at Marshfield Br.	3674 3552	92.7	01 10 1957	02 01 1986	6.30	119	27.5	25	4.3	68004
*68005	Weaver at Audlem	3653 3431	207.0	19 06 1936	07 02 1986	10.30	246	49.6	48	5.0	68005*
68006	Dane at Hulme Walfield	3845 3644	150.0	14 08 1953	02 01 1986	31.00	124	31.1	29	4.0	68006
68007	Wincham Bk at Lostock Gralam	3697 3757	148.0	01 10 1963	02 01 1986	11.20	95	20.3	19	4.7	68007
68010	Fender at Ford	3281 3880	18.4	25 04 1973	30 09 1981	2.60	45	8.4	8	5.3	68010
68011	Arley Brook at Gore Farm	3696 3799	36.5	03 01 1975	30 09 1982	4.00	35	7.7	7	4.5	68011
68014	Sandersons Brook at Sandbach	3754 3652	5.4	20 08 1964	30 09 1969	0.54	34	4.8	3	7.0	68014
68015	Gowy at Huxley	3497 3624	49.0	01 10 1973	06 01 1986	3.20	66	12.2	10	5.4	68015
68018	Dane at Congleton Park	3861 3632	145.0	20 07 1936	26 12 1985	21.00	213	34.4	29	6.2	68018
68020	Gowy at Bridge Trafford	3448 3711	156.0	01 10 1979	06 01 1986	10.10	46	6.2	5	7.4	68020
69001	Mersey at Irlam Weir	3728 3936	679.0	28 09 1934	27 12 1985	87.76	231	51.0	45	4.5	69001
69002	Irwell at Adelphi Weir	3824 3987	559.4	11 11 1935	03 01 1980	108.00	231	43.7	40	5.3	69002
69003	Irk at Scotland Weir	3841 3992	72.5	01 10 1949	06 01 1986	18.40	211	33.7	25	6.3	69003
69006	Bollin at Dunham Massey	3727 3875	256.0	01 10 1936	03 01 1986	28.10	174	44.5	40	3.9	69006
69007	Mersey at Ashton Weir	3772 3936	660.0	11 06 1958	03 01 1986	75.40	131	27.2	23	4.8	69007
69008	Dean at Stanneylands	3846 3830	51.8	29 11 1966	03 01 1986	5.00	90	18.7	15	4.8	69008
69011	Micker Brook at Cheadle	3855 3889	67.3	29 03 1968	03 01 1986	6.90	122	17.8	17	6.9	69011
69012	Bollin at Wilmslow	3850 3815	72.5	01 02 1968	05 01 1986	8.20	91	17.8	15	5.1	69012
69013	Sinderland Brook at Partington	3726 3905	44.8	01 01 1968	27 12 1985	3.80	93	18.0	16	5.2	69013
69015	Etherow at Compstall	3962 3908	156.0	20 03 1969	03 01 1986	21.50	90	16.7	14	5.4	69015
69017	Goyt at Marple Bridge	3964 3898	183.0	20 03 1969	03 01 1986	20.05	130	16.7	11	7.8	69017
69018	Newton Bk at Newton Le Willows	3585 3933	32.8	27 08 1969	01 05 1981	2.05	53	11.7	11	4.5	69018
69019	Worsley Brook at Eccles	3753 3980	24.9	26 08 1969	06 01 1986	2.63	119	16.3	15	7.3	69019
69020	Medlock at London Road	3849 3975	57.5	24 04 1969	06 01 1986	7.20	97	16.7	16	5.8	69020
69023	Roch at Blackford Bridge	3807 4077	186.0	15 02 1949	03 01 1980	32.20	145	30.9	29	4.7	69023
69024	Croal at Farnworth Weir	3743 4068	145.0	15 12 1948	06 11 1985	28.00	214	36.7	35	5.8	69024
69025	Irwell at Manchester Racecourse	3821 4004	557.0	04 01 1980	06 01 1986	108.00	50	6.0	5	8.3	69025
69027	Tame at Portwood	3906 3918	150.0	15 03 1943	03 01 1986	28.00	183	36.2	30	5.1	69027

No.	Name	Grid ref	NRFA Area km²	Record starts	Record ends	THRESH	NPOT	NWYRS NYRS		Ratio	No.
69034	Musbury Brook at Helmshore	3775 4213	3.1	03 01 1960	06 10 1969	2.68	48	9.7	8	5.0	69034
69035	Irwell at Bury Bridge	3797 4109	155.0	06 01 1976	06 01 1986	85.00	48	9.9	8	4.9	69035
69040	Irwell at Stubbins	3793 4188	105.0	01 10 1974	06 01 1986	39.00	54	11.2	9	4.8	69040
69041	Tame at Broomstair Bridge	3938 3953	113.0	13 06 1968	02 01 1986	29.40	60	16.5	13	3.6	69041
69802	Etherow at Woodhead	4102 3998	13.0	23 02 1937	31 12 1975	7.10	205	36.5	27	5.6	69802
70003	Douglas at Central Park Wigan	3587 4061	55.3	01 10 1973	07 01 1986	7.84	78	12.2	10	6.4	70003
70004	Yarrow at Croston Mill	3498 4180	74.4	01 10 1973	07 01 1986	15.00	85	12.2	9	7.0	70004
70005	Lostock at Littlewood Bridge	3497 4197	56.0	01 10 1974	07 01 1986	7.30	84	11.1	7	7.6	70005
70006	Tawd at Newburgh	3469 4107	28.9	15 02 1965	03 07 1981	7.00	78	16.0	13	4.9	70006
71001	Ribble at Samlesbury	3589 4304	1145.0	06 04 1960	07 01 1986	326.00	143	25.1	22	5.7	71001
71003	Croasdale at Croasdale Flume	3706 4546	10.4	04 06 1957	14 11 1977	5.26	119	16.9	14	7.1	71003
71004	Calder at Whalley Weir	3729 4360	316.0	01 10 1969	02 01 1986	96.00	64	16.3	16	3.9	71004
71005	Bottoms Beck at B. Beck Flume	3745 4565	10.6	14 04 1960	31 12 1975	8.40	58	15.1	14	3.8	71005
71006	Ribble at Henthorn	3722 4392	456.0	01 10 1968	02 01 1986	134.00	77	15.2	12	5.1	71006
71007	Ribble at Hodderfoot	3709 4379	720.0	23 07 1965	07 01 1980	285.00	30	14.2	13	2.1	71007
71008	Hodder at Hodder Place	3704 4399	261.0	01 10 1969	02 01 1986	93.00	123	16.2	14	7.6	71008
71009	Ribble at Jumbles Rock	3702 4376	1053.0	14 05 1970	02 01 1986	350.00	71	15.6	15	4.5	71009
71010	Pendle Water at Barden Lane	3837 4351	108.0	01 10 1971	02 01 1986	34.00	92	14.2	13	6.5	71010
71011	Ribble at Arnford	3839 4556	204.0	01 10 1969	02 01 1986	111.00	30	16.2	14	1.9	71011
71013	Darwen at Ewood Bridge	3677 4262	39.5	01 10 1973	07 01 1986	11.60	101	12.3	12	8.2	71013
71014	Darwen at Blue Bridge	3565 4278	128.0	01 10 1974	07 01 1986	42.00	77	11.3	11	6.8	71014
71802	Ribble at Halton West	3850 4552	207.0	29 04 1966	03 10 1969	111.00	15	3.2	2	4.6	71802
71803	Hodder at Higher Hodder Bridge	3697 4411	256.0	23 09 1960	03 10 1969	191.00	53	9.0	9	5.9	71803
72001	Lune at Halton	3503 4647	994.6	01 10 1969	19 01 1977	402.00	22	7.3	7	3.0	72001
72002	Wyre at St Michaels	3463 4411	275.0	14 08 1962	08 01 1986	89.00	99	22.4	20	4.4	72002
72004	Lune at Caton	3529 4653	983.0	19 01 1977	31 12 1984	402.00	35	8.0	7	4.4	72004
72005	Lune at Killington New Bridge	3622 4907	219.0	09 05 1969	03 01 1985	115.00	64	14.8	13	4.3	72005
72006	Lune at Kirkby Lonsdale	3615 4778	507.1	01 10 1968	31 12 1984	275.00	69	16.3	16	4.2	72006
72009	Wenning at Wennington Rd Br.	3615 4701	142.0	27 11 1970	31 12 1984	50.00	67	14.1	13	4.8	72009
72011	Rawthey at Brigg Flatts	3639 4911	200.0	21 06 1968	03 01 1985	170.00	70	15.9	11	4.4	72011
72013	Borrowbeck at Borrow Br. Weir	3609 5014	26.0	20 02 1976	02 02 1981	32.00	19	5.0	4	3.8	72013
72014	Conder at Galgate	3481 4554	28.5	04 09 1975	31 12 1984	16.10	52	9.3	9	5.6	72014
72015	Lune at Lunes Bridge	3612 5029	141.5	02 02 1979	03 01 1985	114.00	27	5.7	3	4.7	72015
72016	Wyre at Scorton Weir	3501 4500	88.8	12 01 1967	03 01 1986	55.26	52	14.5	12	3.6	72016
72804	Lune at Broadraine	3621 4901	222.0	02 07 1963	30 09 1969	130.00	24	6.2	5	3.9	72804
72807	Wenning at Hornby	3586 4684	232.0	01 05 1957	31 12 1984	142.00	125	27.5	26	4.5	72807
73001	Leven at Newby Bridge	3371 4863	241.0	28 12 1938	03 10 1969	46.30	101	30.8	30	3.3	73001
73002	Crake at Low Nibthwaite	3294 4882	73.0	21 08 1963	30 09 1969	10.00	22	6.1	6	3.6	73002
73005	Kent at Sedgwick	3509 4874	209.0	01 10 1968	03 01 1985	72.50	67	16.3	16	4.1	73005
73008	Bela at Beetham	3496 4806	131.0	07 07 1969	31 12 1984	22.00	62	15.5	14	4.0	73008
73009	Sprint at Sprint Mill	3514 4961	34.6	11 03 1970	27 12 1984	19.40	49	14.8	14	3.3	73009
73011	Mint at Mint Bridge	3524 4944	65.8	28 07 1970	27 12 1984	26.00	49	14.4	14	3.4	73011
73013	Rothay at Miller Bridge House	3371 5042	64.0	24 09 1968	28 12 1984	53.60	71	16.3	16	4.4	73013
73014	Brathay at Jeffy Knotts	3360 5034	57.4	07 09 1970	28 12 1984	30.00	68	14.3	14	4.8	73014
73015	Keer at High Keer Weir	3523 4719	48.0	18 05 1971	06 10 1981	7.50	48	10.4	10	4.6	73015
73803	Winster at Lobby Bridge	3424 4885	20.7	01 10 1969	01 10 1981	5.60	56	12.0	12	4.7	73803
73805	Kent at Kendal (nether Bridge)	3517 4919	188.0	13 11 1963	02 10 1969	76.00	29	5.9	5	4.9	73805
74001	Duddon at Duddon Hall	3196 4896	85.7	05 01 1968	28 12 1984	62.50	76	17.0	16	4.5	74001
74002	Irt at Galesyke	3136 5038	44.2	08 12 1967	03 01 1985	9.50	102	16.9	13	6.0	74002
74005	Ehen at Braystones	3009 5061	125.5	25 10 1973	04 01 1985	47.00	61	11.0	9	5.5	74005
74006	Calder at Calder Hall	3035 5045	44.8	01 10 1973	04 01 1985	25.50	45	11.3	11	4.0	74006
75002	Derwent at Camerton	3038 5305	663.0	12 08 1960	03 01 1985	113.50	114	24.4	24	4.7	75002
75004	Cocker at Southwaite Bridge	3131 5281	116.6	05 04 1967	03 01 1985	38.00	39	17.8	17	2.2	75004
75005	Derwent at Portinscale	3251 5239	235.0	17 12 1971	03 01 1985	67.50	52	13.0	12	4.0	75005
75006	Newlands Beck at Braithwaite	3240 5239	33.9	16 08 1968	02 01 1986	20.00	88	17.4	17	5.1	75006

No.	Name	Grid ref	NRFA Area km²	Record starts	Record ends	THRESH	NPOT	NWYRS NYRS	NWYRS Ratio	No.
75007	Glenderamackin at Threlkeld	3323 5248	64.5	01 04 1969	06 05 1981	45.00	47	12.1 11	3.9	75007
75009	Greta at Low Briery	3286 5242	145.6	25 03 1971	03 01 1985	56.00	59	13.7 11	4.3	75009
75010	Marron at Ullock	3074 5238	27.7	28 04 1972	06 05 1981	11.60	35	9.0 8	3.9	75010
75017	Ellen at Bullgill	3096 5384	96.0	30 09 1975	03 01 1985	15.00	64	9.3 9	6.9	75017
76002	Eden at Warwick Bridge	3470 5567	1366.7	13 11 1959	02 01 1985	296.00	96	25.1 24	3.8	76002
76003	Eamont at Udford	3578 5306	396.2	20 04 1961	02 01 1985	92.30	125	23.6 21	5.3	76003
76004	Lowther at Eamont Bridge	3527 5287	158.5	27 07 1962	02 01 1985	77.29	63	22.4 22	2.8	76004
76005	Eden at Temple Sowerby	3605 5283	616.4	01 05 1964	02 01 1985	186.00	68	20.7 20	3.3	76005
76007	Eden at Sheepmount	3390 5571	2286.5	03 02 1967	02 01 1985	410.00	49	17.9 17	2.7	76007
76008	Irthing at Greenholme	3486 5581	334.6	15 08 1967	02 01 1985	85.00	83	17.4 17	4.8	76008
76009	Caldew at Holm Hill	3378 5469	147.2	30 04 1968	03 01 1985	39.00	81	16.7 16	4.9	76009
76010	Petteril at Harraby Green	3412 5545	160.0	13 02 1970	02 01 1985	16.00	51	14.9 14	3.4	76010
76011	Coal Burn at Coalburn	3693 5777	1.5	01 01 1967	22 06 1971	0.88	19	4.3 2	4.4	76011
76014	Eden at Kirkby Stephen	3773 5097	69.4	01 09 1971	01 01 1986	52.50	64	14.3 14	4.5	76014
77001	Esk at Netherby	3390 5718	841.7	24 08 1961	14 04 1983	400.40	71	21.3 19	3.3	77001
77002	Esk at Canonbie	3397 5751	495.0	05 10 1962	07 01 1990	190.00	113	27.3 26	4.1	77002
77003	Liddel Water at Rowanburnfoot	3415 5759	319.0	01 01 1974	04 03 1993	138.00	113	19.2 18	5.9	77003
77005	Lyne at Cliff Bridge	3412 5662	191.0	08 07 1976	02 01 1985	72.00	45	8.5 8	5.3	77005
78003	Annan at Brydekirk	3191 5704	925.0	16 08 1967	29 03 1993	179.00	150	25.6 25	5.9	78003
78004	Kinnel Water at Redhall	3077 5868	76.1	20 11 1960	29 03 1993	37.00	182	31.7 30	5.7	78004
78005	Kinnel Water at Bridgemuir	3091 5845	229.0	01 01 1979	01 06 1993	72.00	78	14.4 13	5.4	78005
79002	Nith at Friars Carse	2923 5851	799.0	01 07 1957	01 04 1993	282.00	147	35.8 35	4.1	79002
79003	Nith at Hall Bridge	2684 6129	155.0	15 10 1959	01 06 1993	45.00	195	33.6 31	5.8	79003
79004	Scar Water at Capenoch	2845 5940	142.0	20 09 1963	02 04 1993	82.00	153	29.5 29	5.2	79004
79005	Cluden Water at Fiddlers Ford	2928 5795	238.0	07 10 1963	01 04 1993	71.60	142	29.5 28	4.8	79005
79006	Nith at Drumlanrig	2858 5994	471.0	24 05 1967	01 04 1993	164.00	142	25.9 25	5.5	79006
80001	Urr at Dalbeattie	2822 5610	199.0	29 10 1963	30 03 1993	56.00	149	29.4 28	5.1	80001
80003	White Laggan Burn at Loch Dee	2468 5781	5.7	01 01 1981	02 06 1993	7.00	74	12.4 11	6.0	80003
80801	Pullaugh Burn at Diversion Wks	2544 5742	18.2	13 12 1961	28 09 1970	9.50	35	8.8 7	4.0	80801
81002	Cree at Newton Stewart	2412 5653	368.0	24 04 1963	31 03 1993	127.50	152	29.9 29	5.1	81002
81003	Luce at Airyhemming	2180 5599	171.0	15 12 1966	27 03 1993	81.00	123	26.3 25	4.7	81003
82001	Girvan at Robstone	2217 5997	245.5	04 09 1963	28 02 1993	60.00	142	29.5 29	4.8	82001
82003	Stinchar at Balnowlart	2108 5832	341.0	01 01 1975	28 02 1993	102.00	86	15.2 12	5.7	82003
83002	Garnock at Dalry	2293 6488	88.8	01 01 1960	31 12 1969	36.60	51	10.0 9	5.1	83002
83004	Lugar at Langholm	2508 6217	181.0	01 01 1973	28 02 1993	63.00	159	20.2 19	7.9	83004
83005	Irvine at Shewalton	2345 6369	380.7	01 01 1973	28 02 1993	90.00	141	20.2 19	7.0	83005
83006	Ayr at Mainholm	2361 6216	574.0	01 01 1976	28 02 1993	170.00	105	17.1 15	6.1	83006
*83802	Irvine at Kilmarnock	2430 6369	218.0	29 08 1913	31 12 1988	48.00	460	70.5 45	6.5	83802*
*84001	Kelvin at Killermont	2558 6705	335.1	01 01 1949	31 12 1993	51.00	278	45.0 44	6.2	84001*
84002	Calder at Muirshiel	2309 6638	12.4	18 03 1952	30 09 1973	11.31	96	19.5 19	4.9	84002
84003	Clyde at Hazelbank	2835 6452	1092.9	27 09 1955	31 12 1993	144.00	253	38.3 38	6.6	84003
84004	Clyde at Sills	2927 6424	741.8	01 10 1955	03 03 1993	112.00	208	37.4 37	5.6	84004
84005	Clyde at Blairston	2704 6579	1704.2	01 10 1955	31 12 1993	219.00	237	38.3 38	6.2	84005
84006	Kelvin at Bridgend	2672 6749	63.7	15 08 1956	31 12 1982	9.41	151	26.3 24	5.7	84006
84007	South Calder W. at Forgewood	2751 6585	93.0	20 01 1965	30 06 1993	9.56	167	27.1 24	6.2	84007
84008	Rotten Calder Water at Redlees	2679 6604	51.3	01 10 1966	31 12 1982	16.50	71	16.3 16	4.4	84008
84009	Nethan at Kirkmuirhill	2809 6429	66.0	01 10 1966	31 12 1982	22.51	79	16.3 16	4.9	84009
84011	Gryfe at Craigend	2415 6664	71.0	26 09 1963	30 06 1993	36.70	217	29.8 29	7.3	84011
84012	White Cart Water at Hawkhead	2499 6629	227.2	27 08 1963	01 03 1993	63.30	235	29.5 29	8.0	84012
84013	Clyde at Daldowie	2672 6616	1903.1	23 05 1963	27 12 1988	221.00	140	24.6 23	5.7	84013
84014	Avon Water at Fairholm	2755 6518	265.5	15 01 1964	01 03 1993	90.00	153	28.9 27	5.3	84014
84015	Kelvin at Dryfield	2638 6739	235.4	01 01 1947	28 12 1988	37.00	271	42.0 41	6.5	84015
84016	Luggie Water at Condorrat	2739 6725	33.9	01 05 1968	28 12 1988	7.50	166	20.7 20	8.0	84016
84017	Black Cart Water at Milliken Park	2411 6620	103.1	04 12 1967	30 09 1973	16.50	30	5.8 5	5.1	84017
84018	Clyde at Tulliford Mill	2891 6404	932.6	01 01 1969	31 12 1982	130.00	83	14.0 13	5.9	84018

No.	Name	Grid ref	NRFA Area km²	Record starts	Record ends	THRESH	NPOT	NWYRS NYRS	NWYRS Ratio	No.
84019	North Calder W. at Calderpark	2681 6625	129.8	18 12 1962	31 12 1993	15.90	198	31.0 30	6.4	84019
84020	Glazert W. at Milton of Campsie	2656 6763	51.9	01 01 1969	28 12 1988	26.00	148	20.0 19	7.4	84020
84023	Bothlin Burn at Auchengeich	2680 6717	35.7	01 01 1974	31 12 1982	5.00	47	9.0 8	5.2	84023
84025	Luggie Water at Oxgang	2666 6734	87.7	01 01 1974	31 12 1982	16.00	43	9.0 8	4.8	84025
84026	Allander Water at Milngavie	2558 6738	32.8	01 01 1974	28 12 1988	11.00	143	15.0 14	9.5	84026
84806	Clyde at Cambusnethan	2786 6522	1260.0	27 09 1955	31 10 1964	171.00	54	9.1 9	5.9	84806
85002	Endrick Water at Gaidrew	2485 6866	219.9	29 09 1963	31 12 1982	77.00	98	19.3 19	5.1	85002
85003	Falloch at Glen Falloch	2321 7197	80.3	01 01 1971	30 09 1988	104.00	100	17.7 17	5.6	85003
86001	Little Eachaig at Dalinlongart	2143 6821	30.8	01 12 1967	30 06 1993	27.50	177	25.6 21	6.9	86001
87801	Allt Uaine at Intake	2263 7113	3.1	01 01 1951	31 12 1971	5.90	104	21.0 20	5.0	87801
89804	Strae at Duiletter	2146 7294	36.2	04 01 1978	05 01 1989	28.44	133	11.0 10	12.1	89804
90801	Nevis at Achreoch	2167 7690	46.6	16 02 1956	30 09 1962	29.50	34	5.9 2	5.8	90801
91002	Lochy at Camisky	2145 7805	1252.0	01 01 1980	05 07 1993	323.50	83	13.5 12	6.1	91002
91802	Allt Leachdach at Intake	2261 7781	6.5	28 12 1938	31 12 1974	4.20	175	34.9 32	5.0	91802
93001	Carron at New Kelso	1942 8429	137.8	01 01 1979	11 06 1993	87.50	88	14.4 13	6.1	93001
94001	Ewe at Poolewe	1859 8803	441.1	01 01 1970	06 07 1993	47.00	108	22.5 21	4.8	94001
*95801	Little Gruinard at Little Gruinard	1944 8897	82.1	15 11 1962	11 02 1968	0.70	35	5.2 3	6.7	95801*
95803	Abhain Cuileg at Braemore	2193 8790	67.3	05 03 1963	01 05 1968	45.00	39	4.3 2	9.0	95803
96001	Halladale at Halladale	2891 9561	204.6	01 01 1975	04 07 1993	56.00	110	18.5 17	5.9	96001
96002	Naver at Apigill	2713 9568	477.0	01 01 1978	05 07 1993	64.00	99	15.5 14	6.4	96002
97002	Thurso at Halkirk	3131 9595	412.8	01 01 1972	05 07 1993	51.00	99	21.5 20	4.6	97002
201002	Fairy Water at Dudgeon Bridge	2406 3758	161.2	01 10 1971	31 12 1993	40.43	124	22.3 22	5.6	201002
201005	Camowen at Camowen Terrace	2460 3730	274.6	28 04 1972	31 12 1993	37.72	167	21.7 21	7.7	201005
201006	Drumragh at Campsie Bridge	2458 3722	324.6	01 01 1973	31 12 1993	58.02	163	21.0 20	7.8	201006
201007	Burn Dennet at Burndennett Br.	2372 4047	145.3	05 05 1975	31 12 1993	38.10	97	18.6 17	5.2	201007
201008	Derg at Castlederg	2265 3842	337.3	29 10 1975	31 12 1993	120.10	110	18.2 17	6.1	201008
201009	Owenkillen at Crosh	2418 3866	442.5	01 01 1980	31 12 1993	157.24	88	14.0 13	6.3	201009
201010	Mourne at Drumnabuoy House	2347 3960	1844.5	17 06 1982	31 12 1993	475.91	39	11.5 11	3.4	201010
202001	Roe at Ardnargle	2674 4247	365.6	10 01 1975	31 12 1993	93.78	104	19.0 18	5.5	202001
202002	Faughan at Drumahoe	2464 4151	272.3	27 08 1976	31 12 1993	91.65	59	17.3 17	3.4	202002
203010	Blackwater at Maydown Bridge	2820 3519	951.4	23 06 1970	31 12 1993	75.08	81	23.5 23	3.4	203010
203011	Main at Dromona	3052 4086	228.8	27 05 1970	31 12 1993	32.00	94	20.4 18	4.6	203011
203012	Ballinderry at Ballinderry Bridge	2926 3799	419.5	07 06 1970	31 12 1993	66.80	133	23.6 23	5.6	203012
203017	Upper Bann at Dynes Bridge	3043 3509	335.6	01 10 1970	25 06 1991	46.69	77	20.7 20	3.7	203017
203018	Six Mile Water at Antrim	3146 3867	277.3	26 08 1970	31 12 1993	24.41	136	23.4 23	5.8	203018
203019	Claudy at Glenone Bridge	2962 4037	130.1	22 12 1970	31 12 1993	19.77	124	23.0 20	5.4	203019
203020	Moyola at Moyola New Bridge	2955 3905	306.5	11 01 1971	31 12 1993	69.20	111	22.8 21	4.9	203020
203021	Kells Water at Currys Bridge	3106 3971	127.0	20 05 1971	31 12 1993	43.97	134	22.6 22	5.9	203021
203022	Blackwater at Derrymeen Bridge	2625 3530	175.7	01 10 1979	31 12 1995	30.00	104	16.3 16	6.4	203022
203024	Cusher at Gamble's Bridge	3048 3471	176.7	15 06 1971	31 12 1993	21.56	157	22.5 22	7.0	203024
*203025	Callan at Callan New Bridge	2893 3524	164.1	31 08 1971	31 12 1993	18.46	132	22.3 22	5.9	203025*
203026	Glenavy at Glenavy	3149 3725	44.6	28 08 1971	31 12 1993	9.15	113	22.1 19	5.1	203026
203027	Braid at Ballee	3097 4014	177.2	17 08 1972	31 12 1993	31.47	121	21.4 21	5.7	203027
203028	Agivey at White Hill	2883 4193	98.9	03 11 1972	31 12 1993	44.51	113	21.2 20	5.3	203028
203033	Upper Bann at Bannfield	3233 3341	100.9	19 03 1975	31 12 1993	38.74	86	18.8 18	4.6	203033
203039	Clogh at Tullynewey	3090 4108	83.6	19 11 1980	31 12 1993	17.73	106	12.9 11	8.2	203039
203042	Crumlin at Cidercourt Bridge	3135 3765	54.0	20 01 1981	31 12 1993	11.89	83	12.9 12	6.4	203042
203043	Oonawater at Shanmoy U/s	2779 3556	91.9	09 02 1981	31 12 1993	18.84	70	11.3 12	6.2	203043
203046	Rathmore at Rathmore Bridge	3198 3854	26.2	11 11 1981	31 12 1993	5.27	50	12.1 11	4.1	203046
203049	Clady at Clady Bridge	3201 3837	30.7	16 06 1982	31 12 1993	10.69	44	11.5 11	3.8	203049
203092	Maine at Dunminning	3051 4111	211.7	25 05 1983	31 12 1993	30.31	86	10.6 10	8.1	203092
203093	Maine at Shanes Viaduct	3086 3896	704.2	01 01 1983	31 12 1993	74.55	92	11.0 9	8.4	203093
204001	Bush at Seneirl	2942 4362	306.1	21 08 1972	31 12 1993	35.03	166	21.1 19	7.9	204001
205003	Lagan at Dunmurry	3299 3679	444.7	02 09 1969	03 01 1985	37.50	50	15.1 12	3.3	205003
205004	Lagan at Newforge	3329 3693	490.4	11 07 1972	31 12 1993	31.28	131	21.5 21	6.1	205004

No.	Name	Grid ref	NRFA Area km²	Record starts	Record ends	THRESH	NPOT	NWYRS			No.
								NYRS		Ratio	
205005	Ravernet at Ravernet	3267 3613	69.5	14 07 1972	31 12 1993	6.41	116	21.5	21	5.4	205005
205008	Lagan at Drummiller	3236 3525	85.2	14 03 1974	31 12 1994	11.19	100	20.4	18	4.9	205008
205011	Annacloy at Kilmore	3448 3509	186.6	23 11 1979	31 12 1993	17.85	91	14.1	13	6.5	205011
205020	Enler at Comber	3459 3697	59.8	01 01 1983	31 12 1993	8.72	58	10.9	9	5.3	205020
205101	Blackstaff at Easons	3318 3721	15.6	01 01 1979	31 12 1993	4.68	88	14.9	12	5.9	205101
206001	Clanrye at Mount Mill Bridge	3086 3309	132.7	26 10 1971	31 12 1993	9.96	127	22.2	21	5.7	206001
206002	Jerretspass at Jerretspass	3064 3332	41.7	09 12 1971	31 12 1993	4.35	88	22.1	21	4.0	206002
206004	Bessbrook at Carnbane	3074 3292	34.5	13 12 1983	31 12 1993	4.10	56	10.1	9	5.6	206004
236005	Colebrooke at Ballindarragh Br.	2331 3359	309.1	01 01 1982	31 12 1993	68.80	62	12.0	11	5.2	236005
236007	Sillees at Drumrainey Bridge	2205 3400	167.6	22 09 1981	31 12 1993	12.65	85	12.3	12	6.9	236007

Appendix B

Register of gauging stations and summary statistics: annual maximum flood data

Table B.1 gives, for 1000 catchments, period of record details and summary statistics following the FEH update of annual maximum data. Catchments marked with an asterisk indicate that part of the record, or in some cases the complete record, has not been used in the Volume 3 analyses (see Table 22.1). Station records marked with a C indicate that the annual maxima are calendar year.

A brief description of some of the variables shown is given below.

Grid ref   Grid reference of the gauging station, taken from the National River Flow Archive. [For automatic generation of an IHDTM catchment boundary a grid reference located exactly on the appropriate drainage path should be sought.]

NRFA area   Catchment area to the gauging station in km², taken from the National River Flow Archive.

Record   Start and finish of record (water years).

Num AM   Number of annual maxima held.

Date max   Date of the largest flood peak for the annual maximum record held.

Max flood   Magnitude of the largest flood peak for the record held, in m^3s^{-1}.

QMED   Median flood of the annual maximum series, in m^3s^{-1}.

QBAR   Arithmetic mean of the annual maximum series, in m^3s^{-1}.

CV   Coefficient of variation of series as a fraction (standard deviation of annual maxima divided by QBAR).

Table B.1 *Period of record details and summary statistics – annual maximum flood data*

No.	Name	Grid ref	NRFA Area km²	Record	Num AM	Date max	Max flood	QMED	QBAR	CV	No.
2001	Helmsdale at Kilphedir	2997 9181	551.4	1975 - 1992	18	01 12 1985	311.93	179.33	188.39	0.27	2001
3001	Shin at Lairg	2581 9062	494.6	1950 - 1955	6	27 12 1954	92.62	62.75	62.71	0.30	3001
3002	Carron at Sgodachail	2490 8921	241.1	1974 - 1992	19	20 09 1981	353.51	193.47	208.98	0.31	3002
3003	Oykel at Easter Turnaig	2403 9001	330.7	1978 - 1992	15	05 10 1978	847.50	374.93	408.99	0.37	3003
3801	Cassley at Duchally	2387 9168	72.3	1950 - 1958	8	18 12 1954	96.80	72.65	73.87	0.22	3801
3803	Tirry at Rhian Bridge	2553 9167	64.2	1950 - 1956	7	24 01 1955	110.85	62.40	68.03	0.37	3803
4001	Conon at Moy Bridge	2482 8547	961.8	1945 - 1955	11	21 11 1947	506.17	312.02	342.63	0.25	4001
4003	Alness at Alness	2654 8695	201.0	1974 - 1992	19	04 10 1981	196.34	83.86	91.59	0.45	4003
5001	Beauly at Erchless	2426 8406	849.5	1950 - 1962	13	12 02 1962	599.68	316.14	318.05	0.30	5001
6001	Ness at Ness Castle Farm	2639 8410	1792.3	1929 - 1961	33	20 12 1936	594.30	370.73	374.23	0.23	6001
6003	Moriston at Invermoriston	2416 8169	391.0	1930 - 1943	14	20 12 1936	557.54	313.56	325.79	0.31	6003
6006	Allt Bhlaraidh at Invermoriston	2377 8168	27.5	1953 - 1961	7	27 10 1957	23.21	16.70	17.69	0.25	6006
6007	Ness at Ness Side	2645 8427	1839.1	1973 - 1992	20	07 02 1989	669.30	372.05	406.89	0.27	6007
6008	Enrick at Mill of Tore	2450 8300	105.9	1980 - 1992	13	18 01 1993	93.13	49.69	52.05	0.40	6008
7001	Findhorn at Shenachie	2826 8337	415.6	1960 - 1992	33	20 09 1981	577.70	239.67	245.40	0.41	7001
7002	Findhorn at Forres	3018 8583	781.9	1958 - 1991	34	16 08 1970	2402.27	358.92	444.57	0.88	7002
7003	Lossie at Sheriffmills	3194 8626	216.0	1958 - 1994	37	17 08 1970	89.82	40.49	43.53	0.45	7003
8001	Spey at Aberlour	3278 8439	2654.7	1939 - 1973	25	17 08 1970	1241.80	407.86	484.32	0.47	8001
8002	Spey at Kinrara	2881 8082	1011.7	1951 - 1994	40	18 12 1966	325.45	134.70	152.53	0.38	8002
8003	Spey at Ruthven Bridge	2759 7996	533.8	1951 - 1972	22	17 12 1966	223.48	102.26	106.94	0.37	8003
8004	Avon at Delnashaugh	3186 8352	542.8	1952 - 1994	43	25 08 1960	532.04	224.71	242.20	0.44	8004
8005	Spey at Boat of Garten	2946 8191	1267.8	1951 - 1994	44	05 02 1990	405.60	158.16	191.47	0.44	8005
8006	Spey at Boat O Brig	3318 8518	2861.2	1952 - 1994	43	17 08 1970	1597.82	516.98	567.41	0.48	8006
8007	Spey at Invertruim	2687 7962	400.4	1952 - 1994	43	17 12 1966	276.92	95.93	121.69	0.53	8007
8008	Tromie at Tromie Bridge	2789 7995	130.3	1952 - 1988	37	06 09 1958	155.07	58.84	65.70	0.54	8008
8009	Dulnain at Balnaan Bridge	2977 8247	272.2	1952 - 1994	43	04 02 1990	204.51	101.25	107.47	0.34	8009
8010	Spey at Grantown	3033 8268	1748.8	1952 - 1994	43	06 02 1990	508.78	245.79	255.05	0.33	8010
8011	Livet at Minmore	3201 8291	104.0	1981 - 1994	14	02 10 1981	51.82	30.27	31.85	0.39	8011
9001	Deveron at Avochie	3532 8464	441.6	1960 - 1994	35	12 09 1995	274.56	119.19	125.97	0.40	9001
9002	Deveron at Muiresk	3705 8498	954.9	1960 - 1994	35	12 09 1995	556.03	230.42	236.95	0.46	9002
9003	Isla at Grange	3494 8506	176.1	1969 - 1994	26	28 10 1990	84.61	41.56	46.07	0.42	9003
9004	Bogie at Redcraig	3519 8373	179.0	1981 - 1994	14	11 09 1995	56.13	23.07	26.58	0.48	9004
10001	Ythan at Ardlethen	3924 8308	448.1	1939 - 1983	45	06 11 1951	97.31	48.55	50.44	0.32	10001
10002	Ugie at Inverugie	4101 8485	325.0	1972 - 1994	23	12 09 1995	93.61	40.97	50.60	0.49	10002
10003	Ythan at Ellon	3947 8303	523.0	1983 - 1994	12	04 11 1984	93.63	63.32	61.21	0.43	10003
11001	Don at Parkhill	3887 8141	1273.0	1970 - 1992	23	13 10 1982	279.46	118.84	130.70	0.43	11001
11002	Don at Haughton	3756 8201	787.0	1972 - 1994	23	13 10 1982	189.11	106.13	112.26	0.33	11002
11003	Don at Bridge of Alford	3566 8170	499.0	1974 - 1994	21	13 10 1982	188.55	92.93	100.20	0.37	11003
11004	Urie at Pitcaple	3721 8260	198.0	1988 - 1994	7	11 09 1995	59.73	19.89	24.01	0.72	11004
12001	Dee at Woodend	3635 7956	1370.0	1929 - 1994	66	24 01 1937	1134.45	428.61	425.73	0.42	12001
12002	Dee at Park	3798 7983	1844.0	1973 - 1994	22	13 10 1982	839.78	572.23	560.39	0.29	12002
12003	Dee at Polhollick	3344 7965	690.0	1976 - 1994	19	17 01 1993	527.20	311.56	314.35	0.32	12003
12004	Girnock Burn at Littlemill	3324 7956	30.3	1969 - 1994	26	02 10 1981	36.19	21.77	21.13	0.40	12004
12005	Muick at Invermuick	3364 7947	110.0	1977 - 1994	18	02 10 1981	122.32	66.75	74.40	0.38	12005
12006	Gairn at Invergairn	3353 7971	150.0	1978 - 1994	17	13 10 1982	101.50	58.72	59.17	0.39	12006
12007	Dee at Mar Lodge	3098 7895	289.0	1982 - 1994	13	04 02 1990	312.69	196.29	194.03	0.32	12007
12008	Feugh at Heugh Head	3687 7928	229.0	1985 - 1994	10	07 10 1993	261.58	137.52	145.01	0.39	12008
13001	Bervie at Inverbervie	3826 7733	123.0	1979 - 1994	16	01 12 1985	67.70	37.03	42.06	0.35	13001
14001	Eden at Kemback	3415 7158	307.4	1967 - 1992	26	06 10 1990	77.23	43.28	44.73	0.37	14001
15001	Isla at Forter	3187 7647	70.7	1947 - 1972	26	29 09 1962	99.08	43.74	47.22	0.37	15001
15002	Newton Burn at Newton	3230 7605	15.4	1949 - 1972	24	30 09 1962	14.58	6.91	7.63	0.37	15002
15003	Tay at Caputh	3082 7395	3211.0	1951 - 1992	42	17 01 1993	1669.30	784.02	834.46	0.35	15003
15004	Inzion at Loch of Lintrathen	3280 7559	24.7	1926 - 1972	44	01 10 1946	10.48	6.41	6.37	0.33	15004
15005	Melgan at Loch of Lintrathen	3275 7558	40.9	1926 - 1966	38	01 10 1940	25.24	15.52	15.38	0.24	15005
15006	Tay at Ballathie	3147 7367	4587.1	1952 - 1992	41	16 01 1993	1765.66	951.06	990.43	0.30	15006

No.	Name	Grid ref	NRFA Area km²	Record	Num AM	Date max	Max flood	QMED	QBAR	CV	No.
15007	Tay at Pitnacree	2924 7534	1149.4	1952 - 1992	41	16 01 1993	837.68	331.60	369.95	0.39	15007
15008	Dean Water at Cookston	3340 7479	177.1	1953 - 1992	40	11 12 1957	46.85	30.02	29.53	0.23	15008
15010	Isla at Wester Cardean	3295 7466	366.5	1972 - 1992	21	17 01 1993	157.35	100.82	102.06	0.31	15010
15013	Almond at Almondbank	3067 7258	174.8	1974 - 1992	19	16 01 1993	272.67	119.50	113.83	0.43	15013
15016	Tay at Kenmore	2782 7467	600.9	1975 - 1992	18	17 01 1993	323.32	187.03	202.95	0.30	15016
15017	Braan at Ballinloan	2979 7406	197.0	1975 - 1980	6	15 11 1978	205.00	120.10	123.23	0.50	15017
15808	Almond at Almond Intake	2758 7332	31.0	1961 - 1972	12	06 10 1967	18.40	12.85	12.83	0.17	15808
15809	Muckle Burn at Eastmill	3223 7604	16.5	1949 - 1972	20	05 11 1951	14.43	7.63	7.78	0.42	15809
16001	Earn at Kinkell Bridge	2933 7167	590.5	1949 - 1992	42	16 01 1993	297.52	193.45	195.36	0.20	16001
16002	Earn at Aberuchill	2754 7216	176.9	1955 - 1972	18	28 01 1973	100.25	57.69	60.51	0.28	16002
16003	Ruchill Water at Cultybraggan	2764 7204	99.5	1960 - 1992	32	13 01 1975	283.26	164.97	175.62	0.29	16003
16004	Earn at Forteviot Bridge	3043 7184	782.2	1974 - 1992	19	16 01 1993	368.44	250.51	252.88	0.23	16004
17001	Carron at Headswood	2832 6820	122.3	1968 - 1992	23	15 11 1978	222.01	81.72	90.54	0.48	17001
17002	Leven at Leven	3369 7006	424.0	1968 - 1972	5	01 12 1970	40.64	29.24	28.98	0.37	17002
17005	Avon at Polmonthill	2952 6797	195.3	1971 - 1992	22	06 10 1990	106.10	59.18	61.07	0.32	17005
18001	Allan Water at Kinbuck	2792 7053	161.0	1957 - 1981	25	30 01 1974	99.00	65.60	69.46	0.19	18001
18002	Devon at Glenochil	2858 6960	181.0	1956 - 1972	17	12 02 1962	64.04	40.80	41.95	0.20	18002
18003	Teith at Bridge of Teith	2725 7011	518.0	1956 - 1972	17	13 12 1961	259.62	183.18	186.65	0.21	18003
18005	Allan Water at Bridge of Allan	2786 6980	210.0	1972 - 1992	21	16 01 1993	281.40	96.39	107.09	0.44	18005
18008	Leny at Anie	2585 7096	190.0	1974 - 1992	19	17 01 1993	168.76	89.86	96.69	0.32	18008
19001	Almond at Craigiehall	3165 6752	369.0	1956 - 1991	36	23 11 1969	177.68	120.23	117.92	0.32	19001
*19002	Almond at Almond Weir	3004 6652	43.8	1961 - 1991	31	03 11 1984	32.57	15.46	18.77	0.40	19002*
19003	Breich Water at Breich Weir	3014 6639	51.8	1961 - 1978	18	31 10 1977	46.00	19.79	19.98	0.40	19003
19004	North Esk at Dalmore Weir	3252 6616	81.6	1961 - 1991	31	06 10 1990	61.31	20.26	21.83	0.47	19004
19005	Almond at Almondell	3086 6686	229.0	1962 - 1992	29	31 10 1977	165.80	77.50	83.51	0.36	19005
19006	Water of Leith at Murrayfield	3228 6732	107.0	1962 - 1991	30	13 08 1966	70.41	30.85	31.39	0.37	19006
19007	Esk at Musselburgh	3339 6723	330.0	1962 - 1991	29	03 11 1984	180.75	69.69	81.43	0.49	19007
19008	South Esk at Prestonholm	3325 6623	112.0	1963 - 1988	26	03 11 1984	78.09	18.93	22.57	0.75	19008
19010	Braid Burn at Liberton	3273 6707	16.2	1968 - 1973	6	19 03 1971	5.56	0.84	1.56	1.26	19010
19011	North Esk at Dalkeith Palace	3333 6678	137.0	1962 - 1991	29	06 10 1990	91.54	40.60	41.13	0.46	19011
20001	Tyne at East Linton	3591 6768	307.0	1959 - 1991	33	06 10 1990	121.19	48.93	55.97	0.54	20001
20002	West Peffer Burn at Luffness	3489 6811	26.2	1966 - 1992	26	04 01 1982	6.87	3.54	3.33	0.55	20002
20003	Tyne at Spilmersford	3456 6689	161.0	1962 - 1991	29	03 11 1984	131.50	31.17	40.87	0.74	20003
20004	East Peffer Burn at Lochhouses	3610 6824	31.1	1965 - 1972	8	14 08 1966	28.22	4.42	7.61	1.19	20004
20005	Birns Water at Saltoun Hall	3457 6688	93.0	1962 - 1991	30	03 11 1984	59.16	22.02	23.55	0.54	20005
20006	Biel Water at Belton House	3645 6768	51.8	1972 - 1992	20	01 04 1992	31.09	14.69	15.27	0.65	20006
20007	Gifford Water at Lennoxlove	3511 6717	64.0	1973 - 1991	19	26 05 1983	60.17	15.28	20.16	0.76	20007
21001	Fruid Water at Fruid	3088 6205	23.7	1947 - 1961	15	15 01 1962	28.94	19.10	18.95	0.25	21001
21002	Whiteadder W. at Hungry Snout	3663 6633	45.6	1958 - 1966	9	04 08 1966	63.14	21.05	25.14	0.58	21002
21003	Tweed at Peebles	3257 6400	694.0	1939 - 1992	46	07 01 1949	1079.27	175.35	212.45	0.75	21003
21005	Tweed at Lyne Ford	3206 6397	373.0	1961 - 1992	32	15 01 1962	232.13	124.34	128.32	0.30	21005
21006	Tweed at Boleside	3498 6334	1500.0	1961 - 1992	32	31 10 1977	1153.10	399.63	433.10	0.40	21006
21007	Ettrick Water at Lindean	3486 6315	499.0	1961 - 1992	32	31 10 1977	564.53	232.88	252.57	0.33	21007
21008	Teviot at Ormiston Mill	3702 6280	1110.0	1960 - 1992	33	03 01 1982	582.45	342.55	342.86	0.29	21008
21009	Tweed at Norham	3898 6477	4390.0	1960 - 1992	33	04 01 1982	1555.73	751.11	791.77	0.34	21009
21010	Tweed at Dryburgh	3588 6320	2080.0	1949 - 1981	33	31 10 1977	1174.10	448.70	537.32	0.38	21010
21011	Yarrow Water at Philiphaugh	3439 6277	231.0	1962 - 1981	20	31 10 1977	205.20	82.51	88.94	0.52	21011
21012	Teviot at Hawick	3522 6159	323.0	1963 - 1992	30	31 10 1977	269.55	183.67	185.44	0.18	21012
21013	Gala Water at Galashiels	3479 6374	207.0	1963 - 1992	30	03 11 1984	223.91	50.60	56.91	0.73	21013
21015	Leader Water at Earlston	3565 6388	239.0	1966 - 1992	27	03 11 1984	238.32	59.73	73.21	0.65	21015
21016	Eye Water at Eyemouth Mill	3942 6635	119.0	1967 - 1992	26	03 11 1984	67.46	34.01	34.32	0.43	21016
21017	Ettrick Water at Brockhoperig	3234 6132	37.5	1965 - 1992	28	30 10 1977	141.32	63.52	67.03	0.31	21017
21019	Manor Water at Cademuir	3217 6369	61.6	1968 - 1992	25	30 10 1977	33.40	24.70	22.64	0.24	21019
21020	Yarrow Water at Gordon Arms	3309 6247	155.0	1967 - 1980	14	30 10 1977	155.92	52.07	62.94	0.55	21020
21021	Tweed at Sprouston	3752 6354	3330.0	1970 - 1992	23	04 01 1982	1411.32	738.84	764.56	0.32	21021

Statistical procedures for flood frequency estimation

No.	Name	Grid ref	NRFA Area km²	Record	Num AM	Date max	Max flood	QMED	QBAR	CV	No.
21022	Whiteadder W. at Hutton Castle	3881 6550	503.0	1970 - 1988	19	03 11 1984	279.80	117.30	136.42	0.58	21022
21023	Leet Water at Coldstream	3839 6396	113.0	1973 - 1981	9	30 10 1977	71.80	48.40	48.97	0.22	21023
21024	Jed Water at Jedburgh	3655 6214	139.0	1972 - 1988	17	03 11 1984	161.88	58.56	65.01	0.47	21024
21025	Ale Water at Ancrum	3634 6244	174.0	1973 - 1992	20	04 01 1982	80.44	42.58	45.77	0.36	21025
21026	Tima Water at Deephope	3278 6138	31.0	1974 - 1992	19	30 10 1977	71.81	52.84	53.36	0.15	21026
21027	Blackadder Water at Mouth Br.	3826 6530	159.0	1974 - 1991	17	03 01 1982	69.44	38.55	42.28	0.38	21027
21029	Tweed at Glenbreck	3063 6215	34.0	1964 - 1973	7	25 09 1965	47.78	37.68	39.21	0.14	21029
21030	Megget Water at Henderland	3231 6232	56.2	1969 - 1973	5	11 12 1972	110.00	85.89	72.10	0.45	21030
21031	Till at Etal	3927 6396	648.0	1956 - 1977	22	20 11 1965	147.97	81.33	83.87	0.36	21031
21032	Glen at Kirknewton	3919 6310	198.9	1961 - 1982	22	02 10 1981	105.00	42.49	44.03	0.46	21032
21034	Yarrow Water at Craig Douglas	3288 6244	116.0	1969 - 1973	5	30 01 1974	63.78	31.65	37.38	0.43	21034
22001	Coquet at Morwick	4234 6044	569.8	1963 - 1992	30	01 04 1992	341.20	139.85	151.91	0.44	22001
22002	Coquet at Bygate	3870 6083	59.5	1969 - 1979	11	22 11 1974	39.56	28.64	26.09	0.35	22002
22003	Usway Burn at Shillmoor	3886 6077	21.4	1966 - 1978	13	05 11 1967	39.85	15.15	18.88	0.49	22003
22004	Aln at Hawkhill	4211 6129	205.0	1960 - 1978	19	13 08 1966	150.27	63.88	70.64	0.51	22004
22006	Blyth at Hartford Bridge	4243 5800	269.4	1961 - 1992	32	01 04 1992	162.78	46.96	64.38	0.63	22006
*22007	Wansbeck at Mitford	4175 5858	287.3	1963 - 1994	30	03 01 1982	237.03	94.84	106.42	0.54	22007*
22008	Alwin at Clennell	3925 6063	27.7	1969 - 1973	5	22 11 1969	21.30	13.90	12.73	0.60	22008
23001	Tyne at Bywell	4038 5617	2175.6	1956 - 1992	37	17 10 1967	1496.93	883.63	904.27	0.25	23001
23002	Derwent at Eddys Bridge	4041 5508	118.0	1955 - 1964	10	28 08 1956	64.46	42.10	42.87	0.31	23002
23003	North Tyne at Reaverhill	3906 5732	1007.5	1959 - 1985	27	23 03 1968	637.71	402.56	418.03	0.27	23003
23004	South Tyne at Haydon Bridge	3856 5647	751.1	1959 - 1992	29	26 08 1986	700.52	415.72	429.61	0.27	23004
23005	North Tyne at Tarset	3776 5861	284.9	1960 - 1978	19	30 08 1975	335.65	213.83	229.92	0.27	23005
23006	South Tyne at Featherstone	3672 5611	321.9	1966 - 1992	27	03 11 1984	309.94	248.09	245.37	0.16	23006
*23007	Derwent at Rowlands Gill	4168 5581	242.1	1963 - 1992	27	05 11 1967	96.27	38.18	44.34	0.44	23007*
23008	Rede at Rede Bridge	3868 5832	343.8	1968 - 1992	22	03 01 1982	266.78	125.81	140.00	0.32	23008
23010	Tarset Burn at Greenhaugh	3789 5879	96.0	1970 - 1978	9	30 08 1975	105.63	61.46	64.97	0.33	23010
23011	Kielder Burn at Kielder	3644 5946	58.8	1970 - 1992	19	03 11 1984	106.67	60.40	65.24	0.33	23011
23012	East Allen at Wide Eals	3802 5583	88.0	1971 - 1980	10	25 11 1979	128.49	79.55	80.76	0.36	23012
23013	West Allen at Hindley Wrae	3791 5583	75.1	1971 - 1981	11	25 11 1979	127.15	53.15	67.85	0.42	23013
23015	North Tyne at Barrasford	3924 5721	1043.8	1947 - 1969	17	02 12 1954	729.67	456.39	475.15	0.23	23015
24001	Wear at Sunderland Bridge	4264 5376	657.8	1957 - 1973	17	05 11 1967	380.89	174.63	189.26	0.35	24001
24002	Gaunless at Bishop Auckland	4215 5306	93.0	1958 - 1982	25	05 11 1967	39.09	19.23	20.17	0.45	24002
24003	Wear at Stanhope	3984 5391	171.9	1958 - 1992	35	23 03 1968	223.93	118.97	119.96	0.26	24003
24004	Bedburn Beck at Bedburn	4118 5322	74.9	1959 - 1992	34	26 08 1986	46.18	24.86	26.11	0.35	24004
24005	Browney at Burn Hall	4259 5387	178.5	1954 - 1992	37	26 08 1986	80.99	31.02	37.53	0.40	24005
24006	Rookhope Burn at Eastgate	3952 5390	36.5	1960 - 1979	20	11 09 1976	38.64	24.62	24.61	0.26	24006
24007	Browney at Lanchester	4165 5462	44.6	1968 - 1982	15	27 12 1978	28.70	12.63	13.86	0.44	24007
24008	Wear at Witton Park	4174 5309	455.0	1974 - 1992	17	26 08 1986	276.27	181.51	190.65	0.21	24008
24009	Wear at Chester Le Street	4283 5512	1008.3	1977 - 1992	15	26 08 1986	354.39	228.01	247.81	0.25	24009
24801	Burnhope Burn at Burnhope Resr	3855 5395	21.0	1950 - 1970	21	18 08 1967	36.47	26.15	26.00	0.27	24801
25001	Tees at Broken Scar	4259 5137	818.4	1956 - 1992	37	26 08 1986	709.83	362.24	389.10	0.30	25001
25002	Tees at Dent Bank	3932 5260	217.3	1959 - 1973	15	23 03 1968	445.58	280.44	262.04	0.36	25002
25003	Trout Beck at Moor House	3759 5336	11.4	1962 - 1992	19	13 08 1966	24.63	15.47	16.95	0.20	25003
25004	Skerne at South Park	4284 5129	250.1	1957 - 1992	36	29 03 1979	59.21	20.95	23.26	0.41	25004
25005	Leven at Leven Bridge	4445 5122	196.3	1959 - 1992	33	28 03 1979	107.40	37.80	43.45	0.47	25005
25006	Greta at Rutherford Bridge	4034 5122	86.1	1960 - 1992	33	25 08 1986	210.40	73.59	76.85	0.41	25006
25007	Clow Beck at Croft	4282 5101	78.2	1964 - 1978	15	14 08 1971	41.90	13.79	18.22	0.65	25007
25008	Tees at Barnard Castle	4047 5166	509.2	1964 - 1992	23	25 03 1968	513.01	225.05	247.05	0.34	25008
25009	Tees at Low Moor	4364 5105	1264.0	1969 - 1992	22	26 08 1986	492.40	341.75	332.38	0.28	25009
25010	Baydale Beck at Mowden Bridge	4260 5156	31.1	1957 - 1973	17	14 08 1971	11.73	5.99	6.61	0.42	25010
25011	Langdon Beck at Langdon	3852 5309	13.0	1969 - 1982	14	17 07 1983	34.60	15.50	17.87	0.45	25011
25012	Harwood Beck at Harwood	3849 5309	25.1	1969 - 1994	26	31 01 1995	63.86	31.24	35.19	0.34	25012
25018	Tees at Middleton In Teesdale	3950 5250	242.1	1972 - 1992	20	21 12 1991	300.23	180.51	186.36	0.31	25018
25019	Leven at Easby	4585 5087	14.8	1971 - 1993	23	11 09 1976	25.18	6.11	6.89	0.79	25019

No.	Name	Grid ref	NRFA Area km²	Record	Num AM	Date max	Max flood	QMED	QBAR	CV	No.
25020	Skerne at Preston Le Skerne	4292 5238	147.0	1976 - 1992	16	28 03 1979	26.58	17.22	17.08	0.26	25020
25021	Skerne at Bradbury	4318 5285	70.1	1975 - 1992	18	29 03 1979	20.97	5.77	7.28	0.56	25021
*25808	Burnt Weir at Moor House	3752 5332	0.05	1954 - 1958	5	10 01 1955	0.11	0.08	0.08	0.17	25808*
*25809	Bog Weir at Moor House	3773 5327	0.05	1954 - 1958	5	07 12 1957	0.08	0.05	0.06	0.21	25809*
*25810	Syke Weir at Moor House	3772 5332	0.04	1956 - 1958	3	24 08 1957	0.11	0.10	0.10	0.08	25810*
26001	West Beck at Wansford Bridge	5064 4560	192.0	1953 - 1974	22	10 12 1965	11.61	5.52	6.29	0.41	26001
26002	Hull at Hempholme Lock	5080 4498	378.1	1949 - 1977	27	03 12 1960	18.94	12.10	12.41	0.30	26002
26003	Foston Beck at Foston Mill	5093 4548	57.2	1959 - 1993	34	10 02 1977	2.96	1.65	1.68	0.49	26003
26004	Gypsey Race at Bridlington	5165 4675	253.8	1971 - 1984	14	03 03 1977	3.50	0.64	1.15	1.02	26004
*26007	Catchwater at Withernwick	5171 4403	15.5	1965 - 1976	12	09 10 1974	3.89	1.67	1.67	0.48	26007*
27001	Nidd at Hunsingore Weir	4428 4530	484.3	1934 - 1993	59	15 09 1993	310.93	127.07	140.98	0.44	27001
27002	Wharfe at Flint Mill Weir	4422 4473	758.9	1936 - 1993	57	15 02 1950	417.35	230.56	247.20	0.28	27002
27004	Calder at Newlands	4365 4220	899.0	1957 - 1976	20	26 11 1960	379.31	209.61	214.22	0.33	27004
27006	Don at Hadfields Weir	4390 3910	373.0	1957 - 1993	36	09 12 1965	346.16	85.06	121.29	0.67	27006
27007	Ure at Westwick Lock	4356 4671	914.6	1955 - 1996	42	01 02 1995	517.62	271.63	273.84	0.31	27007
27008	Swale at Leckby Grange	4415 4748	1345.6	1956 - 1983	28	07 03 1963	259.34	174.63	174.32	0.20	27008
27009	Ouse at Skelton	4568 4554	3315.0	1956 - 1991	36	06 01 1982	622.05	356.83	363.67	0.26	27009
27010	Hodge Beck at Bransdale Weir	4627 4944	18.9	1936 - 1976	41	23 06 1946	31.03	9.42	10.42	0.45	27010
27012	Hebden W. at High Greenwood	3973 4309	36.0	1953 - 1972	20	21 08 1954	26.30	12.26	13.49	0.43	27012
27014	Rye at Little Habton	4743 4771	679.0	1958 - 1972	15	10 10 1960	142.68	85.07	92.18	0.27	27014
27015	Derwent at Stamford Bridge	4714 4567	1634.3	1962 - 1976	15	21 02 1970	159.00	81.60	95.64	0.30	27015
*27021	Don at Doncaster	4569 4040	1256.2	1868 - 1993	110	01 10 1941	348.29	153.46	161.72	0.41	27021*
27022	Don at Rotherham Weir	4427 3928	826.0	1960 - 1968	8	09 12 1965	286.34	121.49	147.49	0.50	27022
27023	Dearne at Barnsley Weir	4350 4073	118.9	1953 - 1993	41	13 04 1970	62.29	28.88	28.68	0.40	27023
27024	Swale at Richmond	4146 5006	381.0	1960 - 1979	20	23 03 1968	430.94	237.26	247.03	0.27	27024
27025	Rother at Woodhouse Mill	4432 3857	352.2	1961 - 1993	32	23 06 1982	105.34	50.33	51.83	0.35	27025
27026	Rother at Whittington	4394 3744	165.0	1960 - 1993	34	16 07 1973	103.86	41.49	46.19	0.45	27026
27027	Wharfe at Ilkley	4112 4481	443.0	1960 - 1972	13	09 12 1965	422.11	266.15	273.67	0.22	27027
27028	Aire at Armley	4281 4340	691.5	1961 - 1993	33	17 10 1967	211.01	138.67	145.96	0.18	27028
27029	Calder at Elland	4124 4219	341.9	1953 - 1972	20	26 11 1960	340.00	140.82	161.87	0.49	27029
27030	Dearne at Adwick	4477 4020	310.8	1964 - 1993	30	13 04 1970	66.63	38.69	38.47	0.36	27030
27031	Colne at Colne Bridge	4174 4199	245.0	1964 - 1993	29	16 10 1967	272.21	117.29	125.33	0.44	27031
*27032	Hebden Beck at Hebden	4025 4643	22.2	1965 - 1993	28	02 01 1976	8.86	3.64	4.10	0.39	27032*
*27033	Sea Cut at Scarborough	5028 4908	33.2	1965 - 1993	29	15 05 1967	59.45	30.33	33.91	0.38	27033*
27034	Ure at Kilgram Bridge	4190 4860	510.2	1967 - 1993	27	23 02 1991	382.61	224.28	242.74	0.24	27034
27035	Aire at Kildwick Bridge	4013 4457	282.3	1967 - 1993	27	27 10 1980	89.15	60.92	62.39	0.13	27035
27036	Derwent at Malton	4789 4715	1421.0	1969 - 1972	4	04 02 1972	100.00	81.76	85.54	0.12	27036
27038	Costa Beck at Gatehouses	4774 4836	7.8	1969 - 1993	25	14 09 1993	4.85	1.21	1.47	0.59	27038
27040	Doe Lea at Staveley	4443 3746	67.9	1970 - 1993	24	25 02 1977	13.73	10.11	10.34	0.29	27040
27041	Derwent at Buttercrambe	4731 4587	1586.0	1974 - 1993	20	29 12 1978	124.73	81.97	84.47	0.26	27041
27042	Dove at Kirkby Mills	4705 4855	59.2	1972 - 1993	22	11 09 1976	56.38	29.26	30.32	0.47	27042
27043	Wharfe at Addingham	4092 4494	427.0	1973 - 1993	21	02 01 1982	413.30	262.55	265.14	0.27	27043
*27048	Derwent at West Ayton	4990 4853	127.0	1972 - 1993	17	05 08 1993	3.83	1.25	1.56	0.50	27048*
27049	Rye at Ness	4696 4791	238.7	1974 - 1993	20	12 09 1976	74.58	48.75	46.96	0.34	27049
27051	Crimple at Burn Bridge	4284 4519	8.1	1972 - 1993	22	09 12 1983	7.40	4.77	4.52	0.31	27051
27052	Whitting at Sheepbridge	4376 3747	50.2	1976 - 1993	18	22 06 1982	43.56	15.72	18.68	0.51	27052
27053	Nidd at Birstwith	4230 4603	217.6	1975 - 1993	19	23 02 1991	282.80	154.67	152.68	0.38	27053
27054	Hodge Beck at Cherry Farm	4652 4902	37.1	1977 - 1993	17	22 03 1981	17.63	12.42	12.55	0.24	27054
27055	Rye at Broadway Foot	4560 4883	131.7	1977 - 1993	17	22 03 1981	78.76	59.86	55.73	0.31	27055
27058	Riccal at Crook House Farm	4661 4810	40.5	1977 - 1993	17	03 01 1982	18.38	11.26	11.79	0.43	27058
27059	Laver at Ripon	4301 4710	87.5	1977 - 1993	17	28 12 1978	39.10	21.37	22.39	0.31	27059
27061	Colne at Longroyd Bridge	4136 4161	72.3	1979 - 1993	15	21 03 1981	38.88	31.74	31.83	0.13	27061
27811	Aire at Brotherton	4495 4243	1900.0	1964 - 1968	5	09 12 1965	573.88	544.41	536.49	0.06	27811
27835	Calder at Midland Br. Dewsbury	4243 4215	691.0	1964 - 1970	7	09 12 1965	376.35	279.93	296.09	0.25	27835
27846	Aire at Ash Bridge	4472 4266	1880.0	1964 - 1968	5	17 10 1967	404.97	391.62	391.28	0.04	27846

No.	Name	Grid NRFA ref	Area km²	Record	Num AM	Date max	Max max	QMED flood	QBAR	CV	No.
27852	Little Don at Langsett Reservoir	4215 4005	21.1	1910 - 1931	22	01 01 1931	39.89	19.27	19.80	0.37	27852
28002	Blithe at Hamstall Ridware	4109 3192	163.0	1937 - 1951	15	17 03 1947	41.53	26.22	26.42	0.24	28002
28003	Tame at Water Orton	4169 2915	408.0	1955 - 1993	38	08 09 1972	108.04	71.56	72.10	0.19	28003
28004	Tame at Lea Marston	4206 2935	795.0	1956 - 1981	26	11 07 1968	78.97	63.94	63.76	0.11	28004
28005	Tame at Elford	4173 3105	1475.0	1956 - 1984	22	25 01 1960	171.69	120.30	118.11	0.27	28005
28006	Trent at Great Haywood	3994 3231	325.0	1956 - 1992	36	24 08 1987	97.88	28.92	31.56	0.47	28006
28007	Trent at Shardlow	4448 3299	4400.0	1955 - 1968	14	05 12 1960	403.29	261.33	270.92	0.25	28007
28008	Dove at Rocester Weir	4112 3397	399.0	1953 - 1993	40	09 12 1965	150.79	81.79	88.72	0.28	28008
28009	Trent at Colwick	4620 3399	7486.0	1958 - 1993	36	26 02 1977	948.04	446.66	468.83	0.34	28009
28010	Derwent at Longbridge Weir	4356 3363	1054.0	1935 - 1987	52	10 12 1965	520.87	140.87	159.40	0.48	28010
28011	Derwent at Matlock Bath	4296 3586	690.0	1958 - 1984	25	09 12 1965	266.20	102.25	109.46	0.45	28011
28012	Trent at Yoxall	4131 3177	1229.0	1959 - 1993	35	24 08 1987	245.82	70.48	80.18	0.55	28012
28014	Sow at Milford	3975 3215	591.0	1959 - 1984	24	04 12 1960	50.08	30.49	30.94	0.32	28014
28015	Idle at Mattersey	4690 3895	529.0	1961 - 1968	8	21 02 1966	19.81	15.11	13.81	0.43	28015
28016	Ryton at Serlby Park	4641 3897	231.0	1962 - 1968	7	03 11 1968	16.87	13.20	12.97	0.23	28016
28017	Devon at Cotham	4787 3476	284.0	1966 - 1981	16	02 11 1968	38.41	26.71	23.27	0.43	28017
28018	Dove at Marston On Dove	4235 3288	883.2	1961 - 1993	32	22 12 1991	226.54	128.10	134.48	0.30	28018
28019	Trent at Drakelow Park	4239 3204	3072.0	1962 - 1993	32	31 12 1981	692.29	183.50	195.41	0.51	28019
28020	Churnet at Rocester	4103 3389	236.0	1954 - 1984	28	27 10 1954	65.74	41.03	40.00	0.27	28020
28021	Derwent at Draycott	4443 3327	1175.0	1965 - 1980	16	14 01 1968	174.14	104.29	111.42	0.31	28021
28022	Trent at North Muskham	4801 3601	8231.0	1968 - 1993	26	26 02 1977	937.95	452.92	462.00	0.29	28022
28023	Wye at Ashford	4182 3696	154.0	1970 - 1984	13	16 07 1973	43.85	16.33	19.03	0.44	28023
28024	Wreake at Syston Mill	4615 3124	413.8	1969 - 1994	25	27 04 1981	109.19	35.55	42.57	0.55	28024
28026	Anker at Polesworth	4263 3034	368.0	1967 - 1984	16	06 05 1969	56.91	41.45	39.92	0.34	28026
28027	Erewash at Stapleford	4482 3364	182.2	1965 - 1982	18	22 06 1982	39.10	19.50	20.72	0.39	28027
28031	Manifold at Ilam	4140 3507	148.5	1968 - 1993	26	21 12 1991	150.02	54.55	62.83	0.42	28031
28032	Meden at Church Warsop	4558 3680	62.8	1964 - 1992	22	25 02 1977	11.55	5.62	5.92	0.47	28032
28033	Dove at Hollinsclough	4063 3668	8.0	1966 - 1984	12	15 07 1973	10.01	3.79	4.48	0.44	28033
28038	Manifold at Hulme End	4106 3595	46.0	1969 - 1981	13	19 10 1971	80.44	49.03	50.92	0.27	28038
28039	Rea at Calthorpe Park	4071 2847	74.0	1974 - 1993	20	23 08 1987	62.98	29.80	32.20	0.35	28039
28040	Trent at Stoke On Trent	3892 3467	53.2	1968 - 1993	25	23 08 1987	48.22	10.32	12.79	0.64	28040
28041	Hamps at Waterhouses	4082 3502	35.1	1968 - 1981	14	10 08 1971	99.60	26.93	32.10	0.66	28041
28043	Derwent at Chatsworth	4261 3683	335.0	1969 - 1993	25	15 07 1973	155.62	64.52	72.56	0.43	28043
28045	Meden at Bothamstall	4681 3732	262.6	1965 - 1981	17	25 02 1977	22.46	9.82	10.49	0.42	28045
28046	Dove at Izaak Walton	4146 3509	83.0	1969 - 1993	25	21 12 1991	28.48	12.61	12.91	0.34	28046
28047	Oldcotes Dyke at Blyth	4615 3876	85.2	1970 - 1993	23	16 07 1973	38.06	10.38	12.21	0.82	28047
28048	Amber at Wingfield Park	4376 3520	139.0	1970 - 1993	24	25 02 1977	31.77	16.83	19.16	0.33	28048
28049	Ryton at Worksop	4575 3794	77.0	1970 - 1993	19	08 04 1979	10.19	6.04	5.73	0.53	28049
28052	Sow at Great Bridgford	3883 3270	163.0	1971 - 1993	23	11 02 1977	18.80	9.47	9.16	0.29	28052
28053	Penk at Penkridge	3923 3144	272.0	1976 - 1993	17	30 12 1981	38.38	26.58	27.67	0.19	28053
28054	Sence at Blaby	4566 2985	133.0	1972 - 1981	10	15 08 1980	31.45	26.21	23.09	0.32	28054
28055	Ecclesbourne at Duffield	4320 3447	50.4	1971 - 1993	14	19 10 1971	28.93	12.88	15.74	0.46	28055
28056	Rothley Brook at Rothley	4580 3121	94.0	1973 - 1993	21	24 02 1977	17.23	13.46	12.17	0.30	28056
28058	Henmore Brook at Ashbourne	4176 3463	42.0	1974 - 1982	9	30 05 1979	21.50	16.22	14.48	0.41	28058
28059	Maun at Mansfield	4548 3623	28.8	1964 - 1981	18	13 10 1979	21.32	11.70	12.09	0.32	28059
28060	Dover Beck at Lowdham	4653 3479	69.0	1972 - 1992	17	12 07 1992	3.48	2.19	2.15	0.32	28060
28061	Churnet at Basford Bridge	3983 3520	139.0	1975 - 1993	16	21 12 1991	36.51	25.52	25.38	0.18	28061
28066	Cole at Coleshill	4183 2874	130.0	1973 - 1992	20	30 05 1979	24.05	16.06	17.06	0.18	28066
28067	Derwent at Church Wilne	4438 3316	1177.5	1974 - 1992	18	25 02 1977	297.27	146.16	159.21	0.40	28067
28069	Tame at Tamworth	4206 3037	1407.0	1969 - 1992	22	30 12 1981	329.60	124.44	143.33	0.42	28069
28070	Burbage Brook at Burbage	4259 3804	9.1	1926 - 1981	56	01 07 1958	27.81	4.30	5.34	0.90	28070
28082	Soar at Littlethorpe	4542 2973	183.9	1971 - 1984	12	28 06 1973	25.24	21.50	19.97	0.25	28082
28804	Trent at Trent Bridge	4582 3384	7490.0	1884 - 1968	82	19 03 1947	1107.33	494.25	522.33	0.42	28804
29001	Waithe Beck at Brigsley	5253 4016	108.3	1960 - 1993	34	26 04 1981	6.94	2.02	2.34	0.56	29001

No.	Name	Grid ref	NRFA Area km²	Record	Num AM	Date max	Max flood	QMED	QBAR	CV	No.
29002	Great Eau at Claythorpe Mill	5416 3793	77.4	1973 - 1993	21	26 04 1981	8.71	4.06	3.83	0.50	29002
29003	Lud at Louth	5337 3879	55.2	1966 - 1993	28	02 11 1968	7.35	2.87	3.06	0.47	29003
29004	Ancholme at Bishopbridge	5032 3911	54.7	1968 - 1993	26	26 04 1981	22.83	6.15	7.12	0.67	29004
29005	Rase at Bishopbridge	5032 3912	66.6	1971 - 1983	13	26 04 1981	23.97	7.25	8.39	0.69	29005
29009	Ancholme at Toft Newton	5033 3877	27.2	1974 - 1993	20	26 04 1981	7.05	2.00	2.23	0.63	29009
30001	Witham at Claypole Mill	4842 3480	297.9	1959 - 1993	35	11 02 1977	37.61	14.72	16.79	0.50	30001
30002	Barlings Eau at Langworth Bridge	5066 3766	210.1	1960 - 1982	21	26 08 1981	41.54	20.27	21.17	0.40	30002
30003	Bain at Fulsby Lock	5241 3611	197.1	1962 - 1993	32	25 04 1981	57.00	18.10	18.43	0.63	30003
30004	Partney Lymn at Partney Mill	5402 3676	61.6	1962 - 1993	31	26 04 1981	15.21	7.13	7.33	0.47	30004
30005	Witham at Saltersford Total	4927 3335	126.1	1968 - 1993	26	09 03 1975	15.20	7.78	7.93	0.49	30005
30006	Slea at Leasingham Mill	5088 3485	48.4	1975 - 1993	19	01 03 1977	5.29	1.87	1.92	0.66	30006
30011	Bain at Goulceby Bridge	5246 3795	62.5	1966 - 1993	26	26 04 1981	16.24	2.54	3.69	1.07	30011
30012	Stainfield Beck at Stainfield	5127 3739	37.4	1974 - 1983	10	26 04 1981	26.58	10.17	11.47	0.58	30012
30013	Heighington Beck at Heighington	5042 3696	21.2	1976 - 1993	18	13 02 1977	1.22	0.65	0.65	0.42	30013
30014	Pointon Lode at Pointon	5128 3313	11.9	1972 - 1993	21	15 08 1980	9.10	2.46	2.87	0.73	30014
30015	Cringle Brook at Stoke Rochford	4925 3297	50.5	1976 - 1993	18	20 05 1983	2.07	1.66	1.51	0.29	30015
30017	Witham at Colsterworth	4929 3246	51.3	1978 - 1993	16	15 08 1980	11.65	5.82	6.62	0.40	30017
31002	Glen at Kates Bridge	5106 3149	341.9	1959 - 1993	35	10 03 1975	36.66	18.66	18.30	0.49	31002
31004	Welland at Tallington	5095 3078	717.4	1967 - 1993	27	10 03 1975	93.26	41.43	43.27	0.43	31004
31005	Welland at Tixover	4970 2997	417.0	1962 - 1993	32	09 03 1975	107.13	35.50	39.21	0.55	31005
31006	Gwash at Belmesthorpe	5038 3097	150.0	1967 - 1972	6	06 05 1969	26.52	12.47	14.89	0.50	31006
31010	Chater at Fosters Bridge	4961 3030	68.9	1968 - 1993	26	15 08 1980	22.79	9.32	10.49	0.51	31010
31021	Welland at Ashley	4819 2915	250.7	1970 - 1981	12	09 03 1975	39.35	29.63	28.35	0.35	31021
31023	West Glen at Easton Wood	4965 3258	4.4	1972 - 1993	22	14 08 1980	7.75	1.86	2.39	0.81	31023
31025	Gwash South Arm at Manton	4875 3051	24.5	1978 - 1993	15	02 06 1981	22.46	11.05	11.69	0.45	31025
31026	Egleton Brook at Egleton	4878 3073	2.5	1978 - 1993	14	11 06 1993	1.68	0.84	0.98	0.39	31026
32002	Willow Brook at Fotheringhay	5067 2933	89.6	1939 - 1993	53	17 03 1947	15.00	5.52	5.55	0.46	32002
*32003	Harpers Brook at Old Mill Bridge	4983 2799	74.3	1939 - 1993	50	26 04 1981	22.00	7.76	9.30	0.64	32003*
32004	Ise Brook at Harrowden Old Mill	4898 2715	194.0	1944 - 1993	50	02 07 1958	30.03	14.96	15.27	0.38	32004
32006	Nene/kislingbury at Upton	4721 2592	223.0	1940 - 1993	53	18 03 1947	63.25	14.52	15.38	0.52	32006
32007	Nene Brampton at St Andrews	4747 2617	232.8	1940 - 1993	53	08 03 1941	31.51	18.17	17.42	0.40	32007
*32008	Nene/kislingbury at Dodford	4627 2607	107.0	1945 - 1993	47	16 03 1947	29.56	9.97	10.08	0.51	32008*
32010	Nene at Wansford	5081 2996	1530.0	1939 - 1993	55	18 03 1947	255.00	62.68	67.31	0.53	32010
32029	Flore at Experimental Catchment	4660 2610	7.0	1964 - 1968	5	30 05 1969	4.23	2.54	2.32	0.60	32029
33002	Bedford Ouse at Bedford	5055 2495	1460.0	1959 - 1992	34	11 03 1975	143.40	82.43	85.87	0.37	33002
33005	Bedford Ouse at Thornborough Mill	4736 2353	388.5	1950 - 1972	23	31 01 1971	30.10	22.00	21.75	0.23	33005
33006	Wissey at Northwold	5771 2965	274.5	1956 - 1992	37	20 11 1974	13.17	6.90	7.16	0.37	33006
33007	Nar at Marham	5723 3119	153.3	1968 - 1992	25	12 02 1977	7.87	3.45	3.80	0.45	33007
33009	Bedford Ouse at Harrold Mill	4951 2565	1320.0	1951 - 1991	41	12 07 1968	183.06	85.85	92.65	0.38	33009
33011	Little Ouse at County Br. Euston	5892 2801	128.7	1961 - 1992	32	13 10 1987	8.00	3.12	3.29	0.59	33011
33012	Kym at Meagre Farm	5155 2631	137.5	1960 - 1992	33	26 04 1981	24.46	16.52	15.51	0.38	33012
33013	Sapiston at Rectory Bridge	5896 2791	205.9	1960 - 1991	32	17 09 1968	15.60	5.32	6.03	0.58	33013
33014	Lark at Temple	5758 2730	272.0	1960 - 1992	33	17 09 1968	21.90	8.44	8.36	0.46	33014
33015	Ouzel at Willen	4882 2408	277.1	1962 - 1972	11	11 07 1968	23.89	16.12	15.42	0.34	33015
33017	Bedford Ouse at St Ives Staunch	5314 2705	2860.0	1949 - 1972	18	16 07 1968	142.11	95.64	96.37	0.28	33017
33018	Tove at Cappenham Bridge	4714 2488	138.1	1962 - 1983	22	09 03 1975	26.40	15.87	16.89	0.35	33018
33019	Thet at Melford Bridge	5880 2830	316.0	1960 - 1992	32	29 04 1981	15.31	7.18	7.77	0.40	33019
*33020	Alconbury Brook at Brampton	5208 2717	201.5	1963 - 1983	21	27 04 1981	16.33	13.10	11.82	0.34	33020*
33021	Rhee at Burnt Mill	5415 2523	303.0	1962 - 1992	31	06 05 1978	13.40	9.18	7.93	0.45	33021
33022	Ivel at Blunham	5153 2509	541.3	1965 - 1992	28	08 04 1979	28.20	21.19	19.20	0.34	33022
33023	Lea Brook at Beck Bridge	5662 2733	101.8	1963 - 1992	29	16 09 1968	4.48	2.68	2.27	0.44	33023
33024	Cam at Dernford	5466 2506	198.0	1963 - 1992	30	02 02 1979	11.62	8.21	7.65	0.38	33024
33027	Rhee at Wimpole	5333 2485	119.1	1965 - 1992	28	06 05 1978	8.88	5.09	4.76	0.50	33027
33028	Flit at Shefford	5143 2393	119.6	1966 - 1992	27	21 10 1987	8.20	5.86	5.59	0.32	33028
33029	Stringside at White Bridge	5716 3006	98.8	1965 - 1992	28	29 01 1988	4.58	2.69	2.60	0.46	33029
33030	Clipstone Brook at Clipstone	4933 2255	40.2	1966 - 1978	13	18 04 1975	17.49	9.20	8.60	0.58	33030

No.	Name	Grid ref	NRFA Area km²	Record	Num AM	Date max	Max flood	QMED	QBAR	CV	No.
33031	Broughton Brook at Broughton	4889 2408	66.6	1970 - 1988	19	15 08 1980	16.48	7.44	7.50	0.52	33031
33032	Heacham at Heacham	5685 3375	59.0	1973 - 1991	19	01 08 1980	1.27	0.43	0.51	0.69	33032
33033	Hiz at Arlesey	5190 2379	108.0	1973 - 1992	20	18 11 1974	6.39	3.53	3.83	0.38	33033
33034	Little Ouse at Abbey Heath	5851 2844	699.3	1968 - 1992	25	13 10 1987	25.29	17.91	16.07	0.37	33034
33037	Bedford Ouse at Newport Pagnell	4877 2443	800.0	1969 - 1992	24	28 12 1979	83.15	63.94	58.73	0.34	33037
33039	Bedford Ouse at Roxton	5160 2535	1660.0	1972 - 1983	12	29 04 1981	108.00	96.21	81.81	0.39	33039
33044	Thet at Bridgham	5957 2855	277.8	1967 - 1992	25	03 02 1979	13.84	7.88	7.77	0.40	33044
33045	Wittle at Quidenham	6027 2878	28.3	1967 - 1992	25	16 09 1968	3.40	1.17	1.29	0.66	33045
33046	Thet at Red Bridge	5996 2923	145.3	1967 - 1992	26	16 09 1968	17.65	7.69	7.62	0.50	33046
33048	Larling Brook at Stonebridge	5928 2907	21.4	1969 - 1990	22	25 08 1987	1.50	0.29	0.35	0.86	33048
33049	Stanford W. at Buckenham Tofts	5834 2953	43.5	1967 - 1979	13	17 05 1969	1.08	0.72	0.74	0.29	33049
33050	Snail at Fordham	5631 2703	60.6	1974 - 1992	19	06 05 1978	2.98	1.75	1.62	0.40	33050
33051	Cam at Chesterford	5505 2426	141.0	1969 - 1992	24	07 03 1972	13.99	8.11	8.03	0.44	33051
33052	Swaffham Lode at Swaf. Bulbeck	5553 2628	36.4	1967 - 1992	24	05 05 1978	0.90	0.34	0.37	0.56	33052
33054	Babingley at Castle Rising	5680 3252	47.7	1976 - 1992	17	11 02 1977	2.14	0.98	1.14	0.48	33054
33055	Granta at Babraham	5510 2504	98.7	1976 - 1992	17	29 01 1988	8.90	3.99	4.32	0.48	33055
33057	Ouzel at Leighton Buzzard	4917 2241	119.0	1976 - 1988	13	20 10 1987	9.47	7.59	7.27	0.17	33057
33058	Ouzel at Bletchley	4883 2322	215.0	1978 - 1992	13	28 12 1979	33.74	22.70	24.04	0.30	33058
33063	Little Ouse at Knettishall	5955 2807	101.0	1980 - 1992	13	27 08 1987	6.75	4.34	3.85	0.49	33063
33805	Beechamwell Bk at Beechamwell	5738 3036	34.4	1964 - 1973	10	03 03 1966	0.54	0.37	0.34	0.42	33805
33809	Bury Brook at Bury Weir	5286 2837	65.3	1963 - 1977	15	09 08 1968	16.20	8.25	7.36	0.60	33809
33813	Mel at Meldreth	5378 2466	8.6	1964 - 1983	20	05 05 1978	0.48	0.26	0.26	0.42	33813
34001	Yare at Colney	6182 3082	231.8	1958 - 1986	29	17 09 1968	21.80	10.75	11.25	0.44	34001
34002	Tas at Shotesham	6226 2994	146.5	1958 - 1993	36	16 09 1968	61.92	7.75	9.54	1.03	34002
34003	Bure at Ingworth	6192 3296	164.7	1959 - 1993	35	26 04 1981	18.30	5.59	6.27	0.57	34003
34004	Wensum at Costessey Mill	6177 3128	570.9	1960 - 1993	31	28 04 1981	37.60	19.80	19.87	0.39	34004
34005	Tud at Costessey Park	6170 3113	73.2	1961 - 1993	33	27 04 1981	11.01	2.98	3.44	0.67	34005
34006	Waveney at Needham Mill	6229 2811	370.0	1963 - 1973	11	17 09 1968	112.79	22.97	33.62	0.96	34006
34007	Dove at Oakley Park	6174 2772	133.9	1966 - 1993	28	16 09 1968	37.15	12.45	13.16	0.69	34007
34008	Ant at Honing Lock	6331 3270	49.3	1966 - 1993	27	26 04 1981	2.64	1.11	1.12	0.37	34008
34010	Waveney at Billingford Bridge	6168 2782	149.4	1968 - 1993	26	26 04 1981	27.11	12.60	12.96	0.61	34010
34011	Wensum at Fakenham	5919 3294	161.9	1966 - 1993	28	12 02 1977	9.81	4.12	4.13	0.47	34011
34012	Burn at Burnham Overy	5842 3428	80.0	1966 - 1993	28	20 02 1977	1.43	0.61	0.66	0.49	34012
34018	Stiffkey at Warham All Saints	5944 3414	87.8	1971 - 1993	23	27 04 1981	11.00	2.97	3.80	0.76	34018
35001	Gipping at Constantine Weir	6154 2441	310.8	1961 - 1977	15	17 09 1968	50.97	19.30	20.28	0.52	35001
35003	Alde at Farnham	6360 2601	63.9	1961 - 1986	26	01 02 1979	11.70	7.94	7.20	0.44	35003
35004	Ore at Beversham Bridge	6359 2583	54.9	1965 - 1993	29	02 02 1979	11.90	5.61	5.66	0.51	35004
35008	Gipping at Stowmarket	6058 2578	128.9	1964 - 1994	29	02 02 1979	34.00	14.71	15.36	0.53	35008
35010	Gipping at Bramford	6127 2465	298.0	1969 - 1986	18	02 02 1979	41.32	14.68	15.20	0.54	35010
35011	Belstead Brook at Belstead	6143 2420	40.4	1967 - 1974	8	13 03 1969	10.76	4.16	4.66	0.69	35011
35014	Bucklesham Mill at Newbourn	6270 2420	27.1	1948 - 1968	17	15 03 1964	0.67	0.47	0.48	0.28	35014
36001	Stour at Stratford St Mary	6042 2340	844.3	1935 - 1974	40	01 01 1968	99.12	29.85	32.84	0.56	36001
36002	Glem at Glemsford	5846 2472	87.3	1963 - 1993	31	15 09 1968	23.00	8.15	8.67	0.45	36002
36003	Box at Polstead	5985 2378	53.9	1963 - 1993	31	29 01 1988	10.05	3.66	3.76	0.57	36003
36004	Chad Brook at Long Melford	5868 2459	47.4	1967 - 1993	27	15 09 1968	28.00	5.34	6.50	0.76	36004
36005	Brett at Hadleigh	6025 2429	156.0	1963 - 1993	31	01 02 1979	28.04	11.42	12.15	0.53	36005
36006	Stour at Langham	6020 2344	578.0	1963 - 1993	31	17 09 1968	90.00	33.80	32.03	0.48	36006
36007	Belchamp Brook at Bardfield Br.	5848 2421	58.6	1964 - 1993	30	29 01 1988	12.15	4.36	5.08	0.68	36007
36008	Stour at Westmill	5827 2463	224.5	1961 - 1993	33	16 09 1968	85.00	19.83	21.20	0.66	36008
36009	Brett at Cockfield	5914 2525	25.7	1968 - 1992	25	29 01 1988	6.10	3.66	3.45	0.49	36009
36010	Bumpstead Bk at Broad Green	5689 2418	28.3	1967 - 1993	27	16 09 1968	21.00	6.84	8.17	0.67	36010
36011	Stour Brook at Sturmer	5696 2441	34.5	1968 - 1993	26	05 05 1978	10.63	6.16	6.22	0.42	36011
36012	Stour at Kedington	5708 2450	76.2	1967 - 1984	18	19 09 1968	42.00	13.13	14.22	0.61	36012
36015	Stour at Lamarsh	5897 2358	480.7	1972 - 1993	21	02 02 1979	61.00	32.94	28.79	0.42	36015
37001	Roding at Redbridge	5415 1884	303.3	1950 - 1993	44	22 11 1974	62.41	22.95	24.71	0.42	37001

No.	Name	Grid ref	NRFA Area km²	Record	Num AM	Date max	Max flood	QMED	QBAR	CV	No.
37003	Ter at Crabbs Bridge	5786 2107	77.8	1964 - 1993	30	14 12 1974	8.89	4.55	4.66	0.42	37003
37005	Colne at Lexden	5962 2261	238.2	1962 - 1993	32	11 10 1987	24.81	12.25	12.95	0.48	37005
37006	Can at Beach's Mill	5690 2072	228.4	1962 - 1985	24	21 11 1974	37.00	19.70	19.87	0.39	37006
37007	Wid at Writtle	5686 2060	136.3	1964 - 1993	30	21 11 1974	38.60	15.58	16.38	0.47	37007
37008	Chelmer at Springfield	5713 2071	190.3	1966 - 1993	28	10 12 1982	26.66	14.45	14.86	0.49	37008
37009	Brain at Guithavon Valley	5818 2147	60.7	1962 - 1993	32	16 10 1987	9.20	3.60	4.11	0.50	37009
37010	Blackwater at Appleford Bridge	5845 2158	247.3	1963 - 1993	31	11 10 1987	27.36	11.62	12.65	0.47	37010
37011	Chelmer at Churchend	5629 2233	72.6	1963 - 1993	31	09 10 1987	19.11	9.67	9.35	0.50	37011
37012	Colne at Poolstreet	5771 2364	65.1	1964 - 1985	22	17 03 1980	34.71	11.10	12.30	0.69	37012
37013	Sandon Brook at Sandon Bridge	5755 2055	75.1	1964 - 1993	30	08 12 1982	15.75	8.40	8.23	0.45	37013
37014	Roding at High Ongar	5561 2040	95.1	1964 - 1993	30	06 05 1978	23.00	11.16	10.65	0.54	37014
37016	Pant at Copford Hall	5668 2313	62.5	1965 - 1985	21	01 02 1979	31.89	7.61	10.52	0.74	37016
37017	Blackwater at Stisted	5793 2243	139.2	1969 - 1993	25	10 10 1987	17.74	13.34	11.88	0.39	37017
37018	Ingrebourne at Gaynes Park	5553 1862	47.9	1970 - 1978	9	21 11 1974	23.50	4.63	7.36	0.91	37018
37019	Beam at Bretons Farm	5515 1853	49.7	1965 - 1993	29	02 10 1993	17.80	9.24	9.66	0.35	37019
37020	Chelmer at Felsted	5670 2193	132.1	1970 - 1993	24	29 01 1988	20.45	13.40	12.26	0.39	37020
37021	Roman at Bounstead Bridge	5985 2205	52.6	1965 - 1984	20	13 03 1969	9.31	3.06	3.90	0.66	37021
37031	Crouch at Wickford	5748 1934	71.8	1962 - 1993	30	15 09 1968	39.60	9.43	13.01	0.64	37031
37033	Eastwood Brook at Eastwood	5859 1888	10.4	1974 - 1992	19	13 09 1975	8.88	4.84	5.43	0.37	37033
c38001	Lea at Feildes Weir	5390 2092	1036.0	1851 - 1994	121	23 10 1857	280.00	39.05	43.05	0.66	38001c
38002	Ash at Mardock	5393 2148	78.7	1939 - 1993	53	13 03 1947	18.40	6.76	6.80	0.50	38002
38003	Mimram at Panshanger Park	5282 2133	133.9	1953 - 1993	41	12 10 1993	3.82	1.97	2.13	0.38	38003
38004	Rib at Wadesmill	5360 2174	136.5	1959 - 1993	35	16 09 1968	42.50	12.20	14.20	0.56	38004
38007	Canons Brook at Elizabeth Way	5431 2104	21.4	1950 - 1993	44	10 06 1993	14.40	7.79	7.91	0.42	38007
38011	Mimram at Fulling Mill	5225 2169	98.7	1957 - 1972	16	16 09 1968	0.65	0.43	0.40	0.34	38011
38013	Upper Lee at Luton Hoo	5118 2185	70.7	1960 - 1993	32	17 06 1984	9.12	2.98	3.40	0.55	38013
38018	Upper Lee at Water Hall	5299 2099	150.0	1971 - 1993	23	30 05 1979	15.82	7.88	8.48	0.41	38018
38020	Cobbins Bk at Sewardstone Rd	5387 1999	38.4	1971 - 1992	20	29 07 1987	40.00	8.33	10.60	0.89	38020
38021	Turkey Brook at Albany Park	5359 1985	42.2	1971 - 1993	23	30 05 1979	20.69	7.55	8.51	0.50	38021
38022	Pymmes Bk at Edmonton Silver St	5340 1925	42.6	1954 - 1993	40	20 07 1965	39.68	22.85	24.05	0.32	38022
38026	Pincey Brook at Sheering Hall	5495 2126	54.6	1974 - 1993	20	09 10 1987	17.60	11.00	9.64	0.52	38026
39001	Thames at Kingston	5177 1698	9948.0	1883 - 1994	112	18 11 1894	1064.82	308.41	323.91	0.41	39001
39002	Thames at Days Weir	4568 1935	3444.7	1938 - 1994	57	17 03 1947	349.19	142.22	145.81	0.38	39002
39003	Wandle at Connollys Mill	5265 1705	176.1	1939 - 1993	46	16 09 1968	56.00	10.33	11.17	0.68	39003
39004	Wandle at Beddington Park	5296 1655	122.0	1939 - 1993	48	30 11 1976	8.70	3.01	3.61	0.48	39004
39005	Beverley Bk at Wimbledon Com.	5216 1717	43.6	1962 - 1993	22	15 09 1968	21.00	13.19	12.10	0.33	39005
39006	Windrush at Newbridge	4402 2019	362.6	1950 - 1993	44	06 12 1960	23.12	11.23	11.44	0.28	39006
39007	Blackwater at Swallowfield	4731 1648	354.8	1953 - 1993	41	17 09 1968	42.27	21.10	21.74	0.24	39007
39008	Thames at Eynsham	4445 2087	1616.2	1951 - 1994	44	07 12 1960	83.08	66.93	66.17	0.23	39008
39010	Colne at Denham	5052 1864	743.0	1952 - 1993	41	14 10 1993	18.40	10.50	10.60	0.29	39010
39011	Wey at Tilford	4874 1433	396.3	1954 - 1970	14	16 09 1968	78.82	24.45	29.53	0.59	39011
39012	Hogsmill at Kingston upon Thames	5182 1688	69.1	1958 - 1993	33	06 08 1981	26.30	13.45	13.32	0.34	39012
39014	Ver at Hansteads	5151 2016	132.0	1957 - 1972	16	15 09 1968	3.11	1.59	1.64	0.36	39014
39015	Whitewater at Lodge Farm	4731 1523	44.5	1963 - 1993	31	03 02 1990	2.24	1.16	1.19	0.30	39015
39016	Kennet at Theale	4649 1708	1033.4	1961 - 1993	33	11 06 1971	71.00	37.25	37.02	0.27	39016
39017	Ray at Grendon Underwood	4680 2211	18.6	1963 - 1993	25	10 07 1968	16.26	5.45	5.79	0.63	39017
39018	Ock at Abingdon	4486 1969	234.0	1962 - 1976	15	06 03 1972	19.01	10.77	10.28	0.45	39018
39019	Lambourn at Shaw	4470 1682	234.1	1962 - 1993	32	13 11 1974	5.05	3.53	3.47	0.26	39019
39020	Coln at Bibury	4122 2062	106.7	1963 - 1993	31	11 02 1990	5.48	3.56	3.53	0.28	39020
39021	Cherwell at Enslow Mill	4482 2183	551.7	1965 - 1982	18	28 12 1979	40.09	25.87	26.34	0.28	39021
39022	Loddon at Sheepbridge	4720 1652	164.5	1965 - 1993	29	16 09 1968	28.52	16.40	16.41	0.29	39022
39023	Wye at Hedsor	4896 1867	137.3	1965 - 1993	29	22 09 1992	4.25	2.94	2.99	0.20	39023
39024	Gatwick Stream at Gatwick	5288 1402	31.1	1952 - 1972	21	15 09 1968	15.23	6.20	7.24	0.39	39024
39025	Enborne at Brimpton	4568 1648	147.6	1967 - 1982	16	11 06 1971	21.24	15.55	15.31	0.19	39025
39026	Cherwell at Banbury	4458 2411	199.4	1967 - 1993	25	28 12 1979	54.10	16.70	20.73	0.64	39026

No.	Name	Grid ref	NRFA Area km²	Record	Num AM	Date max	Max flood	QMED	QBAR	CV	No.
39027	Pang at Pangbourne	4634 1766	170.9	1969 - 1993	25	29 01 1988	4.36	2.13	2.34	0.37	39027
39028	Dun at Hungerford	4321 1685	101.3	1968 - 1993	26	14 11 1974	3.53	2.41	2.38	0.34	39028
39029	Tillingbourne at Shalford	5000 1478	59.0	1975 - 1993	19	10 10 1987	5.09	2.02	2.21	0.45	39029
39031	Lambourn at Welford	4411 1731	176.0	1962 - 1972	11	10 04 1967	2.95	1.95	1.89	0.36	39031
39032	Lambourn at East Shefford	4390 1745	154.0	1966 - 1982	17	06 02 1969	2.50	1.83	1.74	0.33	39032
39033	Winterbourne at St Bagnor	4453 1694	49.2	1962 - 1993	32	15 03 1982	0.60	0.32	0.36	0.37	39033
39034	Evenlode at Cassington Mill	4448 2099	430.0	1970 - 1993	24	28 12 1979	26.70	20.75	19.97	0.24	39034
39035	Churn at Cerney Wick	4076 1963	124.3	1969 - 1993	25	31 01 1971	4.76	3.51	3.41	0.29	39035
39036	Law Brook at Albury	5045 1468	16.0	1968 - 1993	25	06 08 1981	0.77	0.46	0.45	0.40	39036
39037	Kennet at Marlborough	4187 1686	142.0	1972 - 1993	22	07 12 1992	7.09	3.07	3.20	0.54	39037
39038	Thame at Shabbington	4670 2055	443.0	1968 - 1992	22	04 02 1990	28.40	24.42	21.86	0.31	39038
39040	Thames at West Mill Cricklade	4094 1942	185.0	1972 - 1993	22	09 02 1974	10.80	8.10	8.18	0.26	39040
39042	Leach at Priory Mill Lechlade	4227 1994	76.9	1972 - 1993	22	30 12 1979	5.12	3.46	3.47	0.33	39042
39044	Hart at Bramshill House	4755 1593	84.0	1972 - 1992	21	20 10 1987	12.70	8.46	8.25	0.28	39044
39049	Silk Stream at Colindeep Lane	5217 1895	29.0	1929 - 1993	35	16 08 1977	42.00	11.70	14.77	0.70	39049
39052	The Cut at Binfield	4853 1713	50.2	1957 - 1993	36	01 06 1981	18.10	8.32	8.67	0.41	39052
39053	Mole at Horley	5271 1434	89.9	1962 - 1993	32	16 09 1968	61.43	24.32	25.97	0.34	39053
39055	Yeading Bk West at Yeading West	5083 1846	17.6	1974 - 1992	18	17 08 1977	11.49	4.44	5.06	0.46	39055
39056	Ravensbourne at Catford Hill	5372 1732	120.3	1975 - 1993	17	09 06 1992	28.40	15.28	16.56	0.27	39056
39057	Crane at Cranford Park	5103 1778	61.7	1974 - 1993	19	17 08 1977	17.94	14.00	13.49	0.25	39057
39058	Pool at Winsford Road	5371 1725	38.3	1975 - 1993	19	29 02 1984	19.60	10.64	11.45	0.23	39058
39069	Mole at Kinnersley Manor	5262 1462	142.0	1973 - 1993	21	02 10 1993	71.90	45.50	43.08	0.34	39069
39081	Ock at Abingdon	4481 1966	234.0	1979 - 1993	14	16 03 1982	15.60	11.85	11.45	0.17	39081
39086	Gatwick Stream at Gatwick Link	5285 1417	33.6	1975 - 1993	19	15 10 1987	24.10	10.80	11.47	0.41	39086
39088	Chess at Rickmansworth	5066 1947	105.0	1974 - 1993	19	01 04 1993	1.89	1.26	1.29	0.23	39088
39089	Gade at Bury Mill	5053 2077	48.2	1974 - 1993	20	05 07 1983	1.21	0.71	0.75	0.34	39089
39090	Cole at Inglesham	4208 1970	140.0	1976 - 1982	7	28 12 1979	19.86	10.81	12.44	0.29	39090
39092	Dollis Bk at Hendon Lane Bridge	5240 1895	25.1	1952 - 1993	24	07 06 1963	16.42	7.35	8.06	0.44	39092
39093	Brent at Monks Park	5202 1850	117.6	1940 - 1993	54	22 09 1992	56.20	24.62	25.77	0.41	39093
39095	Quaggy at Manor House Gardens	5394 1748	33.9	1962 - 1993	30	09 06 1992	7.82	4.78	4.90	0.32	39095
39096	Wealdstone Brook at Wembley	5192 1862	21.7	1976 - 1993	18	22 09 1992	29.20	12.03	14.53	0.41	39096
39813	Mole at Ifield Weir	5244 1364	12.7	1959 - 1968	10	16 09 1968	19.00	3.23	4.73	1.10	39813
39824	Ravensbourne East at Bromley S	5405 1687	10.3	1963 - 1993	18	15 09 1968	9.34	4.78	4.92	0.37	39824
39827	Pool at Selworthy Road	5369 1722	36.0	1961 - 1968	6	15 09 1968	12.34	5.19	6.24	0.53	39827
39830	Beck at Rectory Road	5370 1697	10.0	1962 - 1968	7	15 09 1968	5.66	2.06	2.50	0.58	39830
39831	Chaffinch Brook at Beckenham	5360 1685	7.0	1962 - 1968	7	15 09 1968	4.25	2.17	2.30	0.40	39831
39834	Brent at Hanwell	5151 1801	132.0	1961 - 1968	8	26 07 1962	38.83	30.24	29.25	0.29	39834
40003	Medway at Teston	5708 1530	1256.1	1956 - 1985	30	16 09 1968	300.42	130.17	148.25	0.44	40003
40004	Rother at Udiam	5773 1245	206.0	1962 - 1990	29	22 11 1974	60.27	41.90	39.26	0.35	40004
40005	Beult at Stile Bridge	5758 1478	277.1	1958 - 1985	28	28 12 1979	106.02	38.80	44.43	0.49	40005
40006	Bourne at Hadlow	5632 1497	50.3	1959 - 1993	29	15 09 1968	56.60	6.77	9.41	1.04	40006
40007	Medway at Chafford Weir	5517 1405	255.1	1960 - 1985	24	03 11 1960	119.38	46.21	50.21	0.41	40007
40008	Great Stour at Wye	6049 1470	230.0	1960 - 1993	32	28 03 1975	35.36	22.96	22.69	0.29	40008
*40009	Teise at Stone Bridge	5718 1399	136.2	1961 - 1985	25	28 12 1979	49.08	29.52	30.14	0.33	40009*
40010	Eden at Penshurst	5520 1437	224.3	1961 - 1992	29	15 09 1968	212.00	28.11	33.21	1.06	40010
40011	Great Stour at Horton	6116 1554	345.0	1964 - 1993	30	22 03 1975	32.37	20.17	20.96	0.28	40011
40012	Darent at Hawley	5551 1718	191.4	1964 - 1982	18	16 09 1968	49.00	2.65	5.29	2.07	40012
40016	Cray at Crayford	5511 1746	119.7	1969 - 1982	14	27 08 1977	32.66	8.15	9.61	0.75	40016
40017	Dudwell at Burwash	5679 1240	27.5	1969 - 1985	17	25 11 1982	48.68	29.34	28.75	0.40	40017
40018	Darent at Lullingstone	5530 1643	118.4	1964 - 1982	18	15 09 1968	23.00	3.28	4.51	1.05	40018
40020	Eridge Stream at Hendal Bridge	5522 1367	53.7	1973 - 1985	12	28 12 1979	34.39	30.25	28.88	0.18	40020
40022	Great Stour at Chart Leacon	5992 1423	72.5	1967 - 1993	26	20 03 1975	13.00	5.39	6.35	0.42	40022
40809	Pippingford Brook at Paygate	5479 1343	24.0	1967 - 1982	15	28 12 1979	9.92	8.67	8.39	0.17	40809
41003	Cuckmere at Sherman Bridge	5533 1051	134.7	1959 - 1980	22	30 01 1961	83.49	32.47	36.35	0.56	41003
41005	Ouse at Gold Bridge	5429 1214	180.9	1960 - 1990	31	22 11 1974	85.25	30.73	37.05	0.52	41005

No.	Name	Grid ref	NRFA Area km²	Record	Num AM	Date max	Max flood	QMED	QBAR	CV	No.
41006	Uck at Isfield	5459 1190	87.8	1964 - 1981	18	28 12 1979	62.12	32.19	34.47	0.38	41006
41007	Arun at Park Mound	5033 1200	403.3	1958 - 1972	15	15 09 1968	291.58	77.55	79.35	0.82	41007
41011	Rother at Iping Mill	4852 1229	154.0	1967 - 1993	27	16 09 1968	157.12	35.15	41.34	0.69	41011
41012	Adur E Branch at Sakeham	5219 1190	93.3	1967 - 1981	14	22 11 1974	35.12	20.97	21.80	0.36	41012
41014	Arun at Pallingham Quay	5047 1229	379.0	1973 - 1981	9	28 12 1979	83.30	70.92	67.57	0.16	41014
41015	Ems at Westbourne	4755 1074	58.3	1967 - 1993	27	18 04 1975	6.42	1.68	2.05	0.70	41015
41016	Cuckmere at Cowbeech	5611 1150	18.7	1967 - 1981	15	21 11 1974	26.50	5.40	9.33	0.85	41016
41018	Kird at Tanyards	5044 1256	66.8	1969 - 1981	13	27 12 1979	43.72	19.99	20.02	0.50	41018
41020	Bevern Stream at Clappers Br.	5423 1161	34.6	1969 - 1981	13	20 01 1975	17.80	12.05	12.24	0.24	41020
41021	Clayhill Stream at Old Ship	5448 1153	7.1	1973 - 1977	5	21 11 1974	4.28	3.69	3.19	0.32	41021
41022	Lod at Halfway Bridge	4931 1223	52.0	1973 - 1993	21	27 12 1979	41.50	16.97	18.96	0.48	41022
41023	Lavant at Graylingwell	4871 1064	87.2	1971 - 1994	22	12 01 1994	7.11	1.23	1.88	0.94	41023
41025	Loxwood Stream at Drungewick	5060 1309	91.6	1973 - 1981	9	27 12 1979	95.92	34.99	41.74	0.52	41025
41026	Cockhaise Brook at Holywell	5376 1262	36.1	1971 - 1981	11	22 11 1974	17.14	10.02	9.29	0.51	41026
41027	Rother at Princes Marsh	4772 1270	37.2	1972 - 1993	22	12 10 1993	27.76	11.60	12.40	0.52	41027
41028	Chess Stream at Chess Bridge	5217 1173	24.0	1965 - 1991	27	21 11 1974	14.25	6.98	7.25	0.34	41028
41801	Hollington Stream at Hollington	5788 1100	3.5	1968 - 1973	6	14 06 1971	3.35	2.03	2.10	0.40	41801
41806	North End Stream at Allington	5385 1138	2.3	1964 - 1978	15	04 11 1967	1.34	0.72	0.76	0.42	41806
41807	Bevern Stream at East Chiltington	5368 1153	5.6	1967 - 1978	12	04 11 1967	6.19	2.97	3.23	0.40	41807
42001	Wallington at North Fareham	4587 1075	111.0	1976 - 1993	16	13 10 1993	34.00	15.11	16.28	0.34	42001
42005	Wallop Brook at Broughton	4311 1330	53.6	1955 - 1990	29	02 03 1966	1.98	0.99	1.05	0.38	42005
42006	Meon at Mislingford	4589 1141	72.8	1958 - 1992	35	04 12 1960	5.94	2.69	2.87	0.39	42006
*42007	Alre at Drove Lane	4574 1326	57.0	1969 - 1993	25	27 01 1994	2.99	2.26	2.35	0.17	42007*
42008	Cheriton Stream at Sewards Br.	4574 1323	75.1	1970 - 1992	23	13 06 1979	2.07	1.33	1.37	0.29	42008
42009	Candover Stream at Borough Br.	4568 1323	71.2	1970 - 1993	23	13 01 1994	1.92	0.97	1.00	0.31	42009
42010	Itchen at Highbridge	4467 1213	360.0	1958 - 1993	35	12 02 1990	13.26	8.82	9.23	0.22	42010
42011	Hamble at Frog Mill	4523 1149	56.6	1972 - 1981	10	29 11 1976	11.16	8.45	7.82	0.34	42011
42012	Anton at Fullerton	4379 1393	185.0	1973 - 1993	21	07 02 1990	5.39	3.46	3.48	0.22	42012
42014	Blackwater at Ower	4328 1174	104.7	1976 - 1993	18	01 04 1993	32.00	17.79	19.00	0.37	42014
42017	Hermitage at Havant	4711 1068	17.0	1953 - 1993	23	22 10 1966	15.57	7.81	7.67	0.37	42017
43001	Avon at Ringwood	4142 1054	1649.8	1959 - 1966	8	01 11 1960	112.82	61.27	65.60	0.31	43001
43002	Stour at Ensbury	4089 964	1056.7	1960 - 1972	12	06 11 1966	210.47	126.61	131.46	0.27	43002
43003	Avon at East Mills Flume	4158 1154	1477.8	1965 - 1984	20	11 03 1967	81.73	43.71	45.12	0.29	43003
43004	Bourne at Laverstock Mill	4157 1304	163.6	1964 - 1983	20	04 03 1966	3.94	2.26	2.38	0.37	43004
43005	Avon at Amesbury	4151 1413	323.7	1965 - 1993	29	04 02 1990	28.54	12.60	12.77	0.41	43005
43006	Nadder at Wilton Park	4098 1308	220.6	1966 - 1993	27	28 12 1979	47.88	15.18	17.84	0.45	43006
43007	Stour at Throop Mill	4113 958	1073.0	1973 - 1993	21	28 12 1979	292.62	106.90	113.83	0.47	43007
43008	Wylye at South Newton	4086 1343	445.4	1967 - 1992	25	07 02 1990	21.52	12.29	12.22	0.33	43008
43009	Stour at Hammoon	3820 1147	523.1	1968 - 1993	26	27 12 1979	234.54	116.97	116.26	0.33	43009
43010	Allen at Loverley Mill	4006 1085	94.0	1970 - 1980	11	21 02 1974	4.96	3.50	3.53	0.36	43010
43012	Wylye at Norton Bavant	3909 1428	112.4	1969 - 1993	22	03 02 1990	7.26	4.70	4.75	0.31	43012
43014	East Avon at Upavon	4133 1559	86.2	1970 - 1992	22	03 02 1990	6.24	3.78	3.77	0.36	43014
43017	West Avon at Upavon	4133 1559	76.0	1970 - 1985	16	27 12 1979	10.48	5.83	5.79	0.36	43017
43018	Allen at Walford Mill	4008 1007	176.5	1974 - 1993	18	14 02 1990	13.06	7.12	6.76	0.41	43018
44002	Piddle at Baggs Mill	3913 876	183.1	1965 - 1993	29	08 01 1968	11.86	8.26	8.15	0.19	44002
44003	Asker at Bridport	3470 928	49.1	1966 - 1978	13	31 05 1979	27.10	12.27	13.00	0.43	44003
44004	Frome at Dorchester Total	3708 903	206.0	1969 - 1984	15	27 12 1979	23.13	15.58	15.65	0.24	44004
44006	Sydling Water at Syd. St Nicholas	3632 997	12.4	1969 - 1985	17	30 05 1979	1.57	0.78	0.86	0.39	44006
44008	S Winterbourne at Wint. Steepleton	3629 897	19.9	1974 - 1985	12	06 02 1979	0.85	0.44	0.43	0.49	44008
44009	Wey at Broadwey	3666 839	7.0	1975 - 1993	16	30 12 1993	5.47	1.67	1.92	0.68	44009
45001	Exe at Thorverton	2936 1016	600.9	1956 - 1993	38	04 12 1960	456.57	175.31	183.77	0.37	45001
45002	Exe at Stoodleigh	2943 1178	421.7	1960 - 1993	34	04 12 1960	339.62	138.85	145.44	0.34	45002
45003	Culm at Wood Mill	3021 1058	226.1	1962 - 1993	32	10 07 1968	202.00	68.15	79.02	0.50	45003
45004	Axe at Whitford	3262 953	288.5	1965 - 1993	29	27 12 1979	243.16	101.35	109.74	0.47	45004
45005	Otter at Dotton	3087 885	202.5	1962 - 1993	32	10 07 1968	348.29	71.98	78.66	0.69	45005

No.	Name	Grid ref	NRFA Area km²	Record	Num AM	Date max	Max flood	QMED	QBAR	CV	No.
45006	Quarme at Enterwell	2919 1356	20.4	1964 - 1972	9	18 12 1965	18.35	9.76	9.90	0.38	45006
45008	Otter at Fenny Bridges	3115 986	104.2	1974 - 1992	19	31 05 1981	131.73	53.30	61.51	0.51	45008
45009	Exe at Pixton	2935 1260	147.6	1966 - 1993	22	19 12 1982	71.61	41.40	42.89	0.31	45009
45011	Barle at Brushford	2927 1258	128.0	1966 - 1980	12	09 03 1981	153.26	85.68	88.01	0.39	45011
45012	Creedy at Cowley	2901 967	261.6	1964 - 1993	28	27 12 1979	195.78	93.77	92.08	0.49	45012
45801	Back Brook at Hawkerland	3058 887	2.5	1967 - 1972	5	16 07 1972	12.04	3.93	4.68	0.92	45801
46002	Teign at Preston	2856 746	380.0	1956 - 1993	38	30 09 1960	411.30	133.44	141.63	0.44	46002
46003	Dart at Austins Bridge	2751 659	247.6	1958 - 1993	36	27 12 1979	549.74	213.13	227.51	0.35	46003
46005	East Dart at Bellever	2657 775	21.5	1964 - 1993	30	27 12 1979	67.06	39.07	39.98	0.30	46005
46006	Erme at Ermington	2642 532	43.5	1974 - 1993	16	01 09 1988	77.63	47.24	48.76	0.33	46006
46007	West Dart at Dunnabridge	2643 742	47.9	1972 - 1980	9	27 12 1979	131.85	75.65	73.76	0.39	46007
46008	Avon at Loddiswell	2719 476	102.3	1971 - 1980	10	27 12 1979	88.95	64.98	59.49	0.36	46008
46801	Erme at Erme Intake	2640 632	14.9	1963 - 1972	9	27 06 1968	32.11	23.37	24.21	0.15	46801
46806	Avon at Avon Intake	2681 641	14.0	1939 - 1955	17	16 11 1944	47.88	24.73	26.39	0.27	46806
47001	Tamar at Gunnislake	2426 725	916.9	1956 - 1993	38	28 12 1979	703.56	264.90	300.98	0.36	47001
47004	Lynher at Pillaton Mill	2369 626	135.5	1961 - 1993	33	27 12 1979	106.99	45.28	45.40	0.37	47004
47005	Ottery at Werrington Park	2336 866	120.7	1961 - 1993	30	27 12 1979	133.07	60.00	60.41	0.41	47005
47006	Lyd at Lifton Park	2388 842	218.1	1962 - 1972	11	04 11 1967	274.70	122.82	131.12	0.45	47006
47007	Yealm at Puslinch	2574 511	54.9	1962 - 1993	32	30 12 1993	30.25	22.74	23.02	0.18	47007
47008	Thrushel at Tinhay	2398 856	112.7	1969 - 1993	25	27 12 1979	124.65	43.14	48.06	0.45	47008
47009	Tiddy at Tideford	2343 595	37.2	1969 - 1994	26	27 12 1979	10.24	5.73	6.12	0.29	47009
47010	Tamar at Crowford Bridge	2290 991	76.7	1972 - 1986	12	20 09 1980	67.85	54.94	55.42	0.18	47010
47011	Plym at Carn Wood	2522 613	79.2	1971 - 1980	10	27 12 1979	113.31	45.61	48.32	0.53	47011
47014	Walkham at Horrabridge	2513 699	43.2	1973 - 1994	22	26 12 1979	69.85	29.36	30.69	0.39	47014
48001	Fowey at Trekeivesteps	2227 698	36.8	1969 - 1993	25	26 12 1979	38.94	15.91	18.11	0.41	48001
48002	Fowey at Restormel	2108 613	171.2	1961 - 1972	12	04 11 1967	98.56	54.48	55.61	0.33	48002
48003	Fal at Tregony	1921 447	87.0	1961 - 1994	29	27 12 1979	58.09	13.43	16.60	0.68	48003
48004	Warleggan at Trengoffe	2159 674	25.3	1969 - 1993	24	26 12 1979	23.91	9.09	10.06	0.49	48004
48005	Kenwyn at Truro	1820 450	19.1	1968 - 1993	23	11 10 1988	30.37	5.64	7.72	0.87	48005
48006	Cober at Helston	1654 273	40.1	1968 - 1987	20	28 12 1979	16.84	5.22	6.10	0.49	48006
48007	Kennall at Ponsanooth	1762 377	26.6	1968 - 1993	24	27 01 1988	6.55	3.93	4.02	0.32	48007
48009	St Neot at Craigshill Wood	2184 662	22.7	1971 - 1982	12	27 12 1979	21.08	8.35	9.82	0.46	48009
48010	Seaton at Trebrownbridge	2299 596	38.1	1972 - 1993	22	27 12 1979	14.35	6.37	6.86	0.39	48010
48011	Fowey at Restormell Ii	2098 624	169.1	1972 - 1993	22	27 12 1979	128.96	43.65	48.54	0.55	48011
49001	Camel at Denby	2017 682	208.8	1957 - 1993	37	12 06 1993	306.40	53.10	71.87	0.76	49001
49002	Hayle at St Erth	1549 342	48.9	1957 - 1993	34	01 01 1963	15.00	4.45	5.60	0.46	49002
49003	De Lank at De Lank	2132 765	21.7	1967 - 1993	23	21 09 1980	35.81	13.62	14.60	0.41	49003
49004	Gannel at Gwills	1829 593	41.0	1970 - 1993	23	11 10 1988	26.68	14.04	15.24	0.45	49004
50001	Taw at Umberleigh	2608 1237	826.2	1958 - 1993	36	09 01 1968	581.78	219.00	241.70	0.41	50001
50002	Torridge at Torrington	2500 1185	663.0	1960 - 1993	33	28 12 1979	730.00	244.40	272.61	0.45	50002
50005	West Okement at Vellake	2557 903	13.3	1967 - 1993	11	17 06 1971	53.00	23.93	25.84	0.44	50005
50006	Mole at Woodleigh	2660 1211	327.5	1965 - 1972	8	09 01 1968	419.15	261.09	283.28	0.34	50006
50007	Taw at Taw Bridge	2673 1068	71.4	1973 - 1993	21	27 12 1979	128.03	34.10	44.82	0.61	50007
50810	Little Dart at Dart Bridge	2669 1137	125.6	1973 - 1980	8	09 03 1981	61.78	35.44	36.56	0.41	50810
51001	Doniford Stream at Swill Bridge	3088 1428	75.8	1966 - 1993	27	10 07 1968	131.33	12.19	19.88	1.25	51001
51002	Horner Water at West Luccombe	2898 1458	20.8	1973 - 1993	15	18 12 1993	11.32	6.38	6.52	0.40	51002
51003	Washford at Beggearn Huish	3040 1395	36.3	1966 - 1993	22	26 05 1983	27.34	5.85	6.70	0.75	51003
52003	Halse Water at Bishops Hull	3206 1253	87.8	1962 - 1993	31	27 12 1979	42.00	9.66	12.10	0.66	52003
52004	Isle at Ashford Mill	3361 1188	90.1	1962 - 1993	32	18 12 1992	28.89	26.19	25.10	0.16	52004
52005	Tone at Bishops Hull	3206 1250	202.0	1961 - 1993	33	11 07 1968	112.66	66.69	66.19	0.43	52005
52006	Yeo at Pen Mill	3573 1162	213.1	1962 - 1987	24	27 12 1979	97.96	43.75	47.24	0.37	52006
52007	Parrett at Chiselborough	3461 1144	74.8	1966 - 1987	13	29 05 1979	58.51	27.55	30.28	0.36	52007
52009	Sheppey at Fenny Castle	3498 1439	59.6	1964 - 1993	29	10 07 1968	9.27	7.45	7.11	0.19	52009
52010	Brue at Lovington	3590 1318	135.2	1964 - 1993	30	30 05 1979	94.77	47.96	49.26	0.40	52010
52011	Cary at Somerton	3498 1291	82.4	1965 - 1993	29	31 05 1979	15.01	9.95	9.91	0.24	52011

No.	Name	Grid ref	NRFA Area km²	Record	Num AM	Date max	Max flood	QMED	QBAR	CV	No.
52014	Tone at Greenham	3078 1202	57.2	1966 - 1980	13	10 07 1968	23.79	14.15	14.66	0.32	52014
52015	Land Yeo at Wraxall Bridge	3483 1716	23.3	1971 - 1993	17	07 10 1993	6.80	2.49	3.05	0.60	52015
52016	Currypool Stream at Currypool Fm	3221 1382	15.7	1971 - 1993	23	01 12 1976	7.70	2.56	3.17	0.59	52016
52017	Congresbury Yeo at Iwood	3452 1631	66.6	1973 - 1993	19	24 12 1979	13.97	7.72	8.50	0.40	52017
52020	Gallica Stream at Gallica Bridge	3571 1100	16.4	1966 - 1978	8	30 05 1979	38.48	20.28	21.46	0.49	52020
52801	Tone at Wadhams Farm	3055 1268	32.1	1967 - 1972	6	10 07 1968	5.05	3.65	3.60	0.34	52801
*53001	Avon at Melksham	3903 1641	665.6	1938 - 1987	49	11 07 1968	197.79	59.62	75.41	0.52	53001*
53002	Semington Brook at Semington	3907 1605	157.7	1973 - 1987	15	27 12 1979	50.00	25.93	26.38	0.35	53002
53003	Avon at Bath St James	3753 1645	1595.0	1940 - 1968	29	04 12 1960	351.52	127.74	156.66	0.45	53003
53004	Chew at Compton Dando	3648 1647	129.5	1958 - 1993	35	10 07 1968	226.48	29.83	37.08	1.01	53004
53005	Midford Brook at Midford	3763 1611	147.4	1961 - 1993	33	10 07 1968	55.19	28.28	29.90	0.39	53005
53006	Frome(bristol) at Frenchay	3637 1772	148.9	1961 - 1993	33	10 07 1968	70.00	29.00	30.72	0.44	53006
53007	Frome(somerset) at Tellisford	3805 1564	261.6	1961 - 1993	33	11 07 1968	113.24	58.00	61.89	0.33	53007
53008	Avon at Great Somerford	3966 1832	303.0	1964 - 1993	30	11 07 1968	106.13	36.82	39.73	0.49	53008
53009	Wellow Brook at Wellow	3741 1581	72.6	1966 - 1993	28	10 07 1968	29.91	13.53	14.89	0.39	53009
53013	Marden at Stanley	3955 1729	99.2	1969 - 1993	25	12 06 1971	33.84	15.02	17.78	0.49	53013
53017	Boyd at Bitton	3681 1698	48.0	1973 - 1993	21	30 05 1979	27.42	12.57	13.49	0.46	53017
53018	Avon at Bathford	3786 1671	1552.0	1969 - 1993	25	27 12 1979	299.29	166.97	168.34	0.34	53018
53019	Woodbridge Brook at Crab Mill	3949 1866	46.6	1964 - 1975	12	11 06 1971	66.45	22.10	26.05	0.72	53019
53020	Gauze Brook at Rodbourne	3937 1840	28.2	1963 - 1993	31	10 07 1968	13.00	3.55	4.67	0.60	53020
53023	Sherston Avon at Fosseway	3891 1870	89.7	1976 - 1993	18	30 11 1992	11.91	6.93	7.33	0.30	53023
53025	Mells at Vallis	3757 1491	119.0	1980 - 1993	14	13 10 1993	40.27	20.82	23.41	0.36	53025
54001	Severn at Bewdley	3782 2762	4325.0	1923 - 1993	71	21 03 1947	671.10	357.34	377.62	0.27	54001
54002	Avon at Evesham	4040 2438	2210.0	1937 - 1990	54	11 07 1968	361.91	146.95	156.02	0.47	54002
54003	Vyrnwy at Vyrnwy Reservoir	3019 3191	94.3	1927 - 1966	40	03 11 1931	240.63	87.24	100.23	0.51	54003
54004	Sowe at Stoneleigh	4332 2731	262.0	1951 - 1993	42	26 03 1955	57.65	31.19	30.68	0.39	54004
54005	Severn at Montford	3412 3144	2025.0	1952 - 1994	43	05 12 1960	467.23	303.54	303.35	0.19	54005
*54006	Stour at Kidderminster	3829 2768	324.0	1952 - 1991	40	27 03 1955	52.20	17.40	19.18	0.51	54006*
54007	Arrow at Broom	4086 2536	319.0	1956 - 1984	29	30 12 1981	91.50	42.19	47.22	0.38	54007
54008	Teme at Tenbury	3597 2686	1134.4	1956 - 1993	38	03 12 1960	261.13	145.74	148.47	0.35	54008
54010	Stour at Alscot Park	4208 2507	319.0	1959 - 1993	32	13 01 1993	82.90	38.53	40.02	0.44	54010
54011	Salwarpe at Harford Mill	3868 2618	184.0	1958 - 1993	31	24 01 1960	46.41	20.31	23.19	0.43	54011
54012	Tern at Walcot	3592 3123	852.0	1959 - 1993	35	03 07 1968	61.07	40.47	39.44	0.27	54012
54013	Clywedog at Cribynau	2944 2855	57.0	1959 - 1964	6	12 12 1964	120.48	69.46	72.84	0.41	54013
54014	Severn at Abermule	3164 2958	580.0	1960 - 1994	35	04 12 1960	616.90	199.57	227.45	0.50	54014
54016	Roden at Rodington	3589 3141	259.0	1961 - 1993	33	03 07 1968	30.75	14.56	14.59	0.33	54016
54017	Leadon at Wedderburn Bridge	3777 2234	293.0	1961 - 1994	34	10 02 1977	48.80	21.72	23.33	0.34	54017
54018	Rea Brook at Hookagate	3466 3092	178.0	1962 - 1993	30	09 12 1965	38.11	22.64	22.80	0.24	54018
54019	Avon at Stareton	4333 2715	347.0	1962 - 1993	32	11 07 1968	98.82	35.09	35.61	0.50	54019
54020	Perry at Yeaton	3434 3192	180.8	1963 - 1993	31	07 02 1990	14.91	9.33	9.52	0.22	54020
54022	Severn at Plynlimon Flume	2853 2872	8.7	1951 - 1972	22	05 08 1973	27.97	11.84	13.95	0.40	54022
54023	Badsey Brook at Offenham	4063 2449	95.8	1968 - 1993	25	14 06 1977	15.82	10.15	9.91	0.34	54023
54024	Worfe at Burcote	3747 2953	258.0	1969 - 1994	25	31 12 1981	15.92	6.80	7.24	0.34	54024
54025	Dulas at Rhos-y-pentref	2950 2824	52.7	1969 - 1994	26	18 10 1987	38.48	21.62	22.11	0.26	54025
54026	Chelt at Slate Mill	3892 2264	34.5	1969 - 1984	16	27 12 1979	10.98	9.02	8.55	0.21	54026
54027	Frome at Ebley Mill	3831 2047	198.0	1971 - 1994	24	30 05 1979	19.08	11.07	11.24	0.28	54027
54028	Vyrnwy at Llanymynech	3252 3195	778.0	1971 - 1993	23	06 08 1973	544.03	280.66	292.24	0.30	54028
54029	Teme at Knightsford Bridge	3735 2557	1480.0	1970 - 1993	24	28 12 1979	276.32	183.25	180.18	0.26	54029
54032	Severn at Saxons Lode	3863 2390	6850.0	1970 - 1993	24	02 02 1990	781.62	462.32	481.92	0.27	54032
54034	Dowles Brook at Dowles	3768 2764	40.8	1971 - 1994	23	10 06 1993	21.62	9.62	11.30	0.44	54034
54036	Isbourne at Hinton On The Green	4023 2408	90.7	1973 - 1993	21	30 05 1979	27.08	15.48	14.85	0.45	54036
54038	Tanat at Llanyblodwel	3252 3225	229.0	1973 - 1993	21	01 01 1991	122.92	78.09	77.86	0.22	54038
54040	Meese at Tibberton	3680 3205	167.8	1973 - 1994	22	31 12 1981	8.90	5.45	5.48	0.25	54040
54041	Tern at Eaton On Tern	3649 3230	192.0	1972 - 1994	23	28 01 1990	20.00	11.16	12.14	0.33	54041
54043	Severn at Upton On Severn	3865 2399	6850.0	1955 - 1969	15	25 01 1960	538.00	470.00	459.27	0.10	54043

No.	Name	Grid ref	NRFA Area km²	Record	Num AM	Date max	Max flood	QMED	QBAR	CV	No.
54044	Tern at Ternhill	3629 3316	92.6	1972 - 1994	23	11 02 1977	12.05	4.73	5.57	0.47	54044
54052	Bailey Brook at Ternhill	3629 3316	34.4	1972 - 1993	22	11 02 1977	4.12	2.52	2.58	0.29	54052
54057	Severn at Haw Bridge	3844 2279	9895.0	1975 - 1991	16	03 02 1990	662.47	493.40	510.36	0.15	54057
54058	Stoke Park Brook at Stoke Park	3644 3260	14.3	1972 - 1977	6	06 08 1973	3.13	2.58	2.62	0.11	54058
54059	Allford Brook at Allford	3654 3223	10.2	1972 - 1977	6	06 08 1973	3.62	0.93	1.32	0.94	54059
54060	Potford Brook at Potford	3634 3220	25.0	1972 - 1977	6	06 08 1973	1.78	0.92	1.00	0.42	54060
54061	Hodnet Brook at Hodnet	3628 3288	5.1	1972 - 1976	5	05 08 1973	0.65	0.22	0.28	0.83	54061
54062	Stoke Brook at Stoke	3637 3280	13.7	1972 - 1984	13	11 02 1977	5.50	0.45	1.46	1.17	54062
54065	Roden at Stanton	3565 3241	210.0	1973 - 1977	5	11 02 1974	18.79	13.93	13.67	0.29	54065
54088	Little Avon at Berkeley Kennels	3683 1988	134.0	1978 - 1993	16	01 05 1983	44.63	27.68	27.63	0.38	54088
54090	Tanllwyth at Tanllwyth Flume	2843 2876	0.9	1973 - 1994	22	15 08 1977	5.46	2.33	2.32	0.34	54090
54091	Severn at Hafren Flume	2843 2878	3.6	1976 - 1994	19	15 08 1977	22.27	6.25	6.70	0.58	54091
54092	Hore at Hore Flume	2846 2873	3.2	1973 - 1994	19	28 10 1989	8.47	6.33	6.26	0.18	54092
55001	Wye at Cadora	3535 2090	4040.0	1937 - 1968	32	20 03 1947	925.88	515.48	539.49	0.24	55001
55002	Wye at Belmont	3485 2388	1895.9	1908 - 1995	84	04 12 1960	958.43	420.95	433.49	0.25	55002
55003	Lugg at Lugwardine	3548 2405	885.8	1940 - 1995	46	26 03 1996	81.50	51.71	52.03	0.14	55003
55004	Irfon at Abernant	2892 2460	72.8	1937 - 1982	46	06 08 1973	129.96	55.30	60.07	0.29	55004
55005	Wye at Rhayader	2969 2676	166.8	1938 - 1968	31	13 12 1964	279.82	115.01	137.01	0.48	55005
55007	Wye at Erwood	3076 2445	1282.1	1938 - 1995	56	04 12 1960	1205.77	556.67	582.53	0.37	55007
55008	Wye at Cefn Brwyn	2829 2838	10.6	1951 - 1994	44	05 08 1973	59.13	18.10	19.82	0.45	55008
55009	Monnow at Kentchurch	3419 2251	357.4	1948 - 1972	22	24 01 1960	192.57	112.55	115.20	0.31	55009
55010	Wye at Pant Mawr	2843 2825	27.2	1952 - 1994	40	05 08 1957	132.63	51.81	57.20	0.35	55010
55011	Ithon at Llandewi	3105 2683	111.4	1959 - 1972	14	09 12 1965	67.64	54.91	51.39	0.21	55011
55012	Irfon at Cilmery	2995 2507	244.2	1966 - 1994	26	07 02 1990	356.66	202.83	218.67	0.40	55012
55013	Arrow at Titley Mill	3328 2585	126.4	1966 - 1995	25	10 01 1986	101.10	36.42	37.41	0.53	55013
55014	Lugg at Byton	3364 2647	203.3	1966 - 1994	26	14 01 1968	54.27	27.46	29.04	0.29	55014
55015	Honddu at Tafolog	3277 2294	25.1	1953 - 1982	30	24 10 1960	54.56	17.29	19.42	0.46	55015
55016	Ithon at Disserth	3024 2578	358.0	1968 - 1995	20	09 01 1992	148.10	104.18	108.29	0.23	55016
55017	Chwefru at Carreg-y-wen	2998 2531	29.0	1968 - 1972	5	06 08 1973	44.84	20.45	23.20	0.54	55017
55018	Frome at Yarkhill	3615 2428	144.0	1968 - 1995	25	26 05 1969	26.83	21.74	20.95	0.18	55018
55021	Lugg at Butts Bridge	3502 2589	371.0	1970 - 1995	18	10 01 1985	64.10	37.40	37.58	0.31	55021
55022	Trothy at Mitchel Troy	3503 2112	142.0	1970 - 1982	10	13 11 1974	40.71	36.15	33.05	0.25	55022
55023	Wye at Redbrook	3528 2110	4010.0	1969 - 1995	25	04 12 1992	808.77	512.57	543.80	0.21	55023
55025	Llynfi at Three Cocks	3166 2373	132.0	1970 - 1995	22	27 12 1979	198.42	48.04	54.27	0.66	55025
55026	Wye at Ddol Farm	2976 2676	174.0	1970 - 1982	13	06 08 1973	252.05	116.34	124.60	0.34	55026
55029	Monnow at Grosmont	3415 2249	354.0	1973 - 1995	19	27 12 1979	200.30	131.37	139.52	0.25	55029
c55030	Clearwyn at Dol Y Mynach	2910 2620	95.3	1928 - 1947	20	01 01 1946	142.19	90.93	90.37	0.25	55030c
55033	Wye at Gwy Flume	2824 2853	3.9	1973 - 1994	19	06 10 1980	10.45	8.54	8.52	0.17	55033
55034	Cyff at Cyff Flume	2824 2842	3.1	1973 - 1994	20	27 01 1995	6.36	5.60	5.56	0.10	55034
55035	Iago at Iago Flume	2826 2854	1.1	1973 - 1987	15	29 12 1986	2.10	1.85	1.82	0.11	55035
56001	Usk at Chain Bridge	3345 2056	911.7	1957 - 1993	37	27 12 1979	945.00	379.69	401.54	0.36	56001
56002	Ebbw at Rhiwderyn	3259 1889	216.5	1957 - 1983	27	27 12 1979	247.30	90.91	100.56	0.44	56002
56003	Honddu at The Forge Brecon	3051 2297	62.1	1963 - 1983	21	27 12 1979	72.82	23.45	24.80	0.54	56003
56004	Usk at Llandetty	3127 2203	543.9	1965 - 1992	28	27 12 1979	774.24	340.10	350.47	0.40	56004
56005	Lwyd at Ponthir	3330 1924	98.1	1966 - 1990	25	07 02 1990	129.06	48.78	53.85	0.43	56005
56006	Usk at Trallong	2947 2295	183.8	1963 - 1992	30	27 12 1979	323.73	164.30	166.16	0.38	56006
56007	Senni at Pont Hen Hafod	2928 2255	19.9	1968 - 1993	23	27 12 1979	49.65	26.17	27.69	0.29	56007
56011	Sirhowy at Wattsville	3206 1912	76.1	1971 - 1981	11	27 12 1979	113.36	30.34	40.38	0.64	56011
56012	Grwyne at Millbrook	3241 2176	82.2	1971 - 1983	13	27 12 1979	61.68	19.94	24.10	0.53	56012
56013	Yscir at Pontaryscir	3003 2304	62.8	1972 - 1993	22	06 10 1985	84.60	31.50	37.74	0.48	56013
*56015	Olway Brook at Olway Inn	3384 2010	105.1	1974 - 1991	16	07 02 1990	21.52	17.88	17.78	0.11	56015*
56019	Ebbw at Aberbeeg	3210 2015	77.0	1975 - 1992	18	15 10 1983	85.53	42.87	49.73	0.37	56019
57003	Taff at Tongwynlais	3132 1818	486.9	1960 - 1977	15	03 12 1960	682.67	320.00	344.76	0.38	57003
57004	Cynon at Abercynon	3079 1956	106.0	1962 - 1993	32	27 12 1979	181.67	72.65	81.37	0.40	57004
57005	Taff at Pontypridd	3079 1897	454.8	1968 - 1993	26	27 12 1979	651.09	288.89	317.86	0.36	57005

No.	Name	Grid ref	NRFA Area km²	Record	Num AM	Date max	Max flood	QMED	QBAR	CV	No.
57006	Rhondda at Trehafod	3054 1909	100.5	1968 - 1993	25	27 12 1979	197.42	99.76	105.55	0.29	57006
57007	Taff at Fiddlers Elbow	3089 1951	194.5	1973 - 1993	21	27 12 1979	320.50	123.08	138.39	0.47	57007
57008	Rhymney at Llanedeyrn	3225 1821	178.7	1972 - 1992	21	07 02 1990	156.89	103.39	98.57	0.27	57008
57009	Ely at St Fagans	3121 1770	145.0	1975 - 1993	18	30 11 1992	84.95	52.24	57.91	0.26	57009
57010	Ely at Lanelay	3034 1827	39.4	1967 - 1993	26	09 01 1986	95.32	43.00	44.12	0.40	57010
57015	Taff at Merthyr Tydfil	3043 2068	104.1	1978 - 1992	15	27 12 1979	313.30	91.85	103.80	0.61	57015
57803	Clun at Cross Inn	3053 1824	25.9	1967 - 1972	6	01 07 1968	23.21	17.10	18.21	0.19	57803
58001	Ogmore at Bridgend	2904 1794	158.0	1960 - 1993	34	03 12 1960	175.63	103.09	103.81	0.28	58001
58002	Neath at Resolven	2815 2017	190.9	1960 - 1982	22	27 12 1979	502.78	172.74	200.08	0.45	58002
58003	Ewenny at Ewenny Priory	2914 1780	62.9	1961 - 1968	8	29 12 1965	22.52	19.60	19.34	0.11	58003
58004	Afan at Cwmavon	2781 1919	85.7	1962 - 1969	8	17 12 1965	158.30	93.24	96.39	0.42	58004
58005	Ogmore at Brynmenyn	2904 1844	74.3	1969 - 1993	25	10 03 1981	95.97	48.38	51.03	0.33	58005
58006	Mellte at Pontneddfechan	2915 2082	65.8	1971 - 1982	12	27 12 1979	128.83	59.23	64.44	0.38	58006
58007	Llynfi at Coytrahen	2891 1855	50.2	1970 - 1995	26	30 10 1994	88.46	43.79	45.60	0.31	58007
58008	Dulais at Cilfrew	2778 2008	43.0	1972 - 1995	24	04 11 1973	85.14	44.07	46.53	0.26	58008
58009	Ewenny at Keepers Lodge	2920 1782	62.5	1972 - 1995	24	30 10 1994	73.68	44.28	42.59	0.38	58009
58010	Hepste at Esgair Carnau	2969 2134	11.0	1975 - 1980	6	27 12 1979	15.18	12.79	12.50	0.20	58010
58011	Thaw at Gigman Bridge	3017 1716	49.2	1973 - 1993	16	30 11 1992	6.86	6.19	6.05	0.09	58011
59001	Tawe at Yynstanglws	2685 1998	227.7	1957 - 1972	16	01 11 1970	272.71	225.29	211.54	0.21	59001
59002	Loughor at Tir-y-dail	2623 2127	46.4	1967 - 1982	16	04 08 1973	144.24	68.69	73.55	0.39	59002
60002	Cothi at Felin Mynachdy	2508 2225	297.8	1961 - 1993	33	18 10 1987	432.29	154.06	171.44	0.40	60002
60003	Taf at Clog-y-fran	2238 2160	217.3	1964 - 1993	30	25 08 1986	94.91	73.58	72.98	0.13	60003
60004	Dewi Fawr at Glasfryn Ford	2290 2175	40.1	1967 - 1982	15	27 12 1979	23.39	17.20	17.92	0.21	60004
60005	Bran at Llandovery	2771 2343	66.8	1968 - 1982	15	05 08 1973	63.60	38.33	40.58	0.35	60005
60006	Gwili at Glangwili	2431 2220	129.5	1968 - 1992	25	01 12 1992	179.75	82.42	90.39	0.34	60006
60007	Tywi at Dolau Hirion	2762 2362	231.8	1968 - 1995	27	18 10 1987	222.46	119.03	123.10	0.30	60007
60009	Sawdde at Felin-y-cwm	2712 2266	81.1	1973 - 1995	23	18 10 1987	228.48	97.24	105.77	0.36	60009
60010	Tywi at Nantgaredig	2491 2204	1090.4	1958 - 1982	25	27 12 1979	571.02	312.83	351.04	0.29	60010
60012	Twrch at Ddol Las	2650 2440	20.7	1970 - 1982	13	29 10 1977	32.78	14.70	17.91	0.48	60012
60013	Cothi at Pont Ynys Brechfa	2537 2301	261.6	1971 - 1979	9	27 12 1979	244.06	120.35	133.86	0.38	60013
61001	W Cleddau at Prendergast Mill	1954 2177	197.6	1961 - 1995	35	18 10 1987	127.12	53.45	61.08	0.36	61001
61002	E Cleddau at Canaston Bridge	2072 2153	183.1	1960 - 1994	35	25 08 1986	125.34	80.29	79.69	0.20	61002
61003	Gwaun at Cilrhedyn Bridge	2005 2349	31.3	1968 - 1982	15	20 11 1971	28.06	15.40	17.30	0.27	61003
62001	Teifi at Glan Teifi	2244 2416	893.6	1959 - 1995	37	19 10 1987	448.33	190.05	206.86	0.32	62001
62002	Teifi at Llanfair	2433 2406	510.0	1971 - 1981	11	27 12 1979	227.48	131.98	142.02	0.36	62002
63001	Ystwyth at Pont Llolwyn	2591 2774	169.6	1961 - 1995	34	12 12 1964	154.35	90.31	92.21	0.26	63001
63002	Rheidol at Llanbadarn Fawr	2601 2804	182.1	1964 - 1982	19	06 08 1973	139.41	78.01	83.03	0.30	63002
63003	Wyre at Llanrhystyd	2542 2698	40.6	1968 - 1978	11	06 08 1973	93.03	26.02	30.50	0.75	63003
64001	Dyfi at Dyfi Bridge	2745 3019	471.3	1962 - 1984	23	06 08 1973	405.74	316.57	306.40	0.19	64001
64002	Dysynni at Pont-y-garth	2632 3066	75.1	1966 - 1984	19	21 11 1980	120.43	63.04	69.61	0.30	64002
64005	Wnion at Dolgellau	2730 3179	110.8	1969 - 1972	4	05 08 1973	185.36	154.15	156.51	0.14	64005
64006	Leri at Dolybont	2635 2882	47.2	1974 - 1984	11	05 12 1979	23.59	16.83	17.36	0.26	64006
65001	Glaslyn at Beddgelert	2592 3478	68.6	1969 - 1984	16	17 07 1973	132.64	93.76	95.03	0.17	65001
65002	Dwyryd at Maentwrog	2670 3415	78.2	1967 - 1972	6	16 07 1973	171.80	143.10	142.06	0.12	65002
65004	Gwyrfai at Bontnewydd	2484 3599	47.9	1971 - 1984	14	21 03 1981	46.95	20.50	22.31	0.37	65004
65005	Erch at Pencaenewydd	2400 3404	18.1	1972 - 1984	13	21 03 1981	19.51	10.95	12.00	0.29	65005
65006	Seiont at Peblig Mill	2493 3623	74.4	1975 - 1984	10	21 03 1981	57.05	40.63	42.65	0.21	65006
65007	Dwyfawr at Garndolbenmaen	2499 3429	52.4	1975 - 1984	10	21 03 1981	57.27	33.79	36.18	0.23	65007
66001	Clwyd at Pont-y-cambwll	3069 3709	404.0	1959 - 1994	36	26 09 1976	81.47	44.30	48.02	0.32	66001
66002	Elwy at Pant Yr Onen	3021 3704	220.0	1961 - 1972	12	12 12 1964	150.45	66.56	80.53	0.45	66002
66003	Aled at Bryn Aled	2957 3703	70.0	1963 - 1989	26	18 10 1987	60.10	27.81	29.56	0.41	66003
66004	Wheeler at Bodfari	3105 3714	62.9	1974 - 1994	18	11 02 1977	5.24	3.20	3.38	0.34	66004
66005	Clwyd at Ruthin Weir	3122 3592	95.3	1972 - 1994	19	29 01 1990	19.04	10.18	11.35	0.28	66005
66006	Elwy at Pont-y-gwyddel	2952 3718	194.0	1974 - 1994	21	14 10 1976	135.21	63.16	71.49	0.35	66006
66011	Conwy at Cwm Llanerch	2802 3581	344.5	1964 - 1984	21	12 12 1964	522.36	367.24	372.93	0.21	66011

No.	Name	Grid ref	NRFA Area km²	Record	Num AM	Date max	Max flood	QMED	QBAR	CV	No.
66801	Upperconway at Blaen Y Coed	2804 3452	10.4	1951 - 1956	6	30 09 1953	18.22	14.68	14.87	0.16	66801
67002	Dee at Erbistock Rectory	3357 3413	1040.0	1938 - 1972	34	08 02 1946	626.58	249.72	285.16	0.43	67002
67003	Brenig at Llyn Brenig Outflow	2974 3539	20.2	1964 - 1972	9	31 07 1972	28.82	14.75	16.72	0.33	67003
*67005	Ceiriog at Brynkinalt Weir	3295 3373	113.7	1952 - 1994	35	09 12 1965	65.13	30.45	32.27	0.39	67005*
67006	Alwen at Druid	3042 3436	184.7	1960 - 1994	35	12 12 1964	186.14	72.38	78.15	0.40	67006
67007	Dee at Glyndyfrdwy	3155 3428	728.0	1964 - 1972	9	13 12 1964	554.40	182.04	237.13	0.58	67007
67008	Alyn at Pont-y-capel	3336 3541	227.1	1965 - 1994	30	25 09 1976	60.27	23.40	24.17	0.35	67008
67009	Alyn at Rhydymwyn	3206 3667	77.8	1957 - 1994	38	26 09 1976	21.87	8.36	8.97	0.40	67009
67010	Gelyn at Cynefail	2843 3420	13.1	1966 - 1994	18	13 11 1994	22.17	15.87	15.86	0.19	67010
67013	Hirnant at Plas Rhiwedog	2946 3349	33.9	1967 - 1978	12	19 10 1971	37.67	24.32	24.58	0.34	67013
67014	Dee at Corwen	3069 3433	655.4	1974 - 1984	11	22 03 1981	271.32	224.65	206.38	0.26	67014
67015	Dee at Manley Hall	3348 3415	1019.3	1974 - 1994	21	18 10 1987	370.20	217.13	219.61	0.25	67015
67018	Dee at New Inn	2874 3308	53.9	1969 - 1994	24	02 09 1983	86.01	72.37	67.49	0.18	67018
*67019	Tryweryn at Weir X	2932 3360	111.2	1960 - 1968	8	04 12 1960	90.23	46.17	51.55	0.41	67019*
67020	Dee at Chester Weir	3418 3663	1816.8	1898 - 1968	71	09 02 1946	455.72	189.55	203.94	0.37	67020
67025	Clywedog at Bowling Bank	3396 3483	98.6	1975 - 1994	20	29 09 1976	43.05	19.91	20.11	0.41	67025
68001	Weaver at Ashbrook	3670 3633	622.0	1937 - 1993	56	08 02 1946	212.37	47.07	54.31	0.52	68001
68002	Gowy at Picton	3443 3714	156.2	1949 - 1978	30	03 07 1968	19.98	16.24	15.65	0.19	68002
68003	Dane at Rudheath	3668 3718	407.1	1949 - 1993	45	13 12 1964	117.05	64.84	67.08	0.31	68003
68004	Wistaston Brook at Marshfield Br.	3674 3552	92.7	1957 - 1993	34	23 08 1987	21.45	11.66	11.64	0.34	68004
*68005	Weaver at Audlem	3653 3431	207.0	1936 - 1993	58	08 02 1946	44.08	20.55	22.15	0.31	68005*
68006	Dane at Hulme Walfield	3845 3644	150.0	1953 - 1984	31	08 09 1965	122.31	51.06	60.14	0.43	68006
68007	Wincham Bk at Lostock Gralam	3697 3757	148.0	1963 - 1993	30	11 02 1977	52.61	24.14	25.02	0.34	68007
68010	Fender at Ford	3281 3880	18.4	1973 - 1980	8	25 09 1976	21.11	4.87	7.85	0.79	68010
68011	Arley Brook at Gore Farm	3696 3799	36.5	1974 - 1981	8	18 11 1981	11.57	7.43	7.75	0.26	68011
68014	Sandersons Brook at Sandbach	3754 3652	5.4	1964 - 1968	5	02 07 1968	1.86	1.45	1.51	0.18	68014
68015	Gowy at Huxley	3497 3624	49.0	1973 - 1991	19	06 08 1981	19.54	7.87	8.51	0.53	68015
68018	Dane at Congleton Park	3861 3632	145.0	1936 - 1984	32	20 09 1946	82.51	37.64	40.41	0.33	68018
68020	Gowy at Bridge Trafford	3448 3711	156.0	1979 - 1993	15	06 08 1981	38.01	22.96	23.52	0.39	68020
69001	Mersey at Irlam Weir	3728 3936	679.0	1934 - 1984	51	08 02 1946	266.11	153.44	166.20	0.28	69001
69002	Irwell at Adelphi Weir	3824 3987	559.4	1936 - 1993	56	20 09 1946	585.00	228.66	237.31	0.38	69002
69003	Irk at Scotland Weir	3841 3992	72.5	1949 - 1989	35	11 06 1970	71.64	39.64	41.04	0.33	69003
69006	Bollin at Dunham Massey	3727 3875	256.0	1936 - 1993	53	13 12 1964	55.30	40.34	40.20	0.17	69006
69007	Mersey at Ashton Weir	3772 3936	660.0	1958 - 1993	35	21 12 1991	563.43	172.69	215.87	0.54	69007
69008	Dean at Stanneylands	3846 3830	51.8	1967 - 1993	26	16 07 1973	20.70	9.36	10.05	0.31	69008
69011	Micker Brook at Cheadle	3855 3889	67.3	1968 - 1984	17	16 07 1973	37.51	18.39	17.98	0.39	69011
69012	Bollin at Wilmslow	3850 3815	72.5	1968 - 1993	26	16 07 1973	23.35	12.77	14.33	0.27	69012
69013	Sinderland Brook at Partington	3726 3905	44.8	1968 - 1993	26	27 11 1983	26.33	8.50	10.16	0.53	69013
69015	Etherow at Compstall	3962 3908	156.0	1969 - 1993	25	21 12 1991	86.30	40.82	42.25	0.37	69015
69017	Goyt at Marple Bridge	3964 3898	183.0	1969 - 1993	24	16 07 1973	165.49	48.27	54.53	0.50	69017
69018	Newton Bk at Newton Le Willows	3585 3933	32.8	1969 - 1979	11	28 12 1978	31.69	10.10	11.80	0.69	69018
69019	Worsley Brook at Eccles	3753 3980	24.9	1969 - 1984	16	28 12 1978	15.01	8.08	7.56	0.47	69019
69020	Medlock at London Road	3849 3975	57.5	1969 - 1984	16	09 12 1983	26.86	14.92	16.09	0.35	69020
69023	Roch at Blackford Bridge	3807 4077	186.0	1949 - 1993	45	27 10 1980	126.93	57.14	63.25	0.32	69023
69024	Croal at Farnworth Weir	3743 4068	145.0	1949 - 1993	45	18 07 1964	119.45	56.92	59.44	0.29	69024
69025	Irwell at Manchester Racecourse	3821 4004	557.0	1977 - 1993	12	27 10 1980	473.98	245.89	270.20	0.31	69025
69027	Tame at Portwood	3906 3918	150.0	1943 - 1993	45	09 12 1983	102.22	54.46	58.17	0.32	69027
69034	Musbury Brook at Helmshore	3775 4213	3.1	1961 - 1968	8	18 07 1964	5.89	5.02	4.87	0.18	69034
69035	Irwell at Bury Bridge	3797 4109	155.0	1976 - 1993	18	27 10 1980	306.05	207.05	187.90	0.33	69035
69040	Irwell at Stubbins	3793 4188	105.0	1974 - 1993	20	15 12 1986	213.08	91.76	102.64	0.37	69040
69041	Tame at Broomstair Bridge	3938 3953	113.0	1968 - 1993	26	09 12 1983	122.23	57.25	57.81	0.34	69041
69802	Etherow at Woodhead	4102 3998	13.0	1937 - 1974	29	29 07 1939	42.24	13.42	14.90	0.47	69802
70002	Douglas at Wanes Blades Bridge	3476 4126	198.0	1967 - 1993	27	22 08 1987	70.33	34.22	35.87	0.28	70002
70003	Douglas at Central Park Wigan	3587 4061	55.3	1973 - 1993	21	09 12 1983	29.98	16.36	17.45	0.31	70003
70004	Yarrow at Croston Mill	3498 4180	74.4	1973 - 1993	21	22 08 1987	191.97	33.89	47.42	0.83	70004

No.	Name	Grid ref	NRFA Area km²	Record	Num AM	Date max	Max flood	QMED	QBAR	CV	No.
70005	Lostock at Littlewood Bridge	3497 4197	56.0	1974 - 1984	11	27 10 1980	46.88	17.51	19.54	0.54	70005
70006	Tawd at Newburgh	3469 4107	28.9	1965 - 1979	14	25 09 1976	47.96	12.65	15.68	0.65	70006
71001	Ribble at Samlesbury	3589 4304	1145.0	1960 - 1993	33	27 10 1980	995.50	610.11	616.55	0.24	71001
71003	Croasdale at Croasdale Flume	3706 4546	10.4	1957 - 1976	15	08 08 1967	30.52	13.31	13.79	0.44	71003
71004	Calder at Whalley Weir	3729 4360	316.0	1962 - 1984	22	27 10 1980	226.60	153.07	155.81	0.22	71004
71005	Bottoms Beck at B. Beck Flume	3745 4565	10.6	1960 - 1973	14	08 08 1967	26.30	15.52	16.34	0.33	71005
71006	Ribble at Henthorn	3722 4392	456.0	1968 - 1993	26	27 10 1980	476.98	226.85	244.51	0.28	71006
71007	Ribble at Hodderfoot	3709 4379	720.0	1965 - 1978	14	16 10 1967	479.58	370.62	374.90	0.20	71007
71008	Hodder at Hodder Place	3704 4399	261.0	1969 - 1993	25	23 10 1980	495.57	209.78	218.91	0.32	71008
71009	Ribble at Jumbles Rock	3702 4376	1053.0	1970 - 1993	24	27 10 1980	1221.90	594.94	618.64	0.29	71009
71010	Pendle Water at Barden Lane	3837 4351	108.0	1971 - 1984	14	27 10 1980	133.66	72.81	74.21	0.30	71010
71011	Ribble at Arnford	3839 4556	204.0	1969 - 1993	25	27 10 1980	143.05	120.28	119.77	0.08	71011
71013	Darwen at Ewood Bridge	3677 4262	39.5	1973 - 1993	16	27 10 1980	56.65	30.62	31.39	0.27	71013
71014	Darwen at Blue Bridge	3565 4278	128.0	1974 - 1993	20	27 10 1980	206.93	111.95	115.26	0.35	71014
71802	Ribble at Halton West	3850 4552	207.0	1966 - 1968	3	23 03 1968	155.04	143.44	146.02	0.06	71802
71803	Hodder at Higher Hodder Bridge	3697 4411	256.0	1960 - 1968	9	11 12 1964	512.28	360.79	361.14	0.19	71803
72001	Lune at Halton	3503 4647	994.6	1959 - 1975	17	23 03 1968	929.59	658.24	649.71	0.23	72001
72002	Wyre at St Michaels	3463 4411	275.0	1962 - 1993	31	23 10 1980	189.47	145.36	141.55	0.21	72002
72004	Lune at Caton	3529 4653	983.0	1977 - 1993	17	19 02 1990	873.62	640.49	651.29	0.20	72004
72005	Lune at Killington New Bridge	3622 4907	219.0	1969 - 1993	13	14 11 1980	315.14	207.88	219.59	0.33	72005
72006	Lune at Kirkby Lonsdale	3615 4778	507.1	1968 - 1983	16	02 01 1982	579.46	441.99	429.88	0.25	72006
72009	Wenning at Wennington Road Br.	3615 4701	142.0	1971 - 1983	13	01 10 1981	131.32	90.13	95.59	0.24	72009
72011	Rawthey at Brigg Flatts	3639 4911	200.0	1968 - 1993	26	22 02 1991	459.76	307.08	307.48	0.28	72011
72013	Borrowbeck at Borrow Br. Weir	3609 5014	26.0	1976 - 1979	4	15 11 1978	80.09	60.88	62.37	0.27	72013
72014	Conder at Galgate	3481 4554	28.5	1975 - 1983	9	08 12 1983	91.06	37.73	49.76	0.59	72014
72015	Lune at Lunes Bridge	3612 5029	141.5	1979 - 1993	15	21 12 1985	461.04	247.28	242.03	0.35	72015
72016	Wyre at Scorton Weir	3501 4500	88.8	1967 - 1993	23	22 11 1980	180.65	92.80	95.75	0.35	72016
c72803	Lune at Halton Upper Weir	3513 4648	981.0	1940 - 1971	32	01 01 1954	1047.00	611.00	602.53	0.27	72803c
72804	Lune at Broadraine	3621 4901	222.0	1963 - 1968	6	06 10 1967	292.12	252.79	243.26	0.22	72804
72807	Wenning at Hornby	3586 4684	232.0	1957 - 1983	27	08 08 1967	1246.76	304.45	338.06	0.61	72807
73001	Leven at Newby Bridge	3371 4863	241.0	1939 - 1968	30	02 12 1954	135.77	61.46	68.45	0.35	73001
73002	Crake at Low Nibthwaite	3294 4882	73.0	1963 - 1968	6	09 10 1967	29.68	22.32	22.51	0.30	73002
73005	Kent at Sedgwick	3509 4874	209.0	1968 - 1983	16	03 01 1982	195.46	112.47	120.87	0.28	73005
73008	Bela at Beetham	3496 4806	131.0	1969 - 1993	25	21 03 1981	55.63	35.32	35.51	0.28	73008
73009	Sprint at Sprint Mill	3514 4961	34.6	1970 - 1993	24	20 12 1985	58.93	32.23	32.35	0.28	73009
73011	Mint at Mint Bridge	3524 4944	65.8	1970 - 1993	24	21 12 1985	72.06	39.02	41.26	0.27	73011
73013	Rothay at Miller Bridge House	3371 5042	64.0	1968 - 1983	16	25 11 1979	185.64	112.42	111.66	0.35	73013
73014	Brathay at Jeffy Knotts	3360 5034	57.4	1970 - 1983	14	02 01 1982	68.90	44.58	44.87	0.21	73014
73015	Keer at High Keer Weir	3523 4719	48.0	1971 - 1980	10	27 10 1980	27.11	12.97	13.05	0.47	73015
73803	Winster at Lobby Bridge	3424 4885	20.7	1969 - 1980	12	27 10 1980	11.84	8.46	8.51	0.17	73803
73805	Kent at Kendal (nether Bridge)	3517 4919	188.0	1964 - 1968	5	08 12 1964	220.71	151.42	157.32	0.32	73805
74001	Duddon at Duddon Hall	3196 4896	85.7	1968 - 1993	26	01 01 1991	181.11	120.18	122.31	0.23	74001
74002	Irt at Galesyke	3136 5038	44.2	1968 - 1993	25	02 10 1968	46.86	20.02	22.56	0.35	74002
74005	Ehen at Braystones	3009 5061	125.5	1974 - 1983	9	30 10 1977	109.47	87.33	83.56	0.21	74005
74006	Calder at Calder Hall	3035 5045	44.8	1973 - 1993	21	30 08 1989	87.19	40.60	41.68	0.37	74006
75002	Derwent at Camerton	3038 5305	663.0	1960 - 1993	34	03 01 1982	258.23	188.32	185.85	0.21	75002
75004	Cocker at Southwaite Bridge	3131 5281	116.6	1967 - 1993	27	31 10 1977	84.72	51.13	53.04	0.30	75004
75005	Derwent at Portinscale	3251 5239	235.0	1972 - 1993	22	21 12 1985	179.99	114.76	119.07	0.26	75005
75006	Newlands Beck at Braithwaite	3240 5239	33.9	1968 - 1984	17	19 12 1982	48.62	45.48	42.51	0.14	75006
75007	Glenderamackin at Threlkeld	3323 5248	64.5	1969 - 1993	17	11 12 1972	77.68	68.12	65.91	0.13	75007
75009	Greta at Low Briery	3286 5242	145.6	1971 - 1992	21	21 12 1985	205.79	112.40	110.45	0.34	75009
75010	Marron at Ullock	3074 5238	27.7	1972 - 1979	8	30 10 1977	35.57	17.59	20.08	0.40	75010
75017	Ellen at Bullgill	3096 5384	96.0	1975 - 1983	9	24 10 1980	63.41	52.85	45.57	0.38	75017
76002	Eden at Warwick Bridge	3470 5567	1366.7	1960 - 1993	34	23 03 1968	860.00	417.10	447.60	0.26	76002
76003	Eamont at Udford	3578 5306	396.2	1961 - 1993	33	23 03 1968	274.92	168.94	172.45	0.23	76003

No.	Name	Grid ref	NRFA Area km²	Record	Num AM	Date max	Max flood	QMED	QBAR	CV	No.
76004	Lowther at Eamont Bridge	3527 5287	158.5	1962 - 1993	32	23 03 1968	231.55	101.70	114.37	0.37	76004
76005	Eden at Temple Sowerby	3605 5283	616.4	1964 - 1993	30	23 03 1968	400.96	251.31	258.26	0.19	76005
76007	Eden at Sheepmount	3390 5571	2286.5	1967 - 1993	27	24 03 1968	1094.19	569.63	588.79	0.29	76007
76008	Irthing at Greenholme	3486 5581	334.6	1967 - 1993	27	03 01 1982	354.28	194.27	207.21	0.34	76008
76009	Caldew at Holm Hill	3378 5469	147.2	1968 - 1993	26	25 11 1979	178.65	80.03	93.72	0.39	76009
76010	Petteril at Harraby Green	3412 5545	160.0	1970 - 1993	24	27 03 1987	47.18	24.66	28.40	0.32	76010
76011	Coal Burn at Coalburn	3693 5777	1.5	1967 - 1969	3	08 10 1967	2.70	2.04	2.12	0.26	76011
76014	Eden at Kirkby Stephen	3773 5097	69.4	1971 - 1984	14	25 11 1979	220.47	123.82	130.45	0.41	76014
77001	Esk at Netherby	3390 5718	841.7	1961 - 1993	33	31 10 1977	1112.20	603.56	676.35	0.26	77001
77002	Esk at Canonbie	3397 5751	495.0	1963 - 1988	26	31 10 1977	636.58	360.28	397.25	0.24	77002
77003	Liddel Water at Rowanburnfoot	3415 5759	319.0	1974 - 1992	19	01 01 1991	422.38	260.61	284.52	0.21	77003
77005	Lyne at Cliff Bridge	3412 5662	191.0	1976 - 1983	8	22 08 1979	138.57	122.86	118.78	0.12	77005
78003	Annan at Brydekirk	3191 5704	925.0	1967 - 1992	26	09 10 1967	477.54	296.45	310.67	0.21	78003
78004	Kinnel Water at Redhall	3077 5868	76.1	1961 - 1992	31	30 10 1977	112.71	69.38	69.27	0.25	78004
78005	Kinnel Water at Bridgemuir	3091 5845	229.0	1979 - 1992	14	21 09 1985	155.08	128.87	127.75	0.18	78005
79002	Nith at Friars Carse	2923 5851	799.0	1957 - 1992	36	15 01 1962	997.44	454.01	475.68	0.28	79002
79003	Nith at Hall Bridge	2684 6129	155.0	1960 - 1992	33	15 01 1962	225.09	75.94	83.09	0.41	79003
79004	Scar Water at Capenoch	2845 5940	142.0	1963 - 1992	30	19 12 1982	255.29	148.46	153.50	0.22	79004
79005	Cluden Water at Fiddlers Ford	2928 5795	238.0	1964 - 1992	29	22 12 1977	270.98	109.28	124.01	0.32	79005
79006	Nith at Drumlanrig	2858 5994	471.0	1967 - 1992	26	30 10 1977	429.62	315.71	308.31	0.19	79006
80001	Urr at Dalbeattie	2822 5610	199.0	1964 - 1992	29	18 10 1982	159.37	102.19	101.61	0.23	80001
80003	White Laggan Burn at Loch Dee	2468 5781	5.7	1981 - 1991	11	20 09 1985	9.53	8.76	8.62	0.09	80003
80801	Pullaugh Burn at Diversion Works	2544 5742	18.2	1962 - 1968	7	13 08 1966	16.33	12.31	12.99	0.18	80801
81002	Cree at Newton Stewart	2412 5653	368.0	1963 - 1992	30	30 03 1993	382.17	224.97	237.57	0.29	81002
81003	Luce at Airyhemming	2180 5599	171.0	1967 - 1991	25	12 08 1987	283.60	155.12	150.32	0.28	81003
82001	Girvan at Robstone	2217 5997	245.5	1963 - 1991	28	19 12 1982	116.20	87.05	87.01	0.16	82001
82003	Stinchar at Balnowlart	2108 5832	341.0	1975 - 1991	15	19 12 1982	271.06	196.62	190.51	0.20	82003
83002	Garnock at Dalry	2293 6488	88.8	1960 - 1968	9	08 08 1961	82.70	54.60	55.40	0.21	83002
83003	Ayr at Catrine	2525 6259	166.3	1969 - 1980	12	17 01 1974	292.00	128.15	162.78	0.47	83003
83004	Lugar at Langholm	2508 6217	181.0	1973 - 1992	20	02 01 1981	270.33	150.02	161.94	0.37	83004
83005	Irvine at Shewalton	2345 6369	380.7	1973 - 1992	20	08 08 1979	375.50	215.29	218.56	0.32	83005
83006	Ayr at Mainholm	2361 6216	574.0	1976 - 1992	16	02 01 1981	365.80	251.05	267.13	0.18	83006
*83802	Irvine at Kilmarnock	2430 6369	218.0	1913 - 1987	70	08 08 1961	227.00	70.78	79.41	0.38	83802*
*84001	Kelvin at Killermont	2558 6705	335.1	1947 - 1992	46	18 10 1954	159.38	95.59	98.03	0.22	84001*
84002	Calder at Muirshiel	2309 6638	12.4	1952 - 1972	18	09 09 1962	35.77	16.31	18.81	0.30	84002
84003	Clyde at Hazelbank	2835 6452	1092.9	1955 - 1993	39	31 10 1977	514.81	271.90	289.49	0.29	84003
84004	Clyde at Sills	2927 6424	741.8	1955 - 1992	38	16 01 1962	443.01	198.53	215.39	0.33	84004
84005	Clyde at Blairston	2704 6579	1704.2	1955 - 1993	39	21 09 1985	669.69	382.77	409.21	0.27	84005
84006	Kelvin at Bridgend	2672 6749	63.7	1956 - 1981	26	08 12 1979	23.40	15.79	15.63	0.24	84006
84007	S Calder Water at Forgewood	2751 6585	93.0	1965 - 1992	26	23 01 1993	60.65	21.15	25.48	0.53	84007
84008	Rotten Calder Water at Redlees	2679 6604	51.3	1966 - 1981	16	08 10 1977	51.50	30.00	30.45	0.31	84008
84009	Nethan at Kirkmuirhill	2809 6429	66.0	1966 - 1981	16	31 10 1977	80.50	38.70	41.02	0.37	84009
84011	Gryfe at Craigend	2415 6664	71.0	1963 - 1992	30	25 11 1979	98.28	62.25	65.77	0.20	84011
84012	White Cart Water at Hawkhead	2499 6629	227.2	1963 - 1992	30	13 01 1984	187.12	123.45	126.69	0.24	84012
84013	Clyde at Daldowie	2672 6616	1903.1	1963 - 1987	23	22 09 1985	755.17	391.54	429.25	0.32	84013
84014	Avon Water at Fairholm	2755 6518	265.5	1964 - 1992	28	13 08 1966	409.78	188.09	189.29	0.35	84014
84015	Kelvin at Dryfield	2638 6739	235.4	1947 - 1987	41	18 09 1985	83.51	61.75	60.23	0.15	84015
84016	Luggie Water at Condorrat	2739 6725	33.9	1968 - 1987	20	18 11 1979	34.66	21.63	21.32	0.35	84016
84017	Black Cart Water at Milliken Park	2411 6620	103.1	1968 - 1972	5	02 11 1969	56.26	27.66	32.84	0.42	84017
84018	Clyde at Tulliford Mill	2891 6404	932.6	1969 - 1981	13	31 10 1977	467.80	239.80	247.07	0.31	84018
84019	North Calder Water at Calderpark	2681 6625	129.8	1963 - 1992	30	05 10 1990	90.56	39.07	40.02	0.43	84019
84020	Glazert W. at Milton of Campsie	2656 6763	51.9	1969 - 1987	19	05 11 1971	76.19	58.05	60.33	0.17	84020
84023	Bothlin Burn at Auchengeich	2680 6717	35.7	1974 - 1981	8	09 09 1978	13.50	11.20	10.12	0.26	84023
84025	Luggie Water at Oxgang	2666 6734	87.7	1974 - 1981	8	02 10 1981	51.70	26.30	29.77	0.37	84025
84026	Allander Water at Milngavie	2558 6738	32.8	1974 - 1987	14	18 09 1985	64.59	32.80	36.68	0.37	84026

No.	Name	Grid ref	NRFA Area km²	Record	Num AM	Date max	Max flood	QMED	QBAR	CV	No.
84806	Clyde at Cambusnethan	2786 6522	1260.0	1955 - 1963	9	16 01 1962	519.57	287.97	310.23	0.30	84806
85001	Leven at Linnbrane	2394 6803	784.3	1963 - 1970	8	19 12 1966	123.22	104.77	106.72	0.10	85001
85002	Endrick Water at Gaidrew	2485 6866	219.9	1963 - 1981	19	27 09 1981	149.90	119.20	121.16	0.12	85002
85003	Falloch at Glen Falloch	2321 7197	80.3	1971 - 1987	17	13 08 1986	185.17	154.58	155.18	0.10	85003
86001	Little Eachaig at Dalinlongart	2143 6821	30.8	1968 - 1992	25	02 11 1979	112.78	53.07	56.69	0.29	86001
86002	Eachaig at Eckford	2140 6843	139.9	1968 - 1972	5	11 10 1968	88.48	80.04	77.69	0.14	86002
87801	Allt Uaine at Intake	2263 7113	3.1	1951 - 1970	20	19 09 1953	11.30	8.50	8.61	0.17	87801
89804	Strae at Duiletter	2146 7294	36.2	1978 - 1987	10	18 10 1983	67.55	57.69	56.68	0.16	89804
90801	Nevis at Achreoch	2167 7690	46.6	1957 - 1960	2	27 10 1957	52.58	49.02	49.02	0.10	90801
91002	Lochy at Camisky	2145 7805	1252.0	1980 - 1992	13	02 01 1992	1539.88	741.53	884.70	0.39	91002
91802	Allt Leachdach at Intake	2261 7781	6.5	1939 - 1973	33	25 05 1953	13.26	6.42	6.96	0.29	91802
93001	Carron at New Kelso	1942 8429	137.8	1979 - 1992	14	02 01 1992	318.45	187.31	203.79	0.36	93001
94001	Ewe at Poolewe	1859 8803	441.1	1971 - 1992	22	31 12 1983	185.93	125.70	121.43	0.22	94001
*95801	Little Gruinard at Little Gruinard	1944 8897	82.1	1963 - 1966	4	16 12 1966	12.55	4.50	5.77	0.84	95801*
95803	Abhain Cuileg at Braemore	2193 8790	67.3	1963 - 1966	2	03 03 1967	146.89	104.08	104.08	0.58	95803
96001	Halladale at Halladale	2891 9561	204.6	1975 - 1992	18	28 10 1990	284.71	140.10	151.80	0.42	96001
96002	Naver at Apigill	2713 9568	477.0	1978 - 1992	15	04 10 1981	291.43	153.62	165.55	0.35	96002
97002	Thurso at Halkirk	3131 9595	412.8	1972 - 1992	21	05 03 1993	209.94	107.06	107.42	0.40	97002
201002	Fairy Water at Dudgeon Bridge	2406 3758	161.2	1971 - 1992	22	22 10 1987	94.36	67.26	67.32	0.18	201002
201005	Camowen at Camowen Terrace	2460 3730	274.6	1972 - 1992	21	22 10 1987	195.99	87.81	91.11	0.32	201005
201006	Drumragh at Campsie Bridge	2458 3722	324.6	1973 - 1992	20	22 10 1987	232.72	106.73	110.55	0.29	201006
201007	Burn Dennet at Burndennett Br.	2372 4047	145.3	1975 - 1992	17	22 10 1987	157.25	78.52	78.11	0.36	201007
201008	Derg at Castlederg	2265 3842	337.3	1976 - 1992	17	21 09 1985	245.46	200.67	202.39	0.12	201008
201009	Owenkillen at Crosh	2418 3866	442.5	1980 - 1992	13	21 10 1987	508.05	291.87	309.37	0.22	201009
201010	Mourne at Drumnabuoy House	2347 3960	1844.5	1982 - 1992	11	22 10 1987	1063.89	604.02	656.67	0.26	201010
202001	Roe at Ardnargle	2674 4247	365.6	1975 - 1992	18	03 10 1981	181.79	147.73	144.84	0.15	202001
202002	Faughan at Drumahoe	2464 4151	272.3	1976 - 1992	17	21 10 1987	253.44	140.71	150.93	0.32	202002
203010	Blackwater at Maydown Bridge	2820 3519	951.4	1970 - 1992	23	23 10 1987	156.99	97.32	101.16	0.26	203010
203011	Main at Dromona	3052 4086	228.8	1970 - 1992	23	01 04 1992	71.19	54.16	53.45	0.20	203011
203012	Ballinderry at Ballinderry Bridge	2926 3799	419.5	1970 - 1992	23	22 10 1987	208.33	123.66	128.15	0.23	203012
203017	Upper Bann at Dynes Bridge	3043 3509	335.6	1970 - 1989	20	29 12 1978	120.05	76.98	75.84	0.24	203017
203018	Six Mile Water at Antrim	3146 3867	277.3	1970 - 1992	23	12 10 1987	190.54	74.97	86.24	0.42	203018
203019	Claudy at Glenone Bridge	2962 4037	130.1	1971 - 1992	22	23 10 1980	67.78	40.37	42.14	0.24	203019
203020	Moyola at Moyola New Bridge	2955 3905	306.5	1971 - 1992	22	19 01 1988	148.84	109.89	105.85	0.17	203020
203021	Kells Water at Currys Bridge	3106 3971	127.0	1971 - 1992	22	26 08 1986	151.02	83.71	86.19	0.29	203021
203022	Blackwater at Derrymeen Bridge	2625 3530	175.7	1979 - 1994	16	22 10 1987	89.35	38.92	45.13	0.37	203022
203024	Cusher at Gamble's Bridge	3048 3471	176.7	1971 - 1992	22	21 10 1987	83.74	55.86	56.09	0.26	203024
*203025	Callan at Callan New Bridge	2893 3524	164.1	1971 - 1992	22	22 10 1987	40.69	36.74	34.47	0.16	203025*
203026	Glenavy at Glenavy	3149 3725	44.6	1971 - 1992	22	21 10 1987	28.72	18.46	18.33	0.31	203026
203027	Braid at Ballee	3097 4014	177.2	1972 - 1992	21	02 10 1981	140.48	72.21	81.93	0.41	203027
203028	Agivey at White Hill	2883 4193	98.9	1973 - 1992	20	21 10 1987	226.33	81.08	93.46	0.43	203028
203033	Upper Bann at Bannfield	3233 3341	100.9	1975 - 1992	18	17 10 1976	108.86	63.07	68.82	0.27	203033
203039	Clogh at Tullynewey	3090 4108	83.6	1981 - 1992	12	28 10 1990	40.97	35.85	36.20	0.09	203039
203042	Crumlin at Cidercourt Bridge	3135 3765	54.0	1981 - 1992	12	21 10 1987	79.45	39.64	44.95	0.36	203042
203043	Oonawater at Shanmoy U/s	2779 3556	91.9	1981 - 1992	9	21 10 1987	104.02	74.47	66.50	0.35	203043
203046	Rathmore at Rathmore Bridge	3198 3854	26.2	1982 - 1992	11	21 10 1987	15.12	11.10	11.42	0.18	203046
203049	Clady at Clady Bridge	3201 3837	30.7	1982 - 1992	11	23 11 1990	37.50	27.20	26.62	0.30	203049
203092	Maine at Dunminning	3051 4111	211.7	1983 - 1992	10	28 10 1990	84.89	62.03	64.45	0.19	203092
203093	Maine at Shanes Viaduct	3086 3896	704.2	1983 - 1992	10	21 10 1987	298.28	209.91	219.39	0.18	203093
204001	Bush at Seneirl	2942 4362	306.1	1972 - 1992	21	03 10 1981	93.96	61.01	64.93	0.21	204001
205003	Lagan at Dunmurry	3299 3679	444.7	1969 - 1983	14	28 12 1978	75.97	60.34	60.31	0.17	205003
205004	Lagan at Newforge	3329 3693	490.4	1972 - 1992	21	29 12 1978	166.43	77.81	89.66	0.38	205004
205005	Ravernet at Ravernet	3267 3613	69.5	1972 - 1992	21	21 10 1987	25.44	14.49	14.92	0.35	205005
205008	Lagan at Drummiller	3236 3525	85.2	1974 - 1993	19	28 12 1978	45.35	27.97	27.06	0.32	205008
205010	Lagan at Banoge	3123 3540	189.8	1977 - 1983	7	28 12 1978	212.21	120.70	127.26	0.39	205010

No.	Name	Grid ref	NRFA Area km²	Record	Num AM	Date max	Max flood	QMED	QBAR	CV	No.
205011	Annacloy at Kilmore	3448 3509	186.6	1980 - 1992	13	03 10 1981	51.77	35.69	36.76	0.21	205011
205020	Enler at Comber	3459 3697	59.8	1983 - 1992	10	16 01 1984	53.98	22.87	28.04	0.51	205020
205101	Blackstaff at Easons	3318 3721	15.6	1979 - 1991	13	02 10 1981	33.74	10.44	12.35	0.58	205101
206001	Clanrye at Mount Mill Bridge	3086 3309	132.7	1971 - 1992	22	20 01 1973	114.37	23.15	28.10	0.74	206001
206002	Jerretspass at Jerretspass	3064 3332	41.7	1972 - 1992	21	22 10 1987	18.56	9.60	9.87	0.35	206002
206004	Bessbrook at Cambane	3074 3292	34.5	1984 - 1992	9	26 07 1985	11.51	9.65	9.17	0.20	206004
206006	Annalong at Recorder	3349 3232	13.8	1895 - 1942	44	24 08 1942	30.51	15.57	15.52	0.34	206006
206999	Woodburn at Control Area	3372 3899	0.3	1959 - 1969	11	15 08 1970	0.19	0.12	0.12	0.29	206999
236005	Colebrooke at Ballindarragh Br.	2331 3359	309.1	1982 - 1992	11	22 10 1987	155.28	102.48	107.30	0.18	236005
236007	Sillees at Drumrainey Bridge	2205 3400	167.6	1981 - 1992	12	21 12 1991	37.33	23.81	24.54	0.20	236007

Appendix C   Glossary of catchment descriptors

ALTBAR   Mean altitude of the catchment (metres above mean sea level)

AREA   Catchment drainage area using an IHDTM-derived boundary (km^2)

ASPBAR   Mean direction of all the inter-nodal slopes in the catchment (bearing in degrees, where north is zero). Represents the dominant aspect of catchment slopes

ASPVAR   Invariability of slope directions, where values near to zero indicate that there is considerable variability in the aspect of catchment slopes. Values approaching one indicate that catchment slopes tend to face one particular direction

BFIHOST   Base Flow Index derived by using the HOST classification

CVALL   CV of the length of all spells when soil moisture defecit (SMD) was above and below 6 mm during 1961-90

CVDRY   CV of the length of all spells when SMD was above 6 mm during 1961-90

CVWET   CV of the length of all spells when SMD was below 6 mm during 1961-90

DPLBAR   Mean of distances between each node (on regular 50 m grid) and the catchment outlet (km). Characterises catchment size and configuration

DPLCV   CV of the distances between each node and catchment outlet

DPSBAR   Mean of all the inter-nodal slopes for the catchment ($m\ km^{-1}$): characterises the overall steepness

FARL   Index of flood attenuation attributable to reservoirs and lakes

LDP   Longest drainage path (km), defined by recording the greatest distance from a catchment node to the defined outlet: principally a measure of catchment size but also reflects catchment configuration

MEDALL   Median length of spells when SMD was above or below 6 mm during 1961-90 (days)

MEDDRY   Median length of spells when SMD was above 6 mm during 1961-90 (days)

MEDWET   Median length of spells when SMD was below 6 mm during 1961-90 (days)

NDUR   Total number of spells when SMD was above and below 6 mm during 1961-90

NWET   Total number of spells when SMD was below, or equal to, 6 mm during 1961-90

PROPWET   Proportion of time when SMD was equal to, or below, 6 mm during 1961-90

RMED-1D	Median annual maximum 1-day rainfall in mm (termed RMED1 in this volume)
RMED-1H	Median annual maximum 1-hour rainfall (mm)
RMED-2D	Median annual maximum 2-day rainfall (mm)
SAAR	Standard period (1961-90) average annual rainfall (mm)
$SAAR_{4170}$	Standard period (1941-70) average annual rainfall (mm)
SMDBAR	Mean SMD for the period 1961-90 calculated from MORECS month-end values (mm)
SPRHOST	Standard percentage runoff derived by using the HOST classification
URBCONC	Concentration of urban and suburban land cover. High index values (approaching one) indicate concentrated urban and/or suburban land cover. Not defined when URBEXT < 0.005
$URBEXT_{1990}$	Extent of urban and suburban land cover (1990)
URBLOC	Location of urban and suburban land cover. Low index values indicate that development is near the catchment outlet. Not defined when URBEXT < 0.005

Index